Oxford Resources for Cambridge

Extended

Cambridge IGCSE®
Complete
Mathematics

David Rayner

Ian Bettison

Mathew Taylor

Editor: Deborah Barton

Neha Kawatra
Bhavana Kotwal
Domnic Odipo
Diano Pesidas
Preeti Verma

OXFORD
UNIVERSITY PRESS

OXFORD
UNIVERSITY PRESS

Great Clarendon Street, Oxford, OX2 6DP, United Kingdom

Oxford University Press is a department of the University of Oxford.

It furthers the University's objective of excellence in research, scholarship, and education by publishing worldwide. Oxford is a registered trade mark of Oxford University Press in the UK and in certain other countries.

British Library Cataloguing in Publication Data

Data available

9781382042529

9781382042536 (ebook)

10 9 8 7 6 5 4 3

The manufacturing process conforms to the environmental regulations of the country of origin.

Printed in the UK by Bell and Bain Ltd, Glasgow

Acknowledgements

The publisher and authors would like to thank the following for permission to use photographs and other copyright material:

Front cover: Melinda Podor/Moment/Getty Images. Photos: p1: Tomas Urbelionis/Shutterstock; p9: beerlogoff/Shutterstock; p10: Stas Moroz/Shutterstock; p32: NPeter/Shutterstock; p52: Everett - Art / Shutterstock; p58: Celso Diniz/Shutterstock; p80(t): Alberto Loyo/Shutterstock; p80(b): UnderTheSea / Shutterstock; p84: Science History Images / Alamy Stock Photo; p91: PriceM / Shutterstock; p92: Don Bendickson / Shutterstock; p97(t): Mike Flippo/Shutterstock; p97(b): Leena Robinson/Shutterstock; p99: Hetman Bohdan/Shutterstock; p105: Supertrooper/Shutterstock; p107(t): dencg/Shutterstock; p107(b): kevin brine/Shutterstock; p108: mentalmind/Shutterstock; p109: Clara/Shutterstock; p111: lzf/Shutterstock; p113: Jag_cz/Shutterstock; p115: Stellar_bones/Shutterstock; p120: Offscreen / Shutterstock; p138: Alvov/Shutterstock; p141: Hryshchyshen Serhii/Shutterstock; p151: IanDagnall Computing / Alamy Stock Photo; p169: Paulpixs/Shutterstock; p196(t): GRANGER - Historical Picture Archive / Alamy Stock Photo; p196(b): Belga News Agency / Alamy Stock Photo; p218: The Granger Collection / Alamy Stock Photo; p247(t): Science History Images / Alamy Stock Photo; p247(b): REUTERS / Alamy Stock Photo; p252: beeboys / Shutterstock; p253: Victor Tyakht / Shutterstock; p263(t): rangizzz / Shutterstock; p263(b): DmitryStock / Shutterstock; p264: Tupungato / Shutterstock; p277: Public Domain; p280: tratong / Shutterstock; p294: Artsiom P / Shutterstock; p297: Art_Photo / Shutterstock; p309: barbara cameron pix / Alamy Stock Photo; p313: Maryna Pleshkun / Shutterstock; p332(t): Science History Images / Alamy Stock Photo; p332(b): Sipa US / Alamy Stock Photo; p342: Kisseleva Katya/Shutterstock; p348(t): Bettmann / Getty Images; p348(b): Granger, NYC. / GRANGER - Historical Picture Archive / Alamy Stock Photo; p358: ArtFamily / Shutterstock; p371(t): History and Art Collection / Alamy Stock Photo; p371(b): Jaguar PS / Shutterstock; p407: Everett Collection / Shutterstock; p445: Food_Studio / Shutterstock; p446: akf ffm / Shutterstock; p451: DeAgostini/Getty Images; p452: LightField Studios / Shutterstock; p455: WHITE RABBIT83 / Shuttestock; p457(t): KSVector / Shutterstock; p457(b): Radu Sebastian / Shutterstock; p462: studiostoks / Shutterstock; p464: de2marco / Shutterstock; p472: Perry Correll / Shutterstock; p473: Okrasiuk / Shutterstock; p474: D-VISIONS / Shutterstock.

Artwork by Aptara, Thompson Digital, and Thompson Digital/Aptara.

Index by LNS Indexing.

Every effort has been made to contact copyright holders of material reproduced in this book. Any omissions will be rectified in subsequent printings if notice is given to the publisher.

This Student Book refers to the Cambridge IGCSE® Mathematics syllabus published by Cambridge Assessment International Education.

This work has been developed independently from and is not endorsed by or otherwise connected with Cambridge Assessment International Education.

Contents

Introduction

About this book

This book is designed specifically for the Cambridge IGCSE® Mathematics course. Experienced examiners have been involved in all aspects of the course, to ensure that the content adheres to the latest syllabus.

Using this book will ensure that you are well prepared for the exam at this level, and also studies beyond the IGCSE level in Mathematics. The features below are designed to make learning as interesting and effective as possible.

Finding your way around

To get the most out of this book when studying or revising, use the:

- **Contents list** to help you find the appropriate units
- **Index** to find key words so you can turn to any concept straight away.

Learning objectives

At the start of each chapter you will find a list of objectives. These will tell you what you should be able to do by the end of the chapter. They are based on what you need to cover for the Cambridge IGCSE syllabus.

Famous mathematicians

These are included at the start of each chapter to give you a brief insight into the life of a mathematician who played an important part in the development of the ideas contained in that chapter.

By finding out about the history of mathematics and considering a topic within the broader context of the subject, you can make connections between topics and develop a greater appreciation of how mathematics has developed over the centuries.

Worked examples

Worked examples are an important feature of the book and can be found in every sub-topic. These show you the important skills techniques required in the exercises below and also provide a model for how to structure your solutions.

Exercises

There are thousands of questions in this book, providing ample opportunities to practise the skills and techniques required in the exam. The exercises contain questions of varying levels of difficulty, so that you can progress through a topic as your knowledge and confidence increases.

Each exercise has an icon to denote whether you can use a calculator or not. This 🧮 means you can use a calculator, while this 🚫 means you should not. The same icons also appear in the Revision Exercises.

Revision Exercise

At the end of each chapter, you will find revision questions to bring together all your knowledge and test your understanding of the contents of the chapter.

Examination-style questions

The revision exercises are followed by exam-style practice questions. These are very similar to the kind of questions you should expect to see in the real exam.

Tips

Yellow boxes throughout the exercises provide further information, hints on how to approach a question, or reminders of other concepts.

Answers

These can be found at the back of this book, so you can find out immediately whether or not you have answered a question correctly. Answers to all the numerical problems in the exercises, the review questions, and the exam-style questions are all included.

kerboodle

Additional support can be found on Kerboodle. There are resources for every sub-topic, including adaptive assessments, personalised Next Steps and data-rich reports. You can also access the Digital Student Book.

1 Number 1

Karl Friedrich Gauss (1777–1855) is thought by many to have been the greatest all-round mathematician of all time. Gauss considered that his finest discovery was the method for constructing a regular seventeen-sided polygon. This was not of the slightest use outside the world of mathematics, but was a great achievement of the human mind. Gauss would not have understood the modern view held by many that mathematics must somehow be 'useful' to be worthy of study.

- Working with different types of numbers, e.g. natural numbers, integers, primes, squares, cubes, common factors, common multiples, rational numbers, irrational numbers, real numbers, reciprocals, powers and roots.
- Calculate with and convert between the following including in contexts: proper fractions, improper fractions, mixed numbers, and decimals.
- Order quantities and understand the symbols $=$, $\neq$, $>$, $<$, $\geqslant$ and $\leqslant$.
- Calculate with integers, decimals and fractions including the correct order of operations and brackets.
- Understand and interpret positive, zero, negative and fractional indices including using the rules of indices.
- Understand and calculate with numbers in standard form $A \times 10^n$ where n is a positive or negative integer and $1 \leqslant A < 10$.
- Round to a given number of decimal places or significant figures and use rounded values to estimate calculations, including choosing an appropriate degree of accuracy when a question is in context.
- Understand and use upper and lower bounds including finding bounds of the results of calculations.

- Effective calculator use including entering values correctly and interpreting values correctly, e.g. time and money.
- Understand and use surds, including calculations, simplifying and rationalising the denominator.
- Understand sequences including continuing a sequence, recognising patterns, term-to-term rules, find and use nth terms and relationships between sequences.

1.1 Arithmetic

Mathematical symbols of equality and inequality

The symbol = means 'equal to'.

The symbol < means 'less than'.

The symbol ⩽ means 'less than or equal to'.

The symbol > means 'greater than'.

The symbol ⩾ means 'greater than or equal to'.

The symbol ≠ means 'not equal to'.

Decimals

Example

Evaluate:

a) $7.6 + 19$

b) $3.4 - 0.24$

c) 7.2×0.21

d) $0.84 \div 0.2$

e) $3.6 \div 0.004$

a)
$$\begin{array}{r} 7.6 \\ + 19.0 \\ \hline 26.6 \end{array}$$

b)
$$\begin{array}{r} 3.40 \\ - 0.24 \\ \hline 3.16 \end{array}$$

c)
$$\begin{array}{r} 7.2 \\ \times 0.21 \\ \hline 72 \\ 1440 \\ \hline 1.512 \end{array}$$
No decimal points in the working, '3 figures after the points in the question *and* therefore in the answer'.

d) Multiply both numbers by 10 so that you can divide by a whole number.

$$0.84 \div 0.2 = \frac{0.84^{\times 10}}{0.2^{\times 10}} = \frac{8.4}{2}$$
$$= 4.2$$

e) $3.6 \div 0.004 = \dfrac{3.6^{\times 1000}}{0.004^{\times 1000}} = \dfrac{3600}{4}$

$$= 900$$

Exercise 1.1A

Evaluate the following.

1. $7.6 + 0.31$ **2.** $15 + 7.22$ **3.** $7.004 + 0.368$ **4.** $0.06 + 0.006$

5. $4.2 + 42 + 420$ **6.** $3.84 - 2.62$ **7.** $11.4 - 9.73$ **8.** $4.61 - 3$

9. $17 - 0.37$ **10.** $8.7 + 19.2 - 3.8$ **11.** $25 - 7.8 + 9.5$ **12.** $3.6 - 8.74 + 9$

13. $20.4 - 20.399$ **14.** 2.6×0.6 **15.** 0.72×0.04 **16.** 27.2×0.08

17. 0.1×0.2 **18.** $(0.01)^2$ **19.** 2.1×3.6 **20.** 2.31×0.34

21. 0.36×1000 **22.** $0.34 \times 100\,000$ **23.** $3.6 \div 0.2$ **24.** $0.592 \div 0.8$

25. $0.1404 \div 0.06$ **26.** $3.24 \div 0.002$ **27.** $0.968 \div 0.11$ **28.** $600 \div 0.5$

29. $0.007 \div 4$ **30.** $2640 \div 200$ **31.** $1100 \div 5.5$ **32.** $(11 + 2.4) \times 0.06$

33. $(0.4)^2 \div 0.2$ **34.** $77 \div 1000$ **35.** $(0.3)^2 \div 100$ **36.** $(0.1)^4 \div 0.01$

37. $\dfrac{92 \times 4.6}{2.3}$ **38.** $\dfrac{180 \times 4}{36}$ **39.** $\dfrac{0.55 \times 0.81}{4.5}$ **40.** $\dfrac{63 \times 600 \times 0.2}{360 \times 7}$

Exercise 1.1B

1. Eric's temperature was measured to be 100.4°F, but after taking medicine, his temperature dropped by 1.7°F. What was his new temperature?

2. Kimmie found the mass of a bowl of rice on her scale, which read 400.8 g. She knew the empty bowl had mass 357.4 g. What was the mass of the rice?

3. Debbie took $5.80 with her to the shops. She spent $3.25. How much did she have left?

4. Sam had a bottle of juice containing 2.5 litres. If she pours out 3 glasses containing 0.375 litres each, how much juice will be left in the bottle?

5. Three friends each earn $9.25 for doing a job. They decide to put their money together and buy a comic book that costs $24.99. They split the change equally between them. How much money do they each now have?

6. An object on Earth weighs 2.64 times what it weighs on Mars. If an object weighs 5 newtons on Mars, how many newtons will it weigh on Earth?

7. A group of people have an average of $4.26 each. If the total of all their money is $51.12, how many people are there?

8. In a relay race, the four members of Team Go ran the following times, in seconds: 45.7, 43.1, 48.2 and 50.4. What was their average time?

9. A group of 11 friends share a restaurant bill of £138.05 equally between them. How much do they each pay?

10. A maths teacher bought 40 calculators at $8.20 each and a number of other calculators costing $2.95 each. In all she spent $387. How many of the cheaper calculators did she buy?

Fractions

Fractions are added or subtracted from one another directly only when they have a common denominator. Find the lowest common multiple of the two denominators to find the lowest common denominator.

Example 1

Evaluate:

a) $\dfrac{3}{4} + \dfrac{2}{5}$ **b)** $2\dfrac{3}{8} - 1\dfrac{5}{12}$

---

a) $\dfrac{3}{4} + \dfrac{2}{5} = \dfrac{15}{20} + \dfrac{8}{20}$

$\qquad\quad = \dfrac{23}{20}$

$\qquad\quad = 1\dfrac{3}{20}$

b) $2\dfrac{3}{8} - 1\dfrac{5}{12} = \dfrac{19}{8} - \dfrac{17}{12}$

$\qquad\qquad\quad = \dfrac{57}{24} - \dfrac{34}{24}$

$\qquad\qquad\quad = \dfrac{23}{24}$

Tip

The order of operations follows the BIDMAS rule: Brackets then Indices then Divide and Multiply then Add and Subtract..

Multiplying fractions is much easier than adding or subtracting them.

To multiply two fractions together, you simply multiply the two numerators together to get the numerator of the answer, and then multiply the two denominators together to get the denominator of the answer.

To divide a fraction by another fraction, you simply turn the second fraction upside down to find its **reciprocal** and then multiply them.

Example 2

Evaluate:

a) $\dfrac{2}{5} \times \dfrac{6}{7}$

b) $2\dfrac{2}{5} \div 6$

c) $1\dfrac{2}{3} - \dfrac{1}{5} \times 4\dfrac{1}{2}$

---

a) $\dfrac{2}{5} \times \dfrac{6}{7} = \dfrac{12}{35}$

b) $2\dfrac{2}{5} \div 6 = \dfrac{12}{5} \div \dfrac{6}{1}$

$= \dfrac{\overset{2}{\cancel{12}}}{5} \times \dfrac{1}{\underset{1}{\cancel{6}}} = \dfrac{2}{5}$

The reciprocal of 6 is $\dfrac{1}{6}$.

c) $1\dfrac{2}{3} - \dfrac{1}{5} \times 4\dfrac{1}{2} = \dfrac{5}{3} - \dfrac{1}{5} \times \dfrac{9}{2}$

$= \dfrac{5}{3} - \dfrac{9}{10}$

$= \dfrac{50}{30} - \dfrac{27}{30}$

$= \dfrac{23}{30}$

Exercise 1.1C

Evaluate each of the following, giving your answer in its simplest form.

1. $\dfrac{3}{4} + \dfrac{4}{5}$

2. $\dfrac{1}{3} + \dfrac{1}{8}$

3. $\dfrac{5}{6} + \dfrac{6}{9}$

4. $\dfrac{3}{4} - \dfrac{1}{3}$

5. $\dfrac{3}{5} - \dfrac{1}{3}$

6. $\dfrac{1}{2} - \dfrac{2}{5}$

7. $\dfrac{2}{3} \times \dfrac{4}{5}$

8. $\dfrac{1}{7} \times \dfrac{5}{6}$

9. $\dfrac{5}{8} \times \dfrac{12}{13}$

10. $\dfrac{1}{3} \div \dfrac{4}{5}$

11. $\dfrac{3}{4} \div \dfrac{1}{6}$

12. $\dfrac{5}{6} \div \dfrac{1}{2}$

13. $\dfrac{3}{8} + \dfrac{1}{5}$

14. $\dfrac{3}{8} \times \dfrac{1}{5}$

15. $\dfrac{3}{8} \div \dfrac{1}{5}$

16. $1\dfrac{3}{4} - \dfrac{2}{3}$

17. $1\dfrac{3}{4} \times \dfrac{2}{3}$

18. $1\dfrac{3}{4} \div \dfrac{2}{3}$

19. $3\dfrac{1}{2} + 2\dfrac{3}{5}$

20. $3\dfrac{1}{2} \times 2\dfrac{3}{5}$

21. $3\dfrac{1}{2} \div 2\dfrac{3}{5}$

22. $\left(\dfrac{3}{4} - \dfrac{2}{3}\right) \div \dfrac{3}{4}$

23. $\left(\dfrac{3}{5} + \dfrac{1}{3}\right) \times \dfrac{5}{7}$

24. $\dfrac{\dfrac{3}{8} - \dfrac{1}{5}}{\dfrac{7}{10} - \dfrac{2}{3}}$

25. $\dfrac{\dfrac{2}{3} + \dfrac{1}{3}}{\dfrac{3}{4} - \dfrac{1}{3}}$

26. Arrange these fractions in order of size. Write your answers in the form $a < b < c$.

a. $\dfrac{7}{12}, \dfrac{1}{2}, \dfrac{2}{3}$

b. $\dfrac{3}{4}, \dfrac{2}{3}, \dfrac{5}{6}$

c. $\dfrac{1}{3}, \dfrac{17}{24}, \dfrac{5}{8}, \dfrac{3}{4}$

d. $\dfrac{5}{6}, \dfrac{8}{9}, \dfrac{11}{12}$

27. Find the fraction that is exactly halfway between each pair of fractions:

a. $\dfrac{2}{5}, \dfrac{3}{5}$ **b.** $\dfrac{5}{8}, \dfrac{7}{8}$ **c.** $\dfrac{2}{3}, \dfrac{3}{4}$

d. $\dfrac{1}{3}, \dfrac{4}{9}$ **e.** $\dfrac{4}{15}, \dfrac{1}{3}$ **f.** $\dfrac{3}{8}, \dfrac{11}{24}$

28. In the equation below all the asterisks represent the same number. What is the number?

$$\left[\dfrac{*}{*} - \dfrac{*}{6} = \dfrac{*}{30} \right]$$

29. The shell of a newly hatched crab is 1 cm across. As it grows, it gets new shells that are each one-third bigger than the previous one. The shell of a fully grown crab is approximately 10 cm across. How many shells does a crab have during its lifetime?

30. Glass A contains 100 ml of water and glass B contains 100 ml of juice.

A 10 ml spoonful of juice is taken from glass B and mixed thoroughly with the water in glass A. A 10 ml spoonful of the mixture from A is returned to B. Is there now more juice in the water or more water in the juice?

Fractions and decimals

A decimal is simply a fraction expressed in tenths, hundredths and so on.

Example 1

Convert:

a) $\dfrac{7}{8}$ to a decimal   **b)** 0.35 to a fraction   **c)** $\dfrac{1}{3}$ to a decimal

---

a) $\dfrac{7}{8}$ (divide 7 by 8)

$$8\overline{)7.000} \quad \to \quad 0.875$$

$$\dfrac{7}{8} = 0.875$$

b) $0.35 = \dfrac{35}{100}$

$$= \dfrac{7}{20}$$

c) $\dfrac{1}{3}$ (divide 1 by 3)

$$\dfrac{1}{3} = 0.\dot{3} \text{ (0.3 recurring)}$$

$$3\overline{)1.0^10^10^1000} \quad \to \quad 0.\,3\ 3\ 3\ 3$$

Example 2

a) Convert $0.\dot{7}$ to a fraction.

This recurring decimal has one place recursion so you multiply it by 10 and set out our working as follows:

$$\text{Let } x = 0.\dot{7}$$
$$x = 0.7777...$$
$$10x = 7.7777...$$
$$10x - x = 7.7777... - 0.7777...$$
$$9x = 7$$
$$x = \frac{7}{9}$$

b) Convert $0.\dot{2}\dot{3}$ to a fraction.

Here you have *two place* recursion so you multiply it by 100:

$$\text{Let } x = 0.\dot{2}\dot{3}$$
$$x = 0.2323...$$
$$100x = 23.2323...$$
$$100x - x = 23.2323... - 0.2323...$$
$$99x = 23$$
$$x = \frac{23}{99}$$

c) Convert $0.5\dot{3}\dot{4}$ to a fraction.

You need to multiply by 1000 and 10 as only two of the three digits recur:

$$\text{Let } x = 0.5\dot{3}\dot{4}$$
$$x = 0.53434...$$
$$10x = 5.3434...$$
$$1000x = 534.3434...$$
$$1000x - 10x = 534.3434... - 5.3434...$$
$$990x = 529$$
$$x = \frac{529}{990}$$

Tip

Despite their appearance, all recurring decimal numbers are rational.

Exercise 1.1D

For Questions **1** to **24**, change the fractions to decimals.

1. $\dfrac{1}{4}$
2. $\dfrac{2}{5}$
3. $\dfrac{4}{5}$
4. $\dfrac{3}{4}$
5. $\dfrac{1}{2}$
6. $\dfrac{3}{8}$

7. $\dfrac{9}{10}$
8. $\dfrac{5}{8}$
9. $\dfrac{5}{12}$
10. $\dfrac{1}{6}$
11. $\dfrac{2}{3}$
12. $\dfrac{5}{6}$

13. $\dfrac{2}{7}$
14. $\dfrac{3}{7}$
15. $\dfrac{4}{9}$
16. $\dfrac{5}{11}$
17. $1\dfrac{1}{5}$
18. $2\dfrac{5}{8}$

19. $2\dfrac{1}{3}$
20. $1\dfrac{7}{10}$
21. $2\dfrac{3}{16}$
22. $2\dfrac{2}{7}$
23. $2\dfrac{6}{7}$
24. $3\dfrac{19}{100}$

For Questions **25** to **40**, change the decimals to fractions and simplify.

25. 0.2
26. 0.7
27. 0.25
28. 0.45
29. 0.36
30. 0.52

31. 0.125
32. 0.625
33. 0.84
34. 2.35
35. 3.95
36. 1.05

37. 3.2
38. 0.27
39. 0.007
40. 0.00011

Evaluate, giving your answer to 2 decimal places:

41. $\dfrac{1}{4} + \dfrac{1}{3}$
42. $\dfrac{2}{3} + 0.75$
43. $\dfrac{8}{9} - 0.24$
44. $\dfrac{7}{8} + \dfrac{5}{9} + \dfrac{2}{11}$

45. $\dfrac{1}{3} \times 0.2$
46. $\dfrac{5}{8} \times \dfrac{1}{4}$
47. $\dfrac{8}{11} \div 0.2$
48. $\left(\dfrac{4}{7} - \dfrac{1}{3}\right) \div 0.4$

Arrange these numbers in order of size (smallest first).

49. $\dfrac{1}{3}, 0.33, \dfrac{4}{15}$
50. $\dfrac{2}{7}, 0.3, \dfrac{4}{9}$
51. $0.71, \dfrac{7}{11}, 0.705$
52. $\dfrac{4}{13}, 0.3, \dfrac{5}{18}$

Convert the following recurring decimals to fractions.

53. $0.\dot{6}$
54. $0.\dot{4}$
55. $0.\dot{1}\dot{2}$
56. $0.4\dot{3}$

57. $0.1\dot{3}\dot{4}$
58. $0.\dot{7}3\dot{1}$
59. $0.2\dot{5}$
60. $0.6\dot{1}\dot{7}$

61. Decide whether each statement is true or false.

    a) $0.7 < \dfrac{7}{9}$
    b) $82\% > 0.8\dot{2}\dot{3}$
    c) $0.\dot{6}\dot{3} \neq \dfrac{7}{11}$

1.2 Negative numbers

- If the weather is very cold and the temperature is 3 degrees below zero, it is written −3°.
- If a golfer is 5 under par for the round, the scoreboard shows −5.
- On a bank statement if someone is $55 overdrawn [or 'in the red'] it appears as −$55.

The above are examples of the use of negative numbers.

An easy way to begin calculations with negative numbers is to think about changes in temperature:

a) Suppose the temperature is −2° and it rises by 7°.

The new temperature is 5°.

You can write −2 + 7 = 5.

b) Suppose the temperature is −3° and it falls by 6°.

The new temperature is −9°.

You can write −3 − 6 = −9.

Tip

You can always draw a number line if you have problems visualising the addition and subtraction of negative numbers.

Exercise 1.2A

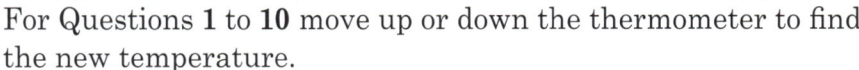

For Questions **1** to **10** move up or down the thermometer to find the new temperature.

1. The temperature is +8° and it falls by 3°.
2. The temperature is −8° and it rises by 4°.
3. The temperature is +4° and it falls by 5°.
4. The temperature is −3° and it rises by 7°.
5. The temperature is +2° and it falls by 6°.
6. The temperature is +4° and it rises by 8°.
7. The temperature is −1° and it falls by 6°.
8. The temperature is +9° and it falls by 14°.
9. The temperature is −5° and it rises by 1°.
10. The temperature is −13° and it rises by 13°.

11. Some of the land in Bangladesh is below sea level.
Here are the heights, relative to sea level, of five villages.

Note: 'sea level' is the base level for measuring elevations and depths. It is defined as 0 m, with all elevations and depths related to it.

A 1 m   **B** −4 m   **C** 21 m **D** −2 m   **E** −1.5 m

a) Which village is safest from flooding?

b) Which village is most at risk from serious flooding?

12. A diver is below the surface of the water at −15 m.
She dives down by 6 m, then rises 4 m.
At what depth is she now?

Operations involving negative numbers

To add two numbers, where one or both may be negative, consider the first number to be your starting point, and the second number to be telling you in which direction to move along the number line.

Example 1

−7 + −3   Begin at −7 and then move 3 in the negative direction.
The answer is −10.

−2 + 8   Begin at −2 and then move 8 in the positive direction.
The answer is 6.

When subtracting, where one or both numbers may be negative, consider the first number to be your starting point, look at what the second number would require you to do if you were adding it, and then go in the opposite direction.

Example 2

−7 − +3   Begin at −7 and then, because the 3 is positive, move 3 in the negative direction.
The answer is −10.

−8 − −7   Begin at −8 and then, because the 7 is negative, move 7 in the positive direction.
The answer is −1.

Exercise 1.2B

Evaluate:

1. $-3 + -9$
2. $-7 + -24$
3. $+0.2 + +5.9$
4. $-8 + -27$
5. $-2 + -3 + -4$
6. $-7 + +4$
7. $+7 + -4$
8. $-9 + +7$
9. $+16 + -30$
10. $+14 + -21$
11. $-19 + +200$
12. $+7.6 + -9.8$
13. $-1.8 + +10$
14. $-7 + +24$
15. $+7 - +5$
16. $+9 - +15$
17. $-6 - +9$
18. $-19 - -7$
19. $-10 - +70$
20. $-5.1 - +8$
21. $-0.2 - +4$
22. $+5.2 - -7.2$
23. $-4 + -3$
24. $+6 - -2$
25. $+8 + -4$
26. $-4 - +6$
27. $+7 - -4$
28. $+10 - +30$
29. $+4 + -7 + -2$
30. $-3 - +2 + -5$
31. $-17 - -1 + -10$
32. $-5 + -7 - +9$
33. $+9 + -7 - -6$
34. $-10.1 + -10.1$
35. $-75 - -25$
36. $-204 - +304$
37. $-7 + -11 - +11$
38. $+17 - +17$
39. $-6 + -7 - +8$
40. $-11 - -4 + +3$
41. $-2 - -8.7$
42. $+7 + -11 + +5$
43. $-610 + -240$
44. $-7 - -3 - -8$
45. $+9 - -6 + -9$
46. $-1 - -5 + -8$
47. $-2.1 + -9.9$
48. $-47 - -16$

When two numbers with the same sign are multiplied together, the result is positive.

- $+7 \times (+3) = +21$
- $-6 \times (-4) = +24$

When two numbers with different signs are multiplied together, the result is negative.

- $-8 \times (+4) = -32$
- $+7 \times (-5) = -35$
- $-3 \times (+2) \times (+5) = -6 \times (+5) = -30$

When dividing numbers, the rules are the same as in multiplication.

- $-70 \div (-2) = +35$
- $+12 \div (-3) = -4$
- $-20 \div (+4) = -5$

> **Tip**
>
> $+ \times + = +$
> $- \times - = +$

> **Tip**
>
> $+ \times - = -$
> $- \times + = -$

Exercise 1.2C

Evaluate:

1. $+2 \times (-4)$　　　　**2.** $+7 \times (+4)$　　　　**3.** $-4 \times (-3)$

4. $-6 \times (-4)$　　　　**5.** $-6 \times (-3)$　　　　**6.** $+5 \times (-7)$

7. $-7 \times (-7)$　　　　**8.** $-4 \times (+3)$　　　　**9.** $+0.5 \times (-4)$

10. $-1\dfrac{1}{2} \times (-6)$　　**11.** $-8 \div (+2)$　　　**12.** $+12 \div (+3)$

13. $+36 \div (-9)$　　　**14.** $-40 \div (-5)$　　　**15.** $-70 \div (-1)$

16. $-56 \div (+8)$　　　**17.** $-\dfrac{1}{2} \div (-2)$　　**18.** $-3 \div (+5)$

19. $+0.1 \div (-10)$　　**20.** $-0.02 \div (-100)$　　**21.** $-11 \times (-11)$

22. $-6 \times (-1)$　　　**23.** $+12 \times (-50)$　　**24.** $-\dfrac{1}{2} \div \left(+\dfrac{1}{2}\right)$

25. $-600 \div (+30)$　　**26.** $-5.2 \div (+2)$　　**27.** $+7 \times (-100)$

28. $-6 \div \left(-\dfrac{1}{3}\right)$　　**29.** $100 \div (-0.1)$　　**30.** -8×-80

31. $-3 \times (-2) \times (-1)$　**32.** $+3 \times (-7) \times (+2)$　**33.** $+0.4 \div (-1)$

34. $-16 \div (+40)$　　**35.** $+0.2 \times (-1000)$　**36.** $-7 \times (-5) \times (-1)$

37. $-14 \div (+7)$　　　**38.** $-7 \div (-14)$　　　**39.** $+1\dfrac{1}{4} \div (-5)$

40. $-6 \times \left(-\dfrac{1}{2}\right) \times (-30)$

1.3 Number facts

- An *integer* is a positive or negative whole number or zero, for example, 2, 0, −3, …

- A *natural number* is a whole number used for counting or ordering, for example, 1, 2, 3, 4, …

- A *prime* number has only two factors: itself and 1.
  The first six prime numbers are: 2, 3, 5, 7, 11, and 13.

- The *multiples* of 12 are 12, 24, 36, 48, …

- The *factors* of 12 are 1, 2, 3, 4, 6, and 12

- The *lowest common multiple* (LCM) of two numbers is the smallest number that is a multiple of both numbers, for example, the LCM of 4 and 10 is 20.

- The *highest common factor* (HCF) of two numbers is the biggest number that is a factor of both of the numbers, for example, the HCF of 16 and 24 is 8.

- Non-prime integers greater than 1 can all be written uniquely as the product of prime numbers. This is called the number's *prime factorisation*, for example, 30 can be written as $2 \times 3 \times 5$.

- A *square number* is the result of multiplying a number by itself, for example, $5 \times 5 = 25$, so 25 is a square number.

- A *cube number* is the result of multiplying a number by itself twice, for example, $5 \times 5 \times 5 = 125$, so 125 is a cube number.

- *Indices* are used as a neat way of writing products.

  $2^4 = 2 \times 2 \times 2 \times 2 = 16$ [2 to the power 4]

  $3^5 = 3 \times 3 \times 3 \times 3 \times 3 = 243$ [3 to the power 5]

- The *reciprocal* of a number is the result of dividing 1 by that number.

  The reciprocal of 4 is $\frac{1}{4}$.

  In general, the reciprocal of n is $\frac{1}{n}$. This can be written as n^{-1}.

A good way to find the HCF and LCM of two numbers, if you know their prime factorisations, is to use a Venn diagram.

Create a set in the Venn diagram for each of the numbers and fill them with their prime factors, making sure to put any primes that belong to both of the numbers into the intersection.

The HCF will be the product of the primes in the intersection.

The LCM will be the product of all the primes in the Venn diagram.

Example

Use a Venn diagram to find the HCF and LCM of 75 and 200.

$75 = 3 \times 5 \times 5$

$200 = 2 \times 2 \times 2 \times 5 \times 5$

The HCF of 75 and 200 is 5×5

The LCM of 75 and 200 is $2 \times 2 \times 2 \times 3 \times 5 \times 5 = 600$

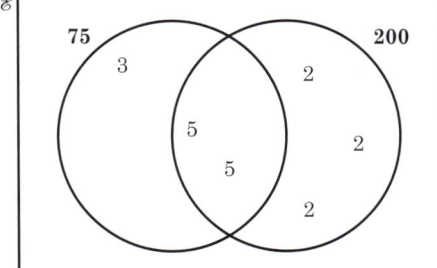

Exercise 1.3A

1. Determine which of the following are prime numbers.

   3, 11, 15, 19, 21, 23, 27, 29, 31, 37, 39, 47, 51, 59, 61, 67, 72, 73, 87, 99

2. Write down the first five multiples of these numbers:

   a) 4   **b)** 6   **c)** 10   **d)** 11   **e)** 20

3. Write down the first six multiples of 4 and of 6. What are the first two *common* multiples of 4 and 6? [i.e. multiples of both 4 and 6]

4. Write down the first six multiples of 3 and of 5. What is the lowest common multiple of 3 and 5?

5. Write down all the factors of the following:

   a) 6   **b)** 9   **c)** 10   **d)** 15   **e)** 24   **f)** 32

6. **a)** Is 263 a prime number?

   By how many numbers do you need to divide 263 so that you can find out?

   b) Is 527 a prime number?

7. Make six prime numbers using the digits 1, 2, 3, 4, 5, 6, 7, 8, 9 once each.

8. Write the following numbers as the product of prime factors:

   a) 24   **b)** 60   **c)** 90

   d) 144   **e)** 1000   **f)** 880

9. Find the highest common factor of

   a) 24 and 60   **b)** 90 and 144   **c)** 60 and 1000

   d) 24 and 880   **e)** 90 and 1000   **f)** 24, 60 and 144

10. Find the lowest common multiple of

    a) 8 and 15   **b)** 10 and 45   **c)** 12 and 20

    d) 6 and 24   **e)** 9 and 21   **f)** 15 and 70

11. Without using a calculator, work out:

    a) 4^2 **b)** 6^2 **c)** 10^2 **d)** 3^3 **e)** 10^3

12. Use the $\boxed{x^2}$ button on the calculator to work out:

    a) 9^2 **b)** 21^2 **c)** 1.2^2 **d)** 0.2^2 **e)** 3.1^2

    f) 100^2 **g)** 25^2 **h)** 8.7^2 **i)** 0.9^2 **j)** 81.4^2

> **Tip**
>
> The circumference and area of a circle will be studied in detail in section 5.2.

13. Find the areas of these squares.

a)

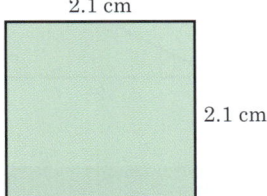

b)

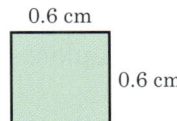

c)

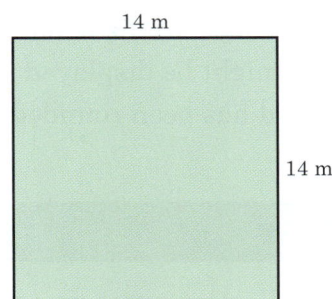

14. 100 million $= 10^x$. Find the value of x.

15. Find the reciprocal of each number.

    a) 7   **b)** 12   **c)** -4

    d) 3.5   **e)** $\dfrac{1}{2}$ **f)** $\dfrac{3}{5}$

For Questions **16** to **20**, work out the value of the number given, both as a fraction and as a decimal.

16. 2^{-1} **17.** 10^{-1} **18.** 5^{-1} **19.** 4^{-1} **20.** 8^{-1}

Rational and irrational numbers

A rational number can always be written exactly in the form $\dfrac{a}{b}$ where a and b are whole numbers providing b is not equal to zero.

$$\frac{3}{7} \qquad 1\frac{1}{2} = \frac{3}{2} \qquad 5.14 = \frac{257}{50} \qquad 0.\dot{6} = \frac{2}{3}$$

All these are rational numbers.

> **Tip**
>
> π is the ratio of the circumference to the diameter of a circle. You will work with π in Chapter 5.

An irrational number cannot be written in the form $\dfrac{a}{b}$.

$\sqrt{2}, \sqrt{5}, \pi, \sqrt[3]{2}$ are all irrational numbers.

In general $\sqrt{n}$ is irrational unless n is a square number.

Negative numbers can be rational as well. For example, -7 is a negative rational number because it can be written as $-\dfrac{7}{1}$.

Thus, the additive inverse of any positive rational number is also rational. From the first bullet point above, $-\frac{3}{7}$, $-\frac{3}{2}$, $-\frac{257}{50}$ and $-\frac{2}{3}$ are all rational.

In this triangle, the length of the hypotenuse is *exactly* $\sqrt{5}$. On a calculator, $\sqrt{5}$ might be displayed as 2.236068. This value of $\sqrt{5}$ is *not* exact and has been rounded to 6 decimal places.

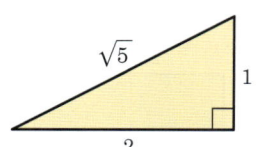

Exercise 1.3B

1. Which of the following numbers are rational?

a) 2.15   **b)** $0.\dot{8}$ **c)** 3π **d)** $2\frac{3}{7}$ **e)** -3

f) $\dfrac{\pi}{2}$ **g)** $\sqrt{5}$ **h)** $\left(\sqrt{17}\right)^2$ **i)** $\sqrt{3}$

j) 3.14   **k)** $\dfrac{\sqrt{12}}{\sqrt{3}}$ **l)** π^2 **m)** $3^{-1} + 3^{-2}$

n) $\dfrac{22}{7}$ **o)** $\sqrt{2} + 1$ **p)** $\sqrt{2.25}$

2. **a)** Write down any rational number between 4 and 6.

   b) Write down any irrational number between 4 and 6.

   c) Find a rational number between $\sqrt{2}$ and $\sqrt{3}$.

   d) Write down any rational number between π and $\sqrt{10}$.

3. **a)** For each shape, state whether the *perimeter* is rational or irrational.

   b) For each shape, state whether the *area* is rational or irrational.

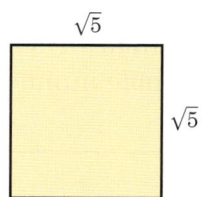

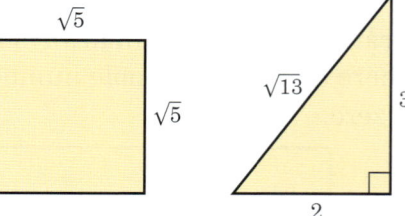

4. The diagram shows a circle of radius 3 cm drawn inside a square. Write down the exact value of the following and state whether the answer is rational or not:

   a) the circumference of the circle

   b) the diameter of the circle

   c) the area of the square

   d) the area of the circle

   e) the shaded area.

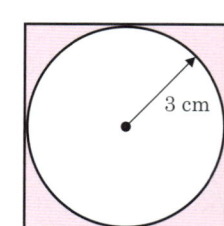

> **Tip**
>
> Circumference = $2\pi r$, where r is the radius.

> **Tip**
>
> Area = πr^2, where r is the radius.

5. Think of two *irrational* numbers x and y such that $\frac{x}{y}$ is a *rational* number.

6. Explain the difference between a rational number and an irrational number.

7. **a)** Is it possible for the product of a rational number and an irrational number to be a rational number? If so, give an example.

   b) Is it possible for the product of two irrational numbers to be rational? If so, give an example.

1.4 Sequences

The terms of a sequence

Look at the sequence which starts 2, 5, 8, 11, …

The numbers that are in the sequence are called **terms** of the sequence.

In this sequence, to get the next term you add 3 to the current term. Therefore, the *term-to-term rule* for this sequence is 'add 3'.

Because the gap between each pair of consecutive terms is always the same, this is a **linear sequence** or an **arithmetic sequence**. They mean the same thing.

Exercise 1.4A

Write down the next two numbers in each sequence.

For Questions **1** to **4**, also state the term-to-term rule.

1. 2, 6, 10, 14 **2.** 2, 9, 16, 23 **3.** 95, 87, 79, 71

4. 13, 8, 3, −2 **5.** 7, 9, 12, 16 **6.** 20, 17, 13, 8

7. 1, 2, 4, 7, 11 **8.** 1, 2, 4, 8 **9.** 55, 49, 42, 34

10. 10, 8, 5, 1 **11.** −18, −13, −9, −6 **12.** 120, 60, 30, 15

13. 27, 9, 3, 1 **14.** 162, 54, 18, 6 **15.** 2, 5, 11, 20

16. 1, 4, 20, 120 **17.** 2, 3, 1, 4, 0 **18.** 720, 120, 24, 6

Finding a formula for the nth term of a linear sequence

In a *linear* sequence, the difference between consecutive terms is always the same number.

Here are some linear sequences. What is the difference between successive terms (the term-to-term difference)?

A: 5, 7, 9, 11, 13

B: 12, 32, 52, 72, 92

C: 20, 17, 14, 11, 8

The expression for the nth term of an linear sequence is always of the form $an + b$.

The *difference* between successive terms is equal to the number a.

For sequence A, the terms go up by 2, so $a = 2$ and the nth term $= 2n + b$

For sequence B, the terms go up by 20, so $a = 2$ and the nth term $= 20n + b$

For sequence C, the terms go *down* by 3, so $a = -3$ and the nth term $= -3n + b$

You can find the value of b in each case by considering the value of the first term in the sequence, when $n = 1$.

For example, in sequence A: when $n = 1$, $\quad 2 \times 1 + b = 5$

$$\text{so } b = 3$$

A formula for the nth term in sequence A is $T_n = 2n + 3$.

Note that the nth term is sometimes abbreviated to T_n, meaning the term at position n. This is also called the position-to-term rule.

Some formulae for nth terms can be found by combining two linear sequences. For example, consider the following sequence:

$$\frac{2}{5}, \frac{3}{10}, \frac{4}{15}, \frac{5}{20}, \frac{6}{25}$$

The numerators of the fractions form the sequence 2, 3, 4, 5, 6, ... or $n + 1$

The denominators of the fractions form the sequence 5, 10, 15, 20, 25, ... or $5n$

Combining these gives $T_n = \dfrac{n + 1}{5n}$.

Exercise 1.4B

For Questions **1** to **16**, find a formula for the nth term of the sequence.

1. 5, 9, 13, 17, …

2. 7, 10, 13, 16, …

3. 4, 9, 14, 19, …

4. 6, 10, 14, 18, …

5. 5, 8, 11, 14, …

6. 25, 22, 19, 16, …

7. 5, 10, 15, 20, …

8. 21, 22, 23, 24, …

9. $\dfrac{1}{2}, \dfrac{2}{3}, \dfrac{3}{4}, \dfrac{4}{5}, \ldots$

10. 7, 14, 21, 28, …

11. 12, 22, 32, 42, …

12. $\dfrac{3}{1}, \dfrac{4}{2}, \dfrac{5}{3}, \dfrac{6}{4}, \ldots$

13. 3, 7, 11, 15, …

14. 5, 7, 9, 11, …

15. 7, 5, 3, 1, …

16. −5, −1, 3, 7, …

17. Write down each sequence and then find the nth term.

    a) 8, 10, 12, 14, 16, …

    b) 3, 7, 11, 15, …

    c) 8, 13, 18, 23, …

18. Write down each sequence and write the formula for T_n.

    a) 11, 19, 27, 35, …

    b) $2\dfrac{1}{2}, 4\dfrac{1}{2}, 6\dfrac{1}{2}, 8\dfrac{1}{2}, \ldots$

    c) −7, −4, −1, 2, 5, …

19. Here is a sequence of shapes made from pencils.

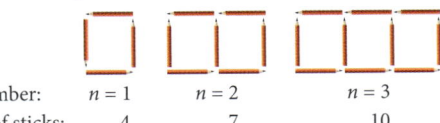

Shape number: $n = 1$ $n = 2$ $n = 3$
Number of sticks: 4   7   10

    The number of pencils makes the sequence 4, 7, 10, 13, …

    a) Find an expression for the nth term in the sequence.

    b) How many pencils are there in shape number 1000?

Quadratic sequences

Consider the sequence 1, 3, 7, 13, 21.

Look at the differences between the consecutive terms, which are: 2, 4, 6, 8.

They are not the same, therefore 1, 3, 7, 13, 21 is not an arithmetic sequence.

Now look at the differences between the differences: 2, 2, 2, 2.

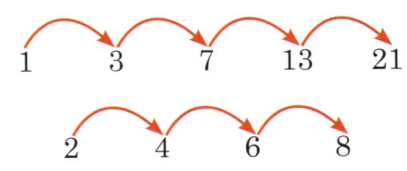

These are the same. If these second differences are all the same, then the original sequence is a quadratic sequence.

Quadratic sequences have an nth term formula of the form $T_n = an^2 + bn + c$.

To find the values of a, b and c, first find the number that appears in the second differences. The value of a will always be half of this number.

Then find the first few terms of the sequence $T_n = an^2$. The difference between this sequence and the sequence you wish to find the nth term formula for will be an arithmetic sequence. You then just need to find the nth term for that arithmetic sequence and add it to an^2 to get the full formula.

Example

Find the nth term formula for the sequence 3, 5, 9, 15, 23, ...

Find the first and second differences: 3   5   9   15   23

First difference   2   4   6   8

Second difference   2   2   2

The second differences are all 2. This implies that $2a = 2$ and $a = 1$.

This means that the sequence is quadratic and that the formula starts with n^2. The sequence n^2 is the sequence of square numbers.

Now subtract the sequence n^2 from the sequence 3, 5, 9, 15, 23, ...

$\quad$ 3   5   9   15   23   (Write the first few terms of the sequence.)

$-$ 1   4   9   16   25   (Subtract the sequence of square numbers.)

$\quad$ 2   1   0   −1   −2

The nth term formula for the sequence 2, 1, 0, −1, −2 is $T_n = -n + 3$.

Therefore the nth term formula for the sequence 3, 5, 9, 15, 23 is $T_n = n^2 - n + 3$.

Exercise 1.4C

Find a formula for the nth term of each sequence.

1. 4, 7, 12, 19, …

2. 2, 8, 18, 32, …

3. 0, 3, 8, 15, …

4. 0.5, 2, 4.5, 8, …

5. −6, −3, 2, 9, …

6. −1, −4, −9, −16, …

7. 0, −3, −8, −15, …

8. 5, 12, 21, 32, …

9. 1, 6, 15, 28, …

10. 3, 9, 17, 27, …

11. 2, 9, 28, 65, …

12. 2, 16, 54, 128, …

13. −1, 6, 25, 62, …

14. 1, 3, 7, 15, …

15. 3, 9, 27, 81, …

> **Tip**
>
> For Question **13**, write out the sequence of *cube* numbers and compare.

> **Tip**
>
> For Question **14**, write out the sequence of 2^n and compare.

Cubic and exponential sequences

As well as linear and quadratic sequences you also need to know about the following types of sequence:

- A *cubic* sequence has an nth term formula of the form $T_n = an^3 + bn^2 + cn + d$.

  You can recognise a cubic sequence because its third differences will all be the same.

- An *exponential* sequence (sometimes called a *geometric* sequence) is a sequence where to move from one term to the next you multiply by a fixed multiplier.

Example 1

Find the nth term formula for the cubic sequence
6, 13, 32, 69, 130, …

Subtract the sequence n^3 from the sequence 6, 13, 32, 69, 130, …

$$
\begin{array}{rccccc}
 & 6 & 13 & 32 & 69 & 130 \\
- & 1 & 8 & 27 & 64 & 125 \\
\hline
 & 5 & 5 & 5 & 5 & 5 \\
\end{array}
$$

Therefore the nth term formula for the sequence
6, 13, 32, 69, 130, … is $T_n = n^3 + 5$.

Example 2

Find the nth term formula for the sequence 3, 6, 12, 24, 48, …

Note that the term-to-term rule here is 'multiply by 2'.

This means it is an exponential sequence.

Because the multiplier is 2, and the first term is 3,

the formula for the nth term is $T_n = 3 \times 2^{n-1}$.

Exercise 1.4D

Find a formula for the nth term of each sequence.

1. 1, 8, 27, 64, …   **2.** 2, 4, 8, 16, …

3. 1, 3, 9, 27, …   **4.** 13, 20, 39, 76, …

5. 6, 18, 54, 162, …   **6.** −4, 3, 22, 59, …

7. 9, 11, 15, 23, …   **8.** 2, 10, 30, 68, …

9. 0, 4, 18, 48, …   **10.** 3, 12, 35, 80, …

1.5 Approximations and estimation

There are several different ways in which you may be required to round a number.

- *To the nearest* something. For example, to the nearest whole number, ten, hundred etc.
- To a certain number of *decimal places*.
- To a certain number of *significant figures*.

Example

a) 7.8126 = 8 to the nearest whole number.

   ↑ This figure is '5 or more'.

b) 7.8126 = 7.81 to three significant figures.

   ↑ This figure is not '5 or more'.

c) 7.8126 = 7.813 to three decimal places.

   ↑ This figure is '5 or more'.

d) $0.078\,126 = 0.0781$ to three significant figures.

    ↑ 7 is the first significant figure.

e) $3596 = 3600$ to two significant figures.

    ↑ This figure is '5 or more'.

Exercise 1.5A

Write the following numbers correct to:

a) the nearest whole number   **b)** three significant figures   **c)** two decimal places.

1. 8.174	**2.** 19.617	**3.** 20.041	**4.** 0.814 52	**5.** 311.14
6. 0.275	**7.** 0.007 47	**8.** 15.62	**9.** 900.12	**10.** 3.555
11. 5.454	**12.** 20.961	**13.** 0.0851	**14.** 0.5151	**15.** 3.071

Write the following numbers correct to one decimal place.

16. 5.71   **17.** 0.7614   **18.** 11.241   **19.** 0.0614   **20.** 0.0081   **21.** 11.12

Measurements and bounds

As all measurement involves some degree of error, all measurement is approximate.

For example, a length could be measured as 145 cm to the nearest cm.

In this situation, the actual length could be anything from 144.5 cm to 145.49999 … cm using the normal rounding conventions.

Since there is no biggest number that is less than 145.5, you say that 145.5 is the **upper bound** of the measurement. The **lower bound** is 144.5.

As an inequality you can write $144.5 \leqslant \text{length} < 145.5$

In general, to find the upper bound of a measurement you add half of the unit in which you are measuring to the value you have, and to find the lower bound you subtract half of the unit in which you are measuring from the value. In the case considered above, the units were centimetres so you added and subtracted half a centimetre from the measurement of 145 cm to find the bounds.

> **Tip**
>
> The 'unit' is 1 so 'half a unit' is 0.5.
>
> The 'unit' is 0.1 so 'half a unit' is 0.05.
>
> The 'unit' is 0.001 so 'half a unit' is 0.0005.

Example

The length of a page in a book is 246 mm to the nearest mm.

a) What is the upper bound of the measurement?
b) What is the lower bound of the measurement?

a) 245.5
b) 246.5

Here are some further examples:

Measurement	Lower bound	Upper bound
The diameter of a CD is 12 cm to the nearest cm.	11.5 cm	12.5 cm
The mass of a coin is 6.2 g to the nearest 0.1 g.	6.15 g	6.25 g
The length of a fence is 330 m to the nearest 10 m.	325 m	335 m
The time waiting for a bus is 15 minutes, to the nearest 5 minutes.	12.5 minutes	17.5 minutes

Exercise 1.5B

1. In a DIY store, the height of a door is given as 195 cm to the nearest cm. Write down the upper bound for the height of the door.

2. A vet measures the mass of a goat at 37 kg to the nearest kg. What is the least possible mass of the goat?

3. A farmer's scales measure mass to the nearest 0.1 kg. What is the upper bound for the mass of a chicken which the scales say has a mass of 3.2 kg?

4. A surveyor using a laser beam device can measure distances to the nearest 0.1 m. What is the least possible length of a warehouse which he measures at 95.6 m?

5. In the 200 m race at school, Stephanie was timed at 28.6 s, correct to 1 d.p. What is the upper bound for her time?

6. Copy and complete the table.

Measurement		Lower bound	Upper bound
a)	temperature in a fridge = 2°C to the nearest degree		
b)	mass of an acorn = 2.3 g to 1 d.p.		
c)	length of telephone cable = 64 m to the nearest m		
d)	time taken to run 100 m = 13.6 s to the nearest 0.1 s		
e)	The time taken to do my homework is 45 minutes, correct to the nearest 5 minutes.		

7. The length of a carton of milk is measured as 193 mm, to the nearest mm. The length lies between:

A	B	C
192 and 194 mm	192.5 and 193.5 mm	188 and 198 mm

8. The mass of a suitcase is 35 kg, to the nearest kg. The mass lies between:

A	B	C
30 and 40 kg	34 and 36 kg	34.5 and 35.5 kg

9. Adra and Leila each measure a different worm and they both say that their worm is 11 cm long to the nearest cm.

a) Does this mean that both worms are the same length?

b) If not, what is the maximum possible difference in the length of the two worms?

10. To the nearest cm, the length L of a stapler is 12 cm. As an inequality you write $11.5 \leqslant L < 12.5$.

For parts **(a)** to **(j)** you are given a measurement. Write the possible values using an inequality as above.

a) mass = 17 kg   (2 s.f.)   **b)** $d = 256$ km   (3 s.f.)

c) length = 2.4 m   (1 d.p.)   **d)** $m = 0.34$ grams   (2 s.f.)

e) $v = 2.04$ m/s   (2 d.p.)   **f)** $x = 12.0$ cm   (1 d.p.)

g) $T = 81.4$ °C   (1 d.p.)   **h)** $M = 0.3$ kg   (1 s.f.)

i) mass = 0.7 tonnes (1 s.f.)   **j)** $n = 52\ 000$ (nearest thousand)

k) time = 220 min   (nearest   **l)** $f = 2750$ (nearest 50)
                             20 min)

11. A card measuring 11.5 cm long (to the nearest 0.1 cm) is to be posted in an envelope which is 12 cm long (to the nearest cm). Can you guarantee that the card will fit inside the envelope? Explain your answer.

11.5 cm

12 cm

Calculating with lower and upper bounds

When adding or multiplying with upper bounds (UB) or lower bounds (LB):

UB + UB = UB   UB × UB = UB

LB + LB = LB   LB × LB = LB

When subtracting or dividing with upper or lower bounds:

UB − LB = UB   UB ÷ LB = UB

LB − UB = LB   LB ÷ UB = LB

Exercise 1.5C

1. The sides of the triangle are measured correct to the nearest cm.

  a) Write down the upper bounds for the lengths of the three sides.

  b) Work out the maximum possible perimeter of the triangle.

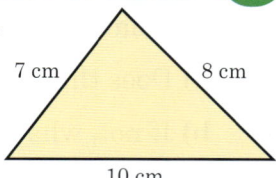

7 cm   8 cm

10 cm

2. The dimensions of a photo are measured correct to the nearest cm. Work out the minimum possible area of the photo.

9 cm

6 cm

3. In this question the value of a is either exactly 4 or 5, and the value of b is either exactly 1 or 2. Work out:

a) the maximum value of $a + b$

b) the minimum value of $a + b$

c) the maximum value of ab

d) the maximum value of $a - b$

e) the minimum value of $a - b$

f) the maximum value of $\frac{a}{b}$

g) the minimum value of $\frac{a}{b}$

h) the maximum value of $a^2 - b^2$.

4. If $p = 7$ cm and $q = 5$ cm, both to the nearest cm, find:

a) the largest possible value of $p + q$

b) the smallest possible value of $p + q$

c) the largest possible value of $p - q$

d) the largest possible value of $\frac{p^2}{q}$.

5. If $a = 3.1$ and $b = 7.3$, correct to one decimal place, find the largest possible value of:

i) $a + b$ **ii)** $b - a$

6. If $x = 5$ and $y = 7$ to one significant figure, find the largest and smallest possible values of:

i) $x + y$ **ii)** $y - x$ **iii)** $\frac{x}{y}$

7. In the diagram, ABCD and EFGH are rectangles with AB = 10 cm, BC = 7 cm, EF = 7 cm and FG = 4 cm, all figures accurate to the nearest cm. Find the largest possible value of the shaded area.

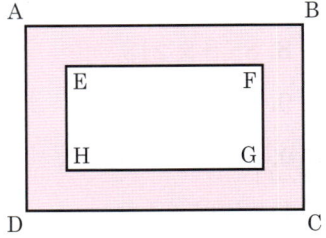

8. When a voltage V is applied to a resistance R the power consumed P is given by $P = \frac{V^2}{R}$.

If you measure V as 12.2 and R as 2.6, correct to 1 d.p., calculate the smallest possible value of P.

Estimation

When you are asked to estimate the value of a calculation, unless you are told otherwise, the standard method is to begin by writing every number in the calculation to 1 significant figure. Then perform the calculation.

Example

Estimate the value of $\frac{57.2 \times 110}{2.146 \times 46.9}$, to one significant figure.

This is approximately $\frac{60 \times 100}{2 \times 50} = 60$

Tip

On a calculator, the value is 62.52 (4 s.f.).

Exercise 1.5D

In this exercise there are 25 questions, each followed by three possible answers. Decide (by estimating) which answer is correct.

1. 7.2×9.8 [52.16, 98.36, 70.56]

2. 2.03×58.6 [118.958, 87.848, 141.116]

3. 23.4×19.3 [213.32, 301.52, 451.62]

4. 313×107.6 [3642.8, 4281.8, 33 678.8]

5. 6.3×0.098 [0.6174, 0.0622, 5.98]

6. 1200×0.89 [722, 1068, 131]

7. 0.21×93 [41.23, 9.03, 19.53]

8. 88.8×213 [18 914.4, 1693.4, 1965.4]

9. 0.04×968 [38.72, 18.52, 95.12]

10. 0.11×0.089 [0.1069, 0.095 9, 0.009 79]

11. $13.92 \div 5.8$ [0.52, 4.2, 2.4]

12. $105.6 \div 9.6$ [8.9, 11, 15]

13. $8405 \div 205$ [4.6, 402, 41]

14. $881.1 \div 99$ [4.5, 8.9, 88]

15. $4.183 \div 0.89$ [4.7, 48, 51]

16. $6.72 \div 0.12$ [6.32, 21.2, 56]

17. $20.301 \div 1010$ [0.0201, 0.211, 0.0021]

18. $0.288\,96 \div 0.0096$ [312, 102.1, 30.1]

19. $0.143 \div 0.11$ [2.3, 1.3, 11.4]

20. $(189.65 - 48.7) \div 2.4$ [60, 70, 75]

21. $(5.6 - 0.21) \times 39$ [389.21, 210.21, 20.51]

22. $\dfrac{17.5 \times 42}{2.5}$ [294, 504, 86]

23. $(906 + 4.1) \times 0.31$ [473.21, 282.131, 29.561]

24. $\dfrac{543 + 472}{18.1 + 10.9}$ [65, 35, 85]

25. $\dfrac{112.2 \times 75.9}{6.9 \times 5.1}$ [242, 20.4, 25.2]

1.6 Indices 1

Rules of indices

1. $a^n \times a^m = a^{n+m}$ For example: $7^2 \times 7^4 = 7^6$

2. $a^n \div a^m = a^{n-m}$ For example: $6^6 \div 6^2 = 6^4$

3. $\left(a^n\right)^m = a^{nm}$ For example: $\left(3^2\right)^5 = 3^{10}$

Also, $a^{-n} = \dfrac{1}{a^n}$ For example: $5^{-2} = \dfrac{1}{5^2}$

$a^{\frac{1}{n}}$ means 'the nth root of a'   For example: $9^{\frac{1}{2}} = \sqrt{9}$

$a^{\frac{m}{n}}$ means 'the nth root of a raised to the power m'

For example: $4^{\frac{3}{2}} = \left(\sqrt{4}\right)^3 = 8$

$a^0 = 1$ for any non-zero value of a.

Example 1

Write as a single power of 5:

a) $5^2 \times 5^4$ **b)** $5^{10} \div 5^3$ **c)** $(5^2)^4$

---

a) $5^2 \times 5^4 = 5^{2+4} = 5^6$ **b)** $5^{10} \div 5^3 = 5^{10-3} = 5^7$ **c)** $(5^2)^4 = 5^{2\times4} = 5^8$

Example 2

Evaluate:

a) $9^{\frac{1}{2}}$

b) 5^{-1}

c) $4^{-\frac{1}{2}}$

d) $25^{\frac{3}{2}}$

e) $\left(5^{\frac{1}{2}}\right)^3 \times 5^{\frac{1}{2}}$

f) 7^0

---

a) $9^{\frac{1}{2}} = \sqrt{9} = 3$

b) $5^{-1} = \dfrac{1}{5}$

c) $4^{-\frac{1}{2}} = \dfrac{1}{4^{\frac{1}{2}}} = \dfrac{1}{\sqrt{4}} = \dfrac{1}{2}$

d) $25^{\frac{3}{2}} = \left(\sqrt{25}\right)^3 = 5^3 = 125$

e) $\left(5^{\frac{1}{2}}\right)^3 \times 5^{\frac{1}{2}} = 5^{\frac{3}{2}} \times 5^{\frac{1}{2}} = 5^2 = 25$

f) $7^0 = 1 \left[\text{consider } \dfrac{7^3}{7^3} = 7^{3-3} = 7^0 = 1 \right]$

You can also express the products of different primes in index form if, for example, you are writing out a number's prime factorisation.

Example

Express the prime factorisation of 200 in index form.

$200 = 2 \times 2 \times 2 \times 5 \times 5 = 2^3 \times 5^2$

Exercise 1.6A

Express in index form:

1. 6×6

2. $4 \times 4 \times 4 \times 4 \times 4$

3. $3 \times 3 \times 5 \times 5$

4. $2 \times 2 \times 2 \times 11$

5. $\dfrac{1}{8 \times 8 \times 8}$

6. $\dfrac{1}{3 \times 3 \times 3 \times 7 \times 7}$

7. $\sqrt{13}$

8. $\sqrt[3]{2}$

9. $\sqrt[5]{10}$

10. $\left(\sqrt{5}\right)^3$

Write as a single power of 3:

11. $3^2 \times 3^9$

12. $3^{15} \div 3^7$

13. $3^3 \times 3^6 \times 3^8$

14. $3^7 \div 3^{10}$

15. $\left(3^5\right)^4$

16. $\dfrac{1}{3 \times 3 \times 3 \times 3}$

Exercise 1.6B

Evaluate:

1. $3^2 \times 3$

2. 100^0

3. 3^{-2}

4. $(5^{-1})^{-2}$

5. $4^{\frac{1}{2}}$

6. $16^{\frac{1}{2}}$

7. $81^{\frac{1}{2}}$

8. $8^{\frac{1}{3}}$

9. $9^{\frac{3}{2}}$

10. $27^{\frac{1}{3}}$

11. $9^{-\frac{1}{2}}$

12. $8^{-\frac{1}{3}}$

13. $1^{\frac{5}{2}}$

14. $25^{-\frac{1}{2}}$

15. $1000^{\frac{1}{3}}$

16. $2^{-2} \times 2^5$

17. $2^4 \div 2^{-1}$

18. $8^{\frac{2}{3}}$

19. $27^{-\frac{2}{3}}$

20. $4^{-\frac{3}{2}}$

21. $36^{\frac{1}{2}} \times 27^{\frac{1}{3}}$

22. $10\,000^{\frac{1}{4}}$

23. $100^{\frac{3}{2}}$

24. $\left(100^{\frac{1}{2}}\right)^{-3}$

25. $\left(9^{\frac{1}{2}}\right)^{-2}$

26. $(-16.371)^0$

27. $81^{\frac{1}{4}} \div 16^{\frac{1}{4}}$

28. $\left(5^{-4}\right)^{\frac{1}{2}}$

29. $1000^{-\frac{1}{3}}$

30. $\left(4^{-\frac{1}{2}}\right)^2$

31. $8^{-\frac{2}{3}}$

32. $100^{\frac{5}{2}}$

33. $1^{\frac{4}{3}}$

34. 2^{-5}

35. $\left(0.01\right)^{\frac{1}{2}}$

36. $\left(0.04\right)^{\frac{1}{2}}$

37. $\left(2.25\right)^{\frac{1}{2}}$

38. $(7.63)^0$

39. $3^5 \times 3^{-3}$

40. $\left(3\frac{3}{8}\right)^{\frac{1}{3}}$

41. $\left(11\frac{1}{9}\right)^{-\frac{1}{2}}$

42. $\left(\frac{1}{8}\right)^{-2}$

43. $\left(\frac{1}{1000}\right)^{\frac{2}{3}}$

44. $\left(\frac{9}{25}\right)^{-\frac{1}{2}}$

45. $(10^{-6})^{\frac{1}{3}}$

46. $7^2 \div \left(7^{\frac{1}{2}}\right)^4$

47. $(0.0001)^{-\frac{1}{2}}$

48. $\dfrac{9^{\frac{1}{2}}}{4^{-\frac{1}{2}}}$

49. $\dfrac{25^{\frac{3}{2}} \times 4^{\frac{1}{2}}}{9^{-\frac{1}{2}}}$

50. $\left(-\frac{1}{7}\right)^2 \div \left(-\frac{1}{7}\right)^3$

1.7 Standard form

When dealing with either very large or very small numbers, it is not convenient to write them out in full in the normal way. It is better to use standard form. Most calculators represent large and small numbers in this way.

The number $A \times 10^n$ is in standard form when $1 \leqslant A < 10$ and n is a positive or negative integer.

Example

Write in standard form:

a) $2000 = 2 \times 1000 = 2 \times 10^3$

b) $150 = 1.5 \times 100 = 1.5 \times 10^2$

c) $0.0004 = 4 \times \dfrac{1}{10\,000} = 4 \times 10^{-4}$

Exercise 1.7A

Write in standard form:

1. 4000	**2.** 500	**3.** 70 000	**4.** 60	**5.** 2400
6. 380	**7.** 46 000	**8.** 46	**9.** 900 000	**10.** 2560
11. 0.007	**12.** 0.0004	**13.** 0.0035	**14.** 0.421	**15.** 0.000 055
16. 0.01	**17.** 564 000	**18.** 19 million		

19. The population of China is estimated at 1 100 000 000.
Write this in standard form.

20. The mass of a hydrogen atom is 0.000 000 000 000 000 000 000 001 67 grams.
Write this mass in standard form.

21. The area of the surface of the Earth is about 510 000 000 km².
Express this in standard form.

22. An atom is 0.000 000 000 25 cm in diameter. Write this in
standard form.

23. The number of cells in the human body is estimated at
3.71×10^{13}. Write this number out in full.

> **Tip**
>
> 1 km = 1000 m
>
> 1 m = 100 cm

24. The speed of light is 300 000 km/s. Express this speed in cm/s
in standard form.

Calculating with standard form

Sometimes it makes sense to convert numbers into standard form before
performing calculations with them. By doing this you will be less likely
to make mistakes, particularly if the numbers contain a lot of zeros.

Example

Work out $1500 \times 8\,000\,000$

$$1500 \times 8\,000\,000 = (1.5 \times 10^3) \times (8 \times 10^6)$$
$$= 12 \times 10^9$$
$$= 1.2 \times 10^{10}$$

Note that you multiply the numbers and the powers of 10
separately.

Exercise 1.7B

For Questions **1** to **15** give the answer in standard form.

1. $(8 \times 10^4) + (2 \times 10^3)$ **2.** $(1.2 \times 10^2) + (6 \times 10^{-1})$

3. $(6 \times 10^{12}) - (1.4 \times 10^{11})$ **4.** $(5.2 \times 10^{-2}) - (2 \times 10^{-4})$

5. $(6 \times 10^4) \times (5 \times 10^3)$ **6.** 0.00007×400 **7.** $(7 \times 10^{-4}) \times (1 \times 10^5)$

8. $8000 \div 0.004$ **9.** $(0.002)^2$ **10.** $(1.5 \times 10^2) \times (6 \times 10^{-4})$

11. $0.000033 \div 500$ **12.** $0.007 \div 20000$ **13.** $(0.0001)^4$

14. $(2000)^3$ **15.** $0.00592 \div 8000$

16. $a = 512 \times 10^2$ $b = 0.478 \times 10^6$ $c = 0.0049 \times 10^7$

Arrange a, b and c in order of size (smallest first).

17. If the number 2.74×10^{15} is written out in full, how many zeros follow the 4?

18. If the number 7.31×10^{-17} is written out in full, how many zeros would there be between the decimal point and the first significant figure?

> **Tip**
>
> The limits of accuracy of 2 to one significant figure are 1.5 to 2.5.

19. If $x = 2 \times 10^5$ and $y = 3 \times 10^{-3}$ correct to one significant figure, find the greatest and least possible values of:

  i) xy **ii)** $\dfrac{x}{y}$

20. Oil flows through a pipe at a rate of 40 m³/s. How long will it take to fill a tank of volume 1.2×10^5 m³? Give your answer in minutes.

21. Given that $L = 2\sqrt{\dfrac{a}{k}}$, find the value of L in standard form when

$a = 4.5 \times 10^{12}$ and $k = 5 \times 10^7$.

22. a) The number 10 to the power 100 is called a 'googol'. If it takes $\frac{1}{5}$ second to write a zero and $\frac{1}{10}$ second to write a 'one', how long would it take to write the number 100 'googols' in full?

  b) The number 10 to the power of a 'googol' is called a 'googolplex'. Using the same speed of writing, how long in years would it take to write 1 'googolplex' in full?

1.8 Surds

Sometimes calculations result in an irrational answer such as $\sqrt{5}$. If this is written as a decimal, it must be rounded and thus is no longer exact. If the value is used again in further calculations the rounding would cause the final answer to be inaccurate. When an exact answer is required, answers should be left in surd form.

A surd means a number left in square root form, such as $\sqrt{5}$ or $\sqrt{7}$.

If the number inside the square root sign is a square number it should be written as an integer rather than in surd form for example, $\sqrt{25} = 5$.

Rules of surds

1. $\sqrt{a} \times \sqrt{b} = \sqrt{ab}$

2. $\sqrt{a} \times \sqrt{a} = a$

3. $\dfrac{\sqrt{a}}{\sqrt{b}} = \sqrt{\dfrac{a}{b}}$

In algebra $5a$ means $5 \times a$.

Surds work in a similar way.

$5\sqrt{3}$ means $5 \times \sqrt{3}$.

In algebra $3x \times 4y$ can be written as $3 \times 4 \times x \times y$ or $12xy$ in its simplest form. This also works for surds. $3\sqrt{7} \times 4\sqrt{5}$ can be written as $3 \times 4 \times \sqrt{7} \times \sqrt{5}$ or $12 \times \sqrt{7 \times 5}$ or $12\sqrt{35}$ as a single surd.

Example

Write each of these as a single surd or integer answer.

a) $\sqrt{3} \times \sqrt{5}$

b) $\sqrt{5} \times \sqrt{5}$

c) $\left(\sqrt{119}\right)^2$

d) $\dfrac{\sqrt{24}}{\sqrt{6}}$

e) $2\sqrt{3} \times 5\sqrt{12}$

f) $35\sqrt{20} \div 5\sqrt{2}$

---

a) $\sqrt{3} \times \sqrt{5} = \sqrt{3 \times 5} = \sqrt{15}$

b) $\sqrt{5} \times \sqrt{5} = \sqrt{5 \times 5} = \sqrt{25} = 5$

c) $\left(\sqrt{119}\right)^2 = \sqrt{119} \times \sqrt{119} = 119$

d) $\dfrac{\sqrt{24}}{\sqrt{6}} = \sqrt{\dfrac{24}{6}} = \sqrt{4} = 2$

e) $2\sqrt{3} \times 5\sqrt{12} = 2 \times 5 \times \sqrt{3 \times 12} = 10\sqrt{36} = 10 \times 6 = 60$

f) $35\sqrt{20} \div 5\sqrt{2} = \dfrac{35\sqrt{20}}{5\sqrt{2}} = \dfrac{7\sqrt{20}}{\sqrt{2}} = 7\sqrt{\dfrac{20}{2}} = 7\sqrt{10}$

Exercise 1.8A

Write each of these as a single surd or integer answer.

1. $\sqrt{2} \times \sqrt{7}$ **2.** $\sqrt{5} \times \sqrt{11}$ **3.** $\dfrac{\sqrt{60}}{\sqrt{6}}$

4. $\sqrt{10} \div \sqrt{2}$ **5.** $\dfrac{\sqrt{45}}{\sqrt{5}}$ **6.** $\sqrt{7} \times \sqrt{7}$

7. $\sqrt{75} \div \sqrt{5}$ **8.** $\sqrt{2} \times \sqrt{3} \times \sqrt{5}$ **9.** $\left(\sqrt{635}\right)^2$

10. $5\sqrt{2} \times 3\sqrt{7}$ **11.** $20\sqrt{20} \div 4\sqrt{4}$ **12.** $2\sqrt{5} \times 3\sqrt{20}$

13. $10\sqrt{8} \div 5\sqrt{2}$ **14.** $\left(\sqrt{3}\right)^4$ **15.** $3\sqrt{3} \times 10\sqrt{14} \div 6\sqrt{6}$

16. Work out the area of these shapes.

a)

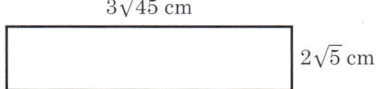

3√45 cm

2√5 cm

b)

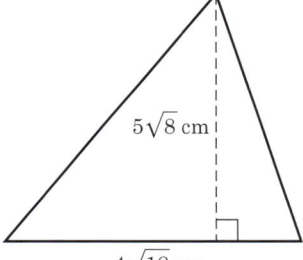

5√8 cm

4√18 cm

17. Given that $a = \sqrt{2}$, $b = \sqrt{30}$ and $c = \sqrt{15}$.

     Work out the value of $\dfrac{ab}{c}$

Simplifying surds

A surd is in its simplest form when the number inside the square root sign is as small as possible. To simplify a surd, write the number being square rooted as a product of two numbers where one is the largest square number possible, then simplify. Simplifying surds can make multiplying or dividing calculations easier.

Example

Simplify, using the rules of surds:

a) $\sqrt{50}$ **b)** $\sqrt{63}$ **c)** $\dfrac{\sqrt{12}}{2}$

d) $\sqrt{75} \times \sqrt{98}$ **e)** $\dfrac{\sqrt{216}}{\sqrt{32} \times \sqrt{147}}$

---

a) $\sqrt{50} = \sqrt{25} \times \sqrt{2} = 5 \times \sqrt{2} = 5\sqrt{2}$

b) $\sqrt{63} = \sqrt{9} \times \sqrt{7} = 3 \times \sqrt{7} = 3\sqrt{7}$

c) $\dfrac{\sqrt{12}}{2} = \dfrac{\sqrt{4} \times \sqrt{3}}{2} = \dfrac{2 \times \sqrt{3}}{2} = \sqrt{3}$

d) $\sqrt{75} \times \sqrt{98}$ $= \sqrt{25} \times \sqrt{3} \times \sqrt{49} \times \sqrt{2}$

$\qquad\qquad\qquad = 5 \times \sqrt{3} \times 7 \times \sqrt{2}$

$\qquad\qquad\qquad = 5 \times 7 \times \sqrt{3} \times \sqrt{2}$

$\qquad\qquad\qquad = 35 \times \sqrt{6}$

$\qquad\qquad\qquad = 35\sqrt{6}$

e) $\dfrac{\sqrt{216}}{\sqrt{32} \times \sqrt{147}} = \dfrac{\sqrt{36} \times \sqrt{6}}{\sqrt{16} \times \sqrt{2} \times \sqrt{49} \times \sqrt{3}}$

$\qquad\qquad\qquad = \dfrac{6 \times \sqrt{6}}{4 \times \sqrt{2} \times 7 \times \sqrt{3}}$

$\qquad\qquad\qquad = \dfrac{6 \times \sqrt{6}}{4 \times 7 \times \sqrt{2} \times \sqrt{3}}$

$\qquad\qquad\qquad = \dfrac{6 \times \sqrt{6}}{28 \times \sqrt{6}}$

$\qquad\qquad\qquad = \dfrac{6}{28}$

$\qquad\qquad\qquad = \dfrac{3}{14}$

Exercise 1.8B

1. Find the value of k in each of these.

    a) $\sqrt{60} = \sqrt{k \times 15}$ **b)** $\sqrt{20} = k\sqrt{5}$ **c)** $\sqrt{18} = 3\sqrt{k}$

2. Simplify:

    a) $\sqrt{45}$ **b)** $\sqrt{28}$ **c)** $\sqrt{72}$

    d) $\sqrt{90}$ **e)** $\dfrac{\sqrt{125}}{5}$ **f)** $\dfrac{\sqrt{54}}{3}$

    g) $\dfrac{\sqrt{20}}{8}$

3. Explain why $\sqrt{30}$ cannot be simplified.

4. Show that $5\sqrt{12}$ in its simplest form is $10\sqrt{3}$.

5. Simplify:

    a) $\sqrt{48}$ **b)** $\sqrt{180}$ **c)** $3\sqrt{50}$ **d)** $2\sqrt{18}$

6. Simplify:

    a) $\sqrt{98} \times \sqrt{54}$ **b)** $\sqrt{28} \times \sqrt{600}$ **c)** $\dfrac{\sqrt{90}}{\sqrt{162} \times \sqrt{45}}$ **d)** $\dfrac{\sqrt{72} \times \sqrt{75}}{\sqrt{288}}$

7. Here is Kyle's method to simplify $\dfrac{\sqrt{60} \times \sqrt{20}}{\sqrt{12}}$:

$$\dfrac{2\sqrt{15} \times 2\sqrt{5}}{2\sqrt{3}} = \dfrac{4\sqrt{75}}{2\sqrt{3}} = \dfrac{4\sqrt{75}}{2\sqrt{3}} = \dfrac{2\sqrt{75}}{\sqrt{3}} = 2\sqrt{\dfrac{75}{3}} = 2\sqrt{25} = 2 \times 5 = 10$$

Amir says, 'Sometimes it is easier not to simplify the surds before multiplying'.

Here is Amir's method to simplify $\dfrac{\sqrt{60} \times \sqrt{20}}{\sqrt{12}}$:

$$\dfrac{\sqrt{1200}}{\sqrt{12}} = \sqrt{\dfrac{1200}{12}} = \sqrt{100} = 10$$

Comment on whose method might be easier in different situations.

8. Find the value of k for each of these.

   a) $2\sqrt{5} \times 3\sqrt{2} = \sqrt{k}$

   b) $\sqrt{2\dfrac{2}{9}} = \dfrac{k\sqrt{5}}{3}$

Adding and subtracting surds

Algebraic terms must be like terms before they can be added or subtracted. For example, $2x + 7x$ simplifies to $9x$ but $2x + 7y$ cannot be simplified. It is the same with surds. $2\sqrt{5} + 7\sqrt{5}$ simplifies to $9\sqrt{5}$ but $2\sqrt{5} + 7\sqrt{6}$ cannot be simplified. Sometimes surds need to be simplified before they can be added or subtracted.

Example
Simplify:

a) $10\sqrt{2} - 7\sqrt{2}$ **b)** $\sqrt{6} + \sqrt{24}$ **c)** $\sqrt{27} - \sqrt{12}$

d) $\sqrt{63} + \sqrt{28} - \sqrt{175}$ **e)** $\sqrt{20} + \sqrt{45} + \sqrt{48}$

---

a) $10\sqrt{2} - 7\sqrt{2} = 3\sqrt{2}$

b) $\sqrt{6} + \sqrt{24} = \sqrt{6} + \sqrt{4 \times 6} = \sqrt{6} + 2\sqrt{6} = 3\sqrt{6}$

c) $\sqrt{27} - \sqrt{12} = \sqrt{9 \times 3} - \sqrt{4 \times 3} = 3\sqrt{3} - 2\sqrt{3} = \sqrt{3}$

d) $\sqrt{63} + \sqrt{28} - \sqrt{175} = \sqrt{9 \times 7} + \sqrt{4 \times 7} - \sqrt{25 \times 7} = 3\sqrt{7} + 2\sqrt{7} - 5\sqrt{7} = 0$

e) $\sqrt{20} + \sqrt{45} + \sqrt{48} = \sqrt{4 \times 5} + \sqrt{9 \times 5} + \sqrt{16 \times 3} = 2\sqrt{5} + 3\sqrt{5} + 4\sqrt{3} = 5\sqrt{5} + 4\sqrt{3}$

Note that part **(e)** cannot be simplified any further as $\sqrt{5}$ and $\sqrt{3}$ are not like surds.

Exercise 1.8C

Give each answer in this exercise in its simplest form.

1. Simplify:

a) $2\sqrt{5} + 10\sqrt{5}$

b) $8\sqrt{3} + 2\sqrt{3} - 6\sqrt{3}$

c) $10\sqrt{3} + \sqrt{75}$

d) $\sqrt{50} + \sqrt{18}$

e) $\sqrt{20} + \sqrt{45}$

f) $\sqrt{200} - \sqrt{18} + \sqrt{72}$

g) $\sqrt{12} + 3\sqrt{48} - \sqrt{75}$

h) $\sqrt{80} - 5\sqrt{45} + 6\sqrt{20}$

2. Write $\sqrt{44} + \sqrt{99}$ in the form $a\sqrt{b}$ where a and b are integers.

3. Find the value of k in each of these.

a) $\sqrt{27} + 2\sqrt{75} = k\sqrt{3}$

b) $\sqrt{k} + \sqrt{24} = 12\sqrt{6}$

c) $\sqrt{45} + 2\sqrt{k} = 7\sqrt{5}$

d) $k\sqrt{12} + \sqrt{75} = 11\sqrt{3}$

4. Find the perimeter of this rectangle.

5. Show that $\left(\sqrt{12} + \sqrt{3}\right)^2 = 27$

6. Find the integer value of $(x + y)^2$ where $x = \sqrt{2}$ and $y = \sqrt{8}$

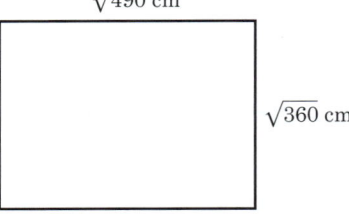

$\sqrt{490}$ cm

$\sqrt{360}$ cm

7. Simplify.

a) $\dfrac{12\sqrt{7} + 6\sqrt{7}}{3\sqrt{7}}$

b) $\dfrac{\sqrt{45} - \sqrt{20}}{\sqrt{80}}$

c) $\dfrac{\sqrt{75} + \sqrt{27}}{\sqrt{48} - \sqrt{12}}$

8. Write $\dfrac{\sqrt{600} + \sqrt{24}}{\sqrt{288}}$ in the form $\sqrt{c}$.

Rationalising the denominator

When a fraction contains a surd in the denominator, make the denominator rational using these rules:

- For fractions in the form $\dfrac{k}{\sqrt{b}}$, multiply by $\dfrac{\sqrt{b}}{\sqrt{b}}$

- For fractions in the form $\dfrac{k}{a + \sqrt{b}}$, multiply by $\dfrac{a - \sqrt{b}}{a - \sqrt{b}}$

- For fractions in the form $\dfrac{k}{a - \sqrt{b}}$, multiply by $\dfrac{a + \sqrt{b}}{a + \sqrt{b}}$

In each case, multiplying the fraction by a number equivalent to a value of 1, means the fraction remains equivalent but no longer contains a surd in the denominator.

Example

Rationalise the denominator.

a) $\dfrac{1}{\sqrt{3}}$

b) $\dfrac{\sqrt{12}}{\sqrt{60}}$

c) $\dfrac{3}{2+\sqrt{5}}$

d) $\dfrac{\sqrt{2}+\sqrt{5}}{\sqrt{5}-\sqrt{2}}$

---

a) $\dfrac{1}{\sqrt{3}} = \dfrac{1}{\sqrt{3}} \times \dfrac{\sqrt{3}}{\sqrt{3}} = \dfrac{\sqrt{3}}{3}$

b) $\dfrac{\sqrt{12}}{\sqrt{60}} = \sqrt{\dfrac{12}{60}} = \dfrac{1}{\sqrt{5}} = \dfrac{1}{\sqrt{5}} \times \dfrac{\sqrt{5}}{\sqrt{5}} = \dfrac{\sqrt{5}}{5}$

c) $\dfrac{3}{2+\sqrt{5}} = \dfrac{3}{2+\sqrt{5}} \times \dfrac{2-\sqrt{5}}{2-\sqrt{5}}$

Note: it is useful to use brackets to remember to multiply both terms in the first denominator by both terms in the second denominator.

$$= \dfrac{3\left(2-\sqrt{5}\right)}{\left(2+\sqrt{5}\right)\left(2-\sqrt{5}\right)} = \dfrac{6-3\sqrt{5}}{4+2\sqrt{5}-2\sqrt{5}-5}$$

$$= \dfrac{6-3\sqrt{5}}{-1} = -6+3\sqrt{5}$$

d) $\dfrac{\sqrt{2}+\sqrt{5}}{\sqrt{5}-\sqrt{2}} = \dfrac{\left(\sqrt{2}+\sqrt{5}\right)\left(\sqrt{5}+\sqrt{2}\right)}{\left(\sqrt{5}-\sqrt{2}\right)\left(\sqrt{5}+\sqrt{2}\right)}$

$$= \dfrac{\sqrt{2}\sqrt{5}+2+5+\sqrt{2}\sqrt{5}}{5+\sqrt{2}\sqrt{5}-\sqrt{2}\sqrt{5}-2} = \dfrac{7+2\sqrt{10}}{3}$$

Exercise 1.8D

Give each answer in this exercise in their simplest form.

1. Copy and complete these calculations.

a) $\dfrac{1}{\sqrt{11}} = \dfrac{1}{\sqrt{11}} \times \dfrac{\sqrt{}}{\sqrt{}} = \dfrac{\sqrt{}}{}$

b) $\dfrac{\sqrt{12}}{\sqrt{84}} = \sqrt{\dfrac{12}{84}} = \sqrt{\dfrac{1}{}} = \dfrac{1}{\sqrt{}} = \dfrac{1}{\sqrt{}} \times \dfrac{\sqrt{}}{\sqrt{}} = \dfrac{\sqrt{}}{}$

c) $\dfrac{5}{2-\sqrt{3}} = \dfrac{5\left(+\sqrt{}\right)}{\left(2-\sqrt{3}\right)\left(+\sqrt{}\right)} = \dfrac{+\sqrt{}}{+\sqrt{}-\sqrt{}-} = \dfrac{+\sqrt{}}{1} = +\sqrt{}$

2. Rationalise the denominators of these fractions.

a) $\dfrac{1}{\sqrt{6}}$

b) $\dfrac{2}{\sqrt{5}}$

c) $\dfrac{18}{\sqrt{6}}$

d) $\dfrac{\sqrt{5}}{\sqrt{55}}$

e) $\dfrac{5\sqrt{7}}{\sqrt{35}}$

f) $\dfrac{12}{5\sqrt{3}}$

3. Work out the integer answers for these calculations.

a) $\left(3 - \sqrt{7}\right)\left(3 + \sqrt{7}\right)$

b) $\left(6 + \sqrt{5}\right)\left(6 - \sqrt{5}\right)$

c) $\left(7 - \sqrt{3}\right)^2 + 14\sqrt{3}$

d) $\left(\sqrt{2} + \sqrt{50}\right)^2$

e) $\left(\sqrt{2} - 3\sqrt{8}\right)^2$

4. Find the value of $(a + b)(a - b)$ when $a = 7$ and $b = \sqrt{11}$.

5. $\left(6 + \sqrt{3}\right)\left(4 - \sqrt{3}\right) = a + b\sqrt{3}$

Find the value of a and the value of b.

6. Rationalise the denominators of these fractions.

a) $\dfrac{1}{5 + \sqrt{3}}$

b) $\dfrac{1}{4 - \sqrt{5}}$

c) $\dfrac{7}{2 + \sqrt{5}}$

d) $\dfrac{2 + \sqrt{3}}{\sqrt{3}}$

e) $\dfrac{1}{\sqrt{6} - \sqrt{3}}$

f) $\dfrac{16}{\sqrt{5} - 1}$

g) $\dfrac{\sqrt{2} + \sqrt{7}}{\sqrt{7} - \sqrt{2}}$

7. The area of this rectangle is 30 cm².

Find the value of x.

Give your answer in the form $a\sqrt{b}$ where a and b are integers.

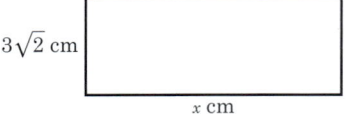

$3\sqrt{2}$ cm

x cm

8. Write each of these in the form $n\sqrt{6}$, where n is an integer.

a) $\dfrac{\sqrt{6} \times \sqrt{50}}{\sqrt{2}}$

b) $\dfrac{\sqrt{12} + \sqrt{108}}{\sqrt{8}}$

c) $\dfrac{10\sqrt{3}}{\sqrt{32} - \sqrt{18}}$

9. Square A and rectangle B are equal in area.

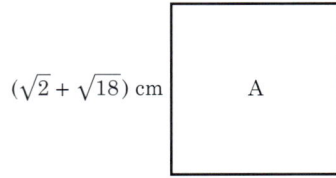

$(\sqrt{2} + \sqrt{18})$ cm   A

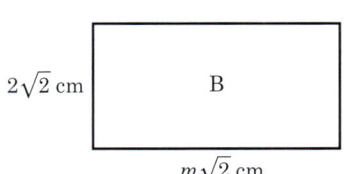

$2\sqrt{2}$ cm   B

$m\sqrt{2}$ cm

Calculate the value of m.

10. Expand and simplify $\left(2 - 2\sqrt{5}\right)\left(1 + 3\sqrt{5}\right)$

Give your answer in the form $a\sqrt{b} - c$.

> **Tip**
>
> For Question **11**, use AB² = AC² + BC²
>
> This is Pythagoras' theorem, which you will use in Chapter 4.

11. Triangle ABC has a right angle at C.

All lengths are measured in centimetres.

Find the value of x.

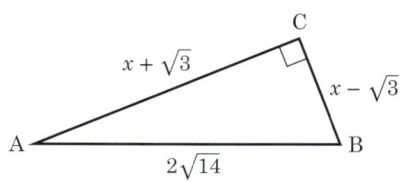

12. Write $\dfrac{\sqrt{75}-\sqrt{12}}{\sqrt{75}+\sqrt{12}}$ as a fraction in its simplest form.

13. Show that the expression $\dfrac{4}{3}\sqrt{\dfrac{300}{4}} + \dfrac{1}{\sqrt{3}}$ can be written in the

form $a\sqrt{b}$, where a and b are integers.

14. Show that these expressions can be written in the form $\dfrac{a}{b}\sqrt{c}$,

where a, b and c are integers.

a) $\left(\dfrac{25}{3}\right)^{\frac{1}{2}} - \left(\dfrac{1}{3}\right)^{-\frac{1}{2}}$

b) $\sqrt{8\dfrac{1}{3}} - \left(\dfrac{16}{3}\right)^{\frac{1}{2}} + 2\sqrt{3}$

1.9 Calculator

In this book, the keys are described thus:

$\boxed{\text{EXP}}$ numbers in standard form (e.g $4\ \boxed{\text{EXP}}\ 7$ is 4×10^7)

$\boxed{+}$ add $\qquad\qquad\quad$ $\boxed{\sqrt{}}$ square root

$\boxed{-}$ subtract $\qquad\quad$ $\boxed{x^2}$ square

$\boxed{\times}$ multiply $\qquad\quad$ $\boxed{1\,/\,x}$ reciprocal

$\boxed{\div}$ divide $\qquad\qquad$ $\boxed{\wedge}$ or $\boxed{y^x}$ raise number y to the power x

$\boxed{=}$ equals $\qquad\qquad$ $\boxed{(}\boxed{)}$ brackets

Your calculator will also have a fraction button that usually looks like this: $\boxed{}$

On your calculator the $\boxed{\text{EXP}}$, $\boxed{1\,/\,x}$ and $\boxed{y^x}$ might look like $\boxed{\times 10^x}$, $\boxed{x^{-1}}$ and $\boxed{x^{\blacksquare}}$, respectively.

Using the $\boxed{\text{ANS}}$ button

The $\boxed{\text{ANS}}$ button can be used as a 'short term memory'.

It holds the answer from the previous calculation.

Example

Evaluate, giving the answers to 4 significant figures:

a) $\dfrac{5}{1.2 - 0.761}$ **b)** $\left(\dfrac{1}{0.084}\right)^4$ **c)** $\sqrt[3]{[3.2 \times (1.7 - 1.64)]}$

a) Find the bottom line first.

$\boxed{5}\ \boxed{\div}\ \boxed{(}\ \boxed{1.2}\ \boxed{-}\ \boxed{0.761}\ \boxed{)}\ \boxed{=}$

or

$\boxed{1.2}\ \boxed{-}\ \boxed{0.761}\ \boxed{=}\ \boxed{5}\ \boxed{\div}\ \boxed{ANS}\ \boxed{=}$

The calculator reads 11.38952164

Answer = 11.39 (4 s.f.)

Note: Sometimes the $\boxed{=}$ button is the $\boxed{EXE}$ button.

> **Tip**
>
> You could also use the fraction button on your calculator to perform this calculation.

b) $\left(\dfrac{1}{0.084}\right)^4$

$\boxed{1}\ \boxed{\div}\ \boxed{0.084}\ \boxed{=}\ \boxed{\wedge}\ \boxed{4}\ \boxed{=}$ or $\boxed{0.084}\ \boxed{1/x}\ \boxed{y^x}\ \boxed{4}\ \boxed{=}$

Answer = 20 090 (4 s.f.)

c) $\sqrt[3]{[3.2(1.7 - 1.64)]}$

$\boxed{\sqrt[3]{}}\ \boxed{3.2}\ \boxed{\times}\ \boxed{(}\ \boxed{1.7}\ \boxed{-}\ \boxed{1.64}\ \boxed{)}\ \boxed{=}$

Answer 0.5769 (to 4 s.f.)

Exercise 1.9A

Use a calculator to evaluate the following, giving the answers to 4 significant figures:

1. $\dfrac{7.351 \times 0.764}{1.847}$ **2.** $\dfrac{0.0741 \times 14\,700}{0.746}$ **3.** $\dfrac{0.0741 \times 9.61}{23.1}$

4. $\dfrac{417.8 \times 0.008\,41}{0.073\,24}$ **5.** $\dfrac{8.41}{7.601 \times 0.008\,47}$ **6.** $\dfrac{4.22}{1.701 \times 5.2}$

7. $\dfrac{9.61}{17.4 \times 1.51}$ **8.** $\dfrac{8.71 \times 3.62}{0.84}$ **9.** $\dfrac{0.76}{0.412 - 0.317}$

10. $\dfrac{81.4}{72.6 + 51.92}$ **11.** $\dfrac{111}{27.4 + 2960}$ **12.** $\dfrac{27.4 + 11.61}{5.9 - 4.763}$

13. $\dfrac{6.51 - 0.1114}{7.24 + 1.653}$ **14.** $\dfrac{5.71 + 6.093}{9.05 - 5.77}$ **15.** $\dfrac{0.943 - 0.788}{1.4 - 0.766}$

16. $\dfrac{2.6}{1.7} + \dfrac{1.9}{3.7}$ **17.** $\dfrac{8.06}{5.91} - \dfrac{1.594}{1.62}$ **18.** $\dfrac{4.7}{11.4 - 3.61} + \dfrac{1.6}{9.7}$

19. $\dfrac{3.74}{1.6 \times 2.89} - \dfrac{1}{0.741}$

20. $\dfrac{1}{7.2} - \dfrac{1}{14.6}$

21. $\dfrac{1}{0.961} \times \dfrac{1}{0.412}$

22. $\dfrac{1}{7} + \dfrac{1}{13} - \dfrac{1}{8}$

23. $4.2\left(\dfrac{1}{5.5} - \dfrac{1}{7.6}\right)$

24. $\sqrt{(9.61 + 0.1412)}$

25. $\sqrt{\left(\dfrac{8.007}{1.61}\right)}$

26. $(1.74 + 9.611)^2$

27. $\left(\dfrac{1.63}{1.7 - 0.911}\right)^2$

28. $\left(\dfrac{9.6}{2.4} - \dfrac{1.5}{0.74}\right)^2$

29. $\sqrt{\left(\dfrac{4.2 \times 1.611}{9.83 \times 1.74}\right)}$

30. $(0.741)^3$

31. $(1.562)^5$

32. $(0.32)^3 + (0.511)^4$

33. $(1.71 - 0.863)^6$

34. $\left(\dfrac{1}{0.971}\right)^4$

35. $\sqrt[3]{(4.714)}$

36. $\sqrt[3]{(0.9316)}$

37. $\sqrt[3]{\left(\dfrac{4.114}{7.93}\right)}$

38. $\sqrt[4]{(0.8145 - 0.799)}$

39. $\sqrt[5]{(8.6 \times 9.71)}$

40. $\sqrt[3]{\left(\dfrac{1.91}{4.2 - 3.766}\right)}$

41. $\left(\dfrac{1}{7.6} - \dfrac{1}{18.5}\right)^3$

42. $\dfrac{\sqrt{(4.79)} + 1.6}{9.63}$

43. $\dfrac{(0.761)^2 - \sqrt{(4.22)}}{1.96}$

44. $\sqrt[3]{\left(\dfrac{1.74 \times 0.761}{0.0896}\right)}$

Example

Work out, to 4 significant figures;

a) $2 \times 10^5 - 1.734 \times 10^4$

b) $(3.6 \times 10^{-4})^2$

a) $\boxed{2}\;\boxed{\times 10^x}\;\boxed{5}\;\boxed{-}\;\boxed{1.734}\;\boxed{\times 10^x}\;\boxed{4}$

Answer: 182 700 (4 s.f.)

b) $\boxed{3.6}\;\boxed{\times 10^x}\;\boxed{-}\;\boxed{4}\;\boxed{x^2}$

Answer: 1.296×10^{-7}

Exercise 1.9B

Use a calculator to evaluate the following, giving your answers to 4 significant figures.

1. $\left(\dfrac{8.6 \times 1.71}{0.43}\right)^3$

2. $\dfrac{9.61 - \sqrt{(9.61)}}{9.61^2}$

3. $\dfrac{9.6 \times 10^4 \times 3.75 \times 10^7}{8.88 \times 10^6}$

4. $\dfrac{8.06 \times 10^{-4}}{1.71 \times 10^{-6}}$

5. $\dfrac{3.92 \times 10^{-7}}{1.884 \times 10^{-11}}$

6. $\left(\dfrac{1.31 \times 2.71 \times 10^5}{1.91 \times 10^4}\right)^5$

7. $\left(\dfrac{1}{9.6} - \dfrac{1}{9.99}\right)^{10}$

8. $\dfrac{\sqrt[3]{86.6}}{\sqrt[4]{4.71}}$

9. $\dfrac{23.7 \times 0.0042}{12.48 - 9.7}$

10. $\dfrac{0.482 + 1.6}{0.024 \times 1.83}$

11. $\dfrac{8.52 - 1.004}{0.004 - 0.0083}$

12. $\dfrac{1.6 - 0.476}{2.398 \times 41.2}$

13. $\left(\dfrac{2.3}{0.791}\right)^7$

14. $\left(\dfrac{8.4}{28.7 - 0.47}\right)^3$

15. $\left(\dfrac{5.114}{7.332}\right)^5$

16. $\left(\dfrac{4.2}{2.3} + \dfrac{8.2}{0.52}\right)^3$

17. $\dfrac{1}{8.2^2} - \dfrac{3}{19^2}$

18. $\dfrac{100}{11^3} + \dfrac{100}{12^3}$

19. $\dfrac{7.3 - 4.291}{2.6^2}$

20. $\dfrac{9.001 - 8.97}{0.95^3}$

21. $\dfrac{10.1^2 + 9.4^2}{9.8}$

22. $(3.6 \times 10^{-8})^2$

23. $(8.24 \times 10^4)^3$

24. $(2.17 \times 10^{-3})^3$

25. $(7.095 \times 10^{-6})^{\frac{1}{3}}$

26. $3\sqrt{\left(\dfrac{4.7}{2.3^2}\right)}$

Checking answers

Here are five calculations, followed by sensible checks.

a) $22.2 \boxed{\div} 6 = 3.7$ check $3.7 \boxed{\times} 6 = 22.2$

b) $31.7 \boxed{-} 4.83 = 26.87$ check $26.87 \boxed{+} 4.83 = 31.7$

c) $42.8 \boxed{\times} 30 = 1284$ check $1284 \boxed{\div} 30 = 42.8$

d) $\sqrt{17} = 4.1231$ check 4.1231^2

e) $3.7 + 17.6 + 13.9$ check $13.9 + 17.6 + 3.7$
            (add in reverse order)

Calculations can also be checked by rounding numbers to a given number of significant figures.

f) $\dfrac{6.1 \times 32.6}{19.3} = 10.3 \left(\text{to 3 s.f.}\right)$

Check this answer by rounding each number to one significant figure and estimating.

$\dfrac{6.1 \times 32.6}{19.3} \approx \dfrac{6 \times 30}{20} = \dfrac{180}{20} = 9$

This is close to 10.3

so the actual answer probably is 10.3

> **Tip**
>
> '$\approx$' means 'approximately equal to'

Exercise 1.9C

1. Use a calculator to work out the following then check the answers as indicated.

   a) $92.5 \times 20 = \boxed{}$ Check $\boxed{} \div 20 = \boxed{}$

   b) $14 \times 328 = \boxed{}$ Check $\boxed{} \div 328 = \boxed{}$

   c) $63 - 12.6 = \boxed{}$ Check $\boxed{} + 12.6 = \boxed{}$

   d) $221.2 \div 7 = \boxed{}$ Check $\boxed{} \times 7 = \boxed{}$

   e) $384.93 \div 9.1 = \boxed{}$ Check $\boxed{} \times 9.1 = \boxed{}$

   f) $13.71 + 25.8 = \boxed{}$ Check $\boxed{} - 25.8 = \boxed{}$

   g) $95.4 \div 4.5 = \boxed{}$ Check $\boxed{} \times 4.5 = \boxed{}$

   h) $8.2 + 3.1 + 19.6 + 11.5 = \boxed{}$ Check $11.5 + 19.6 + 3.1 + 8.2 = \boxed{}$

   i) $\sqrt{39} = \boxed{}$ Check $\boxed{}^2 = 39$

   j) $3.17 + 2.06 + 8.4 + 16 = \boxed{}$ Check $16 + 8.4 + 2.06 + 3.17 = \boxed{}$

2. The numbers below are rounded to one significant figure to *estimate* the answer to each calculation. Match each question below to the correct estimated answer.

   A $\boxed{21.9 \times 1.01}$ **P** $\boxed{10}$

   B $\boxed{\dfrac{19.82^2}{(18.61 + 22.3)}}$ **Q** $\boxed{5}$

   C $\boxed{7.8 \times 1.01}$ **R** $\boxed{0.5}$

   D $\boxed{\dfrac{\sqrt{98.7}}{8.78 + 11.43}}$ **S** $\boxed{8}$

   E $\boxed{\dfrac{21.42 + 28.6}{18.84 - 8.99}}$ **T** $\boxed{20}$

3. Given that $281 \times 36 = 10\,116$, work out the following without using a calculator:

   a) $10\,116 \div 36$ **b)** $10\,116 \div 281$ **c)** 28.1×3.6

4. Mavis is paid a salary of \$49 620 per year.
   Work out a rough estimate for her weekly pay.
   Give your answer correct to one significant figure.

5. In 2011, the population of France was 61 278 514 and the population of Greece was 9 815 972. Roughly how many times bigger was the population of France compared to the population of Greece?

Tip

Round the numbers to one significant figure.

6. Estimate, correct to one significant figure:

a) $41.56 \div 7.88$

b) $\dfrac{5.13 \times 18.777}{0.952}$

c) $\dfrac{1}{5}$ of £14892

d) $\dfrac{0.0974 \times \sqrt{104}}{1.03}$

e) $\dfrac{6.84^2 + 0.983}{5.07^2}$

f) $\dfrac{2848.7 + 1024.8}{51.2 - 9.98}$

g) $\dfrac{2}{3}$ of £3124

h) $18.13 \times (3.96^2 + 2.07^2)$

Time and money

You can use your calculator to work out problems involving time and money. Money can just be treated as a decimal written correct to 2 decimal places.

When working with time, the main thing is to remember that there are 60 minutes in an hour, not 100. This means that 2 hours and 25 minutes is not written as 2.25 hours, since 2.25 hours means $2\frac{1}{4}$ hours, which is 2 hours and 15 minutes.

If you did want to enter 2 hours and 25 minutes into your calculator, the easiest way to do this would be to use the 'hours, minutes and seconds' button, which usually looks like $\boxed{\circ \,{}' \,{}''}$.

To enter 2 hours and 25 minutes, press 2 $\boxed{\circ \,{}' \,{}''}$ 25 $\boxed{\circ \,{}' \,{}''}$.

If the time you want to enter also contains seconds, you can press the button again.

For example, to enter 3 hours 14 minutes and 8 seconds you would press 3 $\boxed{\circ \,{}' \,{}''}$ 14 $\boxed{\circ \,{}' \,{}''}$ 8 $\boxed{\circ \,{}' \,{}''}$.

If you then want to convert that time into a decimal, you can do this using the $\boxed{S \Leftrightarrow D}$ button.

The $\boxed{\circ \,{}' \,{}''}$ button can also be used in reverse to convert a decimal into hours, minutes and seconds. For example, if you type in 2.18 and press $\boxed{\circ \,{}' \,{}''}$, the calculator will display 2°10'48", which means that 2.18 hours is the same as 2 hours, 10 minutes and 48 seconds.

Example

How many hours, minutes and seconds is 3.65 hours?

3.65 $\boxed{\circ\,'\,''}$ $\boxed{=}$ 3°36'36"

So 3.65 hours is 3 hours 36 minutes and 36 seconds.

Exercise 1.9D

1. Convert into a decimal number of hours:

    a) 2 hours 13 minutes and 6 seconds   **b)** 5 hours 42 minutes and 38 seconds

    c) 1 hour 6 minutes and 50 seconds

2. Convert into hours, minutes and seconds:

    a) 2.64 hours   **b)** 3.88 hours   **c)** 8.29 hours

3. Work out in hours, minutes and seconds:

    a) 1.54 hours + 2.83 hours   **b)** 9.82 hours + 4.72 hours

4. How many cents are there in 5.3 dollars?

5. Eric buys 34 cakes at $1.42 each and 28 drinks at $0.89 each.
   How much did he spend in total?

6. Eight people share a prize of $215 000 between them.
   How much do they each get?

7. Four people split a restaurant bill of $34.40 between them.
   How much do they each have to pay?

8. Three singers book 6.75 hours of studio time that they share equally.
   How many hours and minutes do they each get?

Revision exercise 1

You may use a calculator only for Questions **15** and **16**.

1. Evaluate:

   a) $148 \div 0.8$

   b) $0.024 \div 0.000\,16$

   c) $(0.2)^2 \div (0.1)^3$

   d) $2 - \dfrac{1}{2} - \dfrac{1}{3} - \dfrac{1}{4}$

   e) $1\dfrac{3}{4} \times 1\dfrac{3}{5}$

   f) $\dfrac{1\frac{1}{6}}{1\frac{2}{3} + 1\frac{1}{4}}$

2. **a)** $-7 + 24$

   b) $+5 - +18$

   c) $+14 + -9$

   d) $-20 - -10$

3. **a)** $-4 \times (+9)$

   b) $-3 \times (-7)$

   c) $+70 \div (-7)$

   d) $-45 \div (-9)$

4. On each bounce, a ball rises to $\dfrac{4}{5}$ of its previous height. To what height will it rise after the third bounce, if dropped from a height of 250 cm?

5. A man spends $\dfrac{1}{3}$ of his salary on accommodation and $\dfrac{2}{5}$ of the remainder on food.
   What fraction is left for other purposes?

6. Express 0.054 73:

   a) correct to three significant figures

   b) correct to three decimal places

   c) in standard form.

7. Evaluate $\dfrac{2}{3} + \dfrac{4}{7}$, to three decimal places.

8. Evaluate:

   a) $121^{\frac{1}{2}}$

   b) 7^{-1}

   c) $9^{-\frac{1}{2}}$

   d) $16^{\frac{3}{2}}$

   e) $\left(4^{\frac{1}{2}}\right)^3 \times 36^{\frac{1}{2}}$

   f) 12^0

9. Evaluate, giving the answers in standard form:

   a) $3600 \div 0.00012$

   b) $\dfrac{3.33 \times 10^4}{9 \times 10^{-1}}$

   c) $(30\,000)^3$

10. Given that
$$t = 2\pi\sqrt{\left(\dfrac{l}{g}\right)}$$
    find the value of t, to three significant figures, when $l = 2.31$ and $g = 9.81$

11. **a)** From the following numbers, write down:

        1   3   8   9   10

    i) the prime number

    ii) a multiple of 5

    iii) two square numbers

    iv) two factors of 32.

    b) Find two numbers m and n from the list such that $m = \sqrt{n}$ and $n = \sqrt{81}$.

    c) If each of the numbers in the list can be used once, find p, q, r, s, t such that $(p + q)r = 2(s + t) = 36$.

12. The value of t is given by
$$t = 2\pi\sqrt{\left(\dfrac{2.31^2 + 0.9^2}{2.31 \times 9.81}\right)}.$$

    Without using a calculator, and using suitable approximate values for the numbers in the formula, find an estimate for the value of t. (To earn the marks in this question you must show the various stages of your working.)

13. Baichu's heart has beat at an average rate of 72 beats per minute throughout his life. Baichu is sixty years old. How many times has his heart beat during his life? Give the answer in standard form correct to 2 significant figures.

14. Estimate giving the answers to 1 significant figure. Do not use a calculator.

a) $(612 \times 52) \div 49.2$

b) $(11.7 + 997.1) \times 9.2$

c) $\sqrt{\left(\dfrac{91.3}{10.1}\right)}$

d) $\pi\sqrt{5.2^2 + 18.2}$

15. Evaluate giving the answers to 4 significant figures:

a) $\dfrac{0.74}{0.81 \times 1.631}$

b) $\sqrt{\left(\dfrac{9.61}{8.34 - 7.41}\right)}$

c) $\left(\dfrac{0.741}{0.8364}\right)^4$

d) $\dfrac{8.4 - 7.642}{3.333 - 1.735}$

16. Evaluate giving the answers to 3 significant figures:

a) $\sqrt[3]{(9.61 \times 0.0041)}$

b) $\left(\dfrac{1}{9.5} - \dfrac{1}{11.2}\right)^3$

c) $\dfrac{15.6 \times 0.714}{0.0143 \times 12}$

d) $\sqrt[4]{\left(\dfrac{1}{5 \times 10^3}\right)}$

17. Write down the reciprocals of:

a) 20   **b)** $\dfrac{1}{3}$ **c)** 0.4   **d)** 1.5

18. The number of cells in a bacterial culture doubles every hour.

At the end of the first hour there are 2^6 cells. How many cells will there be at the end of the third hour?

19. Rationalise the denominators of these fractions.

a) $\dfrac{1}{\sqrt{5}}$ **b)** $\dfrac{2}{1 + \sqrt{5}}$ **c)** $\dfrac{\sqrt{2} + 1}{\sqrt{2} - 1}$

20. Write down the nth term formulae for the following sequences:

a) $-1, 3, 7, 11, \ldots$

b) $2, 7, 14, 23, \ldots$

c) $3, 10, 29, 66, \ldots$

d) $4, 16, 64, 256, \ldots$

21. The width of a particular book is 2 cm when measured to the nearest cm.

Zac needs to build a bookshelf to hold 50 of these books.

What are the upper and lower bounds for the length of the shelf?

22. Convert into decimals:

a) 43%   **b)** 20%   **c)** 3%

d) 12.5%   **e)** 115%

23. Convert into decimals:

a) $\dfrac{1}{4}$ **b)** $\dfrac{2}{5}$ **c)** $\dfrac{7}{8}$ **d)** $\dfrac{3}{7}$ **e)** $\dfrac{15}{6}$

NON-CALCULATOR SECTION

1. Calculate $\dfrac{3^2}{2^6}$

    a) giving your answer as a fraction   **[1]**

    b) giving your answer as a decimal.   **[1]**

2. Work out the exact value of

$$1 + \cfrac{2}{4 + \cfrac{8}{16 + 32}}$$ **[2]**

3. Write down:

    a) an irrational number between 1 and 2   **[1]**

    b) a prime number between 70 and 80.   **[1]**

4. At 07:20 Mrs Smith bought 150 bagels at a retail shop for 54 cents each. 155 minutes later she sold them all to a supermarket for 85 cents each.

    a) What was the time when she sold the bagels?   **[1]**

    b) Calculate her total profit.   **[1]**

5. Write down the next term in each of the following sequences.

    a) 12.4, 9.4, 6.4, 3.4, 0.4, ...   **[1]**

    b) 3, 5, 9, 15, 23, ...   **[1]**

6. a) The formula for the nth term of the sequence 2, 15, 48, 110, 210, ... is

    $$\dfrac{n(n + 1)(3n - 1)}{2}$$

    Find the 9th term.   **[1]**

    b) The nth term of the sequence 12, 19, 28, 39, 52, ... is $\left(n + 2\right)^2 + 3$

    Write down the formula for the nth term of the sequence 19, 26, 35, 46, 59, ...   **[1]**

7. To raise money for charity, Julie walks 48 km, correct to the nearest kilometre, every day for 5 days.

Copy and complete the statement for the distance, d km, she walks during those 5 days: .... $\leqslant d$ km < ....   **[1]**

8. The distance between London and Chicago is 3900 km correct to the nearest 100 km.

A businessman travelled from London to Chicago and then back to London.

He did this four times in a year.

Between what limits is the total distance he travelled?

Write your answer as ....km $\leqslant$ total distance travelled < ....km.   **[2]**

9. A rectangle has sides of length 8.6 cm and 4.3 cm correct to one decimal place.

Calculate the lower bound for the area of the rectangle as accurately as possible. [2]

10. Write $\dfrac{\sqrt{2}+1}{\sqrt{8}-2}$ as $\dfrac{a}{b}+\sqrt{c}$, where a, b and c are integers. [2]

CALCULATOR SECTION

11. In 2021 there were 58 thousand taxis in London, correct to the nearest thousand.

If the average distance travelled by each taxi in one day was 120 km correct to two significant figures, work out the upper bound for the total distance travelled by all the taxis in one day, correct to the nearest million km. [2]

12. The mass of the Earth is roughly $\dfrac{1}{320}$ of the mass of the planet Jupiter.

The mass of the Earth is 5.97×10^{24} kilograms. Calculate the mass of the planet Jupiter, giving your answer in standard form, correct to 2 significant figures. [3]

13. Use your calculator to work out $\sqrt{(9 + 5 \times 184^{0.1})}$ [1]

2 Algebra 1

Isaac Newton (1642–1727) was an English scientist and mathematician, and a prominent figure in the Scientific Revolution of the 17th century. He went to Trinity College Cambridge in 1661 and by the age of 23 he had made three major discoveries: the nature of colours, calculus and the law of gravitation. He used his version of calculus to give the first satisfactory explanation of the motion of the Sun, the Moon and the stars. Because he was extremely sensitive to criticism, Newton was always very secretive, but he was eventually persuaded to publish his discoveries in 1687.

- Substitute into expressions and formulae.
- Simplify expressions and expand brackets.
- Construct and solving linear equations including those where x appears in the denominator as part of a linear expression.
- Solve simultaneous equations.

2.1 Substitution

In algebra, letters are used to represent numbers. These letters are called *variables*.

Mathematical expressions are made up of one or more terms and operations. A term may be a number, a variable or a combination of both. The expression $5x^2 - 6x + 7$ has three terms:

$5x^2$, $-6x$ and 7

You can evaluate an expression by replacing the variables in the expression with specific values. This is called *substitution*.

For example, when $x = -1$, the expression $5x^2 - 6x + 7$ is evaluated:

$$5(-1)^2 - 6(-1) + 7 = 5 \times 1 + 6 + 7$$
$$= 18$$

Example

When $a = 3$, $b = -2$, and $c = 5$, find the value of:

a) $3a + b$
b) $ac + b^2$
c) $\dfrac{a + c}{b}$
d) $a(c - b)$

a) $3a + b = (3 \times 3) + (-2)$
$\qquad = 9 - 2$
$\qquad = 7$

b) $ac + b^2 = (3 \times 5) + (-2)^2$
$\qquad = 15 + 4$
$\qquad = 19$

c) $\dfrac{a + c}{b} = \dfrac{3 + 5}{-2}$
$\qquad = \dfrac{8}{-2}$
$\qquad = -4$

d) $a(c - b) = 3[5 - (-2)]$
$\qquad = 3(7)$
$\qquad = 21$

Note that working *down* the page makes the steps easy to read and easy to follow.

Tip

When substituting, remember to always use BIDMAS.

Exercise 2.1A

Evaluate the following.

For Questions **1** to **12**, $a = 3$, $c = 2$, $e = 5$.

1. $3a - 2$ **2.** $4c + e$ **3.** $2c + 3a$ **4.** $5e - a$

5. $e - 2c$ **6.** $e - 2a$ **7.** $4c + 2e$ **8.** $7a - 5e$

9. $c - e$ **10.** $10a + c + e$ **11.** $a + c - e$ **12.** $a - c - e$

For Questions **13** to **24**, $h = 3$, $m = -2$, $t = -3$.

13. $2m - 3$ **14.** $4t + 10$ **15.** $3h - 12$ **16.** $6m + 4$

17. $9t - 3$ **18.** $4h + 4$ **19.** $2m - 6$ **20.** $m + 2$

21. $3h + m$ **22.** $t - h$ **23.** $4m + 2h$ **24.** $3t - m$

For Questions **25** to **36**, $x = -2$, $y = -1$, $k = 0$.

25. $3x + 1$ **26.** $2y + 5$ **27.** $6k + 4$ **28.** $3x + 2y$

29. $2k + x$ **30.** xy **31.** xk **32.** $2xy$

33. $2(x + k)$ **34.** $3(k + y)$ **35.** $5x - y$ **36.** $3k - 2x$

Tip

$2x^2$ means $2(x^2)$

$(2x)^2$ means 'work out $2x$ and *then* square it'

$-7x$ means $-7(x)$

$-x^2$ means $-(x^2)$

Example

When $x = -2$, find the value of:

a) $2x^2 - 5x$ **b)** $(3x)^2 - x^2$

a) $\begin{aligned} 2x^2 - 5x &= 2(-2)^2 - 5(-2) \\ &= 2(4) + 10 \\ &= 18 \end{aligned}$ **b)** $\begin{aligned} (3x)^2 - x^2 &= (3 \times -2)^2 - 1(-2)^2 \\ &= (-6)^2 - 1(4) \\ &= 36 - 4 \\ &= 32 \end{aligned}$

Exercise 2.1B

If $x = -3$ and $y = 2$, evaluate:

1. x^2 **2.** $3x^2$ **3.** y^2 **4.** $4y^2$

5. $(2x)^2$ **6.** $2x^2$ **7.** $10 - x^2$ **8.** $10 - y^2$

9. $20 - 2x^2$ **10.** $20 - 3y^2$ **11.** $5 + 4x$ **12.** $x^2 - 2x$

13. $y^2 - 3x^2$ **14.** $x^2 - 3y$ **15.** $(2x)^2 - y^2$ **16.** $4x^2$

17. $(4x)^2$ **18.** $1 - x^2$ **19.** $y - x^2$ **20.** $x^2 + y^2$

21. $x^2 - y^2$ **22.** $2 - 2x^2$ **23.** $(3x)^2 + 3$ **24.** $11 - xy$

25. $12 + xy$ **26.** $(2x)^2 - (3y)^2$ **27.** $2 - 3x^2$ **28.** $y^2 - x^2$

29. $x^2 + y^3$ **30.** $\dfrac{x}{y}$ **31.** $10 - 3x$ **32.** $2y^2$

33. $25 - 3y$ **34.** $(2y)^2$ **35.** $-7 + 3x$ **36.** $-8 + 10y$

37. $(xy)^2$ **38.** xy^2 **39.** $-7 + x^2$ **40.** $17 + xy$

41. $-5 - 2x^2$ **42.** $10 - (2x)^2$ **43.** $x^2 + 3x + 5$ **44.** $2x^2 - 4x + 1$

45. $\dfrac{x^2}{y}$

Example

When $a = -2$, $b = 3$, $c = -3$, evaluate:

a) $\dfrac{2a(b^2 - a)}{c}$ **b)** $\sqrt{(a^2 + b^2)}$

---

a) $(b^2 - a) = 9 - (-2)$
$\qquad\qquad\quad = 11$

$\therefore \dfrac{2a(b^2 - a)}{c} = \dfrac{2 \times (-2) \times (11)}{-3}$

$\qquad\qquad\qquad = \dfrac{-44}{-3}$

$\qquad\qquad\qquad = \dfrac{44}{3}$

$\qquad\qquad\qquad = 14\dfrac{2}{3}$

b) $\sqrt{(a^2 + b^2)} = \sqrt{(-2)^2 + (3)^2}$

$\qquad\qquad\quad = \sqrt{4 + 9}$

$\qquad\qquad\quad = \sqrt{13}$

> **Tip**
>
> In mathematics, the $\therefore$ symbol means 'therefore'.

Exercise 2.1C

Evaluate the following expressions.

For Questions **1** to **16**, $a = 4$, $b = -2$, $c = -3$.

1. $a(b + c)$ **2.** $a^2(b - c)$ **3.** $2c(a - c)$ **4.** $b^2(2a + 3c)$

5. $c^2(b - 2a)$ **6.** $2a^2(b + c)$ **7.** $2(a + b + c)$ **8.** $3c(a - b - c)$

9. $b^2 + 2b + a$ **10.** $c^2 - 3c + a$ **11.** $2b^2 - 3b$ **12.** $\sqrt{(a^2 + c^2)}$

13. $\sqrt{(ab + c^2)}$ **14.** $\sqrt{(c^2 - b^2)}$ **15.** $\dfrac{b^2}{a} + \dfrac{2c}{b}$ **16.** $\dfrac{c^2}{b} + \dfrac{4b}{a}$

For Questions **17** to **32**, $k = -3$, $m = 1$, $n = -4$.

17. $k^2(2m - n)$ **18.** $5m\sqrt{(k^2 + n^2)}$ **19.** $\sqrt{(kn + 4m)}$

20. $kmn(k^2 + m^2 + n^2)$ **21.** $k^2m^2(m - n)$ **22.** $k^2 - 3k + 4$

23. $m^3 + m^2 + n^2 + n$ **24.** $k^3 + 3k$ **25.** $m(k^2 - n^2)$

26. $m\sqrt{(k - n)}$ **27.** $100k^2 + m$ **28.** $m^2(2k^2 - 3n^2)$

29. $\dfrac{2k + m}{k - n}$ **30.** $\dfrac{kn - k}{2m}$ **31.** $\dfrac{3k + 2m}{2n - 3k}$

32. $\dfrac{k + m + n}{k^2 + m^2 + n^2}$

For Questions **33** to **48**, $w = -2$, $x = 3$, $y = 0$, $z = -\dfrac{1}{2}$

33. $\dfrac{w}{z} + x$ **34.** $\dfrac{w + x}{z}$ **35.** $y\left(\dfrac{x + z}{w}\right)$ **36.** $x^2(z + wy)$

37. $x\sqrt{(x + wz)}$ **38.** $w^2\sqrt{(z^2 + y^2)}$ **39.** $2(w^2 + x^2 + y^2)$ **40.** $2x(w - z)$

41. $\dfrac{z}{w} + x$ **42.** $\dfrac{z + w}{x}$ **43.** $\dfrac{x + w}{z^2}$ **44.** $\dfrac{y^2 - w^2}{xz}$

45. $z^2 + 4z + 5$ **46.** $\dfrac{1}{w} + \dfrac{1}{z} + \dfrac{1}{x}$ **47.** $\dfrac{4}{z} + \dfrac{10}{w}$ **48.** $\dfrac{yz - xw}{xz - w}$

49. Find $K = \sqrt{\left(\dfrac{a^2 + b^2 + c^2 - 2c}{a^2 + b^2 + 4c}\right)}$ when $a = 3$, $b = -2$, $c = -1$.

50. Find $W = \dfrac{kmn(k + m + n)}{(k + m)(k + n)}$ when $k = \dfrac{1}{2}$, $m = -\dfrac{1}{3}$, $n = \dfrac{1}{4}$

When a calculation is repeated many times, it is often helpful to use a formula. An example of a scientific formula is the formula for converting between degrees Celsius and degrees Fahrenheit. An example of a mathematical formula is the one for calculating the volume of a sphere.

Example 1

Use the formula $F = \dfrac{9}{5}C + 3$ to convert $45\,°C$ to degrees Fahrenheit.

If $C = 45$, then $F = \dfrac{9}{5} \times 45 + 32 \quad 113\,°F$.

Example 2

Use the formula $V = \dfrac{4}{3}\pi r^3$ to calculate the volume of a sphere with diameter 12 cm.

Leave your answer in terms of π.

The diameter is 12 cm, so the radius is 6 cm.

So $V = \dfrac{4}{3}\pi \times 6^3 = 288\pi \text{ cm}^3$

Tip

Rearranging the formula to convert degrees Fahrenheit to degrees Celsius will be covered in Chapter 8: Changing the subject of a formula.

Exercise 2.1D

1. The final speed v of a car is given by the formula $v = u + at$.

   [u = initial speed, a = acceleration, t = time taken]

   Find v when $u = 15$ m/s, $a = 0.2$ m/s², $t = 30$ s.

2. The period T of a simple pendulum is given by the formula

   $T = 2\pi\sqrt{\left(\dfrac{l}{g}\right)}$, where l is the length of the pendulum and g

   is the gravitational acceleration. Find T when $l = 0.65$ m, $g = 9.81$ m/s² and $\pi = 3.142$.

3. The total surface area A of a cone is related to the radius r and the slant height l by the formula $A = \pi r(r + l)$.
   Find A when $r = 7$ cm and $l = 11$ cm.

4. The sum S of the squares of the integers from 1 to n is given by $S = \dfrac{1}{6}n\,(n + 1)\,(2n + 1)$. Find S when $n = 12$.

Tip

The period of a pendulum is the time it takes to complete one full cycle: a left swing and a right swing.

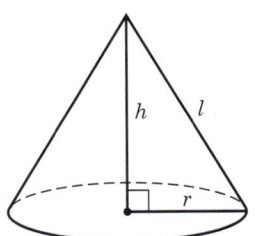

5. The acceleration a of a train is found using the formula
$a = \dfrac{v^2 - u^2}{2s}$.

Find a when $v = 20$ m/s, $u = 9$ m/s and $s = 2.5$ m.

6. Einstein's famous equation relating energy, mass and the speed of light is $E = mc^2$.
Find E when $m = 0.0001$ kg and $c = 3 \times 10^8$ m/s.

7. The distance s travelled by an accelerating rocket is given by $s = ut + \dfrac{1}{2}at^2$.
Find s when $u = 3$ m/s, $t = 100$ s and $a = 0.1$ m/s².

8. Find a formula for the area of the shape below, in terms of a, b and c.

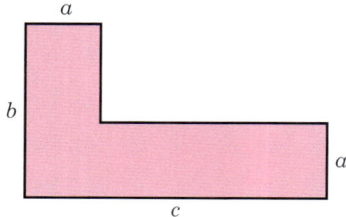

> **Tip**
>
> You can find out more about area in Chapter 5.

9. Find a formula for the length of the shaded part below, in terms of p, q and r.

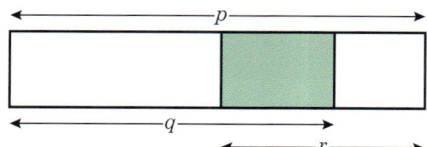

2.2 Brackets and simplifying

A term outside a pair of brackets multiplies each of the terms inside the brackets. This is the *distributive law*.

Example 1
$3(x - 2y) = 3x - 6y$

Example 2
$2x(x - 2y + z) = 2x^2 - 4xy + 2xz$

Example 3

$7y - 4(2x - 3) = 7y - 8x + 12$

In general, like terms can be added:

x terms can be added to x terms

y terms can be added to y terms

x^2 terms can be added to x^2 terms

But they must not be mixed.

Example 4

$2x + 3y + 3x^2 + 2y - x = 2x - x + 3y + 2y + 3x^2$ You can rearrange
$$= x + 5y + 3x^2$$
the expression to group together like terms.

Example 5

$7x + 3x(2x - 3) = 7x + 6x^2 - 9x$
$$= 6x^2 - 2x$$

Exercise 2.2A

Simplify these expressions as far as possible.

1. $3x + 4y + 7y$

2. $4a + 7b - 2a + b$

3. $3x - 2y + 4y$

4. $2x + 3x + 5$

5. $7 - 3x + 2 + 4x$

6. $5 - 3y - 6y - 2$

7. $5x + 2y - 4y - x^2$

8. $x^2 - 2 + 3x + x^2 + 7$

9. $2x - 7y - 2x - 3y$

10. $4a + 3a^2 - 2a$

11. $1 + 7a - 8a^2 + 6 + a^2$

12. $x^2 + 3x^2 - 4x^2 + 5x$

13. $\dfrac{3}{a} + b + \dfrac{7}{a} - 2b$

14. $\dfrac{4}{x} - \dfrac{7}{y} + \dfrac{1}{x} + \dfrac{2}{y}$

15. $\dfrac{m}{x} + \dfrac{2m}{x}$

16. $\dfrac{5}{x} - \dfrac{7}{x} + \dfrac{1}{2}$

17. $\dfrac{3}{a} + b + \dfrac{2}{a} + 2b$

18. $\dfrac{n}{4} - \dfrac{m}{3} - \dfrac{n}{2} + \dfrac{m}{3}$

19. $x^3 + 7x^2 - 2x^3$

20. $(2x)^2 - 2x^2$

21. $(3y)^2 + x^2 - (2y)^2$

22. $(2x)^2 - (2y)^2 - (4x)^2$

23. $5x - 7x^2 - (2x)^2$

24. $\dfrac{3}{x^2} + \dfrac{5}{x^2}$

Expand the brackets and collect like terms to simplify each expression.

25. $3x + 2(x + 1)$

26. $5x + 7(x - 1)$

27. $7 + 3(x - 1)$

28. $9 - 2(3x - 1)$

29. $3x - 4(2x + 5)$

30. $5x - 2x(x - 1)$

31. $7x + 3x(x - 4)$

32. $4(x - 1) - 3x$

33. $5x(x + 2) + 4x$

34. $3x(x - 1) - 7x^2$

35. $3a + 2(a + 4)$

36. $4a - 3(a - 3)$

37. $3ab - 2a(b - 2)$

38. $3y - y(2 - y)$

39. $3x - (x + 2)$

40. $7x - (x - 3)$

41. $5x - 2(2x + 2)$

42. $3(x - y) + 4(x + 2y)$

43. $x(x - 2) + 3x(x - 3)$

44. $3x(x + 4) - x(x - 2)$

45. $y(3y - 1) - (3y - 1)$

46. $7(2x + 2) - (2x + 2)$

47. $7b(a + 2) - a(3b + 3)$

48. $3(x - 2) - (x - 2)$

Two pairs of brackets

To expand two pairs of brackets, multiply each term in the first pair of brackets by each term in the second pair.

Example 1

Expand $(x + 5)(x + 3)$

$(x + 5)(x + 3) = x(x + 3) + 5(x + 3)$ (Multiply each term in the
$\qquad\qquad\quad = x^2 + 3x + 5x + 15$ second bracket by x and by 5.)
$\qquad\qquad\quad = x^2 + 8x + 15$

Example 2

$(2x - 3)(4y + 3) = 2x(4y + 3) - 3(4y + 3)$
$\qquad\qquad\qquad\; = 8xy + 6x - 12y - 9$

Example 3

$3(x + 1)(x - 2) = 3[x(x - 2) + 1(x - 2)]$
$\qquad\qquad\qquad = 3[x^2 - 2x + x - 2]$
$\qquad\qquad\qquad = 3x^2 - 3x - 6$

Exercise 2.2B

Expand the brackets and simplify:

1. $(x + 1)(x + 3)$ **2.** $(x + 3)(x + 2)$ **3.** $(y + 4)(y + 5)$

4. $(x - 3)(x + 4)$ **5.** $(x + 5)(x - 2)$ **6.** $(x - 3)(x - 2)$

7. $(a - 7)(a + 5)$ **8.** $(z + 9)(z - 2)$ **9.** $(x - 3)(x + 3)$

10. $(k - 11)(k + 11)$ **11.** $(2x + 1)(x - 3)$ **12.** $(3x + 4)(x - 2)$

13. $(2y - 3)(y + 1)$ **14.** $(7y - 1)(7y + 1)$ **15.** $(3x - 2)(3x + 2)$

16. $(3a + b)(2a + b)$ **17.** $(3x + y)(x + 2y)$ **18.** $(2b + c)(3b - c)$

19. $(5x - y)(3y - x)$ **20.** $(3b - a)(2a + 5b)$ **21.** $2(x - 1)(x + 2)$

22. $3(x - 1)(2x + 3)$ **23.** $4(2y - 1)(3y + 2)$ **24.** $2(3x + 1)(x - 2)$

25. $4(a + 2b)(a - 2b)$ **26.** $x(x - 1)(x - 2)$ **27.** $2x(2x - 1)(2x + 1)$

28. $3y(y - 2)(y + 3)$ **29.** $x(x + y)(x + z)$ **30.** $3z(a + 2m)(a - m)$

Be careful with an expression like $(x - 3)^2$.
It is not $x^2 - 9$ or even $x^2 + 9$.

$$(x - 3)^2 = (x - 3)(x - 3)$$
$$= x(x - 3) - 3(x - 3)$$
$$= x^2 - 6x + 9$$

Another common mistake occurs with an expression
like $4 - (x - 1)^2$.

A common error is to forget that to multiply a set of brackets
by -1, you need to change the sign of *all* terms inside the brackets.
The following work is correct.

$$4 - (x - 1)^2 = 4 - 1(x - 1)(x - 1)$$
$$= 4 - 1(x^2 - 2x + 1)$$ Using a bracket here helps to get
$$= 4 - x^2 + 2x - 1$$ the signs correct.
$$= 3 + 2x - x^2$$

Exercise 2.2C

Expand the brackets and simplify:

1. $(x + 4)^2$ **2.** $(x + 2)^2$ **3.** $(x - 2)^2$

4. $(2x + 1)^2$ **5.** $(y - 5)^2$ **6.** $(3y + 1)^2$

7. $(x + y)^2$

8. $(2x + y)^2$

9. $(a - b)^2$

10. $(2a - 3b)^2$

11. $3(x + 2)^2$

12. $(3 - x)^2$

13. $(3x + 2)^2$

14. $(a - 2b)^2$

15. $(x + 1)^2 + (x + 2)^2$

16. $(x - 2)^2 + (x + 3)^2$

17. $(x + 2)^2 + (2x + 1)^2$

18. $(y - 3)^2 + (y - 4)^2$

19. $(x + 2)^2 - (x - 3)^2$

20. $(x - 3)^2 - (x + 1)^2$

21. $(y - 3)^2 - (y + 2)^2$

22. $(2x + 1)^2 - (x + 3)^2$

23. $3(x + 2)^2 - (x + 4)^2$

24. $2(x - 3)^2 - 3(x + 1)^2$

Three pairs of brackets

To expand three pairs of brackets, expand the first two pairs of brackets, and then multiply this result by the third pair.

> **Example**
> $$(x + 1)(x + 2)(x + 3) = [x(x + 2) + 1(x + 2)](x + 3)$$
> $$= [x^2 + 2x + x + 2](x + 3)$$
> $$= (x^2 + 3x + 2)(x + 3)$$
> $$= x(x^2 + 3x + 2) + 3(x^2 + 3x + 2)$$
> $$= x^3 + 3x^2 + 2x + 3x^2 + 9x + 6$$
> $$= x^3 + 6x^2 + 11x + 6$$

Exercise 2.2D

Expand the brackets and simplify.

1. $(x + 2)(x - 3)(x - 4)$

2. $(x - 1)(x + 2)(x - 5)$

3. $(x + 6)(x - 3)(x + 5)$

4. $(2x - 1)(x + 1)(x - 1)$

5. $(3x + 1)(2x + 1)(x - 2)$

6. $(x + 2)(4x - 3)(2x + 3)$

7. $(6x - 5)(2x + 7)(3x - 8)$

8. $(x + 1)^2(x - 4)$

9. $(x - 3)(x - 2)^2$

10. $(x - 1)(2x + 3)^2$

11. $(x - 1)^3$

12. $(3x + 2)^3$

13. $(x - 2)^3 - (x + 1)^3$

14. $(x + 3)^3 - (x - 4)^3$

15. $(2x + 1)^3 + 3(x + 1)^3$

2.3 Solving linear equations

If an equation contains only one variable, and the highest power of that variable is 1, then the equation is a *linear equation*. In this section you are going to solve linear equations.

Here are some examples, illustrating a few of the techniques you may use.

- If the x term is negative, add an x term with a positive coefficient to both sides of the equation.

Example 1

Solve $4 - 3x = 2$

$$4 = 2 + 3x \qquad \text{(Add } 3x \text{ to both sides.)}$$
$$2 = 3x \qquad \text{(Subtract 2 from both sides.)}$$
$$\frac{2}{3} = x \qquad \text{(Divide both sides by 3.)}$$

- If there are x terms on both sides, collect them on one side and then simplify.

Example 2

Solve $2x - 7 = 5 - 3x$

$$2x + 3x = 5 + 7 \qquad \text{(Add } 3x \text{ to both sides.)}$$
$$5x = 12$$
$$x = \frac{12}{5} = 2\frac{2}{5} \qquad \text{(Divide both sides by 5 and simplify.)}$$

- If there is a fraction in the x term, multiply out to simplify the equation.

Example 3

Solve $\dfrac{2x}{3} = 10$

$$2x = 30 \qquad \text{(Multiply both sides by 3.)}$$
$$x = \frac{30}{2} = 15 \qquad \text{(Divide both sides by 2 and simplify.)}$$

Exercise 2.3A

Solve:

1. $2x - 5 = 11$

2. $3x - 7 = 20$

3. $2x + 6 = 20$

4. $5x + 10 = 60$

5. $8 = 7 + 3x$

6. $12 = 2x - 8$

7. $-7 = 2x - 10$

8. $3x - 7 = -10$

9. $12 = 15 + 2x$ **10.** $5 + 6x = 7$ **11.** $\dfrac{x}{5} = 7$ **12.** $\dfrac{x}{10} = 13$

13. $7 = \dfrac{x}{2}$ **14.** $\dfrac{x}{2} = \dfrac{1}{3}$ **15.** $\dfrac{3x}{2} = 5$ **16.** $\dfrac{4x}{5} = -2$

17. $7 = \dfrac{7x}{3}$ **18.** $\dfrac{3}{4} = \dfrac{2x}{3}$ **19.** $\dfrac{5x}{6} = \dfrac{1}{4}$ **20.** $-\dfrac{3}{4} = \dfrac{3x}{5}$

21. $\dfrac{x}{2} + 7 = 12$ **22.** $\dfrac{x}{3} - 7 = 2$ **23.** $\dfrac{x}{5} - 6 = -2$ **24.** $4 = \dfrac{x}{2} - 5$

25. $10 = 3 + \dfrac{x}{4}$ **26.** $\dfrac{a}{5} - 1 = -4$ **27.** $100x - 1 = 98$ **28.** $7 = 7 + 7x$

29. $\dfrac{x}{100} + 10 = 20$ **30.** $1000x - 5 = -6$ **31.** $-4 = -7 + 3x$ **32.** $2x + 4 = x - 3$

33. $x - 3 = 3x + 7$ **34.** $5x - 4 = 3 - x$ **35.** $4 - 3x = 1$ **36.** $5 - 4x = -3$

37. $7 = 2 - x$ **38.** $3 - 2x = x + 12$ **39.** $6 + 2a = 3$ **40.** $a - 3 = 3a - 7$

41. $2y - 1 = 4 - 3y$ **42.** $7 - 2x = 2x - 7$ **43.** $7 - 3x = 5 - 2x$ **44.** $8 - 2y = 5 - 5y$

45. $x - 16 = 16 - 2x$ **46.** $x + 2 = 3.1$ **47.** $-x - 4 = -3$ **48.** $-3 - x = -5$

49. $-\dfrac{x}{2} + 1 = -\dfrac{1}{4}$ **50.** $-\dfrac{3}{5} + \dfrac{x}{10} = -\dfrac{1}{5} - \dfrac{x}{5}$

Equations with brackets

Example

Solve $x - 2(x - 1) = 1 - 4(x + 1)$ (Expand the brackets.)

$x - 2x + 2 = 1 - 4x - 4$ (Be careful to get the sign of each term correct.)

$x - 2x + 4x = 1 - 4 - 2$ (Add $4x$ to both sides.)

$3x = -5$ (Simplify.)

$x = -\dfrac{5}{3}$ (Divide both sides by 3.)

Exercise 2.3B

Solve:

1. $x + 3(x + 1) = 2x$ **2.** $1 + 3(x - 1) = 4$

3. $2x - 2(x + 1) = 5x$ **4.** $2(3x - 1) = 3(x - 1)$

5. $4(x - 1) = 2(3 - x)$ **6.** $4(x - 1) - 2 = 3x$

7. $4(1 - 2x) = 3(2 - x)$ **8.** $3 - 2(2x + 1) = x + 17$

9. $4x = x - (x - 2)$ **10.** $7x = 3x - (x + 20)$

11. $5x - 3(x - 1) = 39$ **12.** $3x + 2(x - 5) = 15$

13. $7 - (x + 1) = 9 - (2x - 1)$

14. $10x - (2x + 3) = 21$

15. $3(2x + 1) + 2(x - 1) = 23$

16. $5(1 - 2x) - 3(4 + 4x) = 0$

17. $7x - (2 - x) = 0$

18. $3(x + 1) = 4 - (x - 3)$

19. $3y + 7 + 3(y - 1) = 2(2y + 6)$

20. $4(y - 1) + 3(y + 2) = 5(y - 4)$

21. $4x - 2(x + 1) = 5(x + 3) + 5$

22. $7 - 2(x - 1) = 3(2x - 1) + 2$

23. $10(2x + 3) - 8(3x - 5) + 5(2x - 8) = 0$

24. $2(x + 4) + 3(x - 10) = 8$

25. $7(2x - 4) + 3(5 - 3x) = 2$

26. $10(x + 4) - 9(x - 3) - 1 = 8(x + 3)$

27. $5(2x - 1) - 2(x - 2) = 7 + 4x$

28. $6(3x - 4) - 10(x - 3) = 10(2x - 3)$

29. $3(x - 3) - 7(2x - 8) - (x - 1) = 0$

30. $5 + 2(x + 5) = 10 - (4 - 5x)$

31. $6x + 30(x - 12) = 2\left(x - 1\dfrac{1}{2} \right)$

32. $3\left(2x - \dfrac{2}{3} \right) - 7(x - 1) = 0$

33. $5(x - 1) + 17(x - 2) = 2x + 1$

34. $6(2x - 1) + 9(x + 1) = 8\left(x - 1\dfrac{1}{4} \right)$

35. $7(x + 4) - 5(x + 3) + (4 - x) = 0$

36. $0 = 9(3x + 7) - 5(x + 2) - (2x - 5)$

37. $10(2.3 - x) - 0.1(5x - 30) = 0$

38. $8\left(2\dfrac{1}{2}x - \dfrac{3}{4} \right) - \dfrac{1}{4}(1 - x) = \dfrac{1}{2}$

39. $(6 - x) - (x - 5) - (4 - x) = -\dfrac{x}{2}$

40. $10\left(1 - \dfrac{x}{10} \right) - (10 - x) - \dfrac{1}{100}(10 - x) = 0.05$

Example

Solve $(x + 3)^2 = (x + 2)^2 + 3^2$

$$(x + 3)(x + 3) = (x + 2)(x + 2) + 9$$
$$x^2 + 6x + 9 = x^2 + 4x + 4 + 9$$
$$6x + 9 = 4x + 13$$
$$2x = 4$$
$$x = 2$$

Exercise 2.3C

Solve:

1. $x^2 + 4 = (x + 1)(x + 3)$

2. $x^2 + 3x = (x + 3)(x + 1)$

3. $(x + 3)(x - 1) = x^2 + 5$

4. $(x + 1)(x + 4) = (x - 7)(x + 6)$

5. $(x - 2)(x + 3) = (x - 7)(x + 7)$

6. $(x - 5)(x + 4) = (x + 7)(x - 6)$

7. $2x^2 + 3x = (2x - 1)(x + 1)$

8. $(2x - 1)(x - 3) = (2x - 3)(x - 1)$

9. $x^2 + (x + 1)^2 = (2x - 1)(x + 4)$

10. $x(2x + 6) = 2(x^2 - 5)$

11. $(x + 1)(x - 3) + (x + 1)^2 = 2x(x - 4)$

12. $(2x + 1)(x - 4) + (x - 2)^2 = 3x(x + 2)$

13. $(x + 2)^2 - (x - 3)^2 = 3x - 11$

14. $x(x - 1) = 2(x - 1)(x + 5) - (x - 4)^2$

15. $(2x + 1)^2 - 4(x - 3)^2 = 5x + 10$

16. $2(x + 1)^2 - (x - 2)^2 = x(x - 3)$

17. The area of the rectangle here exceeds the area of the square by 2 cm². Find x.

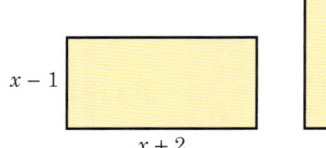

18. The area of the square exceeds the area of the rectangle by 13 m². Find y.

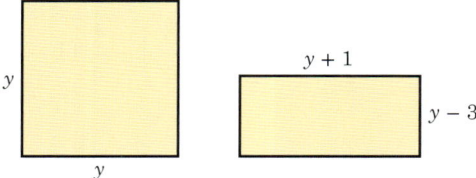

19. The area of the square is half the area of the rectangle. Find x.

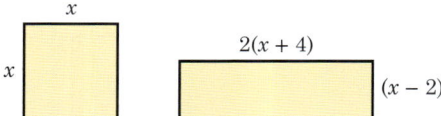

Equations involving fractions

When solving equations involving fractions, multiply both sides of the equation by a suitable number or letter to eliminate the fractions.

Example 1

Solve $\dfrac{5}{x} = 2$

$5 = 2x$ (Multiply both sides by x.)

$\dfrac{5}{2} = x$ (Divide both sides by 2.)

Example 2

Solve $\dfrac{x+3}{4} = \dfrac{2x-1}{3}$

$12 \times \dfrac{(x+3)}{4} = 12 \times \dfrac{(2x-1)}{3}$ (Multiply both sides by 12.)

$3(x+3) = 4(2x-1)$ (Or you can cross multiply.)

$3x + 9 = 8x - 4$

$13 = 5x$ (Subtract $3x$, not $8x$, so that the x term is positive.)

$\dfrac{13}{5} = x$

$x = 2\dfrac{3}{5}$

Example 3

Solve $\dfrac{5}{(x-1)} + 2 = 12$

$\dfrac{5}{(x-1)} = 10$ (2 and 12 are like terms so combine them first.)

$5 = 10(x-1)$

$5 = 10x - 10$

$15 = 10x$

$\dfrac{15}{10} = x$

$x = 1\dfrac{1}{2}$

Exercise 2.3D

Solve:

1. $\dfrac{7}{x} = 21$

2. $30 = \dfrac{6}{x}$

3. $\dfrac{5}{x} = 3$

4. $\dfrac{9}{x} = -3$

5. $11 = \dfrac{5}{x}$

6. $-2 = \dfrac{4}{x}$

7. $\dfrac{x}{4} = \dfrac{3}{2}$

8. $\dfrac{x}{3} = \dfrac{5}{4}$

9. $\dfrac{x+1}{3} = \dfrac{x-1}{4}$

10. $\dfrac{x+3}{2} = \dfrac{x-4}{5}$

11. $\dfrac{2x-1}{3} = \dfrac{x}{2}$

12. $\dfrac{3x+1}{5} = \dfrac{2x}{3}$

13. $\dfrac{8-x}{2} = \dfrac{2x+2}{5}$

14. $\dfrac{x+2}{7} = \dfrac{3x+6}{5}$

15. $\dfrac{1-x}{2} = \dfrac{3-x}{3}$

16. $\dfrac{2}{x-1} = 1$

17. $\dfrac{x}{3} + \dfrac{x}{4} = 1$

18. $\dfrac{x}{3} + \dfrac{x}{2} = 4$

19. $\dfrac{x}{2} - \dfrac{x}{5} = 3$

20. $\dfrac{x}{3} = 2 + \dfrac{x}{4}$

21. $\dfrac{5}{x-1} = \dfrac{10}{x}$

22. $\dfrac{12}{2x-3} = 4$

23. $2 = \dfrac{18}{x+4}$

24. $\dfrac{5}{x+5} = \dfrac{15}{x+7}$

25. $\dfrac{9}{x} = \dfrac{5}{x-3}$

26. $\dfrac{4}{x-1} = \dfrac{10}{3x-1}$

27. $\dfrac{-7}{x-1} = \dfrac{14}{5x+2}$

28. $\dfrac{4}{x+1} = \dfrac{7}{3x-2}$

29. $\dfrac{x+1}{2} + \dfrac{x-1}{3} = \dfrac{1}{6}$

30. $\dfrac{1}{3}(x+2) = \dfrac{1}{5}(3x+2)$

31. $\dfrac{1}{2}(x-1) - \dfrac{1}{6}(x+1) = 0$

32. $\dfrac{1}{4}(x+5) - \dfrac{2x}{3} = 0$

33. $\dfrac{4}{x} + 2 = 3$

34. $\dfrac{6}{x} - 3 = 7$

35. $\dfrac{9}{x} - 7 = 1$

36. $-2 = 1 + \dfrac{3}{x}$

37. $4 - \dfrac{4}{x} = 0$

38. $5 - \dfrac{6}{x} = -1$

39. $7 - \dfrac{3}{2x} = 1$

40. $4 + \dfrac{5}{3x} = -1$

41. $\dfrac{9}{2x} - 5 = 0$

42. $\dfrac{x-1}{5} - \dfrac{x-1}{3} = 0$

43. $\dfrac{x-1}{4} - \dfrac{2x-3}{5} = \dfrac{1}{20}$

44. $\dfrac{4}{1-x} = \dfrac{3}{1+x}$

45. $\dfrac{x+1}{4} - \dfrac{x}{3} = \dfrac{1}{12}$

46. $\dfrac{2x+1}{8} - \dfrac{x-1}{3} = \dfrac{5}{24}$

2.4 Problems solved by linear equations

Step 1 Let the unknown quantity be x (or any other letter) and state the units (where appropriate).

Step 2 Express the given statement in the form of an equation. Do not include the units in the equation.

Step 3 Solve the equation for x and give the answer in *words*. (Do not finish by just writing '$x = 3$'.)

Step 4 Check your solution using the initial problem (not your equation).

Example 1

The sum of three consecutive whole numbers is 78. Find the numbers.

Let the smallest number be x; then the other numbers are $(x + 1)$ and $(x + 2)$.

Form an equation:

$x + (x + 1) + (x + 2) = 78$

$\qquad\quad 3x + 3 = 78$

Solve: $3x = 75$

$\qquad\ x = 25$

In words:

The three numbers are 25, 26 and 27.

Check: $25 + 26 + 27 = 78$

Example 2

The length of a rectangle is three times its width. If the perimeter is 36 cm, find the width.

Let the width of the rectangle be x cm.

Then the length of the rectangle is $3x$ cm.

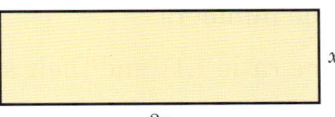

Form an equation.

$x + 3x + x + 3x = 36$ or $\quad 2(x + 3x) = 36$

Solve: $8x = 36$

$\qquad x = \frac{36}{8}$

$\qquad x = 4.5$

In words:

The width of the rectangle is 4.5 cm

Check: If width $\qquad = 4.5$ cm

$\qquad\quad$ length $\qquad = 13.5$ cm

$\qquad\quad$ perimeter $= 36$ cm

Exercise 2.4A

Solve each problem by forming an equation. The first questions are easy but should still be solved using an equation, in order to practise the method.

1. The sum of three consecutive numbers is 276. Find the numbers.

2. The sum of four consecutive numbers is 90. Find the numbers.

3. The sum of three consecutive odd numbers is 177. Find the numbers.

4. Find three consecutive even numbers which add up to 1524.

5. When a number is doubled and then added to 13, the result is 38. Find the number.

6. When a number is doubled and then added to 24, the result is 49. Find the number.

7. When 7 is subtracted from three times a certain number, the result is 28. What is the number?

8. The sum of two numbers is 50. The second number is five times the first. Find the numbers.

9. Two numbers are in the ratio 1:11 and their sum is 15. Find the numbers.

10. The length of a rectangle is twice the width. If the perimeter is 20 cm, find the width.

11. The width of a rectangle is one third of the length. If the perimeter is 96 cm, find the width.

12. If AB is a straight line, find x.

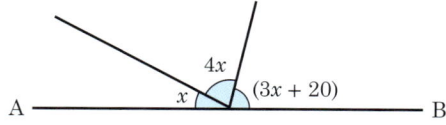

13. If the perimeter of the triangle is 22 cm, find the length of the shortest side.

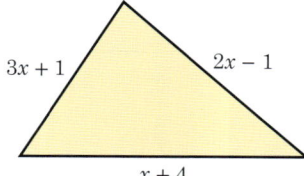

14. If the perimeter of the rectangle is 34 cm, find x.

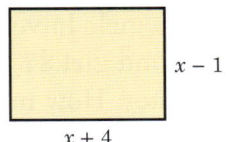

$x - 1$

$x + 4$

15. The difference between two numbers is 9.
Find the numbers if their sum is 46.

16. The three angles in a triangle are in the ratio $1:3:5$.
Find them.

17. The three angles in a triangle are in the ratio $3:4:5$.
Find them.

18. The product of two consecutive odd numbers is 10 more
than the square of the smaller number.
Find the smaller number.

19. The product of two consecutive even numbers is 12 more
than the square of the smaller number. Find the numbers.

20. The sum of three numbers is 66. The second number is
twice the first and six less than the third.
Find the numbers.

21. The sum of three numbers is 28. The second number is
three times the first and the third is 7 less than the second.
What are the numbers?

22. David's mass is 5 kg less than Sucha's, who in turn is 8 kg
lighter than Paul. If their total mass is 197 kg, how heavy
is each person?

23. Nilopal is 2 years older than Devjan who is 7 years older
than John. If their combined age is 61 years, find the age of
each person.

24. Kim has four times as many marbles as Ava. If Kim gave 18
to Ava they would have the same number.
How many marbles has each person?

25. Mukat has five times as many books as Usha. If Mukat
gives 16 books to Usha, they will each have the same
number. How many books does each girl have?

26. The result of multiplying a number by 3 is the same as
adding 12 to it. What is the number?

27. Find the area of the rectangle if the perimeter is 52 cm.

28. The result of multiplying a number by 3 and subtracting
5 is the same as doubling the number and adding 9.
Find the number.

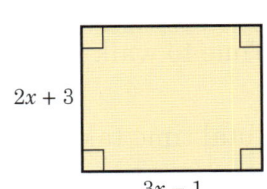

$2x + 3$

$3x - 1$

29. Two girls have $76 between them. If the first girl gave the second girl $7, they would each have the same amount of money. How much does each girl have?

30. A tennis racket costs $12 more than a hockey stick. If the price of the two is $31, find the cost of the tennis racket.

Example

A man leaves home at 16:42 and walks to a library, 6 km away, arriving at 17:30. He walked part of the way at 5 km/h and then, realising the time, he ran the rest of the way at 10 km/h. How far did he run?

Let the distance he ran be x km.

Then the distance he walked $= (6 - x)$ km.

Time taken to walk $(6 - x)$ km

at 5 km/h $= \dfrac{(6 - x)}{5}$ hours.

Time taken to run x km at

10 km/h $= \dfrac{x}{10}$ hours.

> **Tip**
>
> Use the formula
>
> $\text{time} = \dfrac{\text{distance}}{\text{speed}}.$

Total time taken $= 48$ minutes

$$= \dfrac{48}{60} \text{ hour} = \dfrac{4}{5} \text{ hour}$$

$$\therefore \dfrac{(6 - x)}{5} + \dfrac{x}{10} = \dfrac{4}{5}$$

Multiply by 10:

$$2(6 - x) + x = 8$$
$$12 - 2x + x = 8$$
$$4 = x$$

He ran a distance of 4 km.

Check:

Time to run 4 km $= \dfrac{4}{10} = \dfrac{2}{5}$ hour

Time to walk 2 km $= \dfrac{2}{5}$ hour

Total time taken $= \left(\dfrac{2}{5} + \dfrac{2}{5} \right) = \dfrac{4}{5}$ hour

Exercise 2.4B

1. Every year a man is paid $500 more than the previous year. If he receives $17 800 over four years, what was he paid in the first year?

2. Samir buys x cans of soda at 80 cents each and $(x + 4)$ cans of soda at 85 cents each. The total cost was $8.35. Find x.

3. The length of a straight line segment ABC is 5 m. If AB : BC = 2 : 5, find the length of AB.

4. The opposite angles of a cyclic quadrilateral are $(3x + 10)°$ and $(2x + 20)°$. Find the angles.

> **Tip**
>
> Opposite angles of a cyclic quadrilateral add to 180°.

5. The interior angles of a hexagon are in the ratio 1 : 2 : 3 : 4 : 5 : 9. Find the angles.

> **Tip**
>
> Interior angles of a hexagon add to 720°.

6. A woman is 32 years older than her son. Ten years ago, she was three times as old as her son was at that time. Find the current age of the woman and her son.

7. A bus is travelling with 48 passengers. When it arrives at a stop, x passengers get off and 3 get on. At the next stop half the passengers get off and 7 get on. There are now 22 passengers. Find x.

8. A bus is travelling with 52 passengers. When it arrives at a stop, y passengers get off and 4 get on. At the next stop one-third of the passengers get off and 3 get on. There are now 25 passengers. Find y.

9. In a regular polygon with n sides, each interior angle is $\left(180 - \dfrac{360}{n}\right)$ degrees. How many sides does a polygon have if each interior angle is 156°?

10. Consider the equation $\dfrac{k}{x} = 12$ where k is any number between 20 and 65 and x is a positive integer. What are the possible values of x?

11. Mahmoud runs to a marker and back in 15 minutes. His speed on the way to the marker is 5 m/s and his speed on the way back is 4 m/s. Find the distance to the marker.

> **Tip**
>
> Formulae for speed, distance and time are studied in detail in section 3.6 on page 111.

12. A car completes a journey in 10 minutes. For the first half of the journey the speed was 60 km/h and for the second half the speed was 40 km/h. How far is the journey?

2.5 Simultaneous equations

To find the value of two unknowns in a problem, *two* different equations must be given that relate the unknowns to each other. These two equations are called *simultaneous* equations. There are two algebraic ways to solve simultaneous equations: the substitution method and the elimination method. You can also solve simultaneous equations graphically.

Substitution method

This method is used when one equation contains a unit quantity of one of the unknowns, as in equation (2) of the example below.

Example

$3x - 2y = 0$ (1)

$2x + y = 7$ (2)

Label the equations so that the working is made clear.

In this case, write y in terms of x from equation (2).

Substitute this expression for y into equation (1) and solve to find x.

Find y from equation (2) using this value of x.

$2x + y = 7$ (2)

$y = 7 - 2x$

Substituting into (1)

$3x - 2(7 - 2x) = 0$

$3x - 14 + 4x = 0$

$7x = 14$

$x = 2$

Substituting into (2)

$2 \times 2 + y = 7$

$y = 3$

The solutions are $x = 2$, $y = 3$.

$3 \times 2 - 2 \times 3 = 0$

$2 \times 2 + 3 = 7$

These values of x and y are the only pair which simultaneously satisfy *both* equations.

Exercise 2.5A

Use the substitution method to solve these simultaneous equations.

1. $2x + y = 5$
$x + 3y = 5$

2. $x + 2y = 8$
$2x + 3y = 14$

3. $3x + y = 10$
$x - y = 2$

4. $2x + y = -3$
$x - y = -3$

5. $4x + y = 14$
$x + 5y = 13$

6. $x + 2y = 1$
$2x + 3y = 4$

7. $2x + y = 5$
$3x - 2y = 4$

8. $2x + y = 13$
$5x - 4y = 13$

9. $7x + 2y = 19$
$x - y = 4$

10. $b - a = -5$
$a + b = -1$

11. $a + 4b = 6$
$8b - a = -3$

12. $a + b = 4$
$2a + b = 5$

13. $3m = 2n - 6\dfrac{1}{2}$
$4m + n = 6$

14. $2w + 3x - 13 = 0$
$x + 5w - 13 = 0$

15. $x + 2(y - 6) = 0$
$3x + 4y = 30$

16. $2x = 4 + z$
$6x - 5z = 18$

17. $3m - n = 5$
$2m + 5n = 7$

18. $5c - d - 11 = 0$
$4d + 3c = -5$

It is useful at this point to revise the operations of addition and subtraction with negative numbers.

Example

Simplify:

a) $-7 + (-4) = -7 - 4 = -11$

b) $-3x + (-4x) = -3x - 4x = -7x$

c) $4y - (-3y) = 4y + 3y = 7y$

c) $3a + (-3a) = 3a - 3a = 0$

Exercise 2.5B

Evaluate:

1. $7 + -6$

2. $8 + -11$

3. $5 - +7$

4. $6 - -9$

5. $-8 + -4$

6. $-7 - -4$

7. $10 + -12$

8. $-7 - +4$

9. $-10 - +11$

10. $-3 - -4$

11. $4 - +4$

12. $8 - -7$

13. $-5 - +5$

14. $-7 - -10$

15. $16 - +10$

16. $-7 - +4$ **17.** $-6 - -8$ **18.** $10 - +5$

19. $-12 + -7$ **20.** $7 + -11$

Simplify:

21. $3x + -2x$ **22.** $4x + -7x$ **23.** $6x - +2x$

24. $10y - +6y$ **25.** $6y - -3y$ **26.** $7x + -4x$

27. $-5x + -3x$ **28.** $-3x - -7x$ **29.** $5x - +3x$

30. $-7y - -10y$

Elimination method

Often there is a quicker way to solve simultaneous equations than using substitution.

If the coefficient of one of the variables can be made the same number in both equations by multiplying or dividing all the terms, then you can subtract one equation from the other, if the signs of those coefficients are the same, or add the two equations together if they are different.

Example 1

$x + 2y = 8$ (1)
$2x + 3y = 14$ (2)

Label the equations so that the working is made clear.

Multiply one or both equations by a factor or factors, such that the coefficient of one of the unknowns is the same in both equations.

Eliminate this unknown from the two equations by adding or subtracting them, and then solve for the remaining unknown.

Substitute into the first equation and solve for the eliminated unknown.

$$\begin{array}{lll} & x + 2y = 8 & (1) \\ (1) \times 2 & 2x + 4y = 16 & (3) \\ & 2x + 3y = 14 & (2) \end{array}$$

Subtract (2) from (3):

$y = 2$

Substituting into (1):	Check:
$x + 2 \times 2 = 8$	$4 + 2 \times 2 = 8$
$x = 8 - 4$	$2 \times 4 + 3 \times 2 = 14$
$x = 4$	

The solutions are $x = 4$, $y = 2$.

Example 2

$$2x + 3y = 5 \quad\quad (1)$$
$$5x - 2y = -16 \quad\quad (2)$$

$(1) \times 5$	$10x + 15y = 25$	(3)
$(2) \times 2$	$10x - 4y = -32$	(4)
$(3) - (4)$	$15y - (-4y) = 25 - (-32)$	
	$19y = 57$	
	$y = 3$	

Substitute into (1)   Check:

$2x + 3 \times 3 = 5$ $2 \times (-2) + 3 \times 3 = 5$

$2x = 5 - 9 = -4$ $5 \times (-)2 - 2 \times 3 = -16$

$x = -2$

The solutions are $x = -2$, $y = 3$.

Note that you can choose which variable to eliminate. Your choice will often be based on the coefficients of the variables in the original equations. In Example 2, you could have eliminated y instead of x:

$(1) \times 2$	$4x + 6y = 10$	(3)
$(2) \times 3$	$15x - 6y = -48$	(4)

$(3) + (4)$	$19x = -38$
	$x = -2$

You get to the same answer of $x = -2$, $y = 3$ when you substitute $x = -2$ into (1) or (2).

Exercise 2.5C

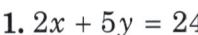

Use the elimination method to solve these simultaneous equations.

1. $2x + 5y = 24$
  $4x + 3y = 20$

2. $5x + 2y = 13$
  $2x + 6y = 26$

3. $3x + y = 11$
  $9x + 2y = 28$

4. $x + 2y = 17$
  $8x + 3y = 45$

5. $3x + 2y = 19$
  $x + 8y = 21$

6. $2a + 3b = 9$
  $4a + b = 13$

7. $2x + 3y = 11$
  $3x + 4y = 15$

8. $3x + 8y = 27$
  $4x + 3y = 13$

9. $2x + 7y = 17$
  $5x + 3y = -1$

10. $5x + 3y = 23$
$2x + 4y = 12$

11. $7x + 5y = 32$
$3x + 4y = 23$

12. $3x + 2y = 4$
$4x + 5y = 10$

13. $3x + 2y = 11$
$2x - y = -3$

14. $3x + 2y = 7$
$2x - 3y = -4$

15. $x + 2y = -4$
$3x - y = 9$

16. $5x - 7y = 27$
$3x - 4y = 16$

17. $3x - 2y = 7$
$4x + y = 13$

18. $x - y = -1$
$2x - y = 0$

19. $y - x = -1$
$3x - y = 5$

20. $x - 3y = -5$
$2y + 3x + 4 = 0$

21. $x + 3y - 7 = 0$
$2y - x - 3 = 0$

22. $3a - b = 9$
$2a + 2b = 14$

23. $3x - y = 9$
$4x - y = -14$

24. $x + 2y = 4$
$3x + y = 9\dfrac{1}{2}$

25. $2x - y = 5$
$\dfrac{x}{4} + \dfrac{y}{3} = 2$

26. $3x - y = 17$
$\dfrac{x}{5} + \dfrac{y}{2} = 0$

27. $3x - 2y = 5$
$\dfrac{2x}{3} + \dfrac{y}{2} = -\dfrac{7}{9}$

28. $2x = 11 - y$
$\dfrac{x}{5} + \dfrac{y}{4} = 1$

29. $4x - 0.5y = 12.5$
$3x + 0.8y = 8.2$

30. $0.4x + 3y = 2.6$
$x - 2y = 4.6$

2.6 Problems solved by simultaneous equations

Example 1

In 1985, a motorist bought 24 litres of fuel and 5 litres of oil for $10.70, while another motorist bought 18 litres of fuel and 10 litres of oil for $12.40. Find the cost of 1 litre of fuel and 1 litre of oil at this garage.

Let cost of 1 litre of fuel be x cents.

Let cost of 1 litre of oil be y cents.

You know: $24x + 5y = 1070$ (1)

$\qquad 18x + 10y = 1240$ (2)

Multiply (1) by 2,

$48x + 10y = 2140 \qquad\qquad$ (3)

Subtract (2) from (3),

$3x = 900$

$x = 30$

Substitute $x = 30$ into equation (2):

$18(30) + 10y = 1240$

$10y = 1240 - 540$

$10y = 700$

$y = 70$

1 litre of fuel cost 30 cents, and 1 litre of oil cost 70 cents.

Example 2

A boat can sail at 18 knots with the current and at 12 knots against it. Find the speed of the current and the speed of the boat in still water.

Let the speed of the boat in still water be x knots.

Let the speed of the current be y knots.

You have: $x + y = 18$ (1)

           $x - y = 12$ (2)

Add (1) to (2):

$2x = 30$

$x = 15$

Substituting $x = 15$ into equation (1) gives $y = 3$.

Therefore, the speed of the boat in still water is 15 knots and the speed of the current is 3 knots.

Exercise 2.6A

Solve each problem by forming a pair of simultaneous equations.

1. Find two numbers with a sum of 15 and a difference of 4.

2. Twice one number added to three times another number gives 21. Find the numbers, if the difference between them is 3 and both the numbers are whole numbers.

3. The average of two numbers is 7, and three times the difference between them is 18. Find the numbers.

Tip

To find the average of two numbers you add them and divide the total by 2.

4. The line, with equation $y + ax = c$, passes through the points (1, 5) and (3, 1). Find a and c.

Tip

For the point (1, 5) put $x = 1$ and $y = 5$ into $y + ax = c$, etc.

5. The line $y = mx + c$ passes through (2, 5) and (4, 13). Find m and c.

6. The curve $y = ax^2 + bx$ passes through (2, 0) and (4, 8). Find a and b.

7. A gardener buys fifty carrot seeds and twenty lettuce seeds for $1.10 and her mother buys thirty carrot seeds and forty lettuce seeds for $1.50. Find the cost of one carrot seed and one lettuce seed.

8. A shop owner can either buy two torches and three boxes of batteries for $17.50 or four torches and one box of batteries for $12.50. Find the cost of one torch and one box of batteries.

9. Half of the difference between two numbers is 2. The sum of the greater number and twice the smaller number is 13. Find the numbers.

10. Three white eggs and two brown eggs have a mass of 13 grams, while five white eggs and four brown eggs have a mass of 24 grams. Find the mass of a brown egg and of a white egg.

11. A tortoise makes a journey in two parts: it can either walk at 4 cm/s or crawl at 3 cm/s. If the tortoise walks the first part and crawls the second, it takes 110 seconds. If it crawls the first part and walks the second, it takes 100 seconds. Find the lengths of the two parts of the journey.

12. A cyclist completes a journey of 500 m in 22 seconds, part of the way at 10 m/s and the remainder at 50 m/s. How far does she travel at each speed?

13. A machine takes only 10 cent and 50 cent coins and contains a total of twenty-one coins altogether. If the value of the coins is $4.90, find the number of coins of each value.

14. Thirty tickets were sold for a concert; some at 60 cents and the rest at $1. If the total raised was $22, how many had the cheaper tickets?

15. A fish can swim at 14 m/s in the direction of the current and at 6 m/s against it. Find the speed of the current and the speed of the fish in still water.

16. If the numerator and denominator of a fraction are both decreased by 1, the new fraction is equivalent to $\frac{2}{3}$. But, if the numerator and denominator are both *increased* by 1, the fraction is equivalent to $\frac{3}{4}$. Find the original fraction.

17. Three years from now, a pet mouse will be as old as his owner was four years ago. Their present ages total 13 years. Find the age of each now.

18. Find two numbers where three times the smaller number exceeds the larger by 5 and the sum of the numbers is 11.

19. A straight line passes through the points (2, 4) and (−1, −5). Find its equation.

20. A wallet containing $40 has three times as many $1 notes as $5 notes. Find the number of each kind.

21. At the present time a man is four times as old as his son. Six years ago he was 10 times as old. Find their present ages.

22. A submarine can travel at 25 knots with the current and at 16 knots against it. Find the speed of the current and the speed of the submarine in still water.

23. The curve $y = ax^2 + bx + c$ passes through the points (1, 8), (0, 5) and (3, 20). Find the values of a, b and c and hence the equation of the curve.

24. The curve $y = ax^2 + bx + c$ passes through the points (1, 4), (−2, 19) and (0, 5). Find the equation of the curve.

25. The curve $y = ax^2 + bx + c$ passes through (1, 8), (−1, 2) and (2, 14). Find the equation of the curve.

26. The curve $y = ax^2 + bx + c$ passes through (2, 5), (3, 12) and (−1, −4). Find the equation of the curve.

> **Tip**
>
> The general form of the equation of a straight line is $y = mx + c$.

Revision exercise 2

1. Solve these equations.

a) $x + 4 = 3x + 9$

b) $9 - 3a = 1$

2. Given $a = 3$, $b = 4$ and $c = -2$, evaluate:

a) $2a^2 - b$

b) $a(b - c)$

c) $2b^2 - c^2$

3. Solve these simultaneous equations.

a) $3x + 2y = 5$

  $2x - y = 8$

b) $2m - n = 6$

  $2m + 3n = -6$

c) $3x - 4y = 19$

  $x + 6y = 10$

d) $3x - 7y = 11$

  $2x - 3y = 4$

4. Given that $x = 4$, $y = 3$, $z = -2$, evaluate:

a) $2x(y + z)$

b) $(xy)^2 - z^2$

c) $x^2 + y^2 + z^2$

d) $(x + y)(x - z)$

e) $\sqrt{x(1 - 4z)}$

f) $\dfrac{xy}{z}$

5. a) Expand and simplify $(x - 2)(x - 3)(x - 4)$.

b) Expand and simplify $(2x - 3)^3$.

6. Solve these equations.

a) $5 - 7x = 4 - 6x$

b) $\dfrac{7}{x} = \dfrac{2}{3}$

7. Find the value of $\dfrac{2x - 3y}{5x + 2y}$ when $x = 2a$ and $y = -a$.

8. Solve these simultaneous equations.

a) $7c + 3d = 29$

  $5c - 4d = 33$

b) $2x - 3y = 7$

  $2y - 3x = -8$

c) $5x = 3(1 - y)$

  $3x + 2y + 1 = 0$

d) $5s + 3t = 16$

  $11s + 7t = 34$

9. Solve these equations.

a) $4(2x - 1) - 3(1 - x) = 0$

b) $\dfrac{x + 3}{x} = 2$

10. Given that $m = -2$, $n = 4$, evaluate:

a) $5m + 3n$

b) $5 + 2m - m^2$

c) $m^2 + 2n^2$

d) $(2m + n)(2m - n)$

e) $(n - m)^2$

f) $n - mn - 2m^2$

11. Given that $a + b = 2$ and that $a^2 + b^2 = 6$, show that $2ab = -2$.
Find also the value of $(a - b)^2$.

12. A jar contains 50 US coins, containing a mixture of dimes (10 cents) and quarters (25 cents). The total value of the coins is $9.35. How many dimes are there?

13. Pat bought 45 stamps, some for 40c and some for 58c. If he spent $22.50 altogether, how many 40c stamps did he buy?

Examination-style exercise 2

NON-CALCULATOR

1. a) $\dfrac{5}{7} + \dfrac{11}{14} = \dfrac{x}{2}$ Work out the value of x.   [1]

   b) $\dfrac{7}{4} \div \dfrac{4}{y} = \dfrac{35}{16}$ Work out the value of y.   [1]

2. Solve these simultaneous equations.

$4x + y = 17$

$3x - 2y = 10$ [3]

3. Solve these equations.

   a) $\dfrac{2x}{3} - 12 = 0$ [2]

   b) $\dfrac{x + 8}{3} = \dfrac{8x - 1}{11}$ [2]

4. Solve these simultaneous equations.

$0.3x + 2y = 17$

$0.6x + 3y = 27$ [3]

5. a) Expand and simplify $(x - 3)^2(3x + 1)$.   [3]

   b) Fully simplify $(x - 3)^2(3x + 1) - (x + 2)^2$.   [3]

Sophie Germain (1776–1831) was a French mathematician. Because it was not then considered appropriate for a woman to learn mathematics, as a child she secretly read books from her father's library. She also wrote to famous mathematicians such as Karl Gauss, using the male pseudonym Monsieur LeBlanc. She became a great mathematician, and in 1816 she became the first woman to win a prize from the Paris Academy of Sciences for her essay on elasticity theory.

- Simplify a ratio, divide a quantity by a ratio. Use ratios in context.
- Understand and use measures of rate including solving problems involving average speed.
- Calculate a percentage of a quantity. Write one quantity as a percentage of another quantity. Solve various problems involving percentages including simple interest, compound interest, percentage increase, percentage decrease and reverse percentages.
- Calculate with time including in terms of the 24-hour and 12-hour clock.
- Calculate with money including converting between currencies.

3.1 Ratio and proportion

Ratio

A ratio expresses the relationship in size between two or more numbers or quantities. Ratios are usually written using a colon, such as $3:5$, which reads 'in a ratio of 3 to 5'. For example, when making bread, a recommended ratio of water to flour is $3:5$. This means that for every 3 g of water, you need 5 g of flour. A ratio is not concerned about the total amount of water and flour; it just tells you how the two quantities are related.

Note that the order of the numbers in the ratio is important. The ratio $3:5$ is *not* the same as $5:3$.

Ratios are also closely related to fractions. If the ratio of a girl's height to her father's height is $4:5$, then the girl's height is $\frac{4}{5}$ of her father's height. This relationship between ratios and fractions is the reason why numbers that can be written as fractions with integer numerators and denominators are called **rational numbers** and numbers that cannot are called **irrational numbers**.

For a ratio to be in its simplest form, it should only contain integers, and those integers should have no common factors greater than 1.

Example 1

Write these ratios in their simplest form

a) $10:30$ **b)** $0.4:0.6$ **c)** $15:25:40$

a) Divide through by 10 to give a ratio of $1:3$.

b) Divide through by 0.2 to give a ratio of $2:3$.

c) Divide through by 5 to give a ratio of $3:5:8$.

Example 2

Change the ratio $2:5$ into the form

a) $1:n$ **b)** $m:1$

a) Divide through by 2 so that the number on the left becomes 1.

$$2:5 = 1:\frac{5}{2}$$

$$= 1:2.5$$

b) Divide through by 5 so that the number on the right becomes 1.

$$2:5 = \frac{2}{5}:1$$

$$= 0.4:1$$

Example 3

Divide $60 between two people, A and B, in the ratio $5:7$.

Consider $60 as 12 equal parts (i.e. $5 + 7$). Each part is worth $5.
Then A receives 5 parts and B receives 7 parts.

$\therefore$ A receives $\dfrac{5}{12}$ of $60 = 25

B receives $\dfrac{7}{12}$ of $60 = 35

Example 4

Divide 200 kg in the ratio $1:3:4$.

$1 + 3 + 4 = 8$. The parts are $\frac{1}{8}, \frac{3}{8}$ and $\frac{4}{8}$ (of 200 kg),
i.e. 25 kg, 75 kg and 100 kg.

Exercise 3.1A

1. Write these ratios in their simplest form.

   a) $2:8$ **b)** $6:16$ **c)** $14:8$ **d)** $2.5:3$

   e) $1.5:3.5$ **f)** $15:4.5$ **g)** $4:8:20$ **h)** $9.8:4.2:2.8$

2. Express these ratios in the form $1:n$.

   a) $2:6$ **b)** $5:30$ **c)** $2:100$ **d)** $5:8$

   e) $4:3$ **f)** $8:3$ **g)** $22:550$ **h)** $45:360$

3. Express these ratios in the form $n:1$.

   a) $12:5$ **b)** $5:2$ **c)** $4:5$ **d)** $2:100$

4. Divide each quantity in the ratio given.

   a) $40; (3:5)$ **b)** $120; (3:7)$ **c)** 250 m; $(14:11)$

   d) $117; (2:3:8)$ **e)** 180 kg; $(1:5:6)$ **f)** 184 minutes; $(2:3:3)$

5. When $143 is divided in the ratio $2:4:5$, what is the difference between the largest share and the smallest share?

6. Divide 180 kg in the ratio $1:2:3:4$

7. Divide \$4000 in the ratio $2:5:5:8$

8. If $\frac{5}{8}$ of the children in a school are boys, what is the ratio of boys to girls?

9. A man and a woman share a prize of \$1000 between them in the ratio $1:4$. The woman shares her part between herself, her mother and her daughter in the ratio $2:1:1$. How much does her daughter receive?

10. Erica and Rachel share a sum of money in the ratio $3:2$. If the sum of money is doubled, in what ratio should they divide it so that Erica still receives the same amount?

11. In a herd of x cattle, the ratio of the number of bulls to cows is $1:6$. Find the number of bulls in the herd in terms of x.

12. If $x:3 = 12:x$, calculate the positive value of x.

13. If $y:18 = 8:y$, calculate the positive value of y.

14. \$400 is divided between Kas, Jaspar and Max so that Kas has twice as much as Jaspar and Jaspar has three times as much as Max. How much does Jaspar receive?

15. A cake mixture of mass 550 g has three dry ingredients: flour, sugar and raisins. There is twice as much flour as sugar and one and a half times as much sugar as raisins. How much flour is there?

16. A brother and sister share out their collection of 5000 stamps in the ratio $5:3$. The brother then shares his stamps with two friends in the ratio $3:1:1$, keeping most for himself. How many stamps do each of his friends receive?

17. \$520 is divided between three people A, B and C. If the ratio of A's share to B's share is $4:1$ and B's share to C's share is $2:3$, calculate:

   a) the ratio of A's share to C's share

   b) how much each person receives.

Proportion

Proportion is closely related to ratio. If two numbers are **directly proportional** to each other, then if one number increases, the other number increases at the same rate. When two ratios are equivalent they are in proportion. In the previous example, you saw that when making bread you need 3 g of water for every 5 g of flour. This means that if you use 300 g of water, you need 500 g of flour. Both numbers have been multiplied by 100. They increase at the same rate. They are directly proportional to each other.

A common way to solve a problem where proportion is involved is to find the value of a unit quantity.

Example 1

If a wire of length 2 metres costs \$10, find the cost of a wire of length 35 cm.

200 cm costs 1000 cents

$\therefore$ 1 cm costs $\dfrac{1000}{200}$ cents = 5 cents

$\therefore$ 35 cm costs 5×35 cents $= 175$ cents $= \$1.75$

Tip

Chapter 8 covers these ideas of **direct** and **inverse** proportion using algebraic methods.

If two numbers are **inversely proportional** to each other, then as one number increases, the other number decreases at the same rate. For example, if you double the number of people working on a job, the time it takes to complete it is halved. In other words, if the number of people working is multiplied by 2, then the time it takes to complete the job is divided by 2.

A good way to solve inverse proportionality problems is to remember that even though one number may be increasing and the other decreasing, the product of the two numbers will always remain the same. In the example of workers doing a job, this is the same as saying that no matter how many workers there are, the total number of days' work to be completed stays the same. This is the number of days it would take if there is only one worker working. Then you need to share that work out equally between however many workers you have at that time.

Example 2

Eight workers can dig a hole in 4 hours. How long will it take five workers to dig the same size hole?

8 workers take 4 hours

1 worker would take $8 \times 4 = 32$ hours   (Multiply as this is inverse proportion.)

5 workers would take $\dfrac{32}{5}$ hours $= 6$ hours 24 minutes

Example 3

25 cleaners can clean 200 hotel rooms in 4 hours.

At this rate **a)** how many rooms would one cleaner clean in 1 hour

b) how many rooms would 5 cleaners clean in 3 hours?

a) If it takes 25 cleaners 4 hours, then there is $25 \times 4 = 100$ hours work to do.

If there are 200 rooms, this means that each room takes

$100 \div 200 = 0.5$ hours to clean.

One cleaner could therefore clean $1 \div 0.5 = 2$ rooms in 1 hour.

b) If one cleaner can clean 2 rooms in 1 hour,

then one cleaner can clean $2 \times 3 = 6$ rooms in 3 hours,

and 5 cleaners can clean $5 \times 6 = 30$ rooms in 3 hours.

Exercise 3.1B

1. Five cans of cola cost $8.50. Find the cost of seven cans of cola.

2. A girl earns $140 in a 5-day week. What is her pay for 3 days?

3. Three people build a wall in 10 days. How long would it take five people?

4. Nine fruit juice bottles contain 4.5 litres of fruit juice between them. How much juice do five bottles hold?

5. A car uses 10 litres of petrol to travel 75 km. How far would it travel on 8 litres?

6. A 11 cm length of wire has a mass of 187 g. What is the mass of 7 cm of this wire?

7. A shopkeeper can buy 36 toys for $20.52. What will she pay for 120 toys?

8. A ship has sufficient food to supply 600 passengers for 3 weeks. How long would the food last for 800 passengers?

9. The cost of a phone call lasting 3 minutes 30 seconds was 52.5 cents. At this rate, what was the cost of a call lasting 5 minutes 20 seconds?

10. 80 machines can produce 4800 identical pens in 5 hours. At this rate

    a) how many pens would one machine produce in one hour?

    b) how many pens would 25 machines produce in 7 hours?

11. Three builders can build a wall in 10 hours. At this rate, how many builders would be needed to build the wall in 7.5 hours?

12. It takes 6 construction workers 4 days to dig a hole 3 metres deep. If they work at this rate, how long will it take 10 of the workers to dig a hole 7 metres deep?

13. Find the cost of 1 km of pipe at 7 cents for every 40 cm.

14. A wheel turns through 90 revolutions per minute. How many degrees does it turn through in 1 second?

15. Find the cost of 200 grams of flour at $6 per kilogram.

16. One Kansas City Place is one of the tallest buildings in the US state of Missouri, standing at a height of 623 feet. Express this height to the nearest metre, using 1 m = 3.281 feet.

17. A floor is covered by 800 square tiles, each with side length 10 cm. How many square tiles of side length 8 cm would be needed to cover the same floor?

18. A battery has enough energy to operate eight toy bears for 21 hours. For how long could the battery operate 15 toy bears?

19. An engine has enough fuel to operate at full power for 20 minutes. For how long could the engine operate at 35% of full power?

20. A wall can be built by 6 people working 8 hours per day in 5 days. How many days will it take 4 people to build the wall if they work only 5 hours per day?

Currency exchange

Money is changed from one currency into another using the method of direct proportion.

The exchange rates for US dollars ($) in September 2022 are shown in the following table.

Country or region	Rate of exchange
Argentina (pesos)	$1 = 146.88 ARS
Australia (dollar)	$1 = 1.53 AUD
Europe (euros, €)	$1 = 1.03 EUR
India (rupees)	$1 = 81.33 INR
Japan (yen)	$1 = 144.00 JPY
Kuwait (dinar)	$1 = 0.31 KWD
UK (pounds, £)	$1 = 0.92 GBP

Tip

These exchange rates vary from day to day.

Example

Use the exchange rates in the table to convert:

a) $22.50 to dinars

b) €300 to US dollars

a) $1 = 0.31 dinar

so $22.50 = 0.31 × 22.50

= 6.98 dinar

b) €1.03 = $1

so $\dfrac{€300}{1.03} = \$291.26$

Exercise 3.1C

Give your answers correct to two decimal places. Use the exchange rates given in the table on page 90.

1. Change the number of dollars into the currency stated.
   a) $20 [euros] b) $70 [pounds] c) $200 [pesos]
   d) $1.50 [rupees] e) $2.30 [yen] f) 90c [dinars]

2. Change the amount of currency into dollars.
   a) €500 b) £2500 c) 7.50 rupees
   d) 900 dinars e) 125.24 pesos f) 750 AUD

3. A book costs £9.50 in London and the identical book costs $9.70 in Chicago. How much cheaper, in UK currency, is the book when bought in the US?

4. A desk lamp costs €20.46 in Spain and £12.60 in the UK. Which is the cheaper in dollars, and by how much?

5. The monthly rent of a flat in New Delhi is 32 860 rupees. How much is this in euros?

6. A Persian kitten is sold in several countries at the prices given below.

   Kuwait   150 dinars
   France   550 euros
   Japan   92 000 yen

   Write out in order (lowest first) a list of the prices converted into GBP.

7. An Australian man has 700 AUD to spend on holiday. If he changes the money at a bank, how many euros will he receive?

3.2 Map scales

You can use proportion to work out map scales. First you need to know these metric equivalents:

1 km = 1000 m   km means kilometre

1 m = 100 cm   m means metre

1 cm = 10 mm   cm means centimetre

                     mm means millimetre

Map scales are an example of direct proportionality. If you measure two distances on a map such that the second distance is twice as far as the first, then in the real world the second distance will also be twice as far as the first.

Example

A map is drawn to a scale of $1:50\,000$. Calculate:

a) the length of a road which appears as 3 cm long on the map

b) the length on the map of a lake which is 10 km long.

a) A scale of $1:50\,000$ means that 1 cm on the map is equivalent to $50\,000$ cm on the Earth.

$\therefore$ 1 cm $\equiv 50\,000$ cm

$\therefore$ 1 cm $\equiv 500$ m

$\therefore$ 1 cm $\equiv 0.5$ km

so 3 cm $\equiv 3 \times 0.5$ km $= 1.5$ km

The road is 1.5 km long.

b) 0.5 km $\equiv$ 1 cm

$\therefore$ 1 km $\equiv$ 2 cm

$\therefore$ 10 km $\equiv 2 \times 10$ cm

$\qquad = 20$ cm

The lake appears 20 cm long on the map.

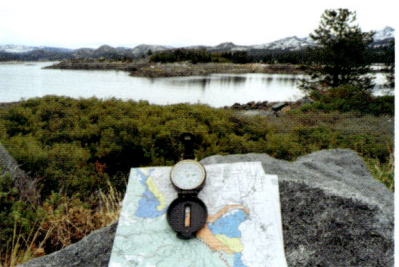

Exercise 3.2A

1. The scale on a drawing is 1 cm to 5 m. Find the actual length represented on the drawing by

   a) 14 cm   **b)** 3.2 cm

   c) 0.71 cm   **d)** 21.7 cm

2. The scale on a drawing is 1 cm to 10 m. Find the length on the drawing that represents

   a) 50 m   **b)** 35 m

   c) 7.2 m   **d)** 28.6 m

3. If the scale is $1:10\,000$, what length will 45 cm on the map represent:

   a) in cm   **b)** in m   **c)** in km?

4. On a map of scale $1:100\,000$, the distance between De'aro and Debeka is 12.3 cm. What is the actual distance in km?

5. On a map of scale $1:15\,000$, the distance between Noordwijk aan Zee and Katwijk aan Zee is 31.4 cm. What is the actual distance in km?

6. If the scale of a map is 1:10 000, what will be the length on this map of a road which is 5 km long?

7. The distance from Hong Kong to Shenzhen is 32 km. How far apart will they be on a map of scale 1:50 000?

8. The 17th hole at St Andrews golf course in Scotland is 420 m in length. How long will it appear on a plan of the course of scale 1:8000?

Area scale factors

An area involves two dimensions multiplied together and hence the scale is multiplied *twice*.

For example, if a map scale is 1:10 000, then 1 cm on the map represents 100 m in real life because 1 cm × 10 000 = 10 000 cm, and 10 000 cm = 100 m.

Now consider a rectangle on the map that measures 2 cm by 3 cm.

It has an area of 2 × 3 = 6 cm² on the map.

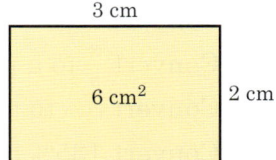

In the real world however, this represents a rectangle with a length of 3 × 100 m = 300 m, and a width of 2 × 100 = 200 m, giving an area of 3 × 100 × 2 × 100 = 3 × 2 × 100² = 60 000 m².

Notice that the area on the map has been multiplied by 100 twice to get the real area.

Exercise 3.2B

1. The scale of a map is 1:1000. What are the actual dimensions of a rectangle which appears as 4 cm by 3 cm on the map? What is the area of the rectangle on the map in cm²? What is the actual area of the rectangle in m²?

2. The scale of a map is 1:100. What area does 1 cm² on the map represent? What area does 6 cm² represent?

3. The scale of a map is 1:20 000. What area does 8 cm² represent?

4. The scale of a map is 1:1000. What is the area, in cm², on the map of a lake of area 5000 m²?

5. The scale of a map is 1 cm to 5 km. A farm is represented by a rectangle measuring 1.5 cm by 4 cm. What is the actual area of the farm?

6. On a map of scale 1 cm to 250 m the area of a car park is 3 cm². What is the actual area of the car park in hectares? (1 hectare = 10 000 m²)

7. The area of the playing surface at the Olympic Stadium in Beijing is $\frac{3}{5}$ of a hectare. What area will it occupy on a plan drawn to a scale of 1:500?

8. On a map of scale $1:20\,000$, the area of a forest is 50 cm². On another map the area of the forest is 8 cm². Find the scale of the second map.

3.3 Percentages

Percentages are a convenient way of comparing fractions or decimals by expressing them as parts out of one hundred.
'50% of $60' means $\frac{50}{100}$ of $60, or more simply $\frac{1}{2}$ of $60.

Percentages are used very frequently in everyday life, but they are misunderstood by many people. What are the implications if 'inflation falls from 10% to 8%'? Does this mean prices will fall?

Example

a) Convert 80% to a fraction.

b) Convert $\frac{3}{8}$ to a percentage.

c) Convert 8% to a decimal.

d) Convert 135% to a decimal.

a) $80\% = \dfrac{80}{100} = \dfrac{4}{5}$

b) $\dfrac{3}{8} = \left(\dfrac{3}{8} \times \dfrac{100}{1} \right)\% = 37\dfrac{1}{2}\%$

c) $8\% = \dfrac{8}{100} = 0.08$

d) $135\% = \dfrac{135}{100} = 1.35$

Exercise 3.3A

1. Convert these percentages to fractions in their simplest form.

   a) 60%   b) 24%   c) 2%   d) 112%

2. Convert these fractions and decimals to percentages.

   a) $\dfrac{1}{4}$ b) $\dfrac{1}{10}$ c) $\dfrac{7}{8}$

   d) $\dfrac{1}{3}$ e) 0.72   f) 1.83

3. Convert these percentages and fractions to decimals.

    a) 36%   **b)** 7%   **c)** 13.4%

    d) 129%   **e)** $\frac{3}{5}$ **f)** $\frac{7}{8}$

4. Arrange in order of size (smallest first).

    a) $\frac{1}{2}$; 45%; 0.6   **b)** 0.38; $\frac{6}{16}$; 4%

    c) 0.111; 11%; $\frac{1}{9}$ **d)** 32%; 0.3; $\frac{1}{3}$

5. The following are marks obtained in various tests. Convert them to percentages.

    a) 17 out of 20   **b)** 31 out of 40   **c)** 19 out of 80

    d) 112 out of 200   **e)** $2\frac{1}{2}$ out of 25   **f)** $7\frac{1}{2}$ out of 20

Percentage increase or decrease

You need to be able to increase or decrease a quantity by a given percentage.

Example 1

A car costing $2400 is reduced in price by 10%.
Find the new price.

Here are two ways to do this.

Method 1

$$10\% \text{ of } \$2400 = \frac{10}{100} \times \frac{2400}{1}$$

$$= \$240$$

$$\text{New price of car} = \$\left(2400 - 240\right)$$

$$= \$2160$$

Method 2

A reduction of 10% means 100% − 10% = 90% of the original price.

90% as a decimal is 0.9

You can now use this as the multiplier.

0.9 × $2400 = $2160

Method 2 is usually the quicker method.

Example 2

After a price increase of 10%, a television costs $286.

What was the price before the increase?

Again, there is more than one way to do this.

Method 1

The price before the increase is 100%.

$\therefore$ 110% of old price = $286

$\quad \therefore$ 1% of old price = $$\dfrac{286}{110}$

$\therefore$ 100% of old price = $$\dfrac{286}{110} \times \dfrac{100}{1}$

$\quad$ Old price of TV = $260

Method 2

1005 + 10% = 110% = 1.10

To increase a number by 10%, you can multiply it by 1.10.

This means that to undo a 10% increase you divide a number by 1.10.

$286 ÷ 1.10 = $260

Again, the decimal multiplier method is the quicker method.

> **Tip**
>
> Notice in Example 2 that subtracting 10% of $286 would not give you the correct answer. That is because it is 10% of the original price that needs to be subtracted, not 10% of the increased price.

Exercise 3.3B

1. Calculate:
   a) 30% of $50
   b) 45% of 2000 kg
   c) 4% of $70
   d) 2.5% of 5000 people.

2. In a sale, a jacket costing $40 is reduced by 20%. What is the sale price?

3. The charge for a telephone call costing 12 cents is increased by 10%. What is the new charge?

4. When peeling potatoes, 4% of the mass of the potatoes is lost as 'peel'. How much is left for use from a bag containing 55 kg of potatoes?

5. Work out, to the nearest cent:
   a) 6.4% of $15.95
   b) 11.2% of $192.66
   c) 8.6% of $25.84
   d) 2.9% of $18.18

6. Find the total bill for the following golf equipment:

5 golf clubs at $18.65 each

60 golf balls at $16.50 per dozen

1 pair of golf shoes at $75.80

Sales tax at 15% is added to the total cost.

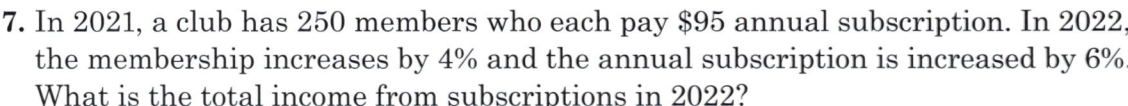

7. In 2021, a club has 250 members who each pay $95 annual subscription. In 2022, the membership increases by 4% and the annual subscription is increased by 6%. What is the total income from subscriptions in 2022?

8. In Thailand, the population of a town is 48 700 men and 41 600 women. What percentage of the total population are men?

9. In South Korea, there are 21 280 000 licensed vehicles on the road. Of these, 16 486 000 are private cars. What percentage of the licensed vehicles are private cars?

10. 70% of Hassan's collection of goldfish died. If he has 60 survivors, how many did he have originally?

11. The average attendance at Parma football club fell by 7% in 2022. If 2030 fewer people went to matches in 2022, how many went in 2021?

12. When heated, an iron bar expands by 0.2%. If the increase in length is 1 cm, what was the original length of the bar?

13. In the last two weeks of a sale, prices are reduced first by 30% and then by a *further* 40% of the new price.

a) What is the final sale price of a shirt which originally cost $15?

b) What is the overall price reduction, expressed as a single percentage?

14. During a Grand Prix car race, the tyres on a car reduce in mass by 3%. If their mass is 388 kg at the end of the race, what was their mass at the start?

15. Over a period of 6 months, a colony of rabbits increases in number by 25% and then by a further 30%. If there were originally 200 rabbits in the colony, how many were there at the end?

16. A television costs $270.25 including 15% tax. How much of the cost in $ is tax?

17. The cash price for a car was $7640. Gurtaj bought the car on the following terms: 'A deposit of 20% of the cash price and 36 monthly payments of $191.60'. Calculate the total amount Gurtaj paid.

Profit and loss

The terms **profit** and **loss**, mean the amount of money you either make or lose as a result of a financial transaction.

In the next exercise use the formulae:

$$\text{percentage profit} = \left(\frac{\text{actual profit}}{\text{original price}} \times 100 \right) \%$$

$$\text{percentage loss} = \left(\frac{\text{actual loss}}{\text{original price}} \times 100 \right) \%$$

Example 1

A radio is bought for $16 and sold for $20.
What is the percentage profit?

actual profit = $4

$$\therefore \text{ percentage profit} = \left(\frac{4}{16} \times \frac{100}{1} \right) \% = 25\%$$

The radio is sold at a 25% profit.

Example 2

A car is sold for $2280, at a loss of 5% on the cost price.
Find the cost price.

Do *not* calculate 5% of $2280!

The loss is 5% of the cost price.

$$\therefore \quad 95\% \text{ of cost price} = \$2280$$

$$1\% \text{ of cost price} = \$ \frac{2280}{95}$$

$$\therefore 100\% \text{ of cost price} = \$ \frac{2280}{95} \times \frac{100}{1}$$

$$\text{cost price} = \$2400$$

Exercise 3.3C

1. The first figure is the cost price and the second figure is the selling price. Calculate the percentage profit or loss in each case.

   a) $20, $25   b) $400, $500   c) $60, $54

   d) $9000, $10 800   e) $460, $598   f) $512, $550.40

   g) $45, $39.60   h) 50c, 23c

> **Tip**
>
> c is the symbol for cents.
>
> 100c = $1

2. A car dealer buys a car for $500, and then sells it for $640. What is the percentage profit?

3. A carpet which cost $180 when new is sold for $100. What is the percentage loss?

4. During the first four weeks of her life, a baby girl's mass increases from 3.2 kg to 4.7 kg. What percentage increase does this represent? (Give your answer to 3 s.f.)

5. When tax is added to the cost of a lipstick, its price increases from $16.50 to $18.48.
What is the rate at which tax is charged?

6. The price of a sports car is reduced from $132 000 to $124 960. What percentage reduction is this?

7. Find the *cost* price of the following:

    a) selling price $55, profit 10%

    b) selling price $558, profit 24%

    c) selling price $680, loss 15%

    d) selling price $11.78, loss 5%

8. A sari is sold for $60 at a profit of 20% on the cost price. What was the cost price?

9. A pair of jeans is sold for $15, at a profit of 25% on the cost price. What was the cost price?

10. A book is sold for $5.40, at a profit of 8% on the cost price. What was the cost price?

11. A can of worms is sold for $0.48, at a loss of 20%. What was the cost price?

12. A used car was sold for $1430, at a loss of 35% on the cost price. What was the cost price?

13. If an employer reduces the working week from 40 hours to 35 hours, with no loss of weekly pay, calculate the percentage increase in the hourly rate of pay.

14. The cost for a television streaming service changed from $80 per year to $8 per month. What is the percentage increase in the yearly cost?

15. A greengrocer sells a melon at a profit of $37\frac{1}{2}\%$ on the price he pays for it. What is the ratio of the cost price to the selling price?

16. Given that $G = ab$, find the percentage increase in G when both a and b increase by 10%.

17. Given that $T = \dfrac{kx}{y}$, find the percentage increase in T when k, x and y all increase by 20%.

18. A book was bought for \$12. Its value increases by 110%. What is its new value?

19. After a successful television series about chess, the number of members of a local chess club increased from 16 to 44. What is this as a percentage increase?

20. The number of sales on a website in December was 583. This was an increase of 112% from November's sales figure. How many sales were there in November?

3.4 Financial mathematics

Simple interest

There are two main types of interest that you need to know about. When you pay money into a bank, the interest you receive is almost always **compound interest**, which you will look at shortly. However, when you take out a loan to borrow money, it is often **simple interest**. This means that a simple fixed percentage of what you borrow is calculated when you take out the loan, and you pay that amount of interest each year. With simple interest, the amount of interest you pay does not change depending on how much you still owe. Simple interest may also be applied to investments.

When a sum of money \$$P$ is invested or borrowed for T years at $R\%$ interest per year, then the interest gained or paid I is given by

$$I = \frac{P \times R \times T}{100}$$

This is the formula for calculating simple interest.

Example 1

Scarlett borrows $1200 for 2 years at 3% per year.

Work out the simple interest paid on this loan.

$P = \$1200 \qquad R = 3 \qquad T = 2$

so $\quad I = \dfrac{1200 \times 3 \times 2}{100}$

$\quad I = \$72$

Example 2

Joel invests $400 for 6 months at 5% per year.

Work out the simple interest gained.

$P = \$400 \qquad R = 5 \qquad T = 0.5 \qquad$ (6 months is half a year)

so $\quad I = \dfrac{400 \times 5 \times 0.5}{100}$

$\quad I = \$10$

Exercise 3.4A

1. Calculate:

   a) the simple interest on $1200 for 3 years at 6% per year

   b) the simple interest on $700 at 8.25% per year for 2 years

   c) the length of time for $5000 to earn $1000 if invested at 10% per year

   d) the length of time for $400 to earn $160 if invested at 8% per year.

2. Khalid invests $6750 at 8.5% simple interest per year. How much interest has he earned and what is the total amount in his account after 4 years?

3. Jeremy takes out a loan for $8000 for 5 years at a rate of 4% simple interest. How much interest will he pay in total?

4. Linda borrows $20 000 to buy a car and pays the loan off over 4 years. $2000 of what she pays back is interest. What was the rate of simple interest on her loan?

5. Petra invests $10 800. After 4 years she has earned $3240 in interest. At what annual rate of interest did she invest her money?

Repeated percentage change

Sometimes you may want to apply a percentage increase or decrease multiple times; for example, if an item increases in value by a fixed percentage each year, or if it loses value by a fixed percentage each year.

Example

A rare book increases in value every year by 12%.

A collector bought the book at an auction for $350.

What was the book worth 3 years later?

The multiplier is 1.12, for an increase of 12%

After one year: $350 \times 1.12 = $392

After two years: $392 \times 1.12 = $439.04

After three years: $439.04 \times 1.12 = 491.72, to the nearest cent.

This calculation can be simplified by doing
$350 \times 1.12^3 = $491.72

You can calculate a repeated percentage change by multiplying the original amount by the percentage change multiplier raised to a power which represents the number of times the change occurs. This power often represents a certain number of years.

Now consider a different situation.

Suppose a shop reduced the price of a coat that originally cost $100 by 20%. Because nobody bought the coat at that price, they reduced it again by another 10%. What does the coat cost now?

To reduce $100 by 20%: $0.8 \times $100 = $80

To reduce again by 10%: $0.9 \times $80 = $72

Note that this is not the same as reducing the original price by 30%. When the shop makes the second reduction, it is by a percentage of the already reduced amount, rather than the original amount.

This is an example of a repeated percentage change, but the percentages are not the same each time.

Exercise 3.4B

1. Jodie plants a tree that is 15 cm tall. Its height increases by 20% each year. What is the height of the tree after 3 years?

2. Emma buys a car for $14 000. Its value depreciates (decreases) by 6% each year. To the nearest dollar, what is the car worth after 4 years?

3. The price of a table is decreased by 25% from its original price of $280. Due to a rise in demand, its price is then increased by 25%. What is its final price?

4. In August 2019, an online gaming club had 200 members. By August 2020, the number of members by increased by 40%. The following year, membership increased again by another 20%. How many members were there in August 2021?

5. Due to high demand, the price of a gaming console that used to cost $450 increased by 30%. The following year its price decreased by 30%. What was its final price?

6. Dinesh bought a guitar for $320. In the first year, its value depreciated by 15%. In the second year its value depreciated by another 12%. What was its value after two years?

7. Daisy bought a bike for $50. In the first year, its value decreased by 16%. In the second year, its value increased by x percent, making it worth $65.52. Find x.

8. Zac bought a graphic novel for $30. In the first year its value increased by 25%. Then the book got damaged and its value went down by p%. If the book was then worth $15, what is p?

9. An increase of 30% followed by another increase of 30% is equivalent to a single increase of how many percent?

10. Samantha works in a shoe shop. A pair of shoes that she likes are reduced by 20% in a sale. Because she works there, she also gets a 15% staff discount. These two reductions can be applied in either order. If Samantha wants to pay the lowest price, would she be better off applying the reductions in a particular order?

Compound interest

When you put money into a bank, the interest you receive is almost always compound interest. This means that each year you receive interest not only on the money you invested, but also on the interest you received the previous year.

Suppose a bank pays a rate of 5% compound interest on money in a deposit account. A person puts $500 into the account.

After one year they have $\qquad$ 500 + 5% of 500 = $525

After two years they have $\qquad$ 525 + 5% of 525 = $551.25

After three years they have $\qquad$ 551.25 + 5% of 551.25 = $578.81

In general, after n years they will have $\qquad$ $\$(500 \times 1.05^n)$

Note that this is just another example of repeated percentage change.

The compound interest formula is often written as:

value of investment $= P\left(1 + \dfrac{r}{100}\right)^n$

where P is the amount invested, r is the percentage rate of interest and n is the number of years it is invested for.

Example

Use the compound interest formula to calculate the amount of money in an account after 5 years if the initial sum invested is $2000 at 4% compound interest.

Amount in account $= 2000 \times 1.04^5 = \$2433.31$

Exercise 3.4C

1. A bank pays compound interest of 9% on money in deposit accounts. Carme puts $2000 in the bank. How much has she after **a)** one year **b)** two years **c)** three years?

2. A bank pays compound interest of 11%. Mamuru puts $5000 in the bank. How much has he after **a)** one year **b)** three years **c)** five years?

3. A student gets a grant of $10 000 per year. Assuming her grant is increased by 7% each year, what will her grant be in four years?

4. Isoke's salary in 2022 is $30 000 per year.
   Every year her salary is increased by 5%.

   In 2023 her salary will be $\qquad$ 30 000 × 1.05 = $31 500

   In 2024 her salary will be $\qquad$ 30 000 × 1.05 × 1.05 = $33 075

   In 2025 her salary will be 30 000 × 1.05 × 1.05 × 1.05 = $34 728.75

   Assuming that this pattern continues,

   a) what will her salary be in 2026

   b) what will her salary be in 2027?

5. Paula is learning Spanish with an app on her phone. In the first month, she earned the maximum amount of 9000 points. From then on, Paula achieved the maximum point total, which was always 6% more than the previous month. She continued this pattern for 10 months. Rounding your answers to the nearest whole number:

   a) How many points did Paula earn in the second month?

   b) How many points did Paula earn in the fifth month?

   c) How many points did Paula earn in the 11th month?

6. Assuming an average inflation rate of 8%, work out the probable cost of the following items in 10 years:

   a) motor scooter $6500

   b) smart phone $340

   c) car $50 000.

7. A new scooter is valued at $15 000. At the end of each year, its value is reduced by 15% of its value at the start of the year. What will it be worth after 3 years?

8. The population of an island increases by 10% each year. After how many whole years will the original population have doubled?

9. A bank pays interest of 11% on $6000 in a deposit account. After how many whole years will the money have trebled?

10. A tree grows in height by 21% per year. It is 2 m tall after one year. After how many more whole years will the tree be over 20 m tall?

11. Which is the better investment over ten years:

   $20 000 at 12% compound interest

   or $30 000 at 8% compound interest?

Income tax

Example

Workers generally pay tax on their earnings. Sometimes they are entitled to a *tax free* allowance before paying a percentage tax on the rest of their earnings.

Vivien earns $42 000 per year and she gets a tax free allowance of $9000. If she pays 20% tax on the next $30 000 and 40% on the rest, how much tax does she pay in total?

$42 000 − $9000 = $33 000

This represents the taxable amount of Vivien's salary.

20% of $30 000 = 0.2 × 30 000 = $6000

She pays $6000 of tax on the first $30 000 of her taxable amount.

$33 000 − $30 000 = $3000

40% of $3000 = 0.4 × 3000 = $1200

She pays $1200 of tax on the final $3000 of her taxable amount.

Total tax = $6000 + $1200 = $7200

Exercise 3.4D

1. Tomas earns $37 000 per year. He gets a tax-free allowance of $8000 and pays 25% tax on the rest. How much tax will he pay in a year?

2. Juliette earns $4500 per month. She gets a tax-free allowance of $10 000 per year and pays tax at 20% on the rest. How much tax will she pay in a year?

3. Elise gets a tax-free allowance of $6000 and pays tax at 25% on the next $20 000. She pays tax at a rate of 30% on the rest. If she earns $72 000 per year, how much tax must she pay?

4. Rohan earns $650 per week and works 48 weeks per year. If he gets a tax-free allowance of $8000, pays tax at a rate of 10% on the next $10 000 and 20% on the rest, how much tax will he pay in a year?

3.5 Time

The 24-hour clock

The times which most people use are measured from midnight or from mid-day (noon). In the morning, 9 o'clock is 9 hours after midnight and is written 9.00 a.m. In the afternoon, 4 o'clock is 4 hours after mid-day (noon) and is written 4.00 p.m.

Using the 24-hour clock, all times are measured from midnight.

This means 9.00 a.m. is written 09:00 and 4.00 p.m. is written 16:00.

Here are three times converted from the 12-hour clock to the 24-hour clock:

a) 8.00 a.m. = 08:00

b) 9.30 p.m. = 21:30

c) 3.15 p.m. = 15:15

> **Tip**
>
> a.m. is an abbreviation of ante meridiem and means before mid-day
>
> p.m. is an abbreviation of post meridiem and means after mid-day.

Exercise 3.5A

Write down the following in the 24-hour clock format.

1. 8.00 a.m.	**2.** 9.30 p.m.	**3.** 6.00 p.m.
4. 5.30 a.m.	**5.** 7.40 p.m.	**6.** 10.00 p.m.
7. 7.15 p.m.	**8.** 10.45 p.m.	**9.** 8.30 a.m.
10. 4.15 a.m.	**11.** 2.25 a.m.	**12.** 1.30 p.m.
13. 7.20 p.m.	**14.** 6.50 a.m.	**15.** 7.10 a.m.

16. Two minutes before midnight.

17. Two and a half hours before midnight.

18. Five minutes before noon.

19. Three and a half hours after noon.

20. One hour after midnight.

21. One and a half hours before noon.

22. Twenty minutes after midnight

23. Five hours before midnight.

24. Six minutes after noon.

25. Fifty minutes after midnight.

Write the following in the 12-hour clock format.

26. 07:00	**27.** 19:30	**28.** 11:20	**29.** 04:45
30. 20:30	**31.** 21:15	**32.** 09:10	**33.** 11:45
34. 23:10	**35.** 20:00	**36.** 12:00	**37.** 01:40
38. 04:00	**39.** 07:07	**40.** 13:13	**41.** 12:15
42. 12:30	**43.** 15:45	**44.** 16:20	**45.** 05:16

Time intervals

Example
Find the time interval between 15:40 and 18:05.

From 15:40 to 16:00 is 20 minutes   (count on to the next hour)
From 16:00 to 18:05 is 2 hours 5 minutes   (count on from 16:00)
The total interval is 2 hours 25 minutes.

Exercise 3.5B

Find the number of hours and minutes between the following.

1. 20:10 and 21:20
2. 21:40 and 23:50
3. 22:15 and 23:10
4. 19:30 and 20:05
5. 20:16 and 23:36
6. 11:25 and 13:10
7. 09:40 and 12:00
8. 21:17 and 23:10
9. 23:04 and 23:57
10. 17:45 and 23:10
11. 05:15 and 07:05
12. 11:26 and 14:40
13. 9.50 a.m. and 11.05 a.m.
14. 9.30 a.m. and 2.05 p.m.
15. 11.10 a.m. and 1.30 p.m.
16. 7.30 a.m. and 7.30 p.m.
17. 10.40 a.m. and 12.40 p.m.
18. 5.40 a.m. and 1.00 p.m.
19. 11.55 a.m. and 3.10 p.m.
20. 1.35 a.m. and 8.40 a.m.
21. 22:30 on Monday to 03:30 on Tuesday
22. 21:00 on Thursday to 01:40 on Friday
23. 17:30 on Monday to 02:00 on Tuesday
24. 23:45 on Saturday to 02:10 on Sunday
25. 22:50 on Thursday to 07:00 on Friday
26. 07:00 on Friday to 02:00 on Saturday
27. 09:30 on Monday to 04:30 on Tuesday
28. 09:15 on Wednesday to 02:45 on Thursday
29. 22:10 on Friday to 07:35 on Saturday
30. 06:30 on Friday to 16:30 on Saturday

Exercise 3.5C

Here is a timetable for trains from Florence to Rome.
Use it to answer Questions **1** to **12**.

Florence	07:10	08:35	11:35	13:50
Pontassieve	07:35	–	12:00	14:15
Figline Valdarno	07:55	09:21	12:21	–
Bucine	08:16	–	12:42	–
Arezzo	08:36	09:54	13:17	15:08
Orvieto	09:24	10:42	14:07	15:48
Orte	10:01	–	14:53	16:34
Rome	10:27	11:42	15:18	16:59

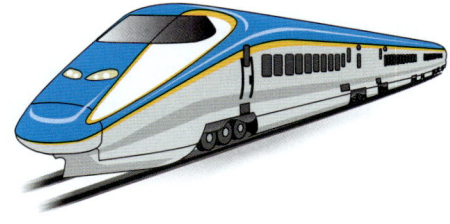

1. How long does it take the 07:10 from Florence to travel to:

   a) Pontassieve   **b)** Figline Valdarno   **c)** Bucine?

2. At how many stations does the 11:35 from Florence stop?

3. At what time does the 08:35 from Florence reach Arezzo?

4. If you had to be in Rome by 15:30, which train would you catch from Florence?

5. You arrive at Florence at 08:20. How long do you have to wait for the next train to Rome?

6. The 11:35 from Florence runs 10 minutes late. At what time will it reach Bucine?

7. How long does it take the 11:35 from Florence to travel to:

   a) Arezzo   **b)** Orvieto   **c)** Rome?

8. At how many stations does the 08:16 from Bucine stop before it reaches Orte?

9. At what time does the 12:21 train from Figline Valdarno reach Orvieto?

10. If you had to be in Rome by 12:00, which train would you catch from Figline Valdarno?

11. You arrive at Florence at 11:08. How long do you have to wait for the next train to Rome?

12. The 08:35 from Florence runs 19 minutes late. At what time will it reach Rome?

13. A flight from London to New York takes exactly 8 hours. The time in New York is 5 hours earlier than the time in London. If a plane takes off from London at 15:00, what time will it be in New York when it lands?

14. A flight from Paris to Istanbul takes 3 hours and 25 minutes. The time in Istanbul is one hour later than the time in Paris. If a plane takes off from Paris at 08:37, what time will it be in Istanbul when the plane lands?

15. A flight from Tokyo to Melbourne takes 10 hours and 25 minutes. The time in Tokyo is 2 hours earlier than the time in Melbourne. If a plane leaves Tokyo at 09:15, what time will it be in Melbourne when the plane lands?

3.6 Rates

In mathematics, a rate is the ratio of one quantity measured against another quantity. These two quantities will usually have different units.

Speed is a common measure of rate. A speed given in kilometres *per* hour tells us how many kilometres you travel in one hour. Other common measures of rate include:

- litres *per* minute, when filling a bath with water, for example
- kilowatt hours *per* day, when measuring energy consumption
- density, the amount of mass in a given volume
- pressure, the amount of force applied to a given area
- population density, the amount of people who live in a given area.

The formulae for these rates can be remembered by thinking about the units that are used to measure them. You just need to remember that 'per' means 'divided by'.

This means that because speed can be measured in km per hour, and because km is a measure of distance and hours is a measure of time, then the formula for speed is distance divided by time.

Speed, distance and time

Calculations involving these three quantities are simpler when the speed is *constant*. The formulae connecting the quantities are as follows:

a) distance = speed × time

b) speed = $\dfrac{\text{distance}}{\text{time}}$

c) time = $\dfrac{\text{distance}}{\text{speed}}$

A helpful way of remembering these formulae is to write the letters D, S and T in a triangle, like this:

to find D, cover D and you have ST

to find S, cover S and you have $\dfrac{D}{T}$

to find T, cover T and you have $\dfrac{D}{S}$

Example 1

A runner is moving at a speed of 8 km/h for a distance of 5200 metres. Find the time taken in minutes.

5200 metres $\qquad\quad = 5.2$ km

time taken in hours $\quad = \left(\dfrac{D}{S}\right) = \dfrac{5.2}{8}$

$\qquad\qquad\qquad\qquad = 0.65$ hours

time taken in minutes $= 0.65 \times 60$

$\qquad\qquad\qquad\qquad = 39$ minutes

Example 2

Convert the speed of 54 km/h into metres per second.

54 km/hour $= 54\,000$ metres/hour

$\qquad\quad = \dfrac{54\,000}{60}$ metres/minute

$\qquad\quad = \dfrac{54\,000}{60 \times 60}$ metres/second

$\qquad\quad = 15$ m/s

Most things do not travel at a constant speed. However, if you know the average speed of an object, you can still use these formulae as though that speed were the constant speed of the object.

Example 3

A car travels at an average speed of 47 km/h for 4 hours.

How far does it travel in that time?

$D = S \times T$

$\quad = 47 \times 4$

$\quad = 188$ km

Exercise 3.6A

1. Find the time taken for the following journeys.

   a) 100 km at a speed of 40 km/h

   b) 250 miles at a speed of 80 miles per hour

   c) 15 metres at a speed of 20 cm/s (answer in seconds)

   d) 10^4 metres at a speed of 2.5 km/h (answer in hours)

2. Convert the units of the following speeds as indicated.

   a) 72 km/h into m/s

   b) 108 km/h into m/s

   c) 300 km/h into m/s

   d) 30 m/s into km/h

   e) 22 m/s into km/h

   f) 0.012 m/s into cm/s

   g) 9000 cm/s into m/s

   h) 600 miles/day into miles per hour

   i) 2592 miles/day into miles per second.

3. Find the speeds of the objects which move as follows.

   a) a distance of 600 km in 8 hours

   b) a distance of 31.64 km in 7 hours

   c) a distance of 136.8 m in 18 seconds

   d) a distance of 4×10^4 m in 10^{-2} seconds

   e) a distance of 5×10^5 cm in 2×10^{-3} seconds

   f) a distance of 10^8 mm in 30 minutes (in km/h)

   g) a distance of 500 m in 10 minutes (in km/h).

4. Find the distance travelled (in metres) for the following rates and times.

   a) 55 km/h for 2 hours

   b) 40 km/h for one quarter of an hour

   c) 338.4 km/h for 10 minutes

   d) 15 m/s for 5 minutes

   e) 14 m/s for 1 hour

   f) 4×10^3 m/s for 2×10^{-2} seconds

   g) 8×10^5 cm/s for 2 minutes.

5. A car travels 60 km at 30 km/h and then a further 180 km at 160 km/h. Find:

   a) the total time taken

   b) the average speed for the whole journey.

6. A cyclist travels 25 kilometres at 20 km/h and then a further 80 kilometres at 25 km/h. Find:

   a) the total time taken

   b) the average speed for the whole journey.

7. A swallow flies at a speed of 50 km/h for 3 hours and then at a speed of 40 km/h for a further 2 hours. Find the average speed for the whole journey.

8. A runner ran two laps around a 400 m track. She completed the first lap in 50 seconds and then decreased her speed by 5% for the second lap. Find:

   a) her speed on the first lap

   b) her speed on the second lap

   c) her total time for the two laps

   d) her average speed for the two laps.

9. An airplane flies 2000 km at a speed of 1600 km/h and then returns due to bad weather at a speed of 1000 km/h. Find the average speed for the whole trip.

10. A train travels from A to B, a distance of 100 km, at a speed of 20 km/h. If it had gone two and a half times as fast, how much earlier would it have arrived at B?

11. Two men running towards each other at 4 m/s and 6 m/s, respectively, are one kilometre apart. How long will it take before they meet?

12. A car travelling at 90 km/h is 500 m behind another car travelling at 70 km/h in the same direction. How long will it take the first car to catch the second?

13. How long is a train which passes a signal in twenty seconds at a speed of 108 km/h?

14. A train of length 180 m approaches a tunnel of length 620 m. How long will it take the train to pass completely through the tunnel at a speed of 54 km/h?

15. An earthworm of length 15 cm is crawling along at 2 cm/s. An ant overtakes the worm in 5 seconds. How fast is the ant moving?

16. A train of length 100 m is moving at a speed of 50 km/h. A horse approaches the train from behind at a speed of 56 km/h. From the moment it is alongside the last carriage of the train, how long will it take for the horse to completely overtake the train?

17. A car completes an outward journey at an average speed of 40 km/h. At what speed must it travel on the return journey if the average speed for the complete journey (out and back) is 60 km/h?

Other rates

Exercise 3.6B

1. Find the following rates in the units given.

   a) 4 litres in 5 minutes (litres per minute)

   b) 12 litres in 45 minutes (litres per hour)

   c) 78 litres in 12 minutes (litres per hour)

   d) 800 kilowatt hours in 2 months (kilowatt hours per year)

   e) 12 kilowatt hours in 3 days (kilowatt hours per year).

2. Find the time taken (in minutes) to fill the following containers.

   a) a 3 litre bowl at a rate of 2 litres per minute

   b) a 30 litre bucket at a rate of 0.2 litres per second

   c) a 120 litre hot water tank at a rate of 80 litres per hour

   d) a 300 ml beaker at a rate of 0.5 litres per hour.

3. A bath is filled with 80 litres of water in 6 minutes. Find the rate at which it is being filled.

4. A typical household uses 4600 kilowatt hours of energy in a year. Find the rate at which the household uses energy in kilowatt hours per day.

5. Water is dripping from a tap at a rate of 5 millilitres per second. How long will it take, in minutes, to fill a bowl with a capacity of 2.5 litres?

6. A rain butt with a capacity of 60 litres fills completely with water each day.

    a) Find the rate of fill in millilitres per hour.

    b) A gardener can use all of the water to hose his garden in 15 minutes. Find the rate of flow of the water from the hose in millilitres per second.

7. Find the pressure exerted by a force of 10 000 N on an area of 40 m².

8. The pressure exerted on a table is 500 N/m². If the force is 750 N, what is the area of the table?

> **Tip**
>
> Use the formula
>
> $$\text{pressure} = \frac{\text{force}}{\text{area}}$$
>
> to give pressure in N/m².

9. A large drum, when full, contains 260 kg of oil of density 0.9 g/cm³. What mass of oil, of density 0.84 g/cm³, can be contained in the drum? Give your answer in kg.

10. In 2020, the population density of Tokyo was 6402 people per square kilometre. The size of Tokyo is 2194 km². How many people lived in Tokyo in 2020? Give your answer accurate to 2 significant figures.

> **Tip**
>
> Use the formula
>
> $$\text{density} = \frac{\text{mass}}{\text{volume}}$$

11. In 2020, there were 28.64 million people living in Texas, which has an area of 695 662 km². What was the population density in people per km²? Give your answer accurate to 3 significant figures.

> **Tip**
>
> Use the formula
>
> $$\text{population density} = \frac{\text{population}}{\text{land area}}$$

Revision exercise 3

1. a) $143 is divided in the ratio $2:3:6$. Calculate the smallest share.

b) A prize is divided between three people X, Y and Z. If the ratio of X's share to Y's share is $3:1$ and Y's share to Z's share is $2:5$, calculate the ratio of X's share to Z's share.

c) If $a:3 = 12:a$, calculate the positive value of a.

2. Labour costs, totalling $47.25, account for 63% of a car repair bill. Calculate the total bill.

3. a) Convert each value to a percentage.

    i) 0.572 **ii)** $\frac{7}{8}$

b) Express 2.6 kg as a percentage of 6.5 kg.

c) In selling a red herring for 92c, a fishmonger makes a profit of 15%. Find the cost price of the fish.

4. The length of a rectangle is decreased by 25% and the width is increased by 40%. Calculate the percentage change in the area of the rectangle.

5. a) What sum of money, invested at 9% simple interest per year, is needed to provide an income of $45 per year?

b) A particle increases its speed from 8×10^5 m/s to 1.1×10^6 m/s. What is the percentage increase?

6. A family on holiday in Australia exchanged $450 for Australian dollars (AUD) when the exchange rate was 1.41 AUD to the dollar. They spent 500 AUD and then changed the rest back into dollars, by which time the exchange rate had become 1.46 AUD to the dollar. How much did the family spend on holiday? (Answer in dollars.)

7. A map is drawn to a scale of $1:10\,000$. Find:

a) the distance between two railway stations which appear on the map 24 cm apart

b) the area, in square kilometres, of a lake which has an area of 100 cm² on the map.

8. A map is drawn to a scale of $1:2000$. Find:

a) the actual distance between two points, which appear 15 cm apart on the map

b) the length on the map of a road, which is 1.2 km in length

c) the area on the map of a field, with an actual area of 60 000 m².

9. a) On a map, the distance between two points is 16 cm. Calculate the scale of the map if the actual distance between the points is 8 km.

b) On another map, two points appear 1.5 cm apart and are in fact 60 km apart. Calculate the scale of the map.

10. a) A painting is bought for $20 000 and sold for $24 400. What is the percentage profit?

b) A piece of fish, initially of mass 2.4 kg, is cooked and subsequently has mass 1.9 kg. What is the percentage loss in mass?

c) An article is sold at a 6% loss for $225.60. What was the cost price?

11. a) Convert into metres per second:

    i) 700 cm/s

    ii) 720 km/h

    iii) 18 km/h

  b) Convert into kilometres per hour:

    i) 40 m/s   **ii)** 0.6 m/s

12. a) Calculate the speed (in metres per second) of a slug which moves a distance of 30 cm in 1 minute.

  b) Calculate the time taken for a bullet to travel 8 km at a speed of 5000 m/s.

c) Calculate the distance flown, in a time of four hours, by a pigeon which flies at a speed of 12 m/s.

13. A motorist travelled 200 km in five hours. Her average speed for the first 100 km was 50 km/h. What was her average speed for the second 100 kilometres?

14. The edges of a cube are all increased by 10%. What is the percentage increase in the volume?

Examination-style exercise 3

CALCULATOR

1. Coraline, Davina and Edward receive $900 from their grandmother in the ratio Coraline : Davina : Edward = 3 : 5 : 7.

  a) Calculate how much money each receives.   [3]

  b) Coraline spends $\frac{1}{6}$ of her money and then invests the rest for four years at 3% per year simple interest.

    How much money does Coraline have at the end of the four years?   [3]

  c) Davina spends all of her money on a new telescope and four years later sells it at a loss of 30%.

    How much money does Davina have at the end of the four years?   [2]

  d) Edward spends some of his money, and at the end of the four years he has $204.

    Write down and simplify the ratio of the amounts of money Coraline, Davina and Edward have at the end of the four years.   [2]

  e) Edward then invests his $204 for four more years at a rate of 6% per year **compound interest**. Calculate to the nearest cent how much money he has at the end of these four years.   [2]

2. In 2019, Patrick had a salary of exactly $32 000.

   a) This was an increase of 9% on his salary in 2017.

   Calculate his salary in 2017. [2]

   b) In 2021 his salary increased again to $33 280.

   Calculate the percentage increase from 2019 to 2021. [2]

3. A student played 20 games of chess and won 13 of them.

   After winning the next x games and losing none, she had now won 80% of all the games she had played.

   Work out the value of x. [4]

4. James and his brother Richard each have $4000 to invest for 5 years.

   a) Northern Bank advertises savings with simple interest at 5% per year.

   James invests his money in this bank.

   How much money will he have at the end of 5 years? [2]

   b) Southern Bank advertises savings with compound interest at 4.8% per year.

   Richard invests his money in this bank.

   At the end of 5 years, how much more money will he have than James? [3]

5. Halima sells fruit and vegetables at the market.

   a) The mass of fruit and vegetables she sells is in the ratio fruit : vegetables = 3 : 2.

   Halima sells 2.52 tonnes of fruit.

   How many tonnes of vegetables does she sell? [3]

   b) The amount of money Halima receives from selling fruit and vegetables is in the ratio fruit : vegetables = 5 : 3.

   Halima receives a total of $1960 from selling fruit and vegetables.

   Calculate how much Halima receives from selling fruit. [2]

   c) Calculate the average price of Halima's vegetables, in cents per kilogram. [2]

   d) Halima sells apples for $0.45 per kilogram.

   She reduces this price by 20%

   Calculate the new price per kilogram. [2]

6. **a)** The scale of a map is 1 : 50 000 000.

   On the map, the distance between Copenhagen and Prague is 4.2 cm.

   i) Calculate the distance, in kilometres, between Copenhagen and Prague. [2]

   ii) The shape of Egypt is roughly a square. It covers an area of approximately 1 002 450 square kilometres. If it were exactly a square, how long would the sides of the square be on the map? [2]

b) i) The actual distance between Paris and Istanbul is 2730 km to the nearest 10 km. On a different map, this distance is represented by 22.75 cm.

Calculate, in the form $1:n$, the scale of this map. [2]

ii) A plane flies the 2730 km from Paris to Istanbul.

It departs from Paris where the time is 10:23 and arrives in Istanbul where the time is 15:48.

Given that the time in Istanbul is 2 hours ahead of Paris, calculate the average speed of the plane, in kilometres per hour. [4]

7. Each year a venue organises a music concert.

a) i) In 2018 the cost of organising the concert was $2500.

In 2019 the cost went up by 15%.

Calculate the cost in 2019. [2]

ii) The cost in 2018 was 25% more than the cost in 2017.

Calculate the cost in 2017. [2]

b) i) In 2018 the number of tickets sold was 870.

The ratio of adult tickets:child tickets was $11:4$.

How many child tickets were sold? [2]

ii) Adult tickets were $12 each and child tickets were $5 each.

Calculate the total amount received from selling the tickets. [2]

iii) What was the percentage profit in 2018? [2]

8. Water flows into a tank at a rate of 3 litres per minute.

a) If the tank fills completely in 450 seconds, what is the capacity of the tank in ml? [2]

A hole is drilled in the bottom of the tank. Water flows out of the hole at a rate of 60 ml per second.

b) How long will the tank take to drain completely if the flow of water into the tank continues at the same rate? [2]

4 Trigonometry 1

Pythagoras (569–500 B.C.E.) was one of the first of the great mathematical names in Greek antiquity. He settled in southern Italy and formed a mysterious brotherhood with his students who were bound by an oath not to reveal the secrets of numbers and who exercised great influence. They laid the foundations of arithmetic through geometry but failed to resolve the concept of irrational numbers. The work of these and others was brought together by Euclid at Alexandria in a book called 'The Elements', which was still studied in English schools as recently as 1900.

- Understand and draw scale drawings including interpreting three-figure bearings.
- Pythagoras' theorem and trigonometry.
- Calculate unknown sides and angles of a right-angled triangle using trigonometry including solving problems in two dimensions and angles of elevation and depression.
- Know exact trigonometric values for $x = 0°$, $30°$, $45°$ and $60°$ (and $90°$ where applicable).

4.1 Pythagoras' theorem

In a right-angled triangle, the square of the hypotenuse is equal to the sum of the squares of the other two sides.

$a^2 + b^2 = c^2$

The *converse* is also true.

If the square of one side of a triangle is equal to the sum of the squares of the other two sides, then the triangle is right-angled.

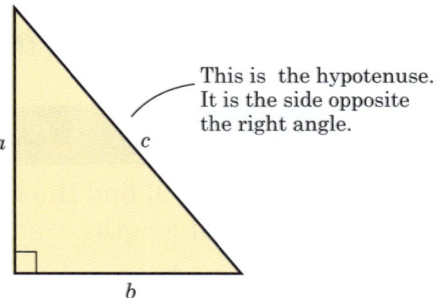

This is the hypotenuse. It is the side opposite the right angle.

Example

In this right-angled triangle, find the length of the side labelled d.

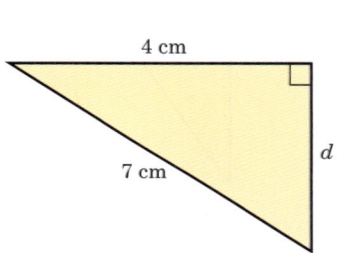

$d^2 + 4^2 = 7^2$

$d^2 = 49 - 16$

$d = \sqrt{33} = 5.74$ cm (3 s.f.)

Tip

If you are asked to give your answer as an exact value then leave your answer as a surd, $\sqrt{33}$. Otherwise you should round to 3 s.f.

Exercise 4.1A

For Questions **1** to **6**, find the length of the side labelled x. All lengths are in cm.

1.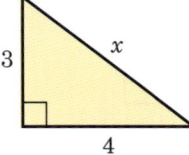

2.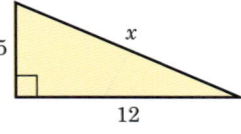

3.

4.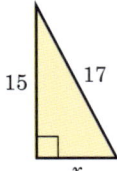

5.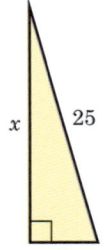

6.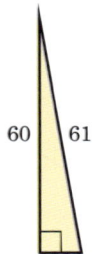

7. The two shorter sides of a right-angled triangle are 33 mm and 56 mm. Find the length of the hypotenuse.

8. The hypotenuse of a right-angled triangle is 85 m and one of the shorter sides is 36 m. Find the length of the other side.

Exercise 4.1B

In Questions **1** to **9**, find the length of the side labelled x, giving your answers as exact values. All lengths are in cm.

1.

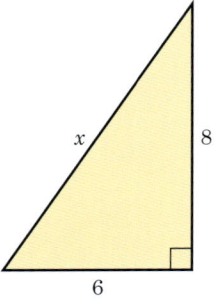

2.

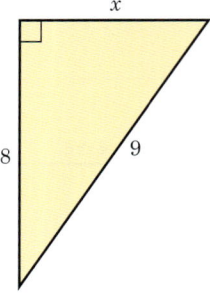

3.

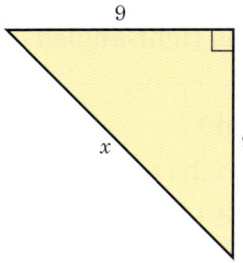

4.

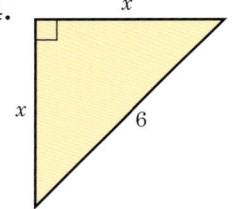

5.

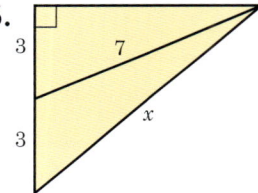

6.

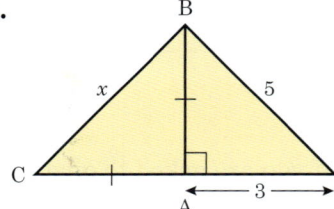

7.

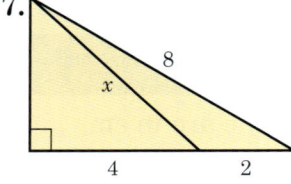

8.

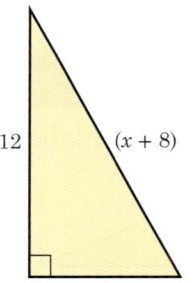

9.

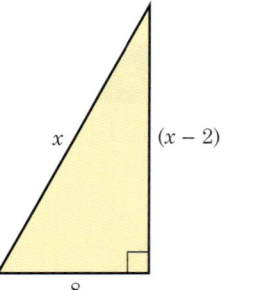

10. Find x.

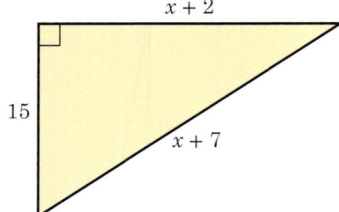

Using Pythagoras' theorem in three dimensions

Pythagoras' theorem can also be used in three dimensions. Look at the cuboid in the diagram. Its base has a length of 12 cm and a width of 9 cm. The height of the cuboid is 8 cm. These are the cuboid's three dimensions.

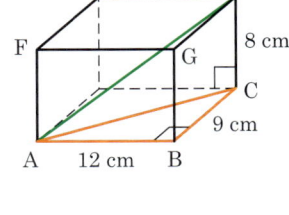

You can adapt Pythagoras' theorem to work out the length of the diagonal that goes up through the centre of the cuboid from A to D.

First consider the triangle (ABC) on the base. The hypotenuse of ABC is $\sqrt{9^2 + 12^2} = \sqrt{225} = 15$ cm. This then becomes the base of triangle ACD, standing up inside the cuboid. Because the height of triangle ACD is 8 cm, you can work out that the length of the diagonal AD is $\sqrt{8^2 + 15^2} = \sqrt{289} = 17$ cm.

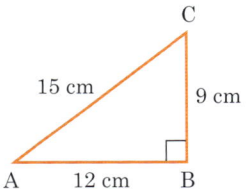
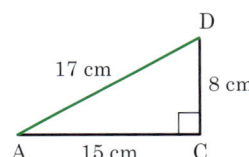

However, you can think of triangle ACD in a slightly different way. Remember that its 15 cm base was the hypotenuse of the triangle ABC. You can therefore label the second triangle in the following way and say that

$$AD^2 = \left(\sqrt{9^2 + 12^2}\right)^2 + 8^2$$
$$AD^2 = 9^2 + 12^2 + 8^2$$

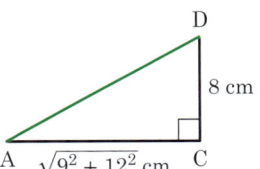

> **Tip**
>
> The length of the diagonal of a cuboid is
> $\sqrt{a^2 + b^2 + c^2}$.

So, for any cuboid with length, width and height a, b and c, and an interior diagonal d, this means that $a^2 + b^2 + c^2 = d^2$.

Exercise 4.1C

1. Find the length of a diagonal of a rectangle of length 9 cm and width 4 cm.

2. A square has diagonals of length 10 cm. Find the side lengths of the square.

3. A 4 m ladder rests against a vertical wall with its foot 2 m from the wall. How far up the wall does the ladder reach?

4. Find the length of a diagonal of a rectangular box of length 12 cm, width 5 cm and height 4 cm.

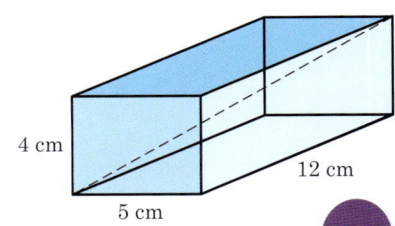

5. Find the length of a diagonal of a rectangular room of length 5 m, width 3 m and height 2.5 m.

6. Find the height of a rectangular box of length 8 cm, width 6 cm where the length of a diagonal is 11 cm.

7. An airplane flies equal distances south-east and then south-west to finish 120 km due south of its starting-point. How long is each part of its journey?

8. The diagonal of a rectangle exceeds the length by 2 cm. If the width of the rectangle is 10 cm, find the length.

9. An aircraft is vertically above a point which is 10 km west and 15 km north of a control tower. If the aircraft is 4000 m above the ground, how far is it from the control tower?

10. It is possible to create right-angled triangles by substituting different values of x into these three expressions:

Hypotenuse: $\qquad 2x^2 + 2x + 1$

Other two sides: $\qquad 2x^2 + 2x \quad$ and $\quad 2x + 1$

a) Find the sides of the triangles when $x = 1, 2, 3, 4$ and 5.

b) Confirm that $(2x + 1)^2 + (2x^2 + 2x)^2 = (2x^2 + 2x + 1)^2$

11. The diagram represents the starting position, AB, and the finishing position, CD, of a ladder as it slips down a vertical wall.

Given: AC = x, OC = 4AC, BD = 2AC and OB = 5 m.

Form an equation in x, then solve for x and hence find the length of the ladder.

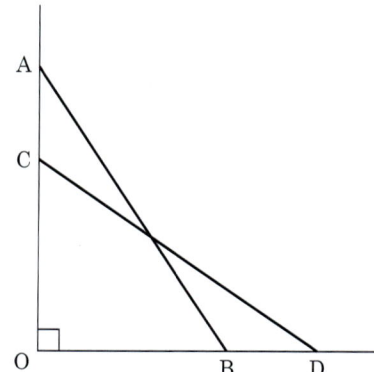

12. A thin wire of length 18 cm is bent into the shape shown. Calculate the straight-line distance from A to B.

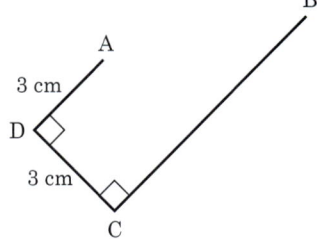

> **Tip**
>
> Think about what triangles you can create by making more line segments between points A, B, C and D.

4.2 Trigonometry

In a right-angled triangle, the side opposite the right angle is called the **hypotenuse**, labelled H in the diagram here. It is always the longest of the three sides.

The other two sides are named the **opposite** and the **adjacent**, but which one is which depends on which of the two acute angles you are working with at the time.

Look at the diagram. Because it is the 35° angle that you are currently concerned with, the side opposite that angle is called the opposite side, O. The other side is called the adjacent side, A. The word adjacent just means 'next to'.

> **Tip**
>
> In Chapter 8 Trigonometry 2, you'll learn and use formulae that can be applied to triangles that contain an obtuse angle.

Sine, cosine and tangent

Three important functions are defined using the opposite, adjacent and hypotenuse. They are called sine, cosine and tangent, but they are usually abbreviated to sin, cos and tan. The three functions are defined as follows:

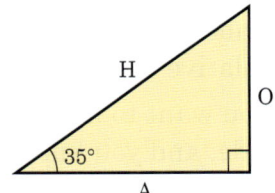

$$\sin x = \frac{O}{H}$$

$$\cos x = \frac{A}{H}$$

$$\tan x = \frac{O}{A}$$

Unlike Pythagoras' theorem which gives the relationship between the three sides of a right-angled triangle, the three trigonometric functions show how two of the sides and one of the angles are related. This means that if you know two of the sides you can work out a missing angle, or if you know an angle and a side length you can work the length of another side.

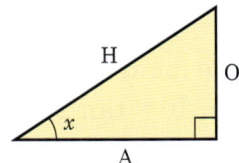

> **Tip**
>
> Check that your calculator is working in degrees.

Exercise 4.2A

You will need a protractor for this exercise.

1. Draw a circle of radius 10 cm on plain paper and construct a tangent to touch the circle at T. To construct the tangent, first draw a radius, label the point T where the radius meets the circle, then use a protractor to construct a right angle at T.

   Draw OA, OB and OC such that AOT = 20°

   $$BOT = 40°$$
   $$COT = 50°$$

   Measure the length AT and compare it with the value for tan 20° given on a calculator. Repeat for BT, CT and for other angles of your own choice. Discuss with a partner what you discover.

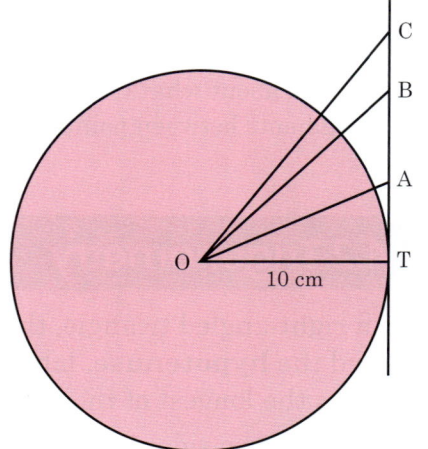

Finding the length of a side

Example 1

Find the length of the side labelled x.

Label the sides of the triangle H, O and A, relative to the 25.4° angle.

You want to find the length of the opposite side, and you know the length of the *adjacent* side, 10 cm. So, you use the tangent function.

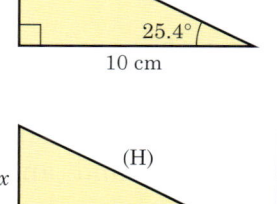

$$\tan 24.4° = \frac{O}{A} = \frac{x}{10}$$

Solve for x.

$$x = 10 \times \tan 25.4° = 4.748$$
$$x = 4.75 \text{ cm (3 s.f.)}$$

Example 2

Find the length of the side labelled z.

Label the sides, relative to the 31.3° angle. The side labelled z is the hypotenuse. The diagram shows that the side *opposite* the 31.3° angle is 7.4 cm. So, you use the sine function.

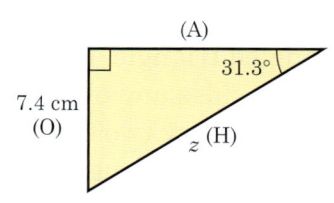

$$\sin 31.3° = \frac{O}{H} = \frac{7.4}{z}$$

Multiply by z.

$z \times (\sin 31.3°) = 7.4$

$$z = \frac{7.4}{\sin 31.3°}$$

On a calculator, press the keys as follows:

$\boxed{7.4} \; \boxed{\div} \; \boxed{\sin} \; \boxed{31.3} \; \boxed{=}$ (You may prefer to use the fraction button to input this calculation.)

$z = 14.2$ cm (3 s.f.)

Exercise 4.2B

For Questions **1** to **21** all lengths are in centimetres. Find the length of the sides labelled with letters. Give your answers to three significant figures.

1.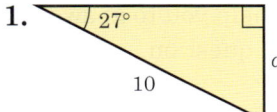

2.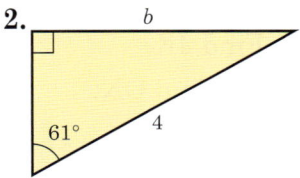

3.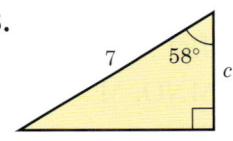

4.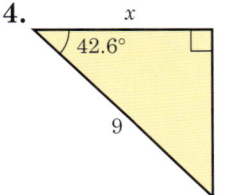

5.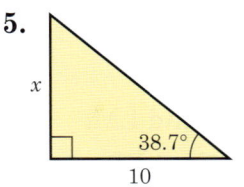

6.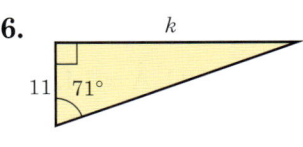

7.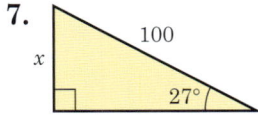

8.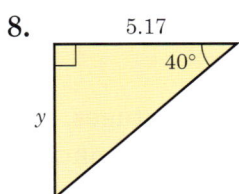

9.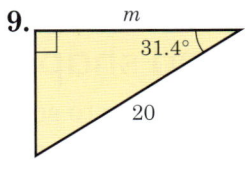

10.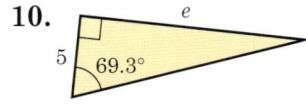

11.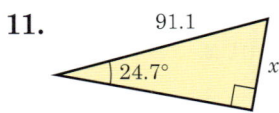

12.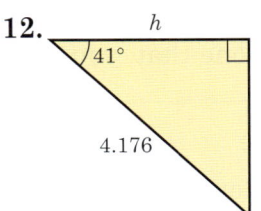

13.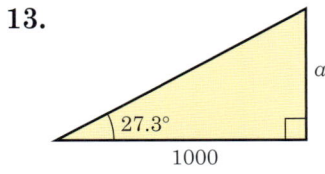

14.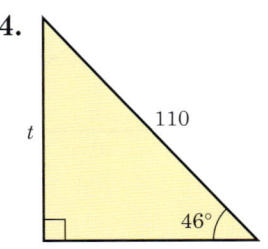

15.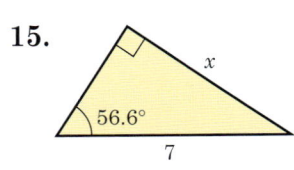

16.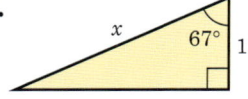

17.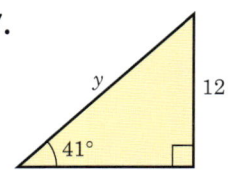

18.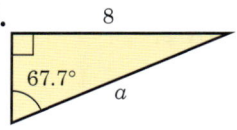

19.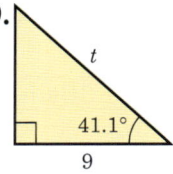

20.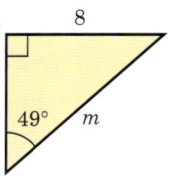

21.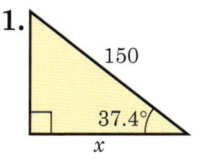

For Questions **22** to **33**, each triangle has a right angle at the middle letter.

22. In $\triangle$ABC, $\hat{C} = 40°$, BC = 4 cm. Find AB.

23. In $\triangle$DEF, $\hat{F} = 35.3°$, DF = 7 cm. Find ED.

24. In $\triangle$GHI, $\hat{I} = 70°$, GI = 12 m. Find HI.

25. In $\triangle$JKL, $\hat{L} = 55°$, KL = 8.21 m. Find JK.

26. In $\triangle$MNO, $\hat{M} = 42.6°$, MO = 14 cm. Find ON.

27. In $\triangle$PQR, $\hat{P} = 28°$, PQ = 5.071 m. Find PR.

28. In $\triangle$STU, $\hat{S} = 39°$, TU = 6 cm. Find SU.

29. In $\triangle$VWX, $\hat{X} = 17°$, WV = 30.7 m. Find WX.

30. In $\triangle$ABC, $\hat{A} = 14.3°$, BC = 14 m. Find AC.

31. In $\triangle$KLM, $\hat{K} = 72.8°$, KL = 5.04 cm. Find LM.

32. In $\triangle$PQR, $\hat{R} = 31.7°$, QR = 0.81 cm. Find PR.

33. In $\triangle$XYZ, $\hat{X} = 81.07°$, YZ = 52.6 m. Find XY.

> **Tip**
>
> Sketch each triangle to help you to answer the question.

Compound shapes

Sometimes you have to solve a problem in two stages. In the following example, you are not given enough information about triangle ABD to immediately solve for x. You need to work out the length of side BD first, using trigonometry on triangle BDC. Once you have done that, you can then work out x.

Example

Find the length of the side labelled x.

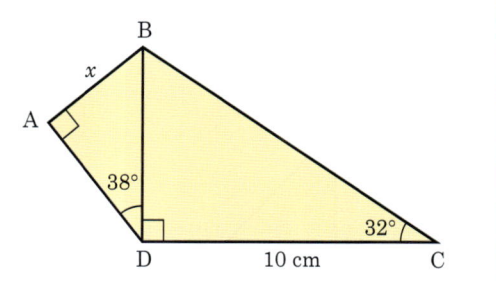

Find the length of BD from triangle BDC.

$$\tan 32° = \frac{BD}{10}$$

$$BD = 10 \times \tan 32° \qquad (1)$$

Now find x from triangle ABD, using the value of BD from (1).

$$\sin 38° = \frac{x}{BD}$$

$\therefore \qquad x = BD \times \sin 38°$

$\qquad\qquad x = 10 \times \tan 32° \times \sin 38°$ (from (1))

$\qquad\qquad x = 3.85$ cm (3 s.f.)

Notice that BD was *not* calculated in (1).

It is better to do all the calculations at one time.

Exercise 4.2C

For Questions **1** to **10**, find the length of each side labelled with a letter. All lengths are in m.

1.

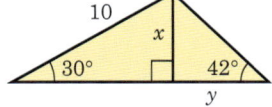

2.

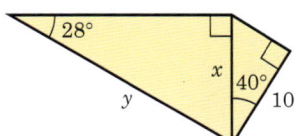

3.

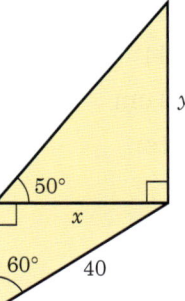

4.

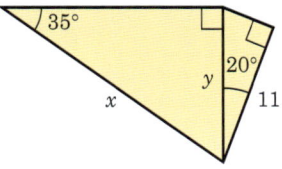

5.

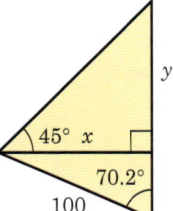

6.

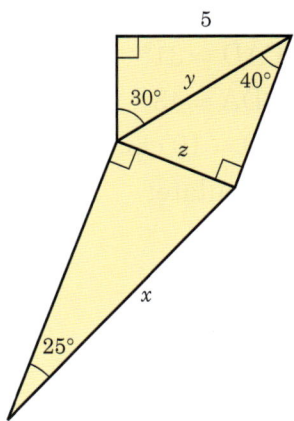

7.

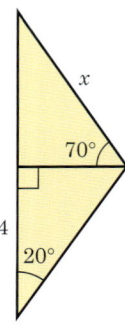

8.

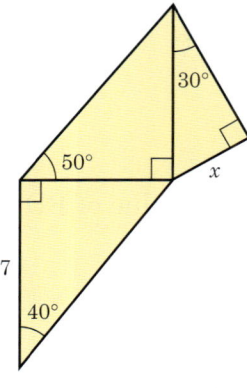

9.

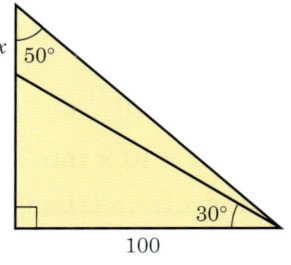

10.

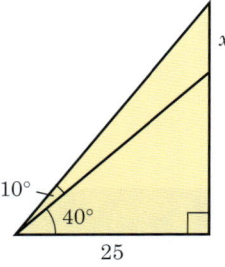

11. $B\hat{A}D = A\hat{C}D = 90°$

$C\hat{A}D = 35°$

$B\hat{D}A = 41°$

$AD = 20$ cm

Calculate:

a) AB

b) DC

c) BD

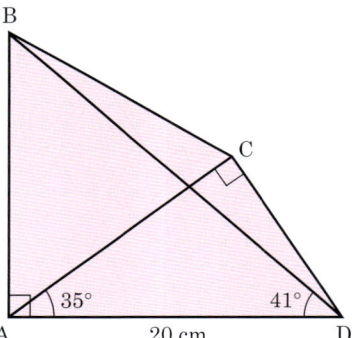

12. $A\hat{B}D = A\hat{D}C = 90°$

$C\hat{A}D = 31°$

$B\hat{D}A = 43°$

$AD = 10$ cm

Calculate:

a) AB

b) CD

c) DB

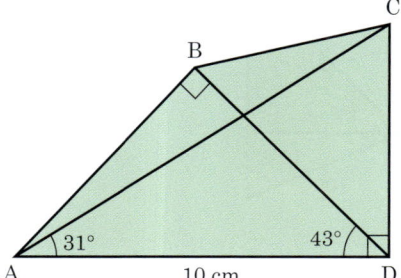

Finding the size of an unknown angle

Example

Find the size of the angle labelled m, accurate to 1 d.p.

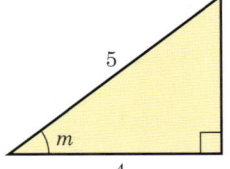

....

Label the sides of the triangle H, O and A in relation to angle m.

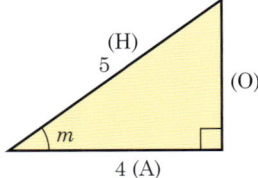

You know the length of the adjacent side and the hypotenuse, so you use the cosine function.

$$\cos m = \left(\frac{A}{H}\right) = \frac{4}{5}$$

Convert $\frac{4}{5}$ to a decimal: $\frac{4}{5} = 0.8$

$\cos m = 0.8$

Press [Shift] and then [cos] on a calculator to access the inverse of cos, which is $\cos^{-1}$.

This will give the angle as $36.86989765°$

So, $m = 36.9°$ (1 d.p.)

Tip

On some calculators press [Inv] [cos]

Exercise 4.2D

For Questions **1** to **15**, find the angle labelled with a letter. All lengths are in cm.

1.

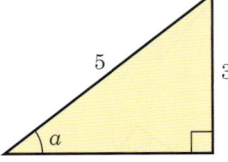

2.

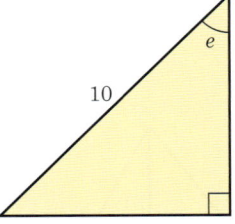

3.

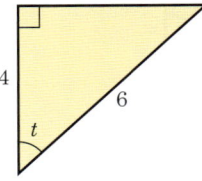

4.

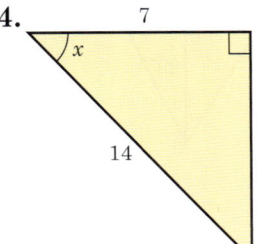

5.

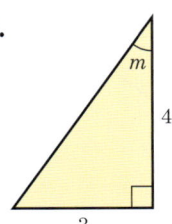

6.

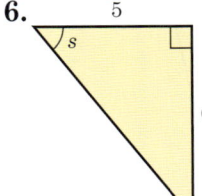

7.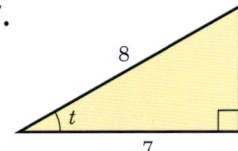

8.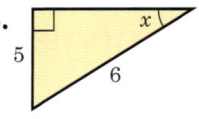

9.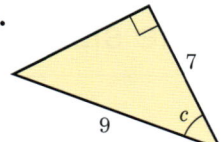

10.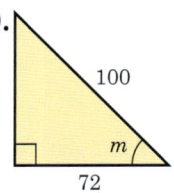

11.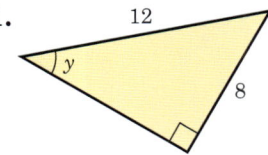

12.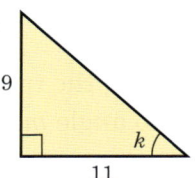

13.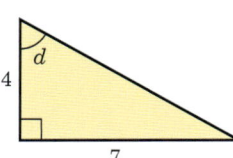

14.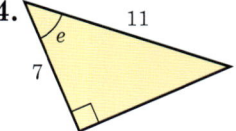

15.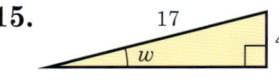

For Questions **16** to **20**, the triangle has a right angle at the middle letter.

16. In △ABC, BC = 4, AC = 7. Find Â.

17. In △DEF, EF = 5, DF = 10. Find F̂.

18. In △GHI, GH = 9, HI = 10. Find Î.

19. In △JKL, JL = 5, KL = 3. Find Ĵ.

20. In △MNO, MN = 4, NO = 5. Find M̂.

For Questions **21** to **26**, find the size of the angle labelled *x*.

> **Tip**
>
> Sketch each triangle to help you to answer the question.

21.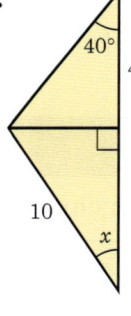

22.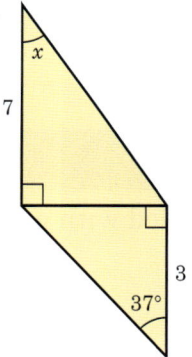

23.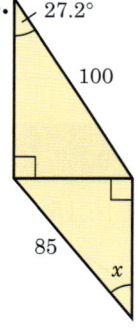

24.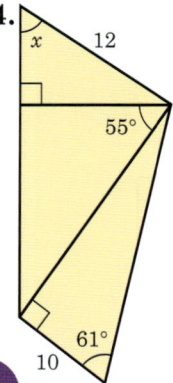

25.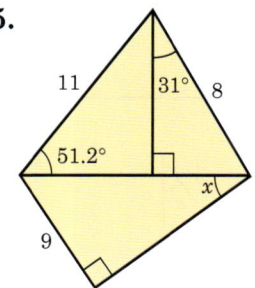

26.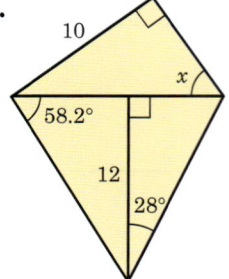

Exact trigonometric values

Consider an equilateral triangle with side length 2.

Look at half of the equilateral triangle and work out the missing side length using Pythagoras' theorem.

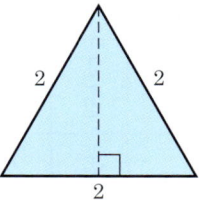

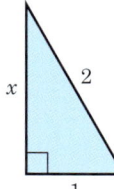

$$x^2 + 1^2 = 2^2$$
$$x^2 = 4 - 1$$
$$x = \sqrt{3}$$

The interior angle of an equilateral triangle is 60° and the half angle is therefore 30°. Use trigonometry to find exact values.

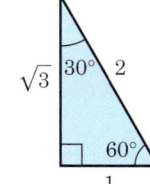

$$\sin 30° = \frac{O}{H} = \frac{1}{2} \qquad \sin 60° = \frac{O}{H} = \frac{\sqrt{3}}{2}$$

$$\cos 30° = \frac{A}{H} = \frac{\sqrt{3}}{2} \qquad \cos 60° = \frac{A}{H} = \frac{1}{2}$$

$$\tan 30° = \frac{O}{A} = \frac{1}{\sqrt{3}} \qquad \tan 60° = \frac{O}{A} = \frac{\sqrt{3}}{1} = \sqrt{3}$$

Now consider a right-angled isosceles triangle with side lengths of 1 for the equal sides.

Work out the missing side length using Pythagoras' theorem.

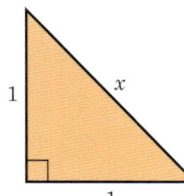

$$x^2 = 1^2 + 1^2$$
$$x^2 = 2$$
$$x = \sqrt{2}$$

The two smaller angles are equal, so they must each be 45°. Use trigonometry to find exact values.

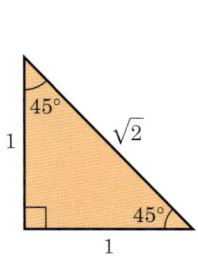

$$\sin 45° = \frac{O}{H} = \frac{1}{\sqrt{2}}$$

$$\cos 45° = \frac{A}{H} = \frac{1}{\sqrt{2}}$$

$$\tan 45° = \frac{O}{A} = \frac{1}{1} = 1$$

These exact values need to be learned.

	0°	30°	45°	60°	90°
sin	0	$\dfrac{1}{2}$	$\dfrac{1}{\sqrt{2}}$	$\dfrac{\sqrt{3}}{2}$	1
cos	1	$\dfrac{\sqrt{3}}{2}$	$\dfrac{1}{\sqrt{2}}$	$\dfrac{1}{2}$	0
tan	0	$\dfrac{1}{\sqrt{3}}$	1	$\sqrt{3}$	–

Tip

Some calculators give the exact values of sin 45° and cos 45° as $\dfrac{\sqrt{2}}{2}$ instead of $\dfrac{1}{\sqrt{2}}$. This is because some calculators give the denominator as a rational number (see surds in Chapter 1). Similarly, tan 30° is sometimes shown as $\dfrac{\sqrt{3}}{3}$ instead of $\dfrac{1}{\sqrt{3}}$. As a calculator is not used in this section, the values from the table at the start of this section should be used, unless a question says otherwise.

Example

a) Calculate the exact value of sin 60° + cos 30°

b) Calculate the exact value of $\dfrac{\tan 45°}{\sin 30°} \times 3 \tan 60°$

c) The diagram shows a right-angled triangle.

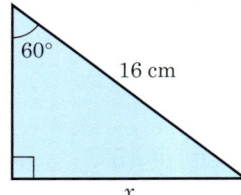

Calculate the exact value of x.

d) The diagram shows a right-angled triangle.

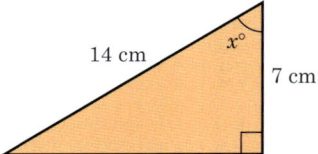

Calculate the value of x.

a) $\sin 60° + \cos 30° = \dfrac{\sqrt{3}}{2} + \dfrac{\sqrt{3}}{2} = \sqrt{3}$

b) $\dfrac{\tan 45°}{\sin 30°} \times 3 \tan 60° = \dfrac{1}{\frac{1}{2}} \times 3\sqrt{3} = 2 \times 3\sqrt{3} = 6\sqrt{3}$

c)

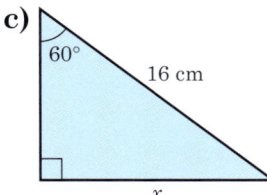

$\sin 60° = \dfrac{x}{16}$

$x = 16 \times \sin 60°$

$x = 16 \times \dfrac{\sqrt{3}}{2}$

$x = 8\sqrt{3}\ \text{cm}$

d)

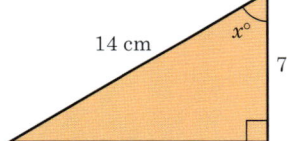

$\cos x = \dfrac{7}{14} = \dfrac{1}{2}$

$\cos 60° = \dfrac{1}{2}$ so $x = 60°$

Exercise 4.2E

In this exercise, do not use a calculator and give all answers as exact and in their simplest form.

1. Using the table of exact values at the start of this section, calculate the following.

   a) $\sin 30° + \cos 60°$

   b) $3 \tan 45° + 2 \cos 60°$

   c) $12 \cos 60° - 8 \sin 30°$

   d) $10 \cos 30° - 2 \tan 60°$

   e) $\cos 60° \times 16 \sin 60°$

> **Tip**
>
> Be confident at working with surds before attempting this exercise.

f) $\cos 0° \times \sin 90°$

g) $\cos 45° \times \sin 45°$

h) $\dfrac{\sin 30°}{\cos 30°} - \tan 30°$

i) $\dfrac{\sin 30°}{\tan 45°} + \dfrac{\sin 90°}{3}$

j) $\dfrac{\sin 60°}{\sin 30°} + 2\cos 30°$

2. Calculate the side length x in each of these triangles.

a)
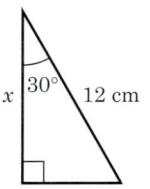
x 30°   12 cm

b)
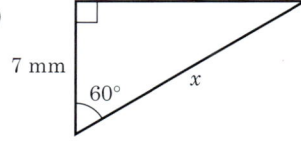
7 mm   60° x

c)
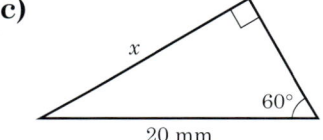
x 60°   20 mm

d)
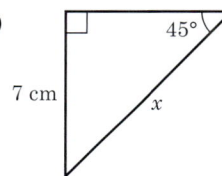
45°   7 cm x

e)
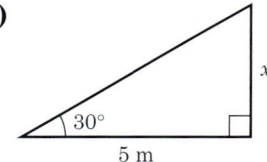
x 30°   5 m

f)
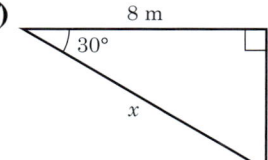
8 m   30° x

3. The diagram shows a right-angled triangle.
Show that angle $x = 30°$.

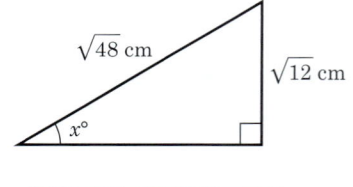
$\sqrt{48}$ cm $\sqrt{12}$ cm $x°$

4. The diagram shows a right-angled triangle.
Calculate the exact value of x.

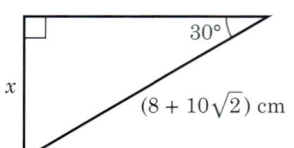
30° x $(8 + 10\sqrt{2})$ cm

5. Calculate each of the following.
Rationalise the denominator if it is irrational.

a) $\sin 45° + \cos 45°$

b) $\tan 60° - \tan 30°$

> **Tip**
>
> You learned how to rationalise the denominator on page 39

6. The diagram shows two right-angled triangles with a common side.

$$y = \frac{x\sqrt{k}}{c}$$

Find the value of k and c.

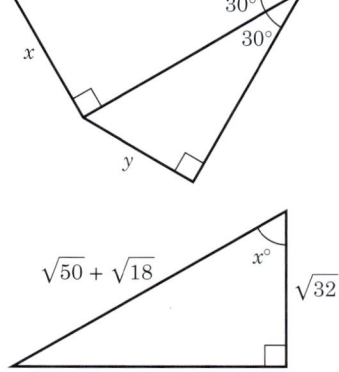

7. The diagram shows a right-angled triangle.

Show that angle $x = 60°$.

4.3 Bearings

Bearings are useful for navigating when you have no recognisable landmarks to help you find your way around. They are extremely useful, for example, if you are on a ship out at sea or flying in a plane up above the clouds.

A bearing is an angle measured *clockwise from north*. It is always given using *three digits*.

In the diagram:

the bearing of B *from A* is 052°

the bearing of A *from B* is 232°

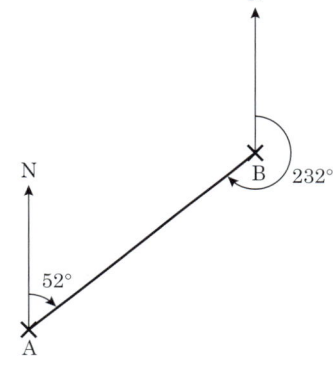

> **Tip**
>
> 'The bearing from A' means that the starting point is A.

Example 1

The bearing of a ship from a lighthouse is 065°.

What is the bearing of the lighthouse from the ship?

....

If you draw a diagram showing the lighthouse and the ship, you will see that there are two equal alternate 65° angles between the two north lines. The bearing of the lighthouse from the ship is therefore 180° bigger than the bearing of the ship from the lighthouse.

It is therefore $65 + 180 = 245°$

In general, if you know the bearing A from B, to find the bearing of B from A you either add or subtract 180°, depending on which one gives you an angle between 0 and 360°. Remember: a bearing is always measured clockwise from north.

Often you will be required to use your knowledge of trigonometry to solve bearings questions.

Example 2

A ship sails 22 km from A on a bearing of 042° to point B, and then a further 30 km on a bearing of 090° to arrive at C. What is the distance and bearing of C from A? Give the bearing accurate to the nearest degree.

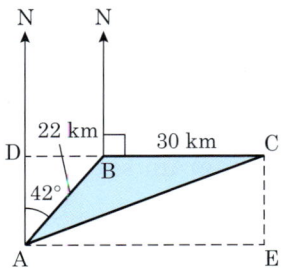

First draw a clear diagram, labelling any extra points that may be helpful.

Then work out a general strategy.

If you knew the lengths of AE and CE you would be able to find the answer.

But notice that AE = BD + 30 and CE = AD.

So you need to find the lengths of BD and AD.

$\sin 42° = \dfrac{BD}{22}$

BD = 22 sin 42° = 14.72 km

$\cos 42° = \dfrac{AD}{22}$

AE = 14.72 + 30 = 44.72 km   AD = 22 cos 42° = 16.35 km

You can now work out the distance AC using Pythagoras' theorem.

$AC^2 = 44.72^2 + 16.35^2$

AC = 47.62 km

The bearing of C from A = 90° − CÂE

$C\hat{A}E = \tan^{-1}\left(\dfrac{CE}{AC}\right) = \tan^{-1}\left(\dfrac{16.35}{47.62}\right) = 18.95°$

Therefore, the bearing of C from A = 90° − 18.95° = 71.05° ≈ 071°

Exercise 4.3A

1. The bearing of Rome from Paris is 134°.
   Find the bearing of Paris from Rome.

2. The bearing of Moscow from Vienna is 059°.
   Find the bearing of Vienna from Moscow.

3. A ship sails 35 km on a bearing of 042°.

   a) How far north has it travelled?

   b) How far east has it travelled?

4. A ship sails 200 km on a bearing of 243.7°.

   a) How far south has it travelled?

   b) How far west has it travelled?

5. A ship sails 20 km due north and then 35 km due east. How far is it from its starting point?

6. An aircraft flies 400 km from a point O on a bearing of 025° and then 700 km on a bearing of 080° to arrive at B.

    a) How far north of O is B?

    b) How far east of O is B?

    c) Find the distance and bearing of B from O.

7. An aircraft flies 500 km on a bearing of 100° and then 600 km on a bearing of 160°.
Find the distance and bearing of the finishing point from the starting point.

8. A ship sails 95 km on a bearing of 140°, then a further 102 km on a bearing of 260° and then returns directly to its starting point. Find the distance and bearing of the return journey.

4.4 Angles of elevation and depression

If you are looking up at something, the angle that your line of sight makes with the horizontal is called an **angle of elevation**.

If you are looking down at something, it is called an **angle of depression**.

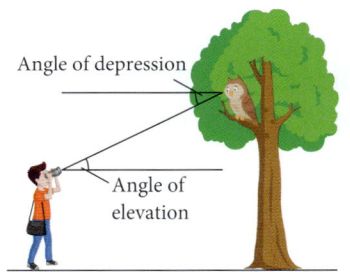

Example 1

A birdwatcher looks up at an owl in a tree through an angle of elevation of 40°.

If he is 15 metres away from the tree, how much higher than the man is the owl?

Let the difference in height be h.

$$\tan 40° = \frac{h}{15}$$
$$h = 15 \tan 40° = 12.6 \text{ m}$$

The owl is 12.6 m higher than the man.

Example 2

John looks down from the top of a tower to his friend who is standing 20 metres away from the base of the tower. If the tower is 52 metres tall, what is the angle of depression between John's line of sight and the horizontal?

Let the angle of depression be θ

$$\tan \theta = \frac{52}{20}$$

$$\theta = \tan^{-1}\left(\frac{52}{20}\right) = 68.96...°$$

The angle of depression is 69.0° to 1 decimal place

Exercise 4.4A

1. A girl looks up at the top of a tower which is 200 m tall. If the angle of elevation through which she looks is 65°, how far away from the base of the tower is she standing?

2. A boy is looking up at his friend who is in a hot air balloon.
If the balloon is 60 m off the ground and the boy is 80 m away from the point on the ground directly below the balloon, through what angle of elevation is he looking?

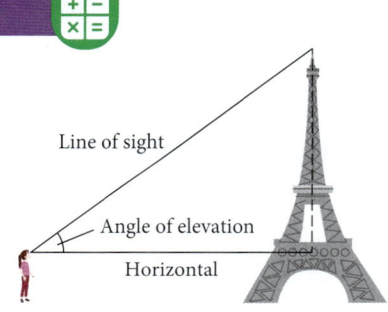

Line of sight
Angle of elevation
Horizontal

3. Tom looks down from the top of a cliff at his friend who is in a boat. Tom knows that the cliff is 60 m tall and that he is 1.8 m tall.
He measures the angle of depression through which he is looking to be 25°.
Roughly how far out to sea is the boat?

4. A kite flying at a height of 55 m is attached to a string which makes an angle of 55° with the horizontal. What is the length of the string?

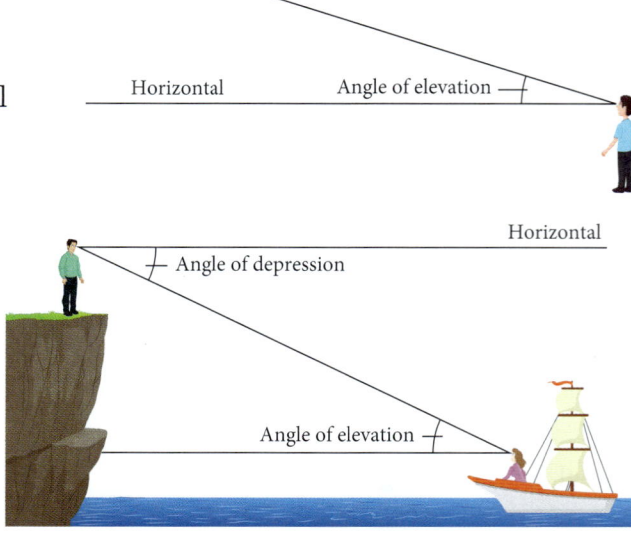

Horizontal
Angle of depression
Horizontal
Angle of elevation
Horizontal
Angle of depression
Angle of elevation

5. A boy is flying a kite from a string of length 150 m. If the string is taut and makes an angle of 67° with the horizontal, what is the height of the kite?

6. From a point 10 m from a vertical wall, the angles of elevation of the bottom and the top of a statue of Sir Isaac Newton, set in the wall, are 40° and 52°. Calculate the height of the statue.

7. From the top of a tower of height 75 m, a person sees two goats, both due west of them. If the angles of depression of the two goats are 10° and 17°, calculate the distance between them.

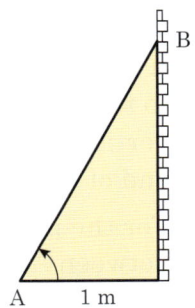

8. Ants can hear each other up to a range of 2 m. An ant at A, 1 m from a wall sees its friend at B about to be eaten by a spider. If the angle of elevation of B from A is 62°, will the spider have a meal or not? (Assume B escapes if it hears A calling.)

9. A hedgehog wishes to cross a road without being run over. This particularly clever hedgehog observes the angle of elevation of a lamp post on the other side of the road to be 27° from the edge of the road and 15° from a point 10 m back from the road.

   a) How wide is the road?

   b) If he can run at 1 m/s, how long will he take to cross?

10. The angle of elevation of the top of a tower is 38° from a point A due south of it. The angle of elevation of the top of the tower from another point B, due east of the tower is 29°. Find the height of the tower if the distance AB is 50 m.

11. An observer at the top of a tower of height 15 m sees a man due west of him at an angle of depression 31°. He sees another man due south at an angle of depression 17°. Find the distance between the men.

12. The angle of elevation of the top of a tower is 27° from a point A due east of it. The angle of elevation of the top of the tower is 11° from another point B due south of the tower. Find the height of the tower if the distance AB is 40 m.

Tip

Draw a diagram and label it with all the information given to you. Use letters to label unknown sides or angles you need to find.

Exercise 4.4B

1. A ladder of length 6 m leans against a vertical wall so that the base of the ladder is 2 m from the wall. Calculate the angle between the ladder and the wall.

2. A ladder of length 8 m rests against a wall so that the angle between the ladder and the wall is 31°. How far is the base of the ladder from the wall?

3. Look at triangle PQR. Find TR if PR = 10 m and QT = 7 m.

4. Look at triangle XYZ. Find d.

5. A rocket flies 10 km vertically, then 20 km at an angle of 15° to the vertical and finally 60 km at an angle of 26° to the vertical. Calculate the vertical height of the rocket at the end of the third stage.

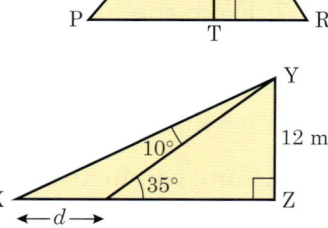

6. For the points A(5, 0) and B(7, 3), calculate the angle between AB and the x-axis.

7. For the points C(0, 2) and D(5, 9), calculate the angle between CD and the y-axis.

8. For the points A(3, 0), B(5, 2) and C(7, −2), calculate the angle BAC.

9. For the points P(2, 5), Q(5, 1) and R(0, −3), calculate the angle PQR.

10. An isosceles triangle has sides of length 8 cm, 8 cm and 5 cm. Find the angle between the two equal sides.

11. The angles of an isosceles triangle are 66°, 66° and 48°. If the shortest side of the triangle is 8.4 cm, find the length of one of the two equal sides.

12. Find the acute angle between the diagonals of a rectangle whose sides are 5 cm and 7 cm.

13. Find x, given that AD = BC = 6 m.

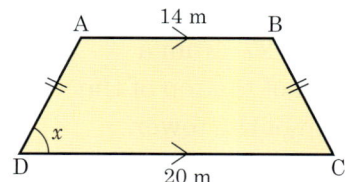

14. Find x.

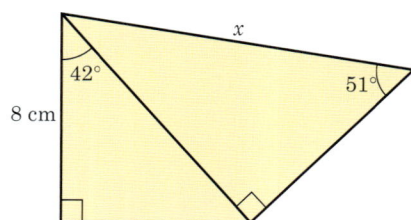

4.5 Scale drawing

When making a scale drawing, the size of the paper you are using will give you a clue as to what sort of scales may be reasonable and practical. Also look at the numbers you are dealing with. This may also be helpful.

For example, look at the quadrilateral in Question **1** below. A scale of 1:100 (which would mean 1 cm per metre) would not be practical, because the longest length on the scale drawing would then be 99 cm long. Similarly, 1:500 (meaning 1 cm per 5 metres) may seem like a good scale, but it is not ideal for the 99 m side. What do you think would be a good scale to use?

Exercise 4.5A

You will need a protractor and a pair of compasses for this exercise.

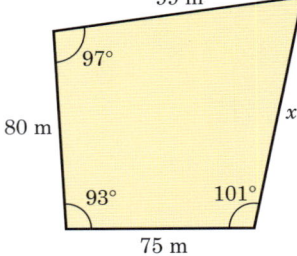

Solve the following problems by making a scale drawing.

1. A field has four sides as shown in the diagram. How long is the side x in metres?

2. Two ships leave a port at the same time. The first ship sails at 38 knots on a bearing of 042° and the second ship sails at 25 knots on a bearing of 315°. How far apart are the ships two hours later?
   [1 knot is a speed of 1 nautical mile per hour.]

3. Two radar stations A and B are 80 km apart and B is due east of A. One aircraft is on a bearing of 030° from A and 346° from B. A second aircraft is on a bearing of 325° from A and 293° from B. How far apart are the two aircraft?

4. A control tower observes the flight of an aircraft. At 09:23, the aircraft is 580 km away on a bearing of 043°. At 09:25, the aircraft is 360 km away on a bearing of 016°. What is the speed and the course of the aircraft?
   [Use a scale of 1 cm to 50 km.]

5. Make a scale drawing of triangle ABC (shown on the right) and find the length of CD in km.

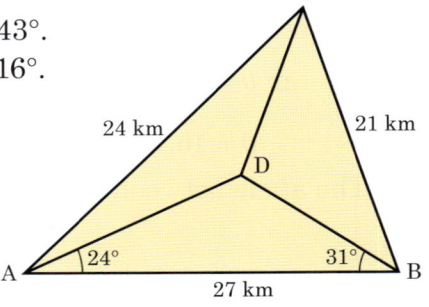

4.6 Three-dimensional trigonometry

Unlike Pythagoras' theorem, where you actually have a new formula for working with three-dimensional problems, with three-dimensional trigonometry the triangles are still two-dimensional; they are just hidden inside three-dimensional shapes.

Look at the example below. Although this is a three-dimensional cuboid, the triangles you need to work with are:

the triangle ABC, lying flat on the base of the cuboid,

and the triangle WAC, which is standing up inside the cuboid.
There are no new formulae to learn.

Example

A rectangular box with top WXYZ and base ABCD has AB = 6 cm, BC = 8 cm and WA = 3 cm.

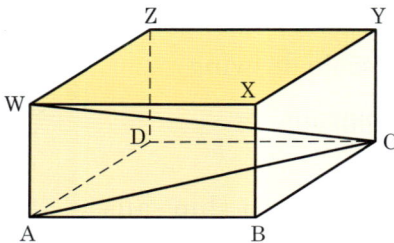

Calculate:

a) the length of AC

b) the angle between WC and the plane ABCD.

a) Redraw triangle ABC.

$$AC^2 = 6^2 + 8^2 = 100$$

$$AC = 10 \text{ cm}$$

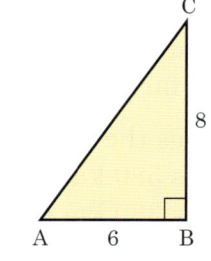

b) Redraw triangle WAC.

Let WCA = θ

$$\tan \theta = \frac{3}{10}$$

$$\theta = 16.7°$$

The angle between WC and AC is 16.7°

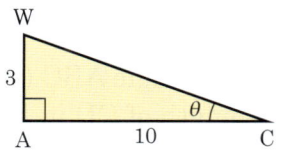

Exercise 4.6A

1. In the rectangular box shown, find:

   a) AC

   b) AR

   c) the angle between AR and the plane ABCD.

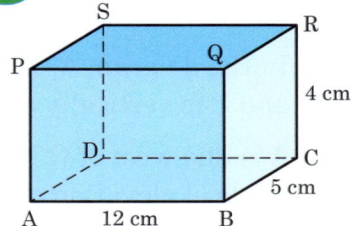

2. A vertical pole BP stands at one corner of a horizontal rectangular field as shown.

   If AB = 10 m, AD = 5 m and angle PAB is 22°, calculate:

   a) the height of the pole

   b) the angle of elevation of P from C

   c) the length of a diagonal of the rectangle ABCD

   d) the angle of elevation of P from D. [This is the angle PDB.]

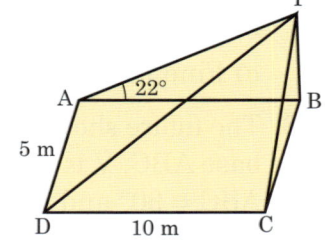

3. In the cube shown, find:

   a) BD

   b) AS

   c) BS

   d) the angle SBD

   e) the angle ASB

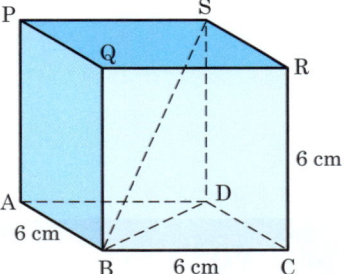

4. In the square-based pyramid, V is vertically above the middle of the base, AB = 10 cm and VC = 20 cm. Find:

   a) AC

   b) the height of the pyramid

   c) the angle between VC and the plane ABCD

   d) the angle AVB

   e) the angle AVC

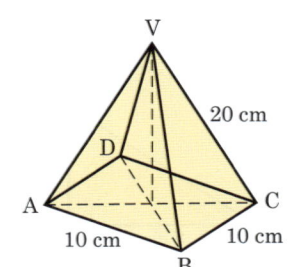

5. In the wedge shown, PQRS is perpendicular to ABRQ; PQRS and ABRQ are rectangles with AB = QR = 6 m, BR = 4 m, RS = 2 m. Find:

   a) BS

   b) AS

   c) angle BSR

   d) angle ASR

   e) angle PAS

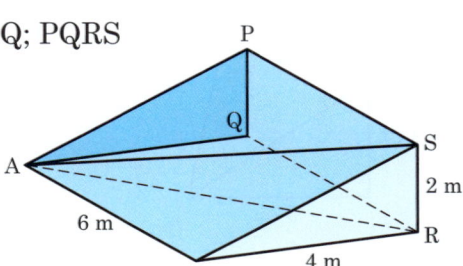

6. The edges of a rectangular box are 4 cm, 6 cm and 8 cm respectively. Find the length of a diagonal and the angle it makes with the diagonal on the largest face.

7. In the diagram A, B and O are points in a horizontal plane and P is vertically above O, where OP = h m.

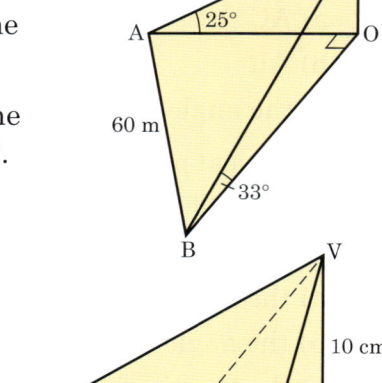

A is due west of O, B is due south of O and AB = 60 m. The angle of elevation of P from A is 25° and angle PBO is 33°.

a) Find the length AO in terms of h.

b) Find the length BO in terms of h.

c) Find the value of h.

8. The figure shows a triangular pyramid on a horizontal base ABC, V is vertically above B where VB = 10 cm, $A\hat{B}C = 90°$ and AB = BC = 15 cm. Point M is the midpoint of AC. Calculate the size of angle VMB.

Revision exercise 4

1. Find the lengths of sides labelled x and y, correct to 3 s.f.

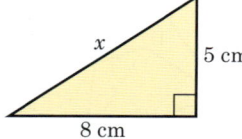

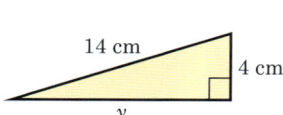

2. Find x.

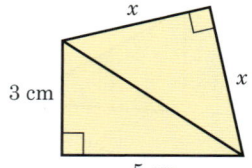

3. Calculate the side or angle labelled with a letter.

a)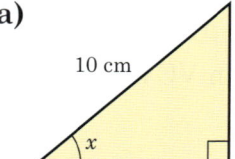

b)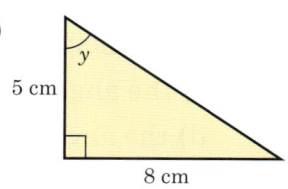

c)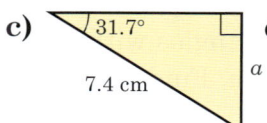

d)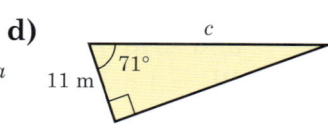

4. Given that x is an acute angle and that
$$3 \tan x - 2 = 4 \cos 35.3°$$

calculate:

a) $\tan x$

b) the value of x in degrees correct to 1 d.p.

5. Without using a calculator, show that the following expression can be simplified to an integer value.

$$\left(\frac{\sin 30° + \tan 45°}{\sin 60°} \right)^2$$

 6. Without using a calculator, find the value of x.

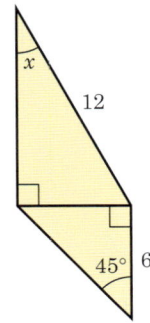

 7. Without using a calculator, find the value of x.

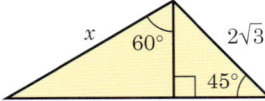

8. Calculate the length of AB.

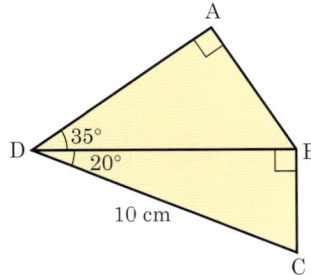

9. a) Point A lies on a bearing of 040° from point B. Calculate the bearing of B from A.

b) The bearing of point X from point Y is 115°. Calculate the bearing of Y from X.

10. Given BD = 1 m, calculate the length AC.

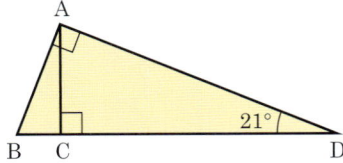

11. In the triangle PQR, angle PQR = 90° and angle RPQ = 31°.

The length of PQ is 11 cm.

Calculate:

a) the length of QR

b) the length of PR

c) the length of the perpendicular from Q to PR.

12. An observer at the top of a tower of height 20 m sees a man due east of him at an angle of depression of 27°. He sees another man due south of him at an angle of depression of 30°. Find the distance between the men on the ground.

13. The figure shows a cube of side 10 cm.

Calculate:

a) the length of AC   **b)** the angle YAC

c) the angle ZBD.

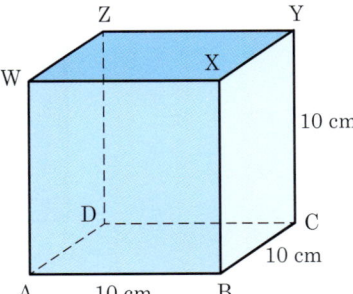

14. The diagram shows a rectangular block.

AY = 12 cm, AB = 8 cm, BC = 6 cm.

Calculate:

a) the length YC

b) the angle YAZ.

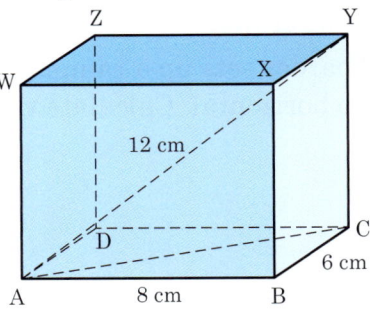

CALCULATOR

1. In the triangle ABC, $AB = 7$ cm, $BC = 8$ cm and $A\hat{B}C = 90°$. Point P lies inside the triangle such that $BP = PC = 5$ cm. Work out:

    a) the perpendicular distance from P to BC [2]

    b) the length AP. [2]

2. In the triangle XYZ, $XY = 14$ cm, $XZ = 17$ cm and angle $YXZ = 25°$. A is the foot of the perpendicular from Y to XZ.

    Calculate:

    a) the length XA [2]

    b) the length YA [2]

    c) the angle $Z\hat{Y}A$ [2]

3. Given that $4\cos x - 3 = \sin 45°$, calculate the value of $\cos x$, giving your answer in the form $\frac{a + \sqrt{b}}{c}$, where a, b and c are integers to be found. [2]

4. $B\hat{A}D = D\hat{C}A = 90°$, $C\hat{A}D = 32.4°$, $B\hat{D}A = 41°$ and $AD = 100$ cm.

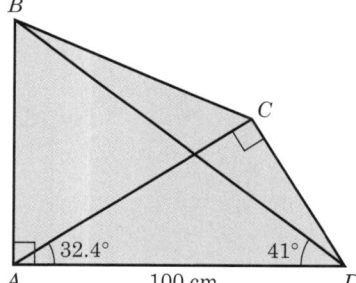

    Calculate:

    a) the length AB [2]

    b) the length DC [2]

    c) the length BD. [2]

5. A man in a castle sees a crow due north of him on top of a 20 m tall tower at an angle of elevation of $35°$. He also sees another crow due west of him on top of another 20 m tall tower at an angle of elevation of $50°$. Find the distance between the crows. [3]

6. A skateboarder sets up a ramp. The ramp is 1.2 metres long and is inclined at $15°$ to the horizontal. Calculate the height, h centimetres, of the ramp. [2]

7. *VABCD* is a pyramid in which the base *ABCD* is a square of side length 8 cm; V is vertically above the centre of the square and *VA* = *VB* = *VC* = *VD* = 10 cm.

   Calculate:

   a) the length *AC* [2]

   b) the height of *V* above the base [2]

   c) the angle *VĈA*. [2]

8. *ABCD*, *BEFC* and *AEFD* are all rectangles.

   ABCD is horizontal, *BEFC* is vertical and *AEFD* represents a road.

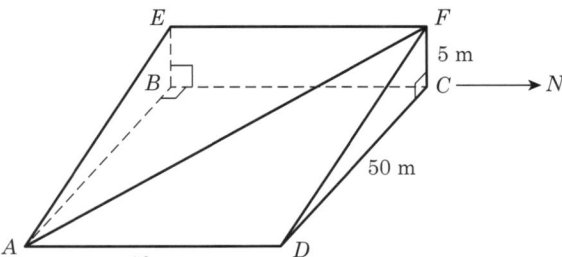

Not to scale

   AF is the route Luke takes as he walks across the road.

   AD = 10 m, *DC* = 50 m and *CF* = 5 m.

   a) Calculate the angle that the path *AF* makes with *ABCD*. [5]

   b) In the diagram *D* is due east of *C*. On what bearing did Luke walk as he crossed the road? [3]

9. The diagram shows a pyramid on a rectangular base *ABCD*, with *AB* = 12 m and *AD* = 9 m. The diagonals *AC* and *BD* intersect at *F*.

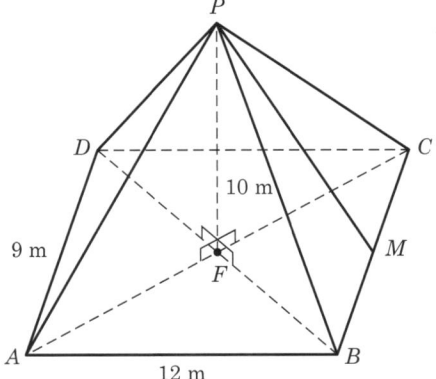

Not to scale

   The vertical height *FP* = 10 m.

   a) Calculate the volume of the pyramid.

   [The volume of a pyramid is $\frac{1}{3}$ × area of base × height.] [2]

   b) The midpoint of *BC* is *M*.

   Calculate the length of *PM*. [2]

    c) Calculate the angle between *PM* and the base. [2]

    d) Calculate the length of *PB*. [2]

    e) Calculate the angle between *PB* and the base. [4]

10. ABCDEFGH is a cuboid.

Work out

    a) the length of the line *FH* [2]

    b) the angle between *CF* and the plane *EFGH*. [2]

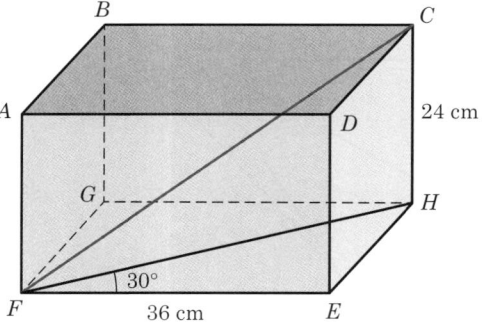

5 Mensuration

Archimedes of Samos (287–212 B.C.E.) studied at Alexandria as a young man. One of the first to apply scientific thinking to everyday problems, he was a practical man of common sense. He gave proofs for finding the area, the volume and the centre of gravity of circles, spheres, conics and spirals. By drawing polygons with many sides, he arrived at a value of π between $3\frac{10}{71}$ and $3\frac{10}{70}$. He was killed in the siege of Syracuse at the age of 75.

- Understand and use the ratio between lengths, areas and volumes of similar shapes and solids including solving problems.
- Use and convert between units of mass, length, area, volume and capacity, including in solving problems.
- Perimeter and area of a triangle, rectangle, parallelogram and trapezium.
- Find the area of a triangle using $\frac{1}{2}ab\sin C$.
- Circumference and area of a circle including arc length and sector area.
- Surface area and volume of a cuboid, prism, cylinder, pyramid, cone and sphere.
- Areas and perimeters of compound shapes. Volumes and surface areas of compound solids.

5.1 Area

Area is the amount of space taken up by a two-dimensional shape or surface. Many 2D geometric shapes have simple formulae for calculating their area.

Quadrilaterals

Rectangle
Trapezium
Kite

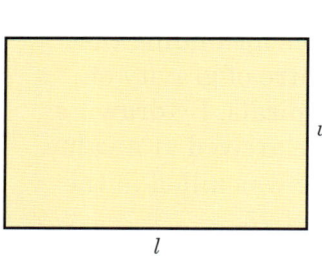

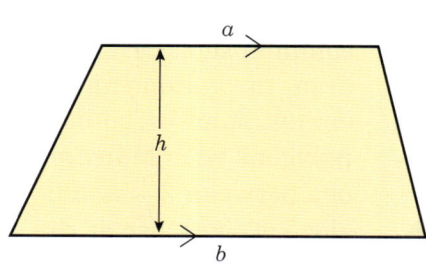

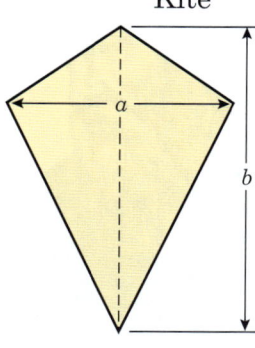

$$\text{area} = l \times w$$

$$\text{area} = \frac{1}{2}(a + b)h$$

$$\text{area} = \frac{1}{2}a \times b$$

$$= \frac{1}{2} \times (\text{product of diagonals})$$

Exercise 5.1A

Use the area formulae for quadrilaterals to find the area of each shape. Note: some diagrams may contain more information than needed.

1.

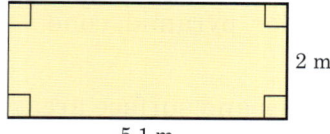

2.

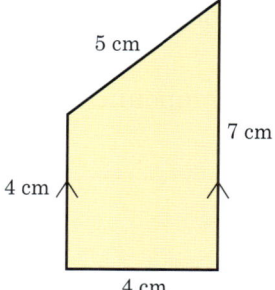

3.

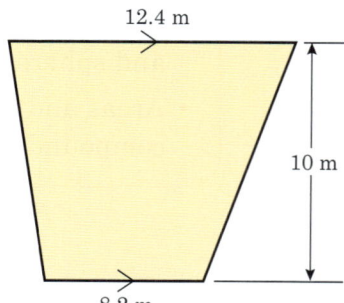

4.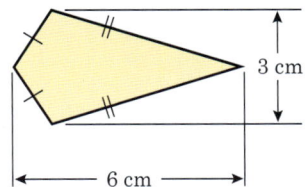
3 cm
6 cm

5.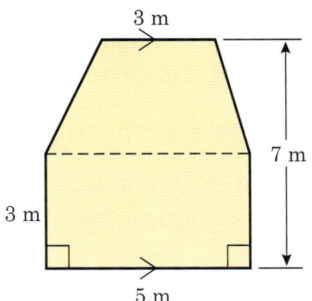
3 m
7 m
3 m
5 m

6.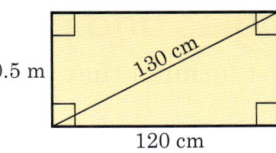
0.5 m
130 cm
120 cm

7.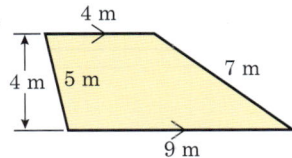
4 m
4 m | 5 m
7 m
9 m

8. Find the area shaded.
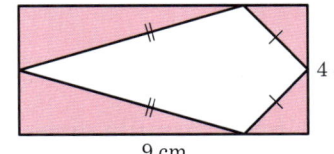
4 cm
9 cm

9. Find the area shaded.
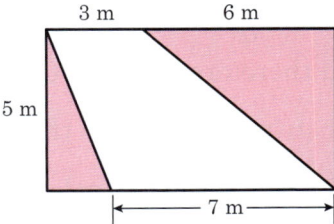
3 m   6 m
5 m
7 m

Exercise 5.1B

1. A rectangle has an area of 117 m² and a width of 9 m. Find its length.

2. A trapezium of area 105 cm² has parallel sides of length 5 cm and 9 cm. Find the perpendicular distance between the parallel sides.

3. A kite of area 252 m² has one diagonal of length 9 m. Find the length of the other diagonal.

4. A kite of area 40 m² has one diagonal 2 m longer than the other. Find the lengths of the diagonals.

5. A trapezium of area 140 cm² has parallel sides 10 cm apart and one of these sides is 16 cm long. Find the length of the other parallel side.

6. A rectangular floor measuring 5 m by 20 m is covered by square tiles of side 20 cm. How many tiles are needed?

7. Draw a set of axes on squared paper and then draw a triangle with vertices at (1, 1), (5, 3) and (3, 5). Find the area of the triangle.

8. Draw a set of axes on squared paper and then draw a quadrilateral with vertices at (1, 1), (6, 2), (5, 5) and (3, 6). Find the area of the quadrilateral.

9. A rectangular field, 400 m long, has an area of 6 hectares. Calculate the perimeter of the field [1 hectare = 10 000 m²].

Triangles and parallelograms

The first formula that you learn for calculating the area of a triangle is

$$\text{Area} = \frac{1}{2} \times \text{base} \times \text{perpendicular height.}$$

There are, however, other formulae that will also achieve the same result. One of them involves trigonometry.

Consider triangle ABC in the diagram.

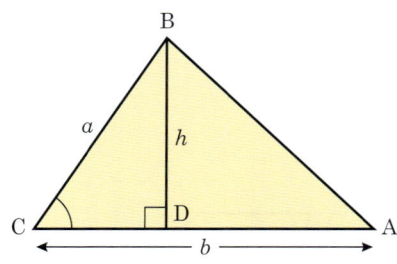

Its area $= \frac{1}{2} \times b \times h$

But look at triangle BCD.

$$\sin C = \frac{h}{a}$$

and therefore $h = a \sin C$

Substituting this into the area $= \frac{1}{2} \times b \times h$ formula gives area $= \frac{1}{2} ab \sin C$.

This means you can calculate the area of any triangle by multiplying two side lengths together, then multiplying that by the sine of the angle between those two sides, then halving the result.

Example

Find the area of this triangle.

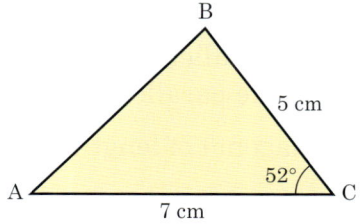

Area $= \frac{1}{2} ab \sin C$

$\quad\ \ = \frac{1}{2} \times 5 \times 7 \times \sin 52°$

$\quad\ \ = 13.8 \text{ cm}^2$ (1 d.p.)

This immediately leads to a new formula for finding the area of a parallelogram.

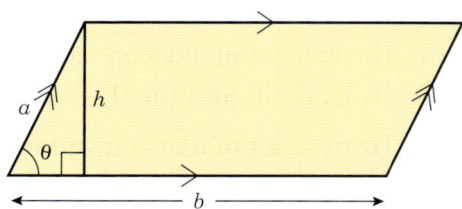

If you know the two side lengths of a parallelogram and the angle between them, you can think of the parallelogram as being two identical triangles joined together.

Since each of the triangles has an area of $\frac{1}{2} ab \sin \theta$, the parallelogram has an area of

$$2 \times \left(\frac{1}{2} ab \sin \theta \right) = ab \sin \theta$$

Exercise 5.1C

In Questions **1** to **12** find the area of $\triangle$ABC where AB = c, AC = b and BC = a.
(For Questions **7** to **12**, start by making your own sketch of the triangle.)

1. $a = 7$ cm, $b = 14$ cm, $\hat{C} = 80°$

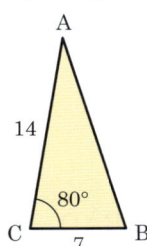

2. $b = 11$ cm, $a = 9$ cm, $\hat{C} = 35°$

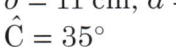
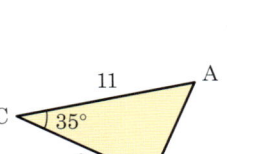

3. $c = 12$ m, $b = 12$ m, $\hat{A} = 67.2°$

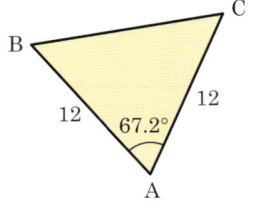

4. $a = 5$ cm, $c = 6$ cm, $\hat{B} = 11.8°$

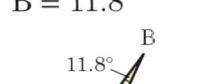
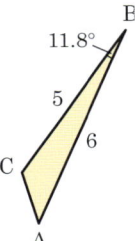

5. $b = 4.2$ cm, $a = 10$ cm, $\hat{C} = 120°$

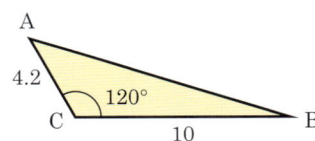

6. $a = 5$ cm, $c = 8$ cm, $\hat{B} = 142°$

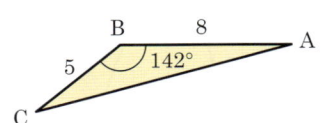

7. $b = 3.2$ cm, $c = 1.8$ cm, $\hat{B} = 10°$, $\hat{C} = 65°$

8. $a = 7$ m, $b = 14$ m, $\hat{A} = 32°$, $\hat{B} = 100°$

9. $a = b = c = 12$ m

10. $a = c = 8$ m, $\hat{B} = 72°$

11. $b = c = 10$ cm, $\hat{B} = 32°$

12. $a = b = c = 0.8$ m

In Questions **13** to **19**, find the area of each shape.

13.

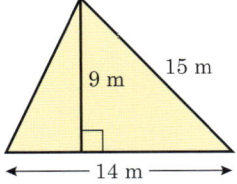

14.

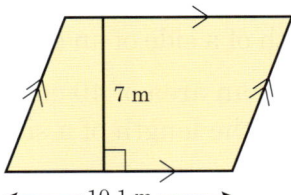

15.

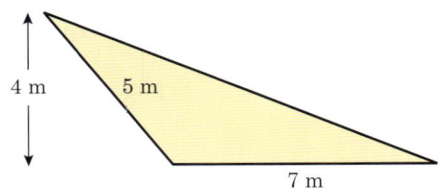

16.

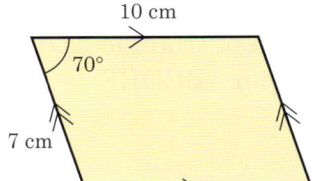

155

17.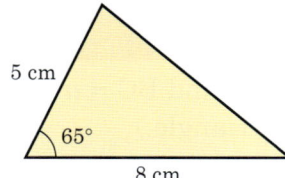

18.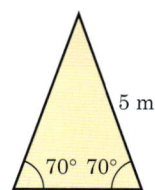

19.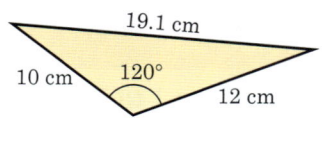

20. Find the shaded area in this diagram.

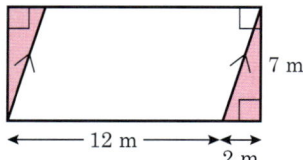

21. Find the area of a parallelogram ABCD with AB = 7 m, AD = 20 m and BÂD = 62°.

22. Find the area of a parallelogram ABCD with AD = 7 m, CD = 11 m and BÂD = 65°.

23. In the diagram, if AE = $\frac{1}{3}$ AB, find the area shaded.

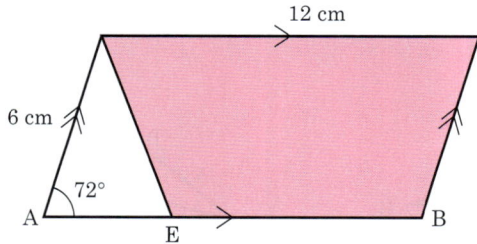

24. The area of an equilateral triangle ABC is 50 cm². Find AB.

25. The area of a triangle ABC is 64 cm². Given AB = 11 cm and BC = 15 cm, find AB̂C.

26. The area of a triangle XYZ is 11 m². Given YZ = 7 m and XŶZ = 130°, find the length of XY.

27. Find the length of a side of an equilateral triangle of area 10.2 m².

28. A rhombus has an area of 40 cm² and adjacent angles of 50° and 130°. Find the length of a side of the rhombus.

29. A regular hexagon is circumscribed by a circle of radius 3 cm with centre O.

    a) Find the size of angle EOD.

    b) Find the area of triangle EOD and hence find the area of the hexagon ABCDEF.

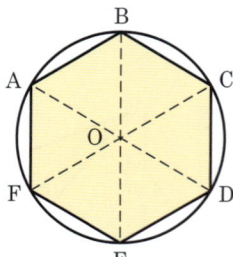

Tip

A **circumscribed** circle is drawn outside another geometric shape such that it passes through all the vertices of the shape.

30. Hexagonal tiles of side 20 cm are used to tile a room which measures 6.25 m by 4.85 m. Assuming the edges are completed by cutting up tiles, how many tiles are needed?

31. Find the area of a regular pentagon of side 8 cm.

32. The area of a regular pentagon is 600 cm². Calculate the length of one side of the pentagon.

5.2 The circle

For any circle, the ratio $\left(\dfrac{\text{circumference}}{\text{diameter}}\right)$ is equal to π.

The value of π is often rounded to 3.142, but this is not an exact value. Through the centuries, mathematicians have been trying to obtain a better value for π.

For example, in the third century A.D., the Chinese mathematician Liu Hui obtained the value 3.1416 by considering a regular polygon having 3072 sides! Ludolph van Ceulen (1540–1610) worked even harder to produce a value correct to 35 decimal places. He was so proud of his work that he had this value of π engraved on his tombstone.

Computer programs can now calculate the value of π to trillions of digits, but its value is still not exact. It was shown in 1761 that π is an *irrational number* which, like $\sqrt{2}$ and $\sqrt{3}$, cannot be expressed exactly as a fraction or a decimal.

There remain a lot of unanswered questions concerning π, and many mathematicians today are still working on them.

The following formulae should be memorised.

$$\text{Circumference} = \pi d$$
$$= 2\pi r$$
$$\text{Area} = \pi r^2$$

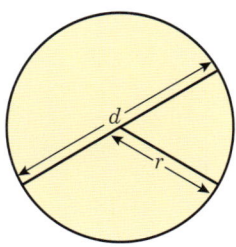

Example

Find the circumference and area of a circle of diameter 8 cm.

Leave your answer in terms of π.

Circumference $= \pi d$

$\qquad = 8\pi$ cm

$\qquad$ Area $= \pi r^2$

$\qquad = \pi \times 4^2$

$\qquad = 16\pi$ cm^2

Exercise 5.2A

In each of these questions, give your answers correct to 3 decimal places.

1. Find the circumference and area of a circle with a radius of 2 cm.

2. Find the circumference and area of a circle with a radius of 8 cm.

3. Find the circumference and area of a circle with a diameter of 10 cm.

4. Find the circumference and area of a circle with a diameter of 14 cm.

5. Find the circumference and area of a circle with a radius of 3.5 cm.

6. Find the circumference and area of a circle with a diameter of 11 cm.

Exercise 5.2B

For each shape, find **a)** the perimeter and **b)** the area. All lengths are in cm. All the arcs are either semi-circles or quarter circles. Leave your answers in terms of π, or $a + b\pi$ as appropriate.

1.

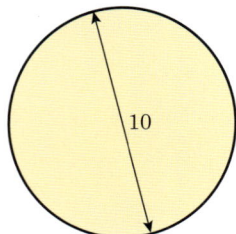

2.

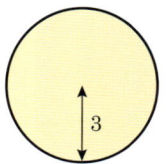

3.

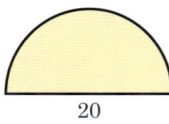

4.

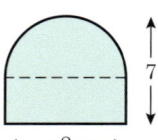

5.

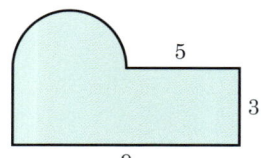

6.

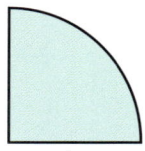

7.

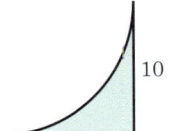

8.

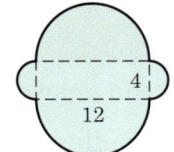

9.

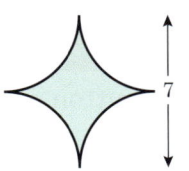

10.

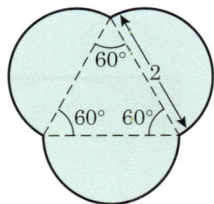

11.

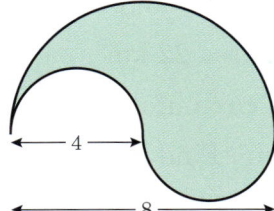

12.

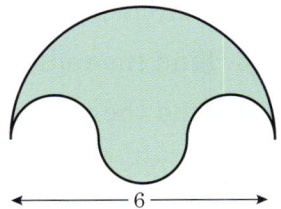

Example 1

Find the radius of a circle that has a circumference of 20 m.

Let the radius of the circle be r m.

Circumference $= 2\pi r$

$\therefore \qquad 2\pi r = 20$

$\therefore \qquad r = \dfrac{20}{2\pi}$

$\qquad\qquad r = 3.183098...$

The radius of the circle is 3.18 m (3 s.f.)

Example 2

Find the radius of a circle that has an area of 45 cm².

Let the radius of the circle be r cm.

$\pi r^2 = 45$

$r^2 = \dfrac{45}{\pi}$

$r = \sqrt{\left(\dfrac{45}{\pi}\right)} = 3.78469...$

The radius of the circle is 3.78 cm (3 s.f.)

Exercise 5.2C

Use the π button on a calculator and give the answers to 3 significant figures.

1. A circle has an area of 15 cm². Find its radius.

2. A circle has a circumference of 190 m. Find its radius.

3. Find the radius of a circle of area 22 km².

4. Find the radius of a circle of circumference 58.6 cm.

5. A circle has an area of 16 mm². Find its circumference.

6. A circle has a circumference of 2500 km. Find its area.

7. A circle of radius 5 cm is inscribed inside a square as shown. Find the area shaded.

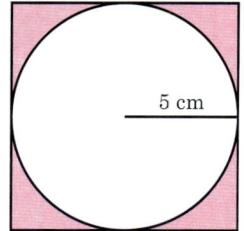

5 cm

> **Tip**
>
> An **inscribed** geometric shape is one that is drawn so that it just touches the sides (or interior) of another geometric shape.

8. A circular pond of radius 6 m is surrounded by a dirt path of width 1 m.

   a) Find the area of the path.

   b) Grass seed is purchased in order to grow grass on the path. Each packet of grass seed will cover an area of 7 m². How many packets would be required?

9. A car tyre has an outer diameter of 30 cm. How many times will the tyre rotate on a journey of 5 km?

10. A golf ball of diameter 1.68 inches rolls a distance of 4 m in a straight line. How many times does the ball rotate completely? (1 inch = 2.54 cm)

11. 100 yards of cotton is wound without stretching onto a reel of diameter 3 cm. How many times does the reel rotate? (1 yard = 0.914 m. Ignore the thickness of the cotton.)

12. A rectangular metal plate has a length of 65 cm and a width of 35 cm. It is melted down and recast into circular discs of the same thickness. How many complete discs can be formed if

    a) the radius of each disc is 3 cm

    b) the radius of each disc is 10 cm?

13. Calculate the radius of a circle whose area is equal to the sum of the areas of three circles of radii 2 cm, 3 cm and 4 cm respectively.

14. The diameter of a circle is given as 10 cm, correct to the nearest cm. Calculate:

    a) the maximum possible circumference
    b) the minimum possible area of the circle consistent with this data.

15. A square is inscribed in a circle of radius 7 cm. Find:

    a) the area of the square
    b) the area shaded.

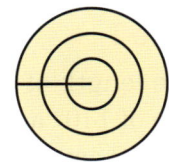

16. An archery target has three concentric regions. The diameters of the regions are in the ratio $1:2:3$.
    Find the ratio of their areas.

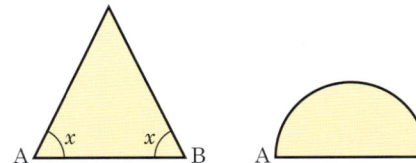

17. The farmer has 100 m of wire fencing. What area can she enclose if she makes a circular pen?

18. The semi-circle and the isosceles triangle have the same base AB and the same area. Find the angle x.

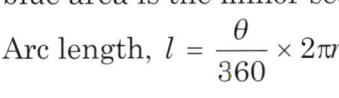

19. Here is a very famous puzzle as an enrichment task. Suppose a very long rope was wrapped tightly around the Earth's equator. This rope would be the same length as the circumference of the Earth. Now imagine that a second rope, rather than being wrapped tightly around the equator, is raised so that at all points it is 1 metre above the first rope. How much longer than the first rope would the second rope need to be?

    Hint: Assume the Earth is a perfect sphere. Also, you do not need to know the circumference of the Earth to solve this puzzle.

5.3 Arc length and sector area

A sector of a circle is the area bounded by two radii and an arc. The smaller area or arc is known as the minor sector or arc. The larger sector or arc is known as the major sector or arc.

In the diagram, the yellow area is the major sector and the smaller blue area is the minor sector.

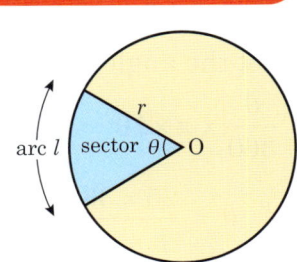

Arc length, $l = \dfrac{\theta}{360} \times 2\pi r$

You take a fraction of the whole circumference, based on the angle at the centre of the circle.

Sector area, $A = \dfrac{\theta}{360} \times \pi r^2$

You take a fraction of the whole area, based on the angle at the centre of the circle.

When an arc is drawn between two radii that meet at an angle, you say that the arc **subtends** the angle.

Example 1

Find the length of an arc which subtends an angle of $140°$ at the centre of a circle of radius 12 cm.

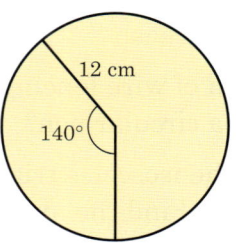

Arc length $= \dfrac{140}{360} \times 2 \times \pi \times 12$

$\qquad\quad = \dfrac{28}{3}\pi$

$\qquad\quad = 29.3215\ldots$

The arc length is 29.3 cm (3 s.f.)

Example 2

A sector of a circle of radius 10 cm has an area of 25 cm². Find the angle at the centre of the circle.

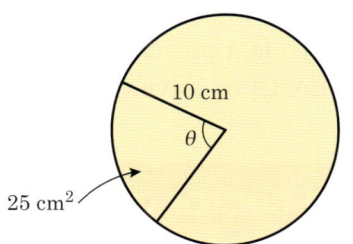

Let the angle at the centre of the circle be θ.

$\dfrac{\theta}{360} \times \pi \times 10^2 = 25$

$\therefore\ \theta = \dfrac{25 \times 360}{\pi \times 100}$

$\quad \theta = 28.6478\ldots$

The angle at the centre of the circle is $28.6°$ (1 d.p.)

Exercise 5.3A

1. Arc AB subtends an angle θ at the centre of circle radius r.

Find the arc length and sector area when:

a) $r = 4$ cm, $\theta = 30°$

b) $r = 10$ cm, $\theta = 45°$

c) $r = 2$ cm, $\theta = 235°$.

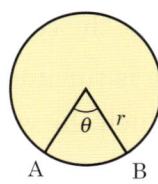

In Questions **2** and **3**, find the total area of the shape.

2.

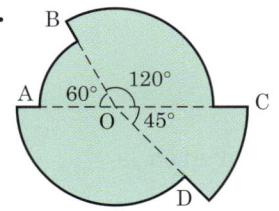

OA = 2 cm
OB = 3 cm
OC = 5 cm
OD = 3 cm

3.

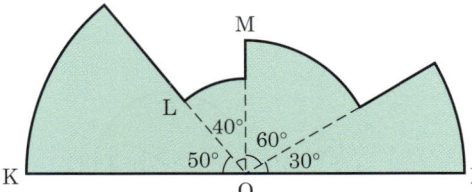

OK = 6 cm
OL = 2 cm
OM = 3 cm
ON = 6 cm

4. Find the shaded areas.

a)

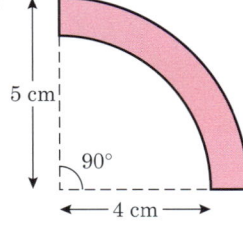

b)

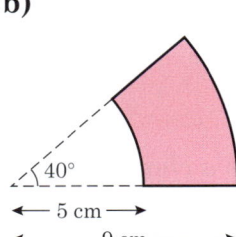

5. In the diagram the arc length is l and the sector area is A.

a) Find θ, when $r = 5$ cm and $l = 7.5$ cm

b) Find θ, when $r = 2$ m and $A = 2$ m^2

c) Find r, when $\theta = 55°$ and $l = 6$ cm

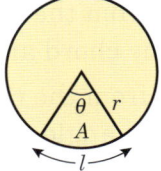

6. The length of the minor arc AB of a circle, centre O, is 2π cm and the length of the major arc is 22π cm. Find:

a) the radius of the circle

b) the acute angle AOB.

7. The lengths of the minor and major arcs of a circle are 5.2 cm and 19.8 cm respectively. Find:

a) the radius of the circle

b) the angle subtended at the centre by the minor arc.

8. A wheel of radius 10 cm is turning at a rate of 5 revolutions per minute. Calculate:

a) the angle through which the wheel turns in 1 second

b) the distance moved by a point on the rim in 2 seconds.

9. The length of an arc of a circle is 12 cm. The corresponding sector area is 108 cm². Find:

a) the radius of the circle

b) the angle subtended at the centre of the circle by the arc.

10. The length of an arc of a circle is 7.5 cm. The corresponding sector area is 37.5 cm². Find:

a) the radius of the circle

b) the angle subtended at the centre of the circle by the arc.

11. In the diagram, the arc length is l and the sector area is A.

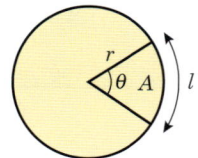

a) Find l, when $\theta = 72°$ and $A = 15$ cm²

b) Find l, when $\theta = 135°$ and $A = 162$ cm²

c) Find A, when $l = 11$ cm and $r = 5.2$ cm

5.4 Chords and segments

In this circle diagram, the line segment AB is a *chord*. The area of a circle cut off by a chord is called a *segment*. In the diagram, the *minor* segment is shaded and the *major* segment is unshaded.

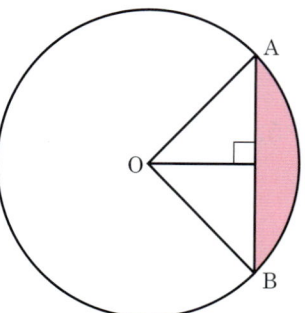

- The line from the centre of a circle to the midpoint of a chord *bisects* the chord at *right angles*.

- The line from the centre of a circle to the midpoint of a chord bisects the angle subtended by the chord at the centre of the circle.

Example

XY is a chord of a circle of radius 10 cm, centre O. The length of XY is 12 cm. Calculate:

a) the angle XOY

b) the area of the minor segment cut off by the chord XY.

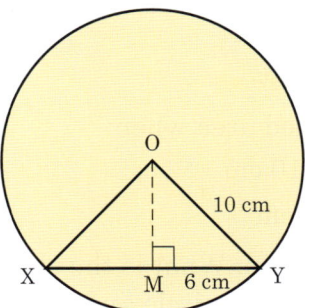

Tip

You can find out more about trigonometry in Chapter 6 on page 209.

a) Let the midpoint of XY be M.

$\therefore \qquad MY = 6$ cm

$$\sin MOY = \frac{6}{10}$$

$\therefore \qquad MOY = 36.87°$

$\therefore \qquad XOY = 2 \times 36.87$
$$= 73.74°$$

b) Area of minor segment = area of sector XOY − area of $\triangle$XOY

$$\text{area of sector XOY} = \frac{73.74}{360} \times \pi \times 10^2$$
$$= 64.32 \text{ cm}^2.$$

$$\text{area of } \triangle\text{XOY} = \frac{1}{2} \times 10 \times 10 \times \sin 73.74°$$
$$= 48.00 \text{ cm}^2$$

$\therefore$ Area of minor segment $= 64.32 − 48.00$
$$= 16.3 \text{ cm}^2 \text{ (3 s.f.)}$$

Exercise 5.4A

1. The chord AB subtends an angle of 130° on a circle with centre O. The radius of the circle is 8 cm. Find:

   a) the length of AB

   b) the area of sector OAB

   c) the area of triangle OAB

   d) the area of the minor segment (shown shaded).

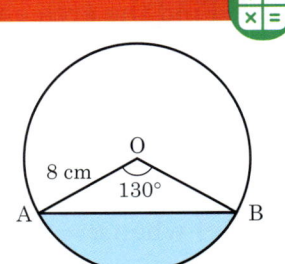

2. Find the shaded area when:

    a) $r = 6$ cm, $\theta = 70°$

    b) $r = 14$ cm, $\theta = 104°$

    c) $r = 5$ cm, $\theta = 80°$

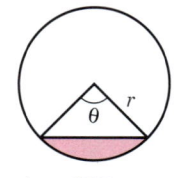

3. Find θ and the shaded area when:

    a) AB $= 10$ cm, $r = 10$ cm

    b) AB $= 8$ cm, $r = 5$ cm

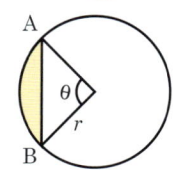

4. A circle has radius 5 cm. What is the shortest distance between the centre of the circle and a chord of length 8 cm?

5. A circle has radius 6 cm. What is the shortest distance between the centre of the circle and a chord of length 9 cm?

6. The diagram shows the cross-section of a cylindrical pipe with water lying in the bottom.

    a) If the maximum depth of the water is 2 cm and the radius of the pipe is 7 cm, find the area shaded.

    b) What is the volume of water in a pipe length of 30 cm?

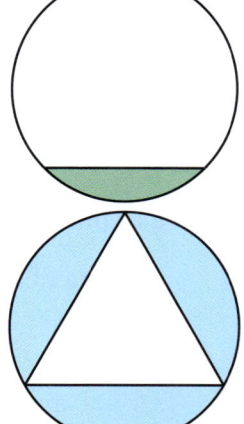

7. An equilateral triangle is inscribed in a circle of radius 10 cm. Find:

    a) the area of the triangle

    b) the area shaded.

8. An equilateral triangle is inscribed in a circle of radius 18.8 cm. Find:

    a) the area of the triangle

    b) the area of the three segments surrounding the triangle.

9. A regular hexagon is circumscribed by a circle of radius 6 cm. Find the area shaded.

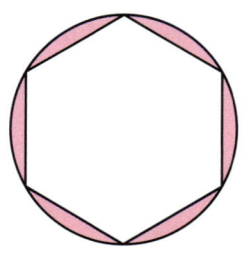

10. A regular octagon is circumscribed by a circle of radius r cm. Find the area enclosed between the circle and the octagon. (Give the answer in terms of r.)

11. Find the radius of the circle:

    a) when $\theta = 90°$, $A = 20$ cm²

    b) when $\theta = 30°$, $A = 35$ cm²

    c) when $\theta = 150°$, $A = 114$ cm²

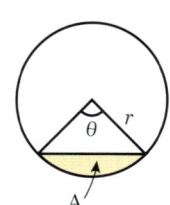

5.5 Volume

Prisms

A *prism* is a 3D object with the same cross-section throughout its length.

$$\text{Volume of prism} = (\text{area of cross-section}) \times \text{length}$$
$$= A \times l$$

A *cuboid* is a prism whose six faces are all rectangles.
A cube is a special case of a cuboid in which all six faces are squares.

Depending on how the prism is positioned, its 'length' may be referred to as its 'height'. The word 'length' that is used in the formula always relates to the direction perpendicular to the face of the cross-section.

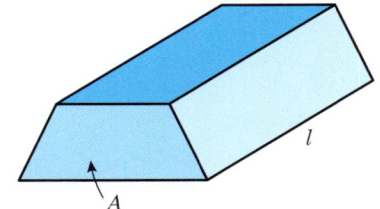

Cylinders

A *cylinder* can be thought of as a prism whose cross-section is a circle.

$$\text{volume of cylinder} = (\text{area of cross-section}) \times \text{height}$$
$$= \pi r^2 h$$

Example

Calculate the height of a cylinder of volume 500 cm³ and base radius 8 cm.

Let the height of the cylinder be h cm.
$$\pi r^2 h = 500$$
$$\pi \times 8^2 \times h = 500$$
$$h = \frac{500}{\pi \times 64}$$
$$h = 2.48679\ldots$$

The height of the cylinder is 2.49 cm (3 s.f.)

Exercise 5.5A

1. Calculate the volume of each prism, giving your answers in terms of π where appropriate. All lengths are in cm.

a)

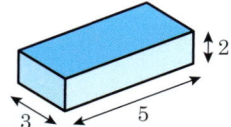

b)

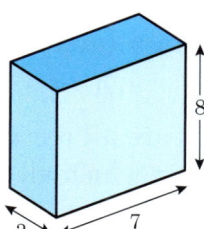

c)

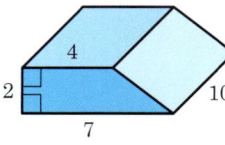

d)

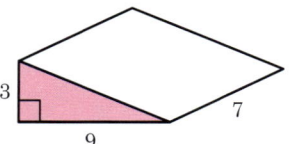

e)

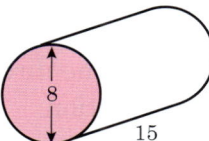

f)

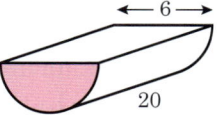

2. Calculate the volume of the following cylinders, giving your answers in terms of π.

   a) $r = 4$ cm, $h = 10$ cm

   b) $r = 11$ m, $h = 2$ m

   c) $r = 2.1$ cm, $h = 0.9$ cm

Exercise 5.5B

1. Find the height of a cylinder of volume 200 cm³ and radius 4 cm.

2. Find the height of a cylinder of volume 2 litres and radius 10 cm.

3. Find the radius of a cylinder of volume 45 cm³ and height 4 cm.

4. A prism has volume 100 cm³ and height 8 cm. If the cross-section is an equilateral triangle, find the length of a side of the triangle.

5. When 3 litres of oil are removed from an upright cylindrical can, the level falls by 10 cm. Find the radius of the can.

6. A solid cylinder of radius 4 cm and height 8 cm is melted down and recast into a solid cube. Find the side of the cube.

7. A solid cuboid of copper measuring 5 cm by 4 cm by 2 cm is drawn out to make a cylindrical wire of diameter 2 mm. Calculate the length of the wire.

> **Tip**
>
> Remember:
> 1 litre = 1000 cm³

8. Water flows through a circular pipe of internal diameter 3 cm at a speed of 10 cm/s. If the pipe is full, how much water flows from the pipe in one minute? (Answer in litres.)

9. Water flows from a hose-pipe of internal diameter 1 cm at a rate of 5 litres per minute. At what speed is the water flowing through the pipe?

10. A cylindrical metal pipe has external diameter of 6 cm and internal diameter of 4 cm.

   a) Calculate the volume of metal in a pipe of length 0.25 m.

   b) If 1 cm³ of the metal has a mass of 8 g, find the mass of the pipe. (Answer in kg.)

11. For two cylinders A and B, the ratio of heights is 3 : 1 and the ratio of diameters is 1 : 2. Calculate the ratio of their volumes.

12. A machine makes boxes which are either perfect cylinders of diameter 4 cm and length 4 cm, or perfect cubes of side 5 cm. Which boxes have the greater volume, and by how much? (Use $\pi = 3$.)

13. Natalia manages a building site where, amongst other building materials, bricks are stored. A shipment of bricks arrives one day and is stacked to measure 6 m by 4 m by 2.5 m. Each brick measures 22 cm by 10 cm by 7 cm. Natalia estimated that there are about 40 000 bricks in this shipment. Is this a reasonable estimate?

14. A cylindrical can of internal radius 20 cm stands upright on a flat surface. It contains water to a depth of 20 cm. Calculate the rise in the level of the water when a brick of volume 1500 cm³ is fully immersed in the water.

15. A cylindrical tin of height 15 cm and radius 4 cm is filled with sand from a rectangular box. How many times can the tin be filled if the dimensions of the box are 50 cm by 40 cm by 20 cm?

16. Rain which falls onto a flat rectangular surface of length 6 m and width 4 m is collected in a cylinder of internal radius 20 cm. What is the depth of water in the cylinder after a storm in which a depth of 1 cm of rain was collected from the rectangular surface?

Pyramids

Imagine a cube with side length $2a$. You can use this to find the volume of a square-based pyramid whose base has a side length of $2a$ and whose height is a.

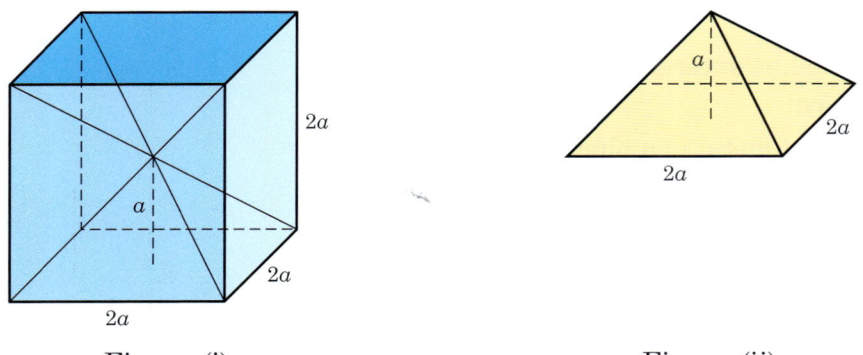

        Figure (i)   Figure (ii)

Figure (i) shows a cube of side $2a$ broken down into six pyramids of height a, as shown in Figure (ii).

If the volume of each pyramid is V, then the cube will have volume $6V$.

$$6V = 2a \times 2a \times 2a$$
$$V = \frac{1}{6} \times \left(2a\right)^2 \times 2a$$
so $$V = \frac{1}{3} \times \left(2a\right)^2 \times a$$
$$V = \frac{1}{3}\left(\text{base area}\right) \times \text{height}$$

In fact, this formula works for pyramids of any base shape and any height.

Cones

$$\text{Volume} = \frac{1}{3}\pi r^2 h$$

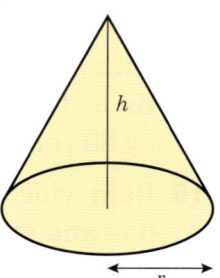

Note that this is $V = \frac{1}{3}$ (base area) × height, where the base area is πr^2.

This means that you can think of a cone as a circular-based pyramid.

Spheres

Volume $= \frac{4}{3}\pi r^3$

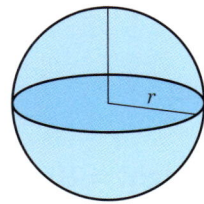

Example 1

A pyramid has a square base of side 5 m and vertical height 4 m. Find its volume.

Volume of pyramid $= \frac{1}{3}(5 \times 5) \times 4$

$$= 33.3 \text{ m}^3 \quad (3 \text{ s.f.})$$

Example 2

Calculate the radius of a sphere of volume 500 cm³.

Let the radius of the sphere be r cm.

$$\frac{4}{3}\pi r^3 = 500$$

$$r^3 = \frac{3 \times 500}{4\pi}$$

$$r = \sqrt[3]{\left(\frac{3 \times 500}{4\pi}\right)} = 4.923725\ldots$$

The radius of the sphere is 4.92 cm (3 s.f.)

Exercise 5.5C

Find the volumes of the following objects, giving your answers in terms of π.

1. cone: height = 5 cm, radius = 2 cm
2. sphere: radius = 5 cm
3. sphere: radius = 10 cm
4. cone: height = 6 cm, radius = 4 cm
5. sphere: diameter = 8 cm
6. cone: height = x cm, radius = $2x$ cm

7. sphere: radius = 0.1 m

8. cone: height $= \dfrac{1}{\pi}$ cm, radius = 3 cm

9. pyramid: rectangular base 7 cm by 8 cm; height = 5 cm

10. pyramid: square base of side 4 m, height = 9 m

11. pyramid: equilateral triangular base of side = 8 cm, height = 10 cm

12. Find the volume of a hemisphere of radius 5 cm.

Exercise 5.5D

1. A cone is attached to a hemisphere of radius 4 cm. If the total height of the object is 10 cm, find its volume.

2. A toy consists of a cylinder of diameter 6 cm 'sandwiched' between a hemisphere and a cone of the same diameter. If the cone is of height 8 cm and the cylinder is of height 10 cm, find the total volume of the toy.

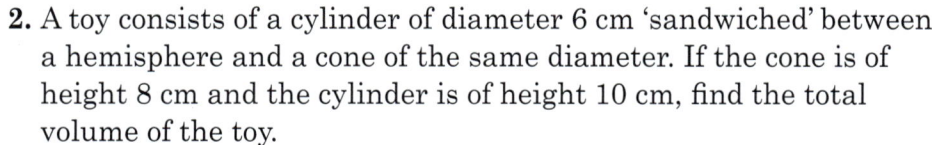

3. Find the height of a pyramid of volume 20 m³ and base area 12 m².

4. Find the radius of a sphere of volume 60 cm³.

5. Find the height of a cone of volume 2.5 litre and radius 10 cm.

6. Six square-based pyramids fit exactly onto the six faces of a cube of side 4 cm. If the volume of the object formed is 256 cm³, find the height of each pyramid.

7. A solid metal cube of side 6 cm is recast into a solid sphere. Find the radius of the sphere.

8. A hollow spherical vessel has internal and external radii of 6 cm and 6.4 cm respectively. Calculate the mass of the vessel if it is made of metal of density 10 g/cm³ and give the answer in kg.

9. Water is flowing into an inverted cone, of diameter and height 30 cm, at a rate of 4 litres per minute. How long, in seconds, will it take to fill the cone?

10. A solid metal sphere is recast into many smaller spheres. Calculate the number of smaller spheres that can be made if the initial and final radii are as follows:

    a) initial radius = 10 cm, final radius = 2 cm

    b) initial radius = 7 cm, final radius $= \dfrac{1}{2}$ cm

    c) initial radius = 1 m, final radius $= \dfrac{1}{3}$ cm

11. A spherical ball is immersed in water contained in a vertical cylinder.

    Assuming the water covers the ball, calculate the rise in the water level if:

    a) sphere radius = 3 cm, cylinder radius = 10 cm

    b) sphere radius = 2 cm, cylinder radius = 5 cm.

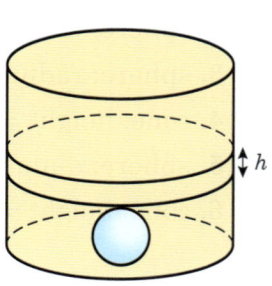

12. A spherical ball is immersed in water contained in a vertical cylinder. The rise in water level is measured in order to calculate the radius of the spherical ball. Calculate the radius of the ball in the following cases:

    a) cylinder of radius 10 cm, water level rises 4 cm

    b) cylinder of radius 100 cm, water level rises 8 cm.

13. One corner of a solid cube of side 8 cm is removed by cutting through the midpoints of three adjacent sides. Calculate the volume of the piece removed.

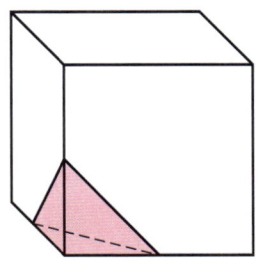

14. The cylindrical end of a pencil is sharpened to produce a perfect cone at the end with no overall loss of length. If the diameter of the pencil is 1 cm, and the cone is of length 2 cm, calculate the volume of the shavings.

15. Metal spheres of radius 2 cm are packed into a rectangular box of internal dimensions 16 cm × 8 cm × 8 cm. When 16 spheres are packed the box is filled with a preservative liquid. Find the volume of this liquid.

16. The diagram shows the cross-section of an inverted cone of height MC = 12 cm. If AB = 6 cm and XY = 2 cm, use similar triangles to find the length NC.

    (You can find out about similar triangles on page 179.)

17. An inverted cone of height 10 cm and base radius 6.4 cm contains water to a depth of 5 cm, measured from the vertex. Calculate the volume of water in the cone.

18. An inverted cone of height 15 cm and base radius 4 cm contains water to a depth of 10 cm. Calculate the volume of water in the cone.

19. An inverted cone of height 12 cm and base radius 6 cm contains 20 cm³ of water. Calculate the depth of water in the cone, measured from the vertex.

20. A frustum of a cone is a cone with the vertex end cut off parallel to its base. In the frustum of the cone shown here, r_1 = 2 cm, r_2 = 5 cm and the height h = 3 cm. Calculate the volume of the frustum.

21. Find the volume, in litres, of a frustum of a cone with end diameters of 60 cm and 20 cm and a depth of 40 cm.

22. The diagram shows a sector of a circle of radius 10 cm.

    a) Find, as a multiple of π, the arc length of the sector.

    The straight edges are brought together to make a cone. Calculate:

    b) the radius of the base of the cone

    c) the vertical height of the cone.

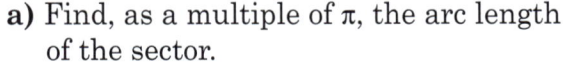

Frustum of a cone

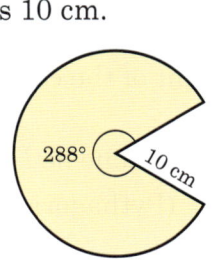

288°   10 cm

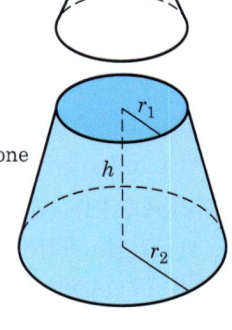

23. Calculate the volume of a regular octahedron whose edges are all 10 cm.

24. A sphere passes through the eight corners of a cube of side 10 cm. Find the volume of the sphere.

25. Find the volume of a regular tetrahedron of side 20 cm.

26. Find the volume of a regular tetrahedron of side 35 cm.

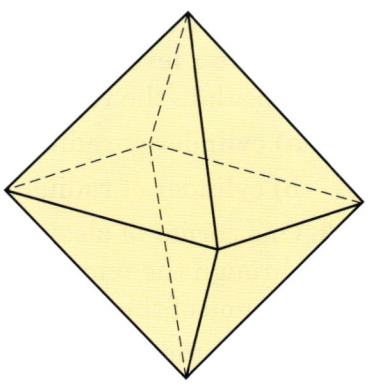

5.6 Surface area

Because a flat, two-dimensional surface is called a plane, we sometimes refer to the flat faces of a solid as plane faces. It is often fairly easy to find the area of these faces. The curved parts of the surface area can be a little more difficult to work out. Here are some useful formulae:

a) Cylinder
Curved surface area $= 2\pi rh$

b) Sphere
Surface area $= 4\pi r^2$

c) Cone
Curved surface area $= \pi rl$
where l is the slant height.

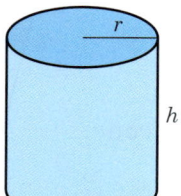

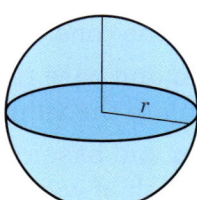

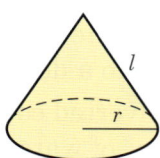

Example 1

Find the total surface area of a solid cone of radius 4 cm and vertical height 3 cm.

The total area is made up of two parts: the curved surface and the circular base.

Viewed from the side, the profile of the cone is an isosceles triangle. The slant height of the cone becomes the hypotenuse of this triangle.

Let the slant height of the cone be l cm.

$$l^2 = 3^2 + 4^2 \qquad \text{(Pythagoras' theorem)}$$
$$l = 5$$

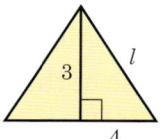

Curved surface area $= \pi r l = \pi \times 4 \times 5$
$$= 20\pi \text{ cm}^2$$
Area of circular base $= \pi r^2 = \pi \times 4^2 = 16\pi \text{ cm}^2$
∴ Total surface area $= 20\pi + 16\pi$
$$= 36\pi \text{ cm}^2$$
$$= 113 \text{ cm}^2 \text{ (3 s.f.)}$$

Example 2

Find the surface area of a prism, whose length is 50 cm and whose cross-section is a regular hexagon with side length 10 cm and area 172 cm².

Area of the two hexagons $= 2 \times 172$
$$= 344 \text{ cm}^2$$

Area of the six rectangular faces $= 6 \times 50 \times 10$
$$= 3000 \text{ cm}^2$$

Total area $= 344 + 3000$
$$= 3344 \text{ cm}^2$$

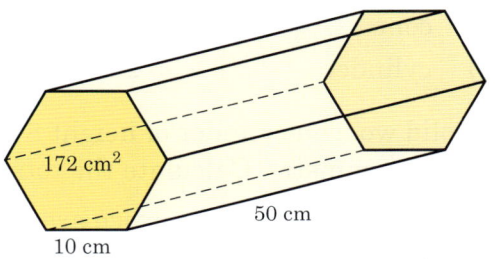

Exercise 5.6A

Use the π button on a calculator unless otherwise instructed.

1. Copy the table and find the quantities marked *. Give your answers as a multiple of π or in terms of π.

	solid object	radius	vertical height	curved surface area	total surface area
a)	sphere	3 cm		*	
b)	cylinder	4 cm	5 cm		*
c)	cone	6 cm	8 cm	*	
d)	cylinder	0.7 m	1 m		*
e)	sphere	10 m		*	
f)	cone	5 cm	12 cm	*	
g)	cylinder	6 mm	10 mm		*
h)	cone	2.1 cm	4.4 cm	*	
i)	sphere	0.01 m		*	
j)	hemisphere	7 cm		*	*

2. Find the radius of a sphere of surface area 34 cm².

3. Find the slant height of a cone that has a curved surface area 20 cm² and radius 3 cm.

4. Find the height of a solid cylinder of radius 1 cm and total surface area 28 cm².

5. Copy the table and find the quantities marked *. (Use π = 3)

	object	radius	vertical height	curved surface area	total surface area
a)	cylinder	4 cm	*	72 cm²	
b)	sphere	*		192 cm²	
c)	cone	4 cm	*	60 cm²	
d)	sphere	*		0.48 m²	
e)	cylinder	5 cm	*		330 cm²
f)	cone	6 cm	*		225 cm²
g)	cylinder	2 m	*		108 m²

6. A solid wooden cylinder of height 8 cm and radius 3 cm is cut in two along a vertical axis of symmetry. Calculate the total surface area of the two pieces.

7. A tin of paint covers a surface area of 60 m² and costs $4.50. Find the cost of painting the outside surface of a hemispherical dome of radius 50 m. (Just the curved part.) You can only buy a whole number of tins of paint.

8. A solid cylinder of height 10 cm and radius 4 cm is to be plated with material costing $11 per cm². Find the cost of the plating.

9. Find the volume of a sphere of surface area 100 cm².

10. Find the surface area of a sphere of volume 28 cm³.

11. Calculate the total surface area of the combined cone/cylinder/hemisphere.

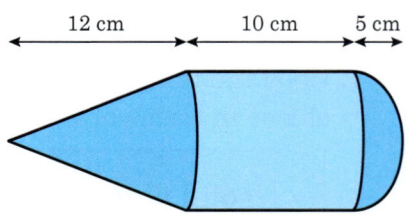

12. An inverted cone of vertical height 12 cm and base radius 9 cm contains water to a depth of 4 cm. Find the area of the interior surface of the cone not in contact with the water.

13. A circular piece of paper of radius 20 cm is cut in half and each half is made into a hollow cone by folding the points A and B inward until they touch. Find the slant height and base radius of each cone.

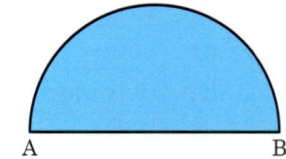

14. A solid cone of radius 3 cm and slant height 6 cm is cut into four identical pieces. Calculate the total surface area of the four pieces.

In Questions **15** to **18**, find the surface area of each prism.

15.

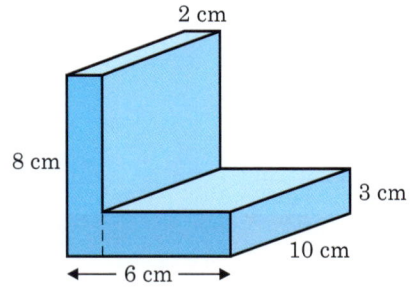

16.

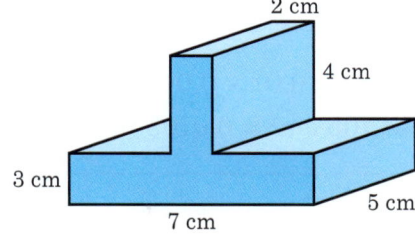

17.

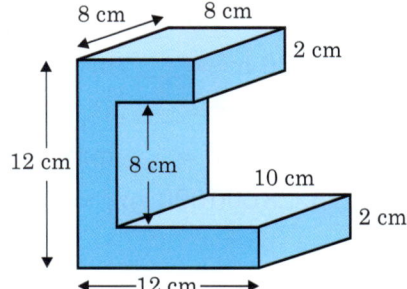

18.

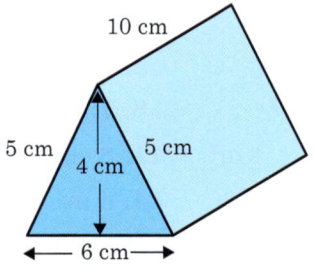

Units for surface areas and volumes

Sometimes you will need to perform unit conversions when dealing with two- or three-dimensional units. In these cases, you need to be very careful as the conversions are not the same as they are when dealing with simple lengths.

Although 1 cm = 10 mm, a 1 cm by 1 cm square measures 10 mm by 10 mm.

Therefore, the area of the square in mm^2 is $10 \times 10 = 100$ mm^2.

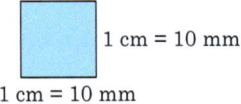

There are similar area conversions for m^2 into cm^2 and km^2 into m^2:

1 m = 100 cm, but 1 m^2 = $100 \times 100 = 10\,000$ cm^2

1 km = 1000 m, but 1 km^2 = $1000 \times 1000 = 1\,000\,000$ m^2

A 1 cm by 1 cm by 1 cm cube measures 10 mm by 10 mm by 10 mm. The volume of the cube is therefore $10 \times 10 \times 10 = 1000$ mm^3.

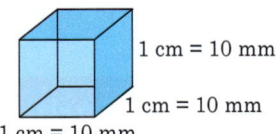

Likewise, 1 m^3 = $100 \times 100 \times 100 = 1\,000\,000$ cm^3

Example

Convert   **a)** 37 cm^2 to mm^2

       b) 88 m^3 to cm^3

       c) 105 cm^2 to m^2

a) 1 cm^2 = $10 \times 10 = 100$ mm^2

so 37 cm^2 = $37 \times 100 = 3700$ mm^2

b) $1 \text{ m}^3 = 100 \times 100 \times 100 = 1\,000\,000 \text{ cm}^3$

so $88 \text{ m}^3 = 88\,000\,000 \text{ cm}^3$

c) $1 \text{ cm}^2 = 0.01 \times 0.01 = 0.0001 \text{ m}^2$

so $105 \text{ cm}^2 = 0.0105 \text{ m}^2$

Exercise 5.6B

Copy and complete these area and volume conversions.

1. $2 \text{ cm}^2 = $ ___ mm^2 　　　　**2.** $45 \text{ cm}^2 = $ ___ mm^2 　　　　**3.** $1600 \text{ mm}^2 = $ ___ cm^2

4. $48 \text{ mm}^2 = $ ___ cm^2 　　　　**5.** $3 \text{ m}^2 = $ ___ cm^2 　　　　**6.** $26 \text{ m}^2 = $ ___ cm^2

7. $8600 \text{ cm}^2 = $ ___ m^2 　　　　**8.** $760 \text{ cm}^2 = $ ___ m^2 　　　　**9.** $5 \text{ km}^2 = $ ___ m^2

10. $4\,500\,000 \text{ m}^2 = $ ___ km^2 　　**11.** $8 \text{ cm}^3 = $ ___ mm^3 　　　**12.** $21 \text{ cm}^3 = $ ___ mm^3

13. $48\,000 \text{ mm}^3 = $ ___ cm^3 　　**14.** $6 \text{ m}^3 = $ ___ cm^3 　　　　**15.** $28\,000\,000 \text{ cm}^3 = $ ___ m^3

16. A cuboid measures 3 cm by 2 cm by 4 cm.

　　a) Find the volume in mm^3. 　　　　**b)** Find the surface area in mm^2.

17. A rectangle measures 40 cm by 80 cm. Find the area in m^2.

18. A sphere has radius 6.2 m.

　　a) Find the surface area in cm^2. 　　**b)** Find the volume in m^3.

　　c) Find the volume in cm^3.

19. A square-based pyramid has base area 300 cm^2 and height 40 mm. Find the volume in mm^3.

20. A cylinder has volume 1200 cm^3. The length of the cylinder is 42 mm. Find the radius of the cylinder in mm.

5.7 Similarity

Two shapes are similar if one of them is an enlargement of the other. Another way of saying this is that two shapes are similar if they are exactly the same shape as each other, but not the same size.

Look at these two rectangles:

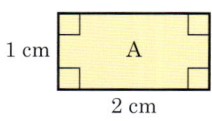

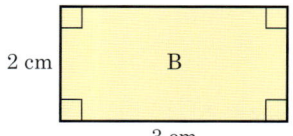

They are not similar because the width has been enlarged by a scale factor of 2, but the length has been enlarged by a scale factor of 1.5. Therefore, rectangle B is not an enlargement of rectangle A. They are different shapes.

Two triangles are always mathematically similar if they have the same angles.

Example 1

Explain why triangles ABC and XYZ are similar.

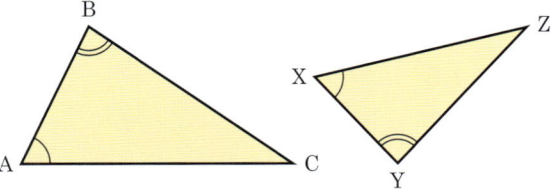

$\widehat{A} = \widehat{X}$ and $\widehat{B} = \widehat{Y}$, therefore $\widehat{C}$ must be equal to $\widehat{Z}$.

The two triangles have the same angles and are therefore similar.

Example 2

Triangles ABC and DEF are similar.

Find the values of x and y.

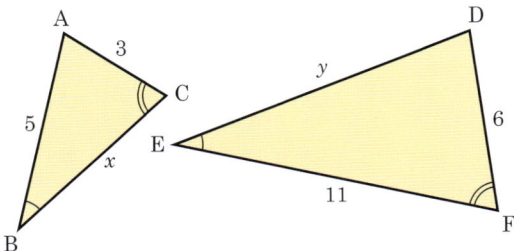

Since $\dfrac{DF}{AC} = \dfrac{6}{3} = 2$, you know that DEF is an enlargement of ABC with a scale factor of 2.

Therefore $x \times 2 = 11$ which gives $x = 5.5$

and $5 \times 2 = y$ which gives $y = 10$

Example 3

Triangles ABC and ADE are similar. Find the lengths of DE and AE.

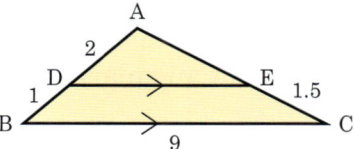

Since $\dfrac{AB}{AD} = \dfrac{3}{2}$, you know that ABC is an enlargement of ADE with a scale factor of $\dfrac{3}{2}$.

Therefore $DE \times \dfrac{3}{2} = 9$ which gives $DE = \dfrac{2 \times 9}{3} = 6$.

and $\dfrac{AE + 1.5}{AE} = \dfrac{3}{2}$ which means that $AE = \dfrac{3}{2} \times AE - 1.5$

$1.5 = \dfrac{3}{2} \times AE - AE = \dfrac{AE}{2} \Rightarrow AE = 3$

Note that the answer of AE = 3 in the example above looks like common sense, because on the left-hand side of the triangle you double the 1 to get the 2, so on the right-hand side you double the 1.5 to get 3. You must be careful, though, because this can sometimes cause you to lose sight of the fact that the scale factor of enlargement here between the two triangles is $\frac{3}{2}$, not 2.

Exercise 5.7A

Each Question **1** to **11** includes two similar triangles. Find the sides labelled with letters. All side lengths are in centimetres.

1.

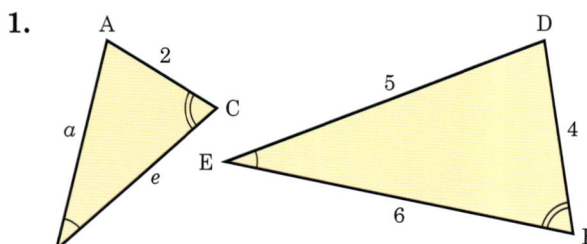

2.

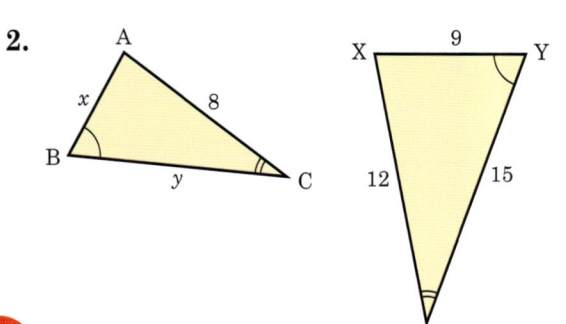

3.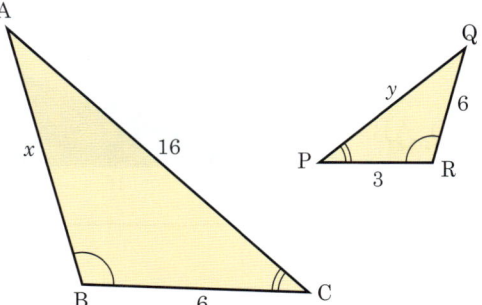

4.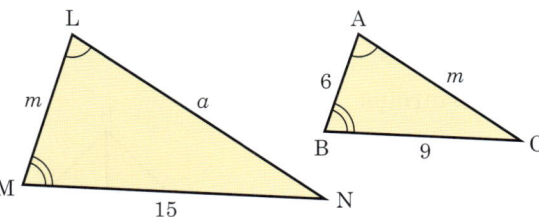

5.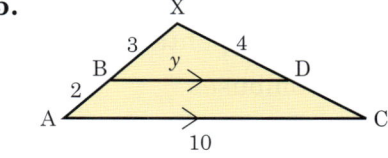

6.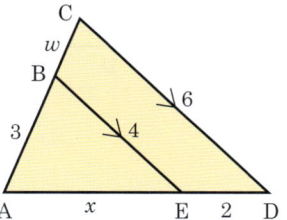

7.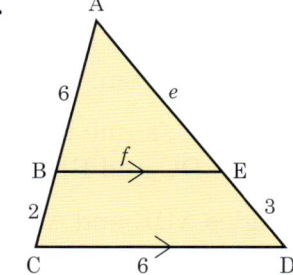

8.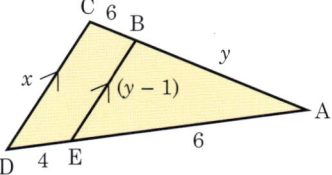

9. $\widehat{BAC} = \widehat{DBC}$

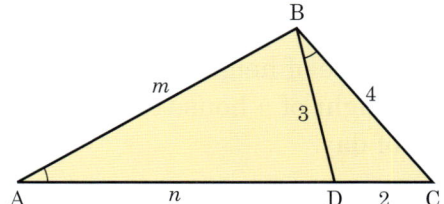

10.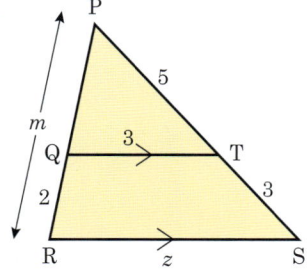

11.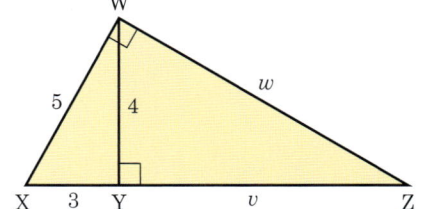

12. The photo shows a rectangular picture 16 cm × 8 cm surrounded by a border of width 4 cm. Are the two rectangles similar?

13. The diagonals of a trapezium ABCD intersect at O. AB is parallel to DC, AB = 3 cm and DC = 6 cm. If CO = 4 cm and OA = 3 cm, find BO and DO.

14. Which of the following must be similar to each other?

   a) two equilateral triangles   **b)** two rectangles

   c) two isosceles triangles   **d)** two squares

   e) two regular pentagons   **f)** two kites

   g) two rhombuses   **h)** two circles

15. In the diagram $A\widehat{B}C = A\widehat{D}B = 90°$, AD = p and DC = q.

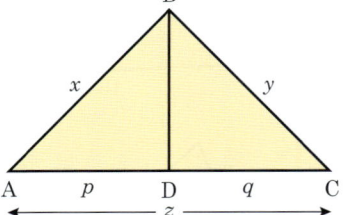

   a) Use similar triangles to show that $x^2 = pz$.

   b) Find a similar expression for y^2.

   c) Add the expressions for x^2 and y^2 and hence prove Pythagoras' theorem.

16. In a triangle ABC, a line is drawn parallel to BC to meet AB at D and AC at E. DC and BE meet at X. Prove that:

   a) the triangles ADE and ABC are similar

   b) the triangles DXE and BXC are similar

   c) $\dfrac{AD}{AB} = \dfrac{EX}{XB}$

17. A tree of height 4 m casts a shadow of length 6.5 m. Find the height of a house casting a shadow 26 m long at the same time of day.

Areas of similar shapes

The two rectangles here are similar, the ratio of their corresponding sides being $1 : k$.

$$\text{area of ABCD} = ab$$
$$\text{area of WXYZ} = ka \times kb = k^2ab$$
$$\therefore \quad \frac{\text{area WXYZ}}{\text{area ABCD}} = \frac{k^2ab}{ab} = k^2$$

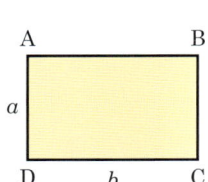

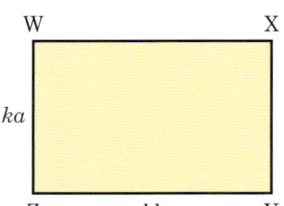

This illustrates an important general rule for all similar shapes:

If two shapes are similar and the ratio of their corresponding sides is $1:k$, then the ratio of their corresponding areas is $1:k^2$.

Note: k is sometimes called the *linear scale factor*.

Tip

This result also applies for the surface areas of similar three-dimensional objects.

Example 1

XY is parallel to BC.

$$\frac{AB}{AX} = \frac{3}{2}$$

If the area of $\triangle AXY = 4 \text{ cm}^2$, find the area of $\triangle ABC$.

The triangles ABC and AXY are similar.

Ratio of corresponding sides $(k) = \dfrac{3}{2}$

$\therefore$ Ratio of areas $(k^2) = \dfrac{9}{4}$

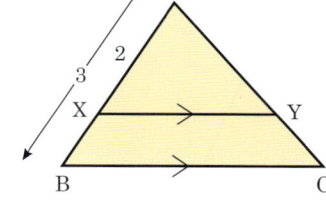

Area of $\triangle ABC = \dfrac{9}{4} \times$ (area of $\triangle AXY$)

$$= \frac{9}{4} \times 4 = 9 \text{ cm}^2$$

Example 2

Two similar triangles have areas of 18 cm^2 and 32 cm^2 respectively. If the base of the smaller triangle is 6 cm, find the base of the larger triangle.

Ratio of areas $(k^2) = \dfrac{32}{18} = \dfrac{16}{9}$

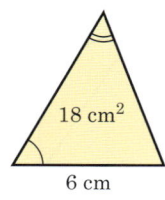

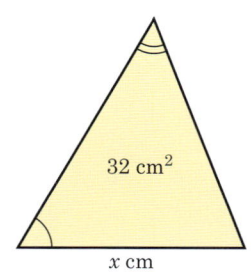

$$\therefore \quad \text{ratio of corresponding sides } (k) = \sqrt{\left(\frac{16}{9}\right)}$$

$$= \frac{4}{3}$$

$$\therefore \qquad \text{base of larger triangle} = 6 \times \frac{4}{3} = 8 \text{ cm}$$

Exercise 5.7B

In this exercise, a number written inside a figure represents the area of the shape. All pairs of shapes in this exercise are similar.

In Questions **1** to **6**, find the unknown area A.

1.

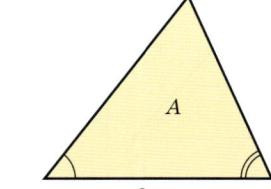

2.

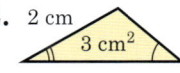

3.

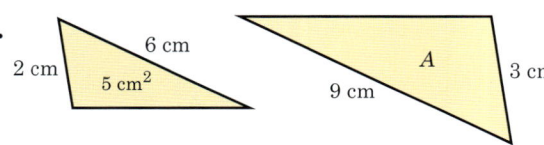

4.

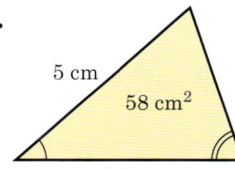

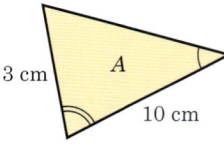

5.

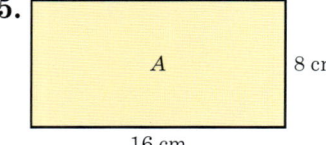

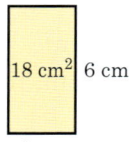

6.

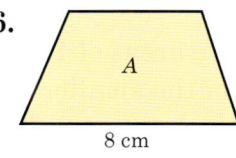

In Questions **7** to **12**, find the length of each side labelled with a letter.

7.

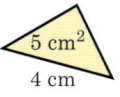

8.

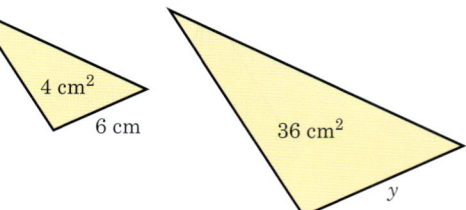

9.

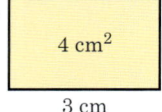

10.

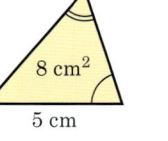

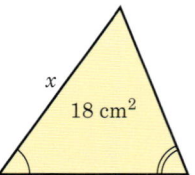

11.

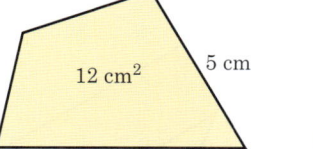

12.

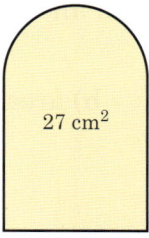
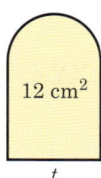

Exercise 5.7C

In Questions **1** to **4** you have a pair of similar three-dimensional objects.
Find the surface area indicated.

1.

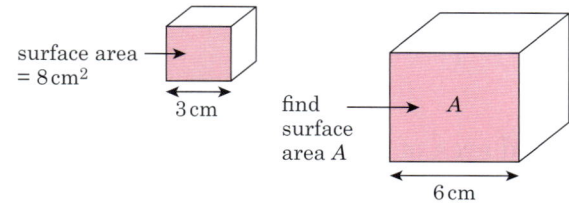

surface area = 8 cm²

3 cm

find surface area *A*

6 cm

2.

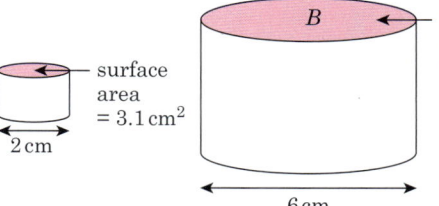

surface area = 3.1 cm²

2 cm

6 cm

B

find surface area B

3.

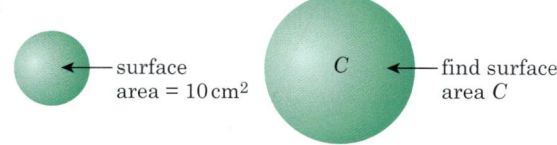

surface area = 10 cm²

C

find surface area *C*

The radius of the large sphere is twice the radius of the small sphere.

4. surface area = 100 cm²   find surface area *D*

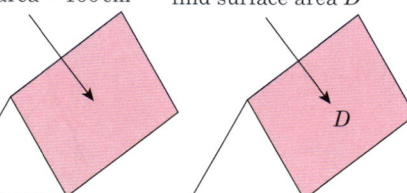

D

The length of large solid is 1.5 times the length of the small solid.

5. Given: AD = 3 cm, AB = 5 cm and area of △ADE = 6 cm².
Find:

a) area of △ABC   **b)** area of DECB

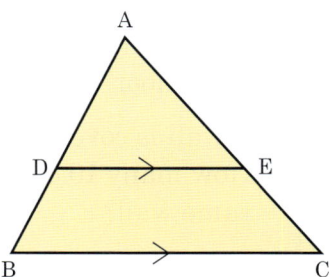

6. Given: XY = 5 cm, MY = 2 cm and area of △MYN = 4 cm². Find:

   a) area of △XYZ   **b)** area of MNZX

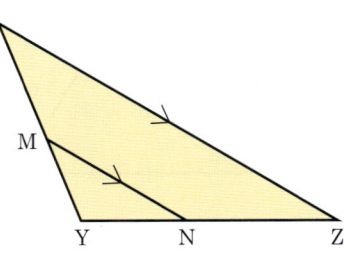

7. Given XY = 2 cm, BC = 3 cm and area of XYCB = 10 cm², find the area of △AXY.

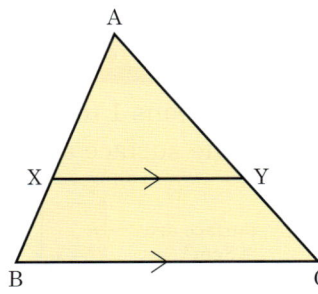

8. Given KP = 3 cm, area of △KOP = 2 cm² and area of OPML = 16 cm², find the length of PM.

9. The triangles ABC and EBD are similar (AC and DE are *not* parallel).

   If AB = 8 cm, BE = 4 cm and the area of △DBE = 6 cm², find the area of △ABC.

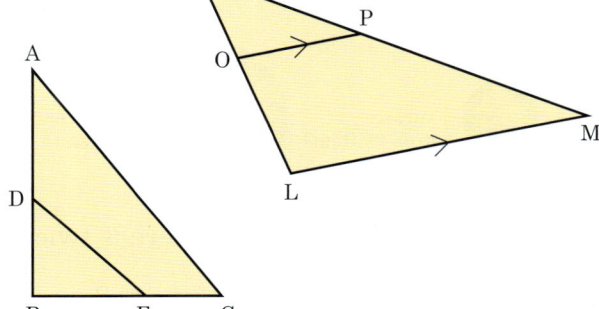

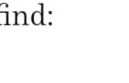

10. Given AZ = 3 cm, ZC = 2 cm, MC = 5 cm and BM = 3 cm, find:

    a) XY
    b) YZ
    c) the ratio of areas AXY : AYZ
    d) the ratio of areas AXY : ABM

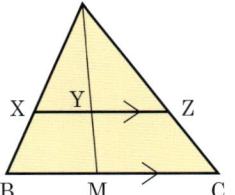

11. A floor is covered by 600 tiles which are 10 cm by 10 cm. How many 20 cm by 20 cm tiles are needed to cover the same floor?

12. A wall is covered by 160 tiles which are 15 cm by 15 cm. How many 10 cm by 10 cm tiles are needed to cover the same wall?

Volumes of similar objects

Cube A and cube B are similar, and the ratio of their corresponding sides is $1:k$.

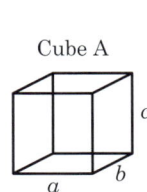

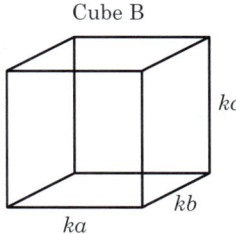

Cube A

Cube B

volume of cube A = abc

volume of cube B = $ka \times kb \times kc = k^3abc$

$\therefore \quad \dfrac{\text{volume of cube B}}{\text{volume of cube A}} = \dfrac{k^3abc}{abc} = k^3$

If two three-dimensional objects are similar and the ratio of their corresponding sides is $1:k$, then the ratio of their corresponding volumes is $1:k^3$.

Example 1

Two similar cylinders have heights of 3 cm and 6 cm respectively. If the volume of the smaller cylinder is 30 cm³, find the volume of the larger cylinder.

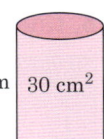

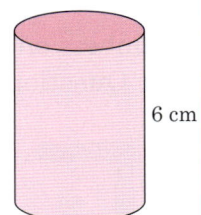

If linear scale factor = k,

then ratio of heights $(k) = \dfrac{6}{3} = 2$

$\therefore \qquad$ ratio of volume $(k^3) = 2^3$

$\qquad\qquad\qquad\quad = 8$

and volume of larger cylinder = 8×30

$\qquad\qquad\qquad\qquad\qquad = 240 \text{ cm}^3$

Example 2

Two similar spheres made of the same material have masses of 32 kg and 108 kg respectively. If the radius of the larger sphere is 9 cm, find the radius of the smaller sphere.

You can take the ratio of masses to be the same as the ratio of volumes.

$$\text{ratio of volume } (k^3) = \frac{32}{108}$$

$$= \frac{8}{27}$$

$$\text{ratio of corresponding lengths } (k) = \sqrt[3]{\left(\frac{8}{27}\right)}$$

$$= \frac{2}{3}$$

$$\therefore \qquad \text{radius of smaller sphere} = \frac{2}{3} \times 9$$

$$= 6 \text{ cm}$$

Exercise 5.7D

In this exercise, the pairs of 3D shapes are similar and a number written inside a figure represents the volume of the object in cm³.

Numbers on the outside give linear dimensions in cm.

For Questions **1** to **8**, find the unknown volume V.

1.

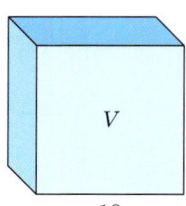

2.

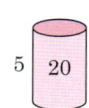

3.

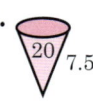

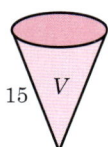

4.

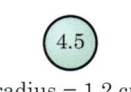

radius = 1.2 cm

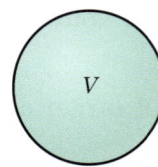

radius = 12 cm

5.

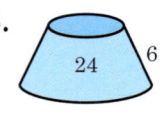

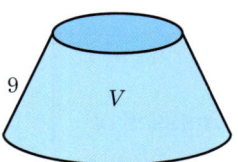

6.

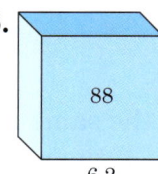

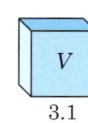

7.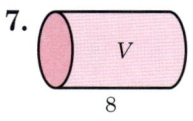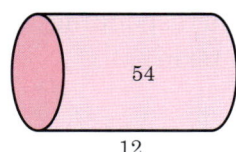

V

8

54

12

8.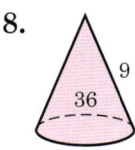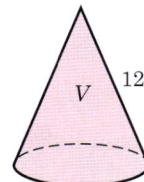

9

36

V

12

For Questions **9** to **14**, find the lengths marked by a letter.

9.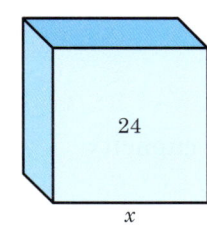

3

2

24

x

10.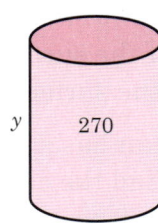

7 | 10

y | 270

11.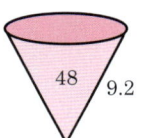

6 z

48 | 9.2

12.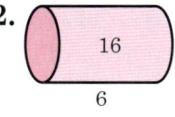

16

6

54

m

13.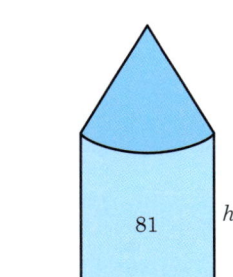

3 | 2.2

81 | h

14. ←—3—→ | ←— d —→

80

270

15. Two similar jugs have heights of 4 cm and 6 cm, respectively. If the capacity of the smaller jug is 50 cm³, find the capacity of the larger jug.

16. Two similar cylindrical tins have base radii of 6 cm and 8 cm respectively. If the capacity of the larger tin is 252 cm³, find the capacity of the smaller tin.

17. Two solid metal spheres have masses of 5 kg and 135 kg respectively. If the radius of the smaller one is 4 cm, find the radius of the larger one.

18. Two similar cones have surface areas in the ratio 4:9. Find the ratio of:

   a) their lengths   **b)** their volumes.

19. The area of the bases of two similar statues are in the ratio 4:25. Find the ratio of their volumes.

Tip

Remember that an object's mass is directly proportional to its volume.

20. Two similar solids have volumes V_1 and V_2 and corresponding sides of length x_1 and x_2. State the ratio $V_1 : V_2$ in terms of x_1 and x_2.

21. Two solid spheres have surface areas of 5 cm² and 45 cm², respectively, and the mass of the smaller sphere is 2 kg. Find the mass of the larger sphere.

22. The masses of two similar objects are 24 kg and 81 kg, respectively. If the surface area of the larger object is 540 cm², find the surface area of the smaller object.

23. A cylindrical can has a circumference of 40 cm and a capacity of 4.8 litres. Find the capacity of a similar cylinder of circumference 50 cm.

24. A container has a surface area of 5000 cm² and a capacity of 12.8 litres. Find the surface area of a similar container which has a capacity of 5.4 litres.

Revision exercise 5

1. Find the area of the following shapes:

a)

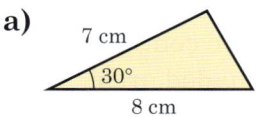

7 cm
30°
8 cm

b)

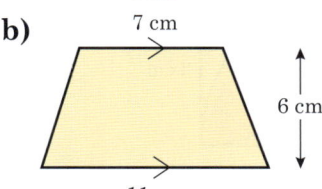

7 cm
6 cm
11 cm

c)

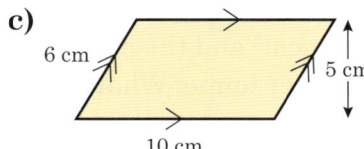

6 cm
5 cm
10 cm

d)

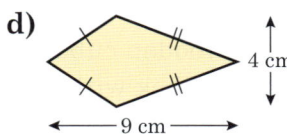

4 cm
9 cm

2. a) A circle has radius 9 m. Find its circumference and area.

b) A circle has circumference 34 cm. Find its diameter.

c) A circle has area 50 cm². Find its radius.

3. A target consists of concentric circles of radii 3 cm and 9 cm.

a) Find the area of A, in terms of π.

b) Find the ratio of the area of B to the area of A.

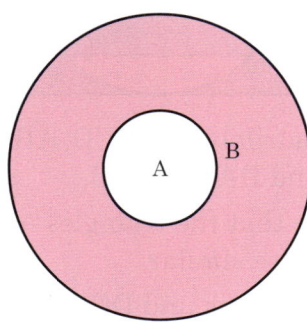

4. In Figure 1, a circle of radius 4 cm is inscribed in a square. In Figure 2 a square is inscribed in a circle of radius 4 cm.

Calculate the shaded area in each diagram.

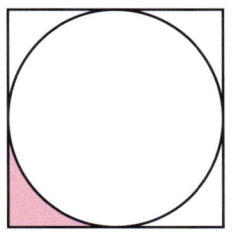   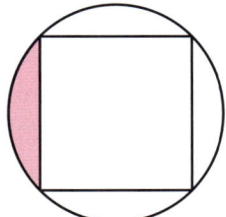

Figure 1   Figure 2

5. Given that OA = 10 cm and $A\widehat{O}B = 70°$ (where O is the centre of the circle), calculate:

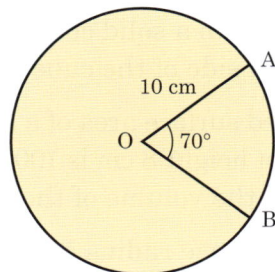

A
10 cm
O
70°
B

a) the arc length AB

b) the area of minor sector AOB.

6. The points X and Y lie on the circumference of a circle, of centre O and radius 8 cm, where $X\widehat{O}Y = 80°$. Calculate:

a) the length of the minor arc XY

b) the length of the chord XY

c) the area of sector XOY

d) the area of triangle XOY

e) the area of the minor segment of the circle cut off by XY.

7. Given that ON = 10 cm and minor arc MN = 18 cm, calculate the angle MON (shown as $x°$).

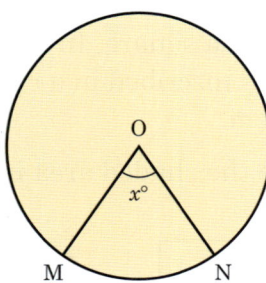

8. A cylinder of radius 8 cm has a volume of 2 litres. Calculate the height of the cylinder.

9. Calculate:

   a) the volume of a sphere of radius 6 cm

   b) the radius of a sphere whose volume is 800 cm³.

10. A sphere of radius 5 cm is melted down and made into a solid cube. Find the length of a side of the cube.

11. The curved surface area of a solid circular cylinder of height 8 cm is 100 cm². Calculate the volume of the cylinder.

12. A cone has base radius 5 cm and vertical height 10 cm, correct to the nearest cm. Calculate the maximum and minimum possible volumes of the cone, consistent with this data.

13. Calculate the radius of a hemispherical solid whose total surface area is 48π cm².

14. Calculate:

   a) the area of an equilateral triangle of side 6 cm

   b) the area of a regular hexagon of side 6 cm

   c) the volume of a regular hexagonal prism of length 10 cm, where the side of the hexagon is 12 cm.

15. A cube of side 10 cm is melted down and made into ten identical spheres. Calculate the surface area of one such sphere.

16. The square has sides of length 3 cm and the circular arcs have centres at the corners. Find the shaded area.

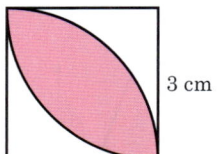

3 cm

17. A copper pipe has external diameter 18 mm and thickness 2 mm. The density of copper is 9 g/cm³ and the price of copper is $150 per tonne. What is the cost of the copper in a length of 5 m of this pipe?

18. Twenty-seven small wooden cubes fit exactly inside a cubical box without a lid. How many of the cubes are touching the sides or the bottom of the box?

19. In the diagram, a small square is circumscribed by a circle, and a larger square is circumscribed on the circle. The area of the smaller square is 10 cm². Find the area of the larger square.

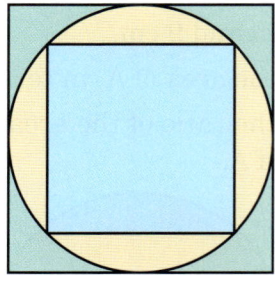

20. In a quadrilateral ABCD, AB is parallel to DC and $D\hat{A}B = D\hat{B}C$.

   a) Prove that the triangles ABD and DBC are similar.

   b) If AB = 4 cm and DC = 9 cm, calculate the length of BD.

21. A rectangle 11 cm by 6 cm is similar to a rectangle 2 cm by x cm. Find the two possible values of x.

22. In the diagram, triangles ABC and EBD are similar but DE is not parallel to AC. Given that AD = 5 cm, DB = 3 cm and BE = 4 cm, calculate the length of BC.

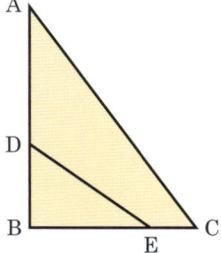

23. The radii of two spheres are in the ratio $2:5$. The volume of the smaller sphere is 16 cm³. Calculate the volume of the larger sphere.

24. A car is an enlargement of a model, the scale factor being 10.

a) If the windscreen of the model has an area of 100 cm², find the area of the windscreen on the actual car (answer in m²).

b) If the capacity of the boot of the car is 1 m³, find the capacity of the boot on the model (answer in cm³).

Examination-style exercise 5

NON-CALCULATOR SECTION

1. In triangle PQR, the bisector of $P\hat{Q}R$ meets PR at S and the point T lies on PQ such that ST is parallel to RQ.

  a) Show that $QT = TS$.   [2]

  b) Show that the triangles PTS and PQR are similar.   [2]

  c) Given that $PT = 5$ cm and $TQ = 2$ cm, calculate the length of QR.   [2]

2. Calculate the area of the isosceles triangle.

Give your answer in the form $a\sqrt{b}$, where a and b are integers.   [3]

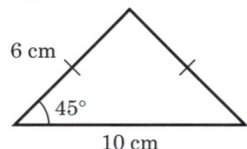

3. A piece of wood, to be used for making a ramp, has been cut into the shape of a prism, whose cross-section is a right-angled triangle with side lengths 9 cm, 12 cm and 15 cm. The length of the ramp is 25 cm.

a) Calculate the volume of the ramp. [2]

b) Calculate the surface area of the ramp. [2]

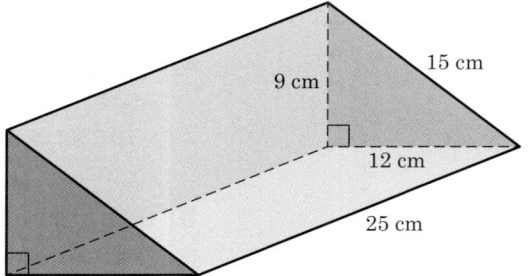

4. The surface areas of two similar jugs are 50 cm² and 450 cm² respectively.

a) If the height of the larger jug is 10 cm, find the height of the smaller jug. [2]

b) If the smaller jug can hold 60 cm³, how much can the larger jug hold? [2]

5. Paul and Debbie buy their son a magic set. The box is a prism with a cross-section that is a trapezium, as shown in the diagram.

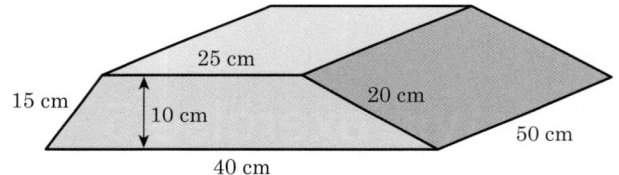

a) Calculate the area of the cross-section. [2]

b) Calculate the volume of the box. [2]

c) Calculate the surface area of the box. [3]

6. The shape here is made by removing a small semi-circle from a large semi-circle.

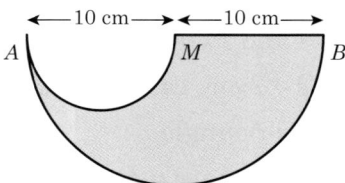

$AM = MB = 10$ cm [3]

Calculate the area of the shape, giving your answer in terms of π.

CALCULATOR SECTION

7. The International Space Station (ISS) made 10 000 orbits of the Earth and travelled a distance of 4.259×10^8 kilometres.

   a) Based on those numbers, calculate the distance travelled by the ISS in one orbit. [2]

   b) If the orbit of the ISS is a circle, what is the radius of the orbit correct to the nearest ten kilometres? [2]

8. Ten spheres of radius 1 cm are immersed in liquid contained in a vertical cylinder of radius 6 cm. Calculate the rise in the level of the liquid in the cylinder.

9. In triangle ABC, $AB = 8$ cm, $AC = 10$ cm, and $BC = 14$ cm. Angle $ACB = 29.2°$.

Calculate the area of the triangle ABC. [2]

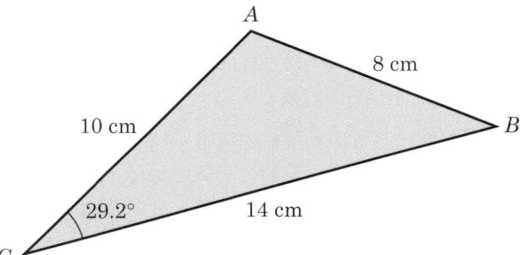

Not to scale

10. A conical beaker has a base radius of 8 cm and a height of 15 cm.

A conical tank full of acid is a similar shape to the beaker.

The beaker can be filled with acid from the tank exactly 1728 times.

Work out the base radius and height of the tank. [3]

11. A solid concrete block is in the shape of a cuboid of length of 350 cm. The cross-section is a square of side x cm.

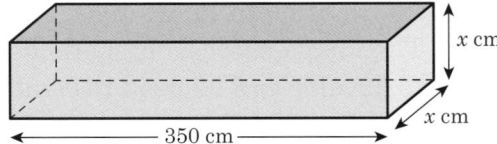

Not to scale

The volume of the cuboid is $2\,528\,750$ cm^3.

   a) Show that $x = 85$. [2]

   b) The mass of 1 cm^3 of the metal is 2.4 grams. Calculate the mass of the whole metal bar in kilograms. [2]

6 Algebra 2

Srinivasa Ramanujan (1887–1920) was a self-taught, Indian mathematician who made a huge contribution to the subject in the early 20th century. In 1914, he travelled to England to work with G. H. Hardy at Trinity College in Cambridge, but he was plagued by ill-health and returned to India five years later. During his time at Cambridge, he made contributions to many areas of mathematics, including analysis and number theory, and solved many problems that were at that time considered unsolvable. He was made a Fellow of the Royal Society in 1918, two years before his death at the age of 32.

Ingrid Daubechies (1954–) is a Belgian physicist and mathematician, best known for her work on image compression technology. Her work has also enabled scientists to extract information from samples of bones and teeth. The image processing methods she has helped to develop can be used to establish the age and authenticity of works of art and have been used on paintings by artists such as Vincent van Gogh and Rembrandt.

- Factorising and completing the square.
- Solve simultaneous equations, where one is linear and one is nonlinear.
- Solve quadratic equations including by factorising, completing the square and using the quadratic formula.

6.1 Factorising

In Chapter 2 you expanded expressions such as $x(3x - 1)$ to give $3x^2 - x$.

The reverse of this process is called **factorising**. When you factorise an expression, you look for the *highest* common factor of all terms.

Example

Factorise: **a)** $4x + 4y$ **b)** $x^2 + 7x$ **c)** $3y^2 - 12y$

          d) $6a^2b - 10ab^2$ **e)** $12ax^2 + 4ax + 8a^2x$

a) 4 is common to $4x$ and $4y$

    $4x + 4y = 4(x + y)$

b) x is common to x^2 and $7x$

    $x^2 + 7x = x(x + 7)$

c) $3y$ is common to both terms

    $3y^2 - 12y = 3y(y - 4)$

d) $2ab$ is common to both terms

    $6a^2b - 10ab^2 = 2ab(3a - 5b)$

e) $4ax$ is common to all three terms

    $12ax^2 + 4ax + 8a^2x = 4ax(3x + 1 + 2a)$

When a question asks you to factorise, you must factorise fully. This means all common factors will be written outside of the brackets. In part **(c)** of the example above, if you had just written $3(y^2 - 4y)$ this would not be correct as it is only partially factorised.

Exercise 6.1A

Factorise:

1. $5a + 5b$
2. $7x + 7y$
3. $7x + x^2$
4. $y^2 + 8y$
5. $2y^2 + 3y$
6. $6y^2 - 4y$
7. $3x^2 - 21x$
8. $16a - 2a^2$
9. $6c^2 - 21c$
10. $15x - 9x^2$
11. $56y - 21y^2$
12. $ax + bx + 2cx$
13. $x^2 + xy + 3xz$
14. $x^2y + y^3 + z^2y$
15. $3a^2b + 2ab^2$
16. $x^2y + xy^2$
17. $6a^2 + 4ab + 2ac$
18. $ma + 2bm + m^2$
19. $2kx + 6ky + 4kz$
20. $ax^2 + ay + 2ab$
21. $x^2k + xk^2$
22. $a^3b + 2ab^2$
23. $abc - 3b^2c$
24. $2a^2e - 5ae^2$
25. $a^3b + ab^3$
26. $x^3y + x^2y^2$
27. $6xy^2 - 4x^2y$
28. $3ab^3 - 3a^3b$
29. $2a^3b + 5a^2b^2$
30. $ax^2y - 2ax^2z$
31. $2abx + 2ab^2 + 2a^2b$
32. $ayx + yx^3 - 2y^2x^2$

> ### Example 1
>
> Factorise $ah + ak + bh + bk$.
>
> ---
>
> Divide into pairs: $(ah + ak) + (bh + bk)$
>
> a is common to the first pair.
>
> b is common to the second pair.
>
> $a(h + k) + b(h + k)$
>
> $(h + k)$ is common to both terms.
>
> Therefore, the answer is $(h + k)(a + b)$

> ### Example 2
>
> Factorise $6mx - ny - 3nx + 2my$.
>
> ---
>
> You may need to rearrange the expression first. In this case, rearrange to $6mx - 3nx + 2my - ny$ so that there are terms next to each other with common factors.
>
> $(6mx - 3nx) + (2my - ny) = 3x(2m - n) + y(2m - n)$
> $$= (2m - n)(3x + y)$$

Exercise 6.1B

Factorise:

1. $ax + ay + bx + by$
2. $xm + xn + m + n$
3. $ah - ak + bh - bk$
4. $am - bn - bm + an$
5. $hs + ht + ks + kt$
6. $ax + by - ay - bx$
7. $xs - xt - ys + yt$
8. $hx - hy - bx + by$
9. $am - bm - an + bn$
10. $xk - xm - kz + mz$
11. $2ax + 6ay + bx + 3by$
12. $2ax + 2ay + bx + by$
13. $2mh - 2mk - h + k$
14. $2mh + 3mk - 2nh - 3nk$
15. $6ax + 2bx + 3ay + by$
16. $2ax - 2ay - bx + by$
17. $x^2a + x^2b + ya + yb$
18. $ms + 2mt^2 - ns - 2nt^2$

Quadratic expressions

When factorising a quadratic expression, first look at the constant term and identify pairs of numbers that multiply to make that term.

For example, if you were trying to factorise $x^2 + 6x + 8$, you would be looking for pairs of numbers that multiply to give +8.

These would be: 1 and 8, 2 and 4, −1 and −8, −2 and −4.

Then find out which of these pairs add together to make the coefficient of x, which in this case is 6.

In this case, the pair is 2 and 4.

Those are the two numbers that you put into your brackets, therefore:

$x^2 + 6x + 8 = (x + 2)(x + 4)$

Example

Factorise: **a)** $x^2 + 2x - 15$

           b) $x^2 - 6x + 8$

           c) $x^2 - 25$

a) Two numbers that multiply to give −15 and add to give +2 are −3 and 5.

$x^2 + 2x - 15 = (x - 3)(x + 5)$

b) Two numbers that multiply to give +8 and add to give −6 are −2 and −4.

$x^2 - 6x + 8 = (x - 2)(x - 4)$

c) Think of this as $x^2 + 0x - 25$

Two numbers that multiply to give −25 and add to give 0 are −5 and 5.

$x^2 - 25 = (x - 5)(x + 5)$

Exercise 6.1C

Factorise:

1. $x^2 + 7x + 10$
2. $x^2 + 7x + 12$
3. $x^2 + 8x + 15$
4. $x^2 + 10x + 21$
5. $x^2 + 8x + 12$
6. $y^2 + 12y + 35$
7. $y^2 + 11y + 24$
8. $y^2 + 10y + 25$
9. $y^2 + 15y + 36$
10. $a^2 - 3a - 10$
11. $a^2 - a - 12$
12. $z^2 + z - 6$
13. $x^2 - 2x - 35$
14. $x^2 - 5x - 24$
15. $x^2 - 6x + 8$
16. $y^2 - 5y + 6$
17. $x^2 - 8x + 15$
18. $a^2 - a - 6$
19. $a^2 + 14a + 45$
20. $b^2 - 4b - 21$
21. $x^2 - 8x + 16$
22. $y^2 + 2y + 1$
23. $y^2 - 3y - 28$
24. $x^2 - x - 20$
25. $x^2 - 8x - 240$
26. $x^2 - 26x + 165$
27. $y^2 + 3y - 108$
28. $x^2 - 49$
29. $x^2 - 9$
30. $x^2 - 16$

If the coefficient of x^2 is not 1, there are two main methods you can use to factorise a quadratic. The first is by inspection.

Example 1

Factorise $2x^2 + 7x + 3$.

Since 2 is a prime number, you know that the brackets must start with $2x$ and x.

This means that $2x^2 + 7x + 3 = (2x + a)(x + b)$, for some a and b.

Since the constant term is 3, you know that a and b must be either 1 and 3 (in some order) or -1 and -3 (in some order).

If you expand $(2x + a)(x + b)$ you get
$2x^2 + 2bx + ax + ab = 2x^2 + (a + 2b)x + ab$.

This means that $a + 2b = 7$

The pair of values for which this is true is $a = 1$ and $b = 3$.

The factorisation of $2x^2 + 7x + 3$ is therefore $(2x + 1)(x + 3)$.

Sometimes it may be too difficult to factorise a quadratic expression by inspection. This could be because the coefficient of x^2 or the constant term (or both) has a lot of factors, which means there are too many possible options to check. In these instances, there is a second method that can be used.

If the quadratic expression to be factorised is of the form $ax^2 + bx + c$, this method starts by looking for two numbers whose product is ac and whose sum is b.

Example 2

Factorise $3x^2 + 13x + 4$.

Here, $a = 3$, $b = 13$ and $c = 4$. Thus $ac = 3 \times 4 = 12$

Find two numbers that multiply to give 12 (ac) and add to 13 (b).

In this case the numbers you want are 1 and 12.

First, you split the '$13x$' term into x and $12x$:
$3x^2 + x + 12x + 4$

Then you factorise the first and second terms as a pair followed by the third and fourth as a pair:
$x(3x + 1) + 4(3x + 1)$

Note that at this stage the brackets in both factorisations will always be the same.

Finally, factorise one more time: $(x + 4)(3x + 1)$

Exercise 6.1D

Factorise:

1. $2x^2 + 5x + 3$

2. $2x^2 + 7x + 3$

3. $3x^2 + 7x + 2$

4. $2x^2 + 11x + 12$

5. $3x^2 + 8x + 4$

6. $2x^2 + 7x + 5$

7. $3x^2 - 5x - 2$

8. $2x^2 - x - 15$

9. $2x^2 + x - 21$

10. $3x^2 - 17x - 28$

11. $6x^2 + 7x + 2$

12. $12x^2 + 23x + 10$

13. $3x^2 - 11x + 6$

14. $3y^2 - 11y + 10$

15. $4y^2 - 23y + 15$

16. $6y^2 + 7y - 3$

17. $6x^2 - 27x + 30$

18. $10x^2 + 9x + 2$

19. $6x^2 - 19x + 3$

20. $8x^2 - 10x - 3$

21. $12x^2 + 4x - 5$

22. $16x^2 + 19x + 3$

23. $4a^2 - 4a + 1$

24. $12x^2 + 17x - 14$

25. $15x^2 + 44x - 3$

26. $48x^2 + 46x + 5$

27. $64y^2 + 4y - 3$

28. $120x^2 + 67x - 5$

29. $9x^2 - 1$

30. $4a^2 - 9$

The difference of two squares

When an expression can be seen as the difference of two perfect squares, for example $x^2 - y^2$, then it can be factorised as $(x - y)(x + y)$.

$$x^2 - y^2 = (x - y)(x + y)$$

Remember this result.

Example

Factorise: **a)** $4a^2 - b^2$ **b)** $25m^2 - 81n^2$ **c)** $3x^2 - 27y^2$

a) $\begin{aligned}4a^2 - b^2 &= (2a)^2 - b^2 \\ &= (2a - b)(2a + b)\end{aligned}$

b) $\begin{aligned}25m^2 - 81n^2 &= (5m)^2 - (9n)^2 \\ &= (5m - 9n)(5m + 9n)\end{aligned}$

c) $\begin{aligned}3x^2 - 27y^2 &= 3(x^2 - 9y^2) \\ &= 3(x^2 - (3y)^2) \\ &= 3(x - 3y)(x + 3y)\end{aligned}$

Exercise 6.1E

Factorise the following:

1. $y^2 - a^2$ **2.** $m^2 - n^2$ **3.** $x^2 - t^2$ **4.** $y^2 - 1$

5. $x^2 - 9$ **6.** $a^2 - 25$ **7.** $x^2 - \dfrac{1}{4}$ **8.** $x^2 - \dfrac{1}{9}$

9. $4x^2 - y^2$ **10.** $a^2 - 4b^2$ **11.** $25x^2 - 4y^2$ **12.** $9x^2 - 16y^2$

13. $x^2 - \dfrac{y^2}{4}$ **14.** $9m^2 - \dfrac{4}{9}n^2$ **15.** $16t^2 - \dfrac{4}{25}s^2$ **16.** $4x^2 - \dfrac{z^2}{100}$

17. $x^3 - x$ **18.** $a^3 - ab^2$ **19.** $4x^3 - x$ **20.** $8x^3 - 2xy^2$

21. $12x^3 - 3xy^2$ **22.** $18m^3 - 8mn^2$ **23.** $5x^2 - 1\dfrac{1}{4}$ **24.** $50a^3 - 18ab^2$

25. $12x^2y - 3yz^2$ **26.** $36a^3b - 4ab^3$ **27.** $50a^5 - 8a^3b^2$ **28.** $36x^3y - 225xy^3$

Evaluate:

29. $81^2 - 80^2$ **30.** $102^2 - 100^2$ **31.** $225^2 - 215^2$ **32.** $1211^2 - 1210^2$

33. $723^2 - 720^2$ **34.** $3.8^2 - 3.7^2$ **35.** $5.24^2 - 4.76^2$ **36.** $1234^2 - 1235^2$

37. $3.81^2 - 3.8^2$ **38.** $540^2 - 550^2$ **39.** $7.68^2 - 2.32^2$ **40.** $0.003^2 - 0.002^2$

Cubic expressions

The techniques you have learned so far mean that you can now also factorise many simple cubic expressions of the form $ax^3 + bx^2 + cx$. Because there is no constant term and every term contains x, you can simply take x, or a multiple of x, out as a factor, leaving you then with only a quadratic to factorise.

Example

Factorise: **a)** $x^3 + 7x^2 + 10x$ **b)** $2x^3 + 10x^2 - 12x$

a) $x^3 + 7x^2 + 10x = x(x^2 + 7x + 10) = x(x + 2)(x + 5)$

b) $2x^3 + 10x^2 - 12x = 2x(x^2 + 5x - 6) = 2x(x - 1)(x + 6)$

Exercise 6.1F

Factorise the following:

1. $x^3 + 3x^2 + 2x$ **2.** $x^3 - x^2 - 6x$ **3.** $x^3 + 3x^2 - 4x$

4. $x^3 + 8x^2 + 15x$ **5.** $x^3 + 4x^2 - 60x$ **6.** $x^3 + 3x^2 - 28x$

7. $x^3 - 8x^2 + 15x$ **8.** $x^3 - 15x^2 + 44x$ **9.** $2x^3 - 3x^2 - 2x$

10. $3x^3 + 5x^2 - 2x$

11. $2x^3 + x^2 - 3x$

12. $4x^3 + x^2 - 3x$

13. $5x^3 + 17x^2 - 12x$

14. $6x^3 + x^2 - x$

15. $8x^3 - 2x^2 - x$

16. $15x^3 + 13x^2 + 2x$

17. $12x^3 + 40x^2 - 7x$

18. $6x^3 + x^2 - 40x$

19. $2x^3 - 2x$

20. $3x^3 - 3x^2 - 6x$

21. $15x^3 + 50x^2 - 40x$

22. $12x^3 - 20x^2 - 48x$

23. $-2x^3 - 32x^2 - 126x$

24. $-30x^3 + 5x^2 + 75x$

6.2 Quadratic equations

A quadratic equation is an equation of the form $ax^2 + bx + c = 0$. Unlike linear equations, which only have one solution, quadratic equations can have zero, one, or two solutions.

For an equation $ax^2 + bx + c = 0$ to be quadratic, a cannot be zero, but b and c are allowed to be zero. There must be an x^2 term, but there cannot be any terms containing a higher power of x than 2.

Example

Which of the following equations are quadratic? Explain your reasoning.

a) $x^2 - 7x + 12 = 0$ **b)** $3x^2 + 14 = 0$ **c)** $-8x^2 = 0$

d) $-13x + 4 = 0$ **e)** $x^3 - x^2 + 4x - 9 = 0$

a) Yes. It is of the form $ax^2 + bx + c = 0$, and a is not zero.

b) Yes. It is of the form $ax^2 + bx + c = 0$. The value of b is zero, but this is allowed.

c) Yes. It is of the form $ax^2 + bx + c = 0$. The values of b and c are zero, but this is allowed.

d) No. It has no x^2 term.

e) No. It has a term with a power of x greater than 2.

Solution by factorising

If the product of two numbers is zero, then one of those two numbers must be zero.

You can use this fact to help you solve some quadratic equations.

Example 1

Solve the equation $x^2 + x - 12 = 0$.

Factorising, this becomes $(x - 3)(x + 4) = 0$

The product of the two brackets can only be zero if one of the brackets equals zero.

This could be because $x - 3 = 0$, which is the case if $x = 3$.

Alternatively, it could be because $x + 4 = 0$, which would be the case if $x = -4$.

The solutions to this equation are therefore $x = 3$ or $x = -4$.

Example 2

Solve the equation $6x^2 + x - 2 = 0$.

Factorising, this becomes $(2x - 1)(3x + 2) = 0$

Either $2x - 1 = 0$, which is the case if $x = \dfrac{1}{2}$

Or $3x + 2 = 0$, which is the case if $x = -\dfrac{2}{3}$

The solutions to this equation are therefore $x = \dfrac{1}{2}$ or $x = -\dfrac{2}{3}$

Example 3

Solve the equation $3x^2 - 2x = 14x - 5$.

First, rearrange to get all the terms on one side of the equals sign.

$3x^2 - 16x + 5 = 0$

Then solve in the same way as Example 2.

Factorising gives $(3x - 1)(x - 5) = 0$.

Therefore $x = \dfrac{1}{3}$ or $x = 5$.

Exercise 6.2A

Solve the following equations:

1. $x^2 + 7x + 12 = 0$
2. $x^2 + 7x + 10 = 0$
3. $x^2 + 2x - 15 = 0$

4. $x^2 + x - 6 = 0$
5. $x^2 - 8x + 12 = 0$
6. $x^2 + 10x + 21 = 0$

7. $x^2 - 5x + 6 = 0$
8. $x^2 = 4x + 5$
9. $x^2 + 5x - 14 = 0$

10. $2 = 2x^2 - 3x$
11. $3x^2 + 10x - 8 = 0$
12. $2x^2 + 7x - 15 = 0$

13. $6x^2 - 13x + 6 = 0$
14. $4x^2 - 29x + 7 = 0$
15. $10x^2 - 2 = 1 + x$

16. $y^2 - 15y + 56 = 0$
17. $12y^2 - 16y + 5 = 0$
18. $y^2 + 2y - 63 = 0$

19. $x^2 = -1 - 2x$
20. $x^2 - 3x = 3x - 9$
21. $x^2 + 10x + 25 = 0$

22. $x^2 - 7x + 5 = 7x - 44$
23. $6a^2 - a - 1 = 0$
24. $6a^2 - 3a - 11 = 2a^2 - 1$

25. $z^2 - 8z - 65 = 0$
26. $x^2 + 17x + 6 = 9 - 5x^2$
27. $10k^2 + 19k - 2 = 0$

28. $y^2 - 2y + 1 = 0$
29. $36x^2 + x - 2 = 0$
30. $14x^2 + x - 3 = 8x - 6x^2$

Example 1

Solve the equation $x^2 - 7x = 0$.

Factorising, $x(x - 7) = 0$

Either $x = 0$ or $x - 7 = 0$

$x = 7$

The solutions are $x = 0$ and $x = 7$.

Example 2

Solve the equation $4x^2 - 9 = 0$.

a) Factorising, $(2x - 3)(2x + 3) = 0$

Either $2x - 3 = 0$ or $2x + 3 = 0$

$2x = 3$ $\qquad\qquad$ $2x = -3$

$x = \dfrac{3}{2}$ $\qquad\qquad$ $x = -\dfrac{3}{2}$

b) Alternative method:

$4x^2 - 9 = 0$

$4x^2 = 9$

$x^2 = \dfrac{9}{4}$

$x = +\dfrac{3}{2}$ or $-\dfrac{3}{2}$

> **Tip**
>
> You must give both the solutions. A common error is to only give the positive square root.

Exercise 6.2B

Solve the following equations:

1. $x^2 - 3x = 0$
2. $x^2 + 7x = 0$
3. $2x^2 - 2x = 0$
4. $3x^2 - x = 0$
5. $x^2 - 16 = 0$
6. $x^2 - 49 = 0$
7. $4x^2 - 1 = 0$
8. $9x^2 - 4 = 0$
9. $6y^2 + 9y = 0$
10. $6a^2 - 9a = 0$
11. $10x^2 - 55x = 0$
12. $16x^2 - 1 = 0$
13. $y^2 - \dfrac{1}{4} = 0$
14. $56x^2 - 35x = 0$
15. $36x^2 - 3x = 0$
16. $x^2 = 6x$
17. $x^2 = 11x$
18. $2x^2 = 3x$
19. $x^2 = x$
20. $4x = x^2$
21. $3x - x^2 = 0$

22. $4x^2 = 1$ **23.** $9x^2 = 16$ **24.** $x^2 = 12 - x$

25. $12x = 5x^2$ **26.** $1 - 9x^2 = 0$ **27.** $x^2 = \dfrac{x}{4}$

28. $2x^2 = \dfrac{x}{3}$ **29.** $4x^2 = \dfrac{1}{4}$ **30.** $\dfrac{x}{5} - x^2 = 0$

Solution by the quadratic formula

The solutions of the quadratic equation $ax^2 + bx + c = 0$ are given by the quadratic formula, one of the most well-known formulae in mathematics:

$$x = \frac{-b \pm \sqrt{\left(b^2 - 4ac \right)}}{2a}$$

You need to learn this formula, but you should only use it if you are unable to solve the equation by factorisation. Note that if you use the formula and discover that the number under the square root is a square number, then you could have solved the equation by factorising. The factorisation, however, may not have been easy to spot.

Example

Solve the equation $2x^2 - 3x - 4 = 0$, giving your answers:

a) in surd form

b) accurate to 2 decimal places.

a) Comparing with the general form $ax^2 + bx + c = 0$, you have $a = 2$, $b = -3$, $c = -4$

Using the quadratic formula gives

$$x = \frac{-(-3) \pm \sqrt{(-3)^2 - (4 \times 2 \times -4)}}{2 \times 2} = \frac{3 \pm \sqrt{9 + 32}}{4} = \frac{3 \pm \sqrt{41}}{4}$$

The solutions in surd form are $x = \dfrac{3 + \sqrt{41}}{4}$ or $x = \dfrac{3 - \sqrt{41}}{4}$

b) Accurate to 2 decimal places:

$$x = \frac{3 + \sqrt{41}}{4} = 2.35 \quad \text{or} \quad x = \frac{3 - \sqrt{41}}{4} = -0.85$$

Exercise 6.2C

For Questions **1** to **27**, solve the equations and give your answers in surd form where necessary.

1. $2x^2 + 11x + 5 = 0$
2. $3x^2 + 11x + 6 = 0$
3. $6x^2 + 7x + 2 = 0$
4. $3x^2 - 10x + 3 = 0$
5. $5x^2 - 7x + 2 = 0$
6. $6x^2 - 11x + 3 = 0$
7. $2x^2 + 6x + 3 = 0$
8. $x^2 + 4x + 1 = 0$
9. $5x^2 - 5x + 1 = 0$
10. $x^2 - 7x + 2 = 0$
11. $2x^2 + 5x - 1 = 0$
12. $3x^2 + x - 3 = 0$
13. $3x^2 + 8x - 6 = 0$
14. $3x^2 - 7x - 20 = 0$
15. $2x^2 - 7x - 15 = 0$
16. $x^2 - 3x - 2 = 0$
17. $6x^2 - 11x - 7 = 0$
18. $3x^2 + 25x + 8 = 0$
19. $3y^2 - 2y - 5 = 0$
20. $2 - x - 6x^2 = 0$
21. $20x^2 + 17x - 63 = 0$
22. $x^2 + 2.5x - 6 = 0$
23. $0.3y^2 + 0.4y - 1.5 = 0$
24. $10 - x - 3x^2 = 0$
25. $x^2 + 3.3x - 0.7 = 0$
26. $12 - 5x^2 - 11x = 0$
27. $5x - 2x^2 + 187 = 0$

For Questions **28** to **36**, solve the equations and give your answers correct to two decimal places.

28. $2x^2 + 6x - 1 = 0$
29. $2y^2 - 5y + 1 = 0$
30. $\dfrac{1}{2}y^2 + 3y + 1 = 0$
31. $3 + 4x - 2x^2 = 0$
32. $1 - 5x - 2x^2 = 0$
33. $3x^2 - 1 + 4x = 0$
34. $5x - x^2 + 2 = 0$
35. $24x^2 - 22x - 35 = 0$
36. $36x^2 - 17x - 35 = 0$

The solution to a problem may involve an equation which does not at first appear to be quadratic. The terms in the equation may need to be rearranged as shown in the next example.

Example

Solve: $2x(x - 1) = (x + 1)^2 - 5$

$2x^2 - 2x = x^2 + 2x + 1 - 5$

$2x^2 - 2x - x^2 - 2x - 1 + 5 = 0$

$x^2 - 4x + 4 = 0$

$(x - 2)(x - 2) = 0$

$x = 2$

In this example the quadratic has a repeated solution of $x = 2$.

Exercise 6.2D

Solve the following, giving answers to two decimal places where necessary:

1. $x^2 = 6 - x$

2. $x(x + 10) = -21$

3. $3x + 2 = 2x^2$

4. $x^2 + 4 = 5x$

5. $6x(x + 1) = 5 - x$

6. $(2x)^2 = x(x - 14) - 5$

7. $(x - 3)^2 = 10$

8. $(x + 1)^2 - 10 = 2x(x - 2)$

9. $(2x - 1)^2 = (x - 1)^2 + 8$

10. $3x(x + 2) - x(x - 2) + 6 = 0$

11. $2x^2 = 7x$

12. $16 = \dfrac{1}{x^2}$

Solution by completing the square

Another way to solve a quadratic equation of the form $x^2 + bx + c = 0$ ($a = 1$) is to rearrange the equation to make x the subject. This, however, appears to be tricky at first because x appears twice in the equation and in one of those instances it is squared.

The key here is to notice that $(x + n)^2 = x^2 + 2nx + n^2$, where n is a number.

Rearranging this gives $x^2 + 2nx = (x + n)^2 - n^2$

This means that if you have an expression of the form $x^2 + 2nx$ you can swap it for an expression of the form $(x + n)^2 - n^2$. This turns out to be very useful.

Suppose you want to solve the equation $x^2 + 6x + 4 = 0$.

Note that $x^2 + 6x$ is an expression of the form $x^2 + 2nx$ where $n = 3$.

This means you can swap $x^2 + 6x$ for $(x + 3)^2 - 3^2$. Note that the 3 is just half of the 6.

This turns $x^2 + 6x + 4 = 0$ into $(x + 3)^2 - 3^2 + 4 = 0$

Rearranging this gives us $(x + 3)^2 = 5$

Note that on the left-hand side of the equation you now have a perfect square.

For this reason, this method of solving quadratic equations is called 'completing the square'.

Now you can finish solving the equation: $x + 3 = \pm\sqrt{5}$

$$x = -3 \pm \sqrt{5}$$

Example 1

Solve the quadratic equation $x^2 - 12x = 0$ by completing the square.

$x^2 - 12x = (x - 6)^2 - 36 = 0$

$(x - 6)^2 = 36$

$x - 6 = \pm 6$

$x = 6 + 6 = 12 \quad \text{or} \quad x = 6 - 6 = 0$

Example 2

Solve the quadratic equation $x^2 - 10x - 17 = 0$ by completing the square, giving your answers in surd form.

$x^2 - 10x - 17 = 0$

$(x - 5)^2 - 5^2 - 17 = 0$

$(x - 5)^2 = 25 + 17 = 42$

$x - 5 = \pm\sqrt{42}$

$x = 5 + \sqrt{42} \quad \text{or} \quad x = 5 - \sqrt{42}$

Example 3

Solve the quadratic equation $x^2 + 3x - 11 = 0$ by completing the square, giving your answers correct to 2 decimal places.

$x^2 + 3x - 11 = 0$

$(x - 1.5)^2 - 1.5^2 - 11 = 0$

$(x - 1.5)^2 = 2.25 + 11 = 13.25$

$x - 1.5 = \pm\sqrt{13.25}$

$x = 1.5 + \sqrt{13.25} = 5.14 \ (2 \text{ d.p.}) \text{ or}$

$x = 1.5 - \sqrt{13.25} = -2.14 \ (2 \text{ d.p.})$

If in $ax^2 + bx + c = 0$, $a \neq 1$, the method can be adapted, as shown in Example 4.

Example 4

Solve the quadratic equation $2x^2 - 12x + 7 = 0$ by completing the square, giving your answers correct to 2 decimal places.

$2x^2 - 12x + 7 = 0$

$2(x^2 - 6x) + 7 = 0$

$2[(x - 3)^2 - 9] + 7 = 0$

$2(x - 3)^2 - 18 + 7 = 0$

$2(x - 3)^2 = 18 - 7 = 11$

$(x - 3)^2 = 5.5$

$x - 3 = \pm\sqrt{5.5}$

$x = 3 + \sqrt{5.5} = 5.35$ (2 d.p.) or

$x = 3 - \sqrt{5.5} = 0.65$ (2 d.p.)

Example 5

Given that $y = x^2 - 8x + 18$, show that $y \geqslant 2$ for all values of x.

Completing the square, $y = (x - 4)^2 - 16 + 18$
$$= (x - 4)^2 + 2$$

Now $(x - 4)^2$ is always greater than or equal to zero because it is 'something squared'.

Therefore, $y \geqslant 2$

Exercise 6.2E

For Questions **1** to **10**, complete the square for each expression by writing them in the form $(x + a)^2 + b$, where a and b can be positive or negative.

1. $x^2 + 8x$ **2.** $x^2 - 12x$ **3.** $x^2 + x$ **4.** $x^2 + 4x + 1$

5. $x^2 - 6x + 9$ **6.** $x^2 + 2x - 15$ **7.** $2x^2 + 16x + 5$ **8.** $2x^2 - 10x$

9. $6 + 4x - x^2$ **10.** $3 - 2x - x^2$

11. Solve these equations by completing the square.

    a) $x^2 + 4x - 3 = 0$ **b)** $x^2 - 3x - 2 = 0$ **c)** $x^2 + 12x = 1$

12. Try to solve the equation $x^2 + 6x + 10 = 0$ by completing the square. Explain why you can find no solutions.

13. Given $y = x^2 + 6x + 12$, show that $y \geqslant 3$ for all values of x.

14. Given $y = x^2 - 7x + \frac{1}{4}$, show that the least possible value of y is -12.

15. If $y = x^2 + 4x + 7$ find:

    a) the smallest possible value of y

    b) the value of x for which this smallest value occurs

    c) the greatest possible value of $\dfrac{1}{(x^2 + 4x + 7)}$

6.3 Solving problems using quadratic equations

Example

The area of rectangle A is 16 cm² greater than the area of rectangle B.

Find the height of rectangle A.

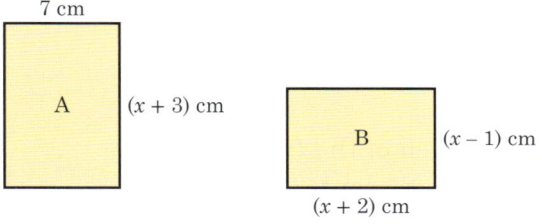

Area of rectangle A $= 7(x + 3)$

Area of rectangle B $= (x + 2)(x - 1)$

You are given $(x + 2)(x - 1) + 16 = 7(x + 3)$

Solve this equation $x^2 + 2x - x - 2 + 16 = 7x + 21$

$$x^2 + x + 14 = 7x + 21$$
$$x^2 - 6x - 7 = 0$$
$$(x - 7)(x + 1) = 0$$
$$x = 7 \ \text{ or } \ x = -1$$

However, x is a length so must be positive; therefore $x = 7$.

The height of rectangle A, $x + 3$, is therefore $7 + 3 = 10$ cm.

Exercise 6.3A

Solve each problem by forming a quadratic equation.

1. Two positive numbers that differ by 3, have a product of 88. Find these numbers.

2. The product of two positive consecutive odd numbers is 143. Find the numbers.

3. The length of a rectangle exceeds the width by 7 cm. If the area is 60 cm², find the length of the rectangle.

4. The length of a rectangle exceeds the width by 2 cm. If the diagonal is 10 cm long, find the width of the rectangle.

5. The area of the rectangle exceeds the area of the square by 24 m². Find the value of x.

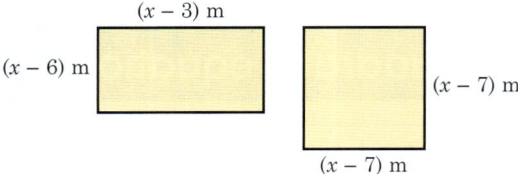

6. The perimeter of a rectangle is 68 cm. If the diagonal is 26 cm, find the dimensions of the rectangle.

7. Sang Jae walks a certain distance due north and then the same distance plus a further 7 km due east. If the final distance from the starting point is 17 km, find the distances he walks north and east.

8. A farmer makes a profit of x cents on each of the $(x + 5)$ eggs her hen lays. If her total profit was 84 cents, find the number of eggs the hen lays.

9. Sirak buys x eggs at $(x - 8)$ cents each and $(x - 2)$ bread rolls at $(x - 3)$ cents each. If the total bill is \$1.75, how many eggs does he buy?

10. In Figure 1, ABCD is a rectangle with AB = 12 cm and BC = 7 cm. AK = BL = CM = DN = x cm. If the area of KLMN is 54 cm², find the value of x.

11. In Figure 1, AB = 14 cm, BC = 11 cm and AK = BL = CM = DN = x cm. If the area of KLMN is now 97 cm², find the possible values of x.

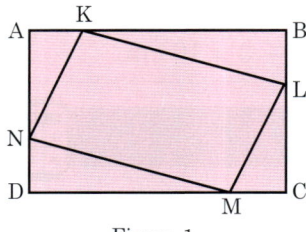

Figure 1

12. The perimeters of a square and a rectangle are equal. One side of the rectangle is 11 cm and the area of the square is 4 cm² more than the area of the rectangle. Find the possible lengths of the side of the square.

6.4 Nonlinear simultaneous equations

Sometimes you may be given a pair of simultaneous equations where one equation is linear and one is nonlinear. When this happens, you will not be able to use the elimination method that you sometimes used in Chapter 2 when both equations were linear. In these instances, you have no choice but to use substitution.

Example 1

Solve the simultaneous equations $y = x + 1$ and $y = x^2 + 3x - 2$.

$y = x + 1$ (1)

$y = x^2 + 3x - 2$ (2)

Substitute (1) into (2):

$\quad x + 1 = x^2 + 3x - 2$

$\quad\quad 0 = x^2 + 2x - 3$

Solve the resulting quadratic equation by factorising:

$\quad 0 = (x + 3)(x - 1)$

$\quad x = -3 \text{ or } x = 1$

Substitute the x-values into (1).

When $x = -3$, $y = -2$

When $x = 1$, $y = 2$

Example 2

Solve the simultaneous equations $2x - y = 3$ and $y = 2x^2 + 9x - 1$.

$2x - y = 3$ (1)

$y = 2x^2 + 9x - 1$ (2)

Rearrange (1) to make y the subject:

$\quad\quad 2x = y + 3$

$\quad 2x - 3 = y$

Substitute into (2):

$\quad 2x - 3 = 2x^2 + 9x - 1$

$\quad\quad\quad 0 = 2x^2 + 7x + 2$

Solve the resulting quadratic equation using the formula:

$$x = \frac{-7 \pm \sqrt{7^2 - 4(2)(2)}}{2(2)} = \frac{-7 \pm \sqrt{33}}{4}$$

> **Tip**
>
> If you have to solve the quadratic equation by using the formula, use the exact x-values when finding y, then round both answers at the end.

Either $x = \dfrac{-7 + 5.74456\ldots}{4} = -0.31386\ldots$

$\Rightarrow y = -3.6277\ldots$

or $\quad x = \dfrac{-7 - 5.74456\ldots}{4} = -3.18614\ldots$

$\Rightarrow y = -9.3722\ldots$

The solutions are:

$x = -0.31$, $y = -3.63$ and $x = -3.19$, $y = -9.37$ (all to 2 d.p.)

Exercise 6.4A

Solve the following pairs of simultaneous equations. Give your answers to two decimal places where necessary.

1. $y = 20 - 2x$
$y = x^2 - 16x + 68$

2. $y = 6x - 8$
$y = x^2 + 2x - 5$

3. $y = 2 - 2x$
$y = x^2 - 4x + 3$

4. $y + 2x = 9$
$y = x^2 - 6x + 12$

5. $y + 10x + 31 = 0$
$y + 6 = x^2$

6. $y + 12x = x^2 + 40$
$y + 8x = 38$

7. $y - 7 = x^2 + 2x$
$y - 9 = 4x$

8. $y - x^2 - 14x = 54$
$43 = y - 6x$

9. $y + 2x + 7 = 4$
$y - 8 = x^2 + 6x + 2$

10. $2y - 3x = 1$
$y = x^2 + 3x - 7$

11. $3y + 4x = 15$
$y = 2x^2 - 3x + 5$

12. $3y - 2x + 5 = 0$
$y = 7 - 2x - 3x^2$

13. $y = x + 1$
$x^2 + y^2 = 6$

14. $y = x - 3$
$y = \dfrac{2}{x}$

15. $x^2 + y^2 = 6$
$4x + 3y = 2$

Revision exercise 6

1. Factorise these expressions.

   a) $4x^2 - y^2$

   b) $2x^2 + 8x + 6$

   c) $6m + 4n - 9km - 6kn$

   d) $2x^2 - 5x - 3$

   e) $4x^3 + 10x^2 + 4x$

2. Solve these equations.

   a) $2x^2 - 7x = 0$

   b) $x^2 + 5x + 6 = 0$

   c) $\dfrac{1}{x} + \dfrac{1}{4} = \dfrac{1}{3}$

3. Factorise these expressions.

   a) $z^3 - 16z$

   b) $x^2y^2 + x^2 + y^2 + 1$

   c) $2x^2 + 11x + 12$

4. Solve these simultaneous equations.

a) $y = x + 4$

$y = x^2 + 4x + 4$

b) $2y - 3x - 1 = 0$

$y = 2x^2 - 4x + 3$

5. Solve these equations.

a) $4(y + 1) = \dfrac{3}{1 - y}$

b) $x^2 = 5x$

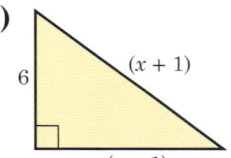 **6.** Solve these equations, giving your answers correct to two decimal places.

a) $2x^2 - 3x - 1 = 0$

b) $x^2 - x - 1 = 0$

c) $3x^2 + 2x - 4 = 0$

d) $x + 3 = \dfrac{7}{x}$

7. In each triangle, find the value of x by forming a suitable equation.

a) 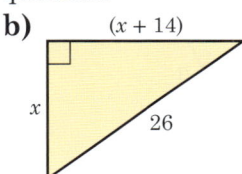 **b)**

8. A car travels for x hours at a speed of $(x + 2)$ km/h. If the distance travelled is 15 km, write down an equation for x and solve it to find the speed of the car.

9. ABCD is a rectangle, where $AB = x$ cm and BC is 1.5 cm less than AB.

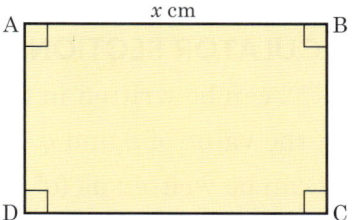

If the area of the rectangle is 52 cm², form an equation in x and solve it to find the dimensions of the rectangle.

 **10.** Solve these equations.

a) $(2x + 1)^2 = (x + 5)^2$

b) $x^2 - 7x + 5 = 0$, giving the answers correct to two decimal places.

11. The sides of a right-angled triangle have lengths $(x - 3)$ cm, $(x + 11)$ cm and $2x$ cm, where $2x$ is the hypotenuse. Find the value of x.

12. When each edge of a cube is decreased by 1 cm, its volume is decreased by 91 cm³. Find the length of a side of the original cube.

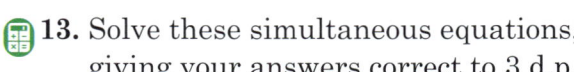 **13.** Solve these simultaneous equations, giving your answers correct to 3 d.p.

$x^2 + y^2 = 16$

$y = x + 1$

Examination-style exercise 6

NON-CALCULATOR SECTION

1. $x^2 + 6x - 12$ can be written in the form $(x + p)^2 + q$.

   Work out the value of p and q. [3]

2. $a^4 - 81b^4$ can be written as $(a^2 - kb^2)(a^2 + kb^2)$.

   a) Write down the value of k. [1]

   b) Fully factorise the expression $a^4b - 81b^5$. [2]

3. Solve the equation $x^2 + 4x - 11 = 0$ by completing the square.

   Leave your answers in surd form. [3]

4. In parallelogram ABCD, the line AD is parallel to BC, *and* the line CD is parallel to AB.

   The line EF is perpendicular to lines AB and CD.

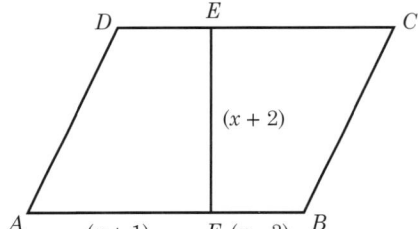

   The area of parallelogram ABCD is 176 cm².

   a) Show that $x^2 + x - 90 = 0$. [3]

   b) Solve the equation $x^2 + x - 90 = 0$. [2]

   c) Calculate the length of AB. [2]

5. Solve these simultaneous equations.

   $x^2 + y^2 = 25$

   $x + y = -1$ [3]

CALCULATOR SECTION

6. **a)** **i)** Write down an expression for the area of rectangle S, in the diagram below, in the form $ax^2 + bx + c$. [1]

   ii) Show that the total area of rectangles S and T is $(7x^2 + 6x + 8)$ cm². [1]

b) The total area of rectangles S and T is 221 cm².

Calculate the value of x correct to 1 decimal place. [4]

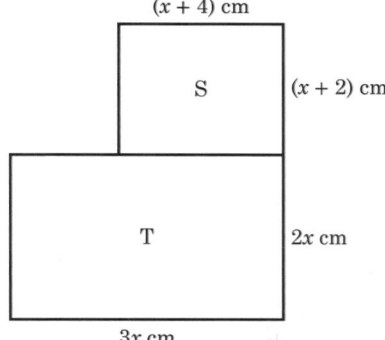

7. Solve these simultaneous equations, giving your answers accurate to 3 d.p.

$$y = \frac{1}{x}$$

$$y = x + 1$$ [3]

8. One solution of the equation $2x^2 - 7x + k = 0$ is $x = -\frac{1}{2}$

a) Work out the value of k. [2]

b) Work out the other value of x. [2]

Geometry

Euclid (300 B.C.E.) was a Greek mathematician. He is most famous for writing the thirteen books known collectively as *The Elements*, in which he laid the foundations for modern geometry. Amazingly, unlike many other works of Euclid, this book has not been lost, and many of the theorems that are taught in schools today can be found in *The Elements*, including ideas relating to prime numbers, Pythagoras' theorem, and all of the circle theorems in this book.

- Use and interpret geometric terms and vocabulary.
- Geometrical drawings and constructions including triangles and nets.
- Symmetry in 2D and 3D shapes including line symmetry, order of rotational planes of symmetry and axes of symmetry.
- Use and understand geometrical properties including: angles at a point, angles on a straight line, vertically opposite angles, sum of angles in a triangle, sum of angles in a quadrilateral, angles in parallel lines, and angle properties of regular and irregular polygons.
- Understand and use geometrical properties of circles including: angle between tangent and radius, angle in a semi-circle, angle at the centre and angle at the circumference, opposite angles in a cyclic quadrilateral, angles in the same segment, alternate segment theorem, equal chords are equal distances from the centre, the perpendicular bisector of a chord passes through the centre of the circle, and tangents from an external point are equal.

7.1 Angles

You should already be familiar with the following results. They are used throughout this chapter and are listed here for reference.

- Angles on a straight line add up to 180°:

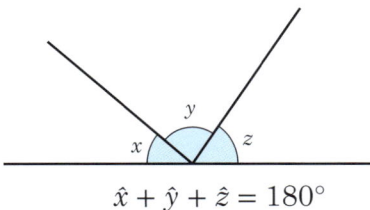

$$\hat{x} + \hat{y} + \hat{z} = 180°$$

- Angles at a point add up to 360°:

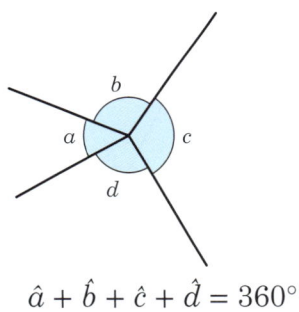

$$\hat{a} + \hat{b} + \hat{c} + \hat{d} = 360°$$

- Vertically opposite angles are equal:

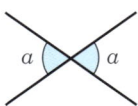

- The angle sum of any triangle is 180°.

- An isosceles triangle has 2 sides of equal length, and 2 angles of equal measure:

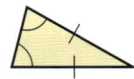

- The angle sum of a quadrilateral is 360°.

- An equilateral triangle has 3 sides of equal length, and 3 angles of equal measure. Thus, each angle in an equilateral triangle is 60°:

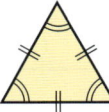

Sometimes you will need to combine these ideas with algebra to solve problems.

Example 1

Find the value of x.

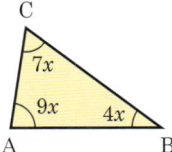

The interior angles of a triangle add up to 180°.

In this triangle, $7x + 9x + 4x = 20x = 180°$

Therefore $x = \dfrac{180}{20} = 9°$

Example 2

Find the size of the largest angle in the diagram.

Angles at a point add up to 360°, so:

$$90° + 49° + 2a + 2a + 9a = 360°$$
$$139° + 13a = 360°$$
$$13a = 221°$$
$$a = 17°$$

Therefore $9a = 153°$

The largest angle measures 153°.

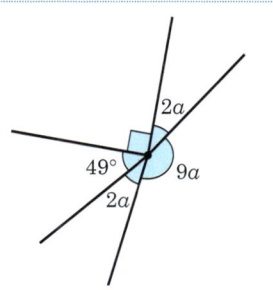

Exercise 7.1A

Find the size of the angles marked with letters.
(AB is a straight line in the diagrams.)

1.

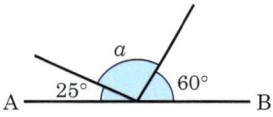

2.

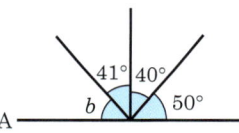

3.

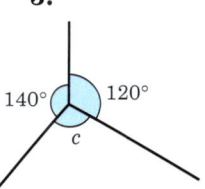

4.

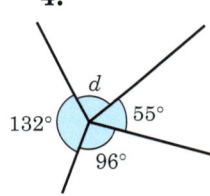

5.

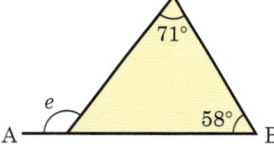

6.

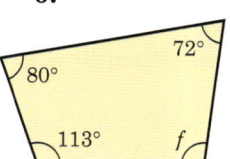

7.

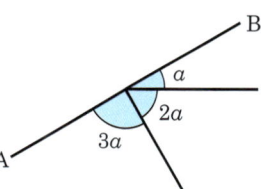

8.

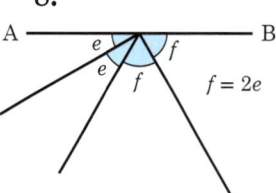

$f = 2e$

9.

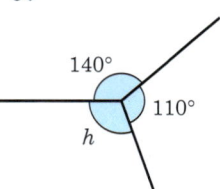

10.

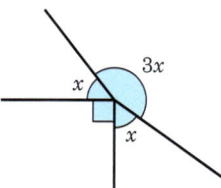

11.

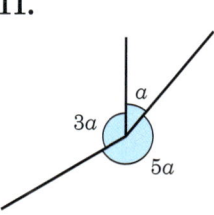

12.

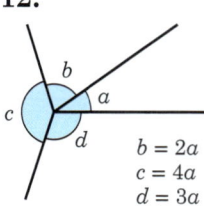

$b = 2a$
$c = 4a$
$d = 3a$

13.

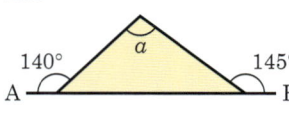

14.

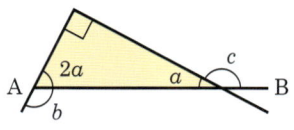

15.

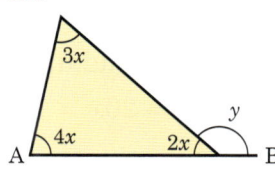

16.

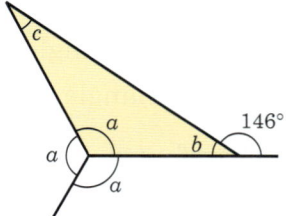

17.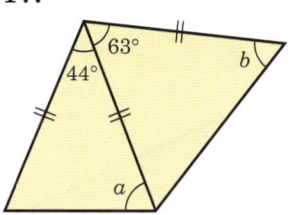

18.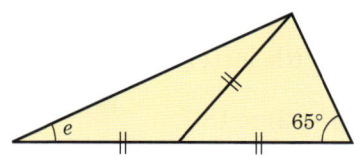

19.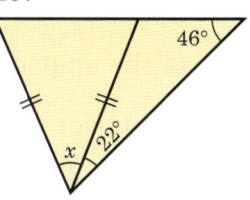

20.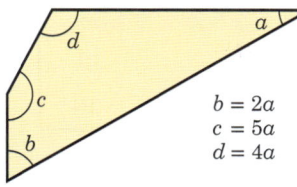

$b = 2a$
$c = 5a$
$d = 4a$

21.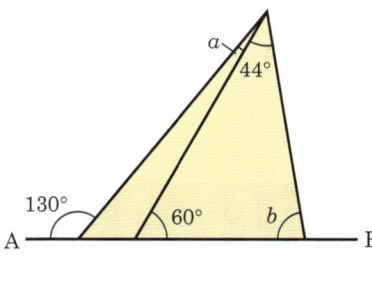

22.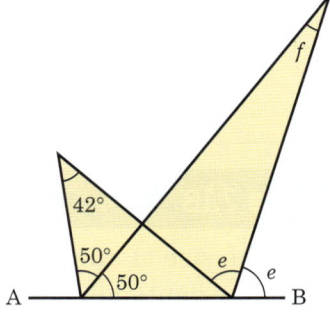

23. The largest angle in a triangle is eight times each of the other two angles. Find the size of the largest angle.

24. In △ABC, Â is a right angle and D is a point on AC such that BD bisects B̂. If BD̂C = 100°, calculate Ĉ.

25. WXYZ is a quadrilateral in which Ŵ = 108°, X̂ = 88°, Ŷ = 57° and WX̂Z = 31°. Calculate WẐX and XẐY.

26. In quadrilateral ABCD, AB extended is perpendicular to DC extended. If Â = 44° and Ĉ = 148°, calculate D̂ and B̂.

27. In the diagram, triangles ABD, CBD and ADC are all isosceles. Find the angle x.

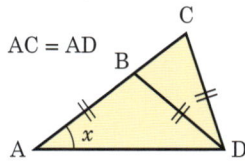

AC = AD

Polygons

- The **exterior** angles of a polygon add up to 360° $(\hat{a} + \hat{b} + \hat{c} + \hat{d} + \hat{e} = 360°)$
- The sum of the **interior** angles of a polygon is $(n - 2) \times 180°$, where n is the number of sides of the polygon.
- In a **regular** polygon, all sides are the same length and all angles are the same size.

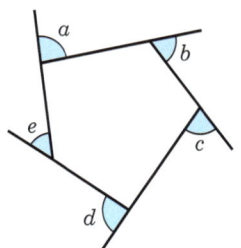

> **Tip**
>
> **Pent**agon = 5 sides
>
> **Hex**agon = 6 sides
>
> **Oct**agon = 8 sides
>
> **Dec**agon = 10 sides

Example

Find the size of the angles marked with letters.

The sum of the interior angles $= (n - 2) \times 180°$
where n is the number of sides of the polygon.
In this case, $n = 6$.

$$110° + 120° + 94° + 114° + 2t = (6 - 2) \times 180°$$
$$438° + 2t = 720°$$
$$2t = 282°$$
$$t = 141°$$

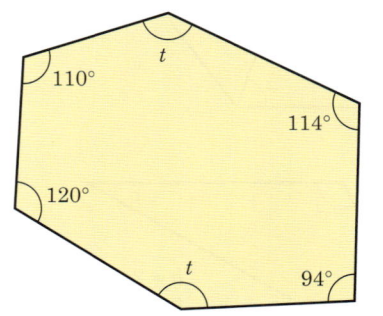

Exercise 7.1B

1. Find the size of angles a and b for a regular pentagon.

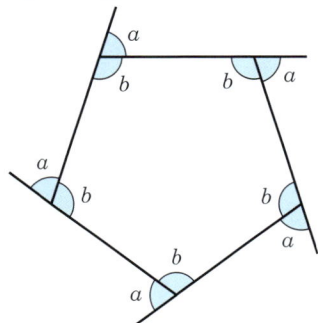

2. Find the size of angles x and y.

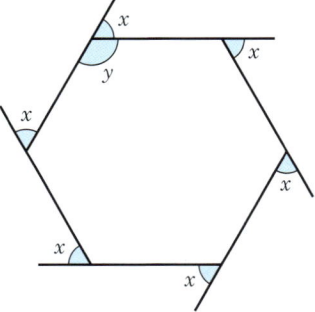

3. Find the value of m.

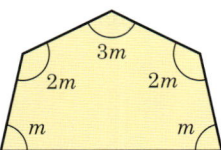

4. Find the value of a.

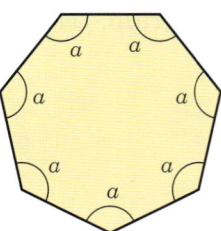

5. Find the value of x.

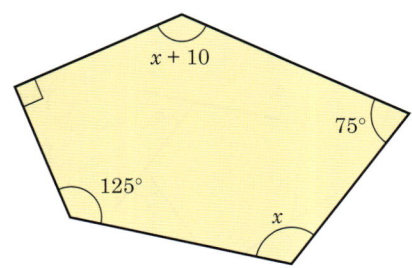

6. Calculate the number of sides of a regular polygon whose **interior** angles are each 156°.

7. Calculate the number of sides of a regular polygon whose **interior** angles are each 150°.

8. Calculate the number of sides of a regular polygon whose **exterior** angles are each 40°.

9. In a regular polygon each interior angle is 140° greater than each exterior angle. Calculate the number of sides of the polygon.

10. In a regular polygon each interior angle is 120° greater than each exterior angle. Calculate the number of sides of the polygon.

11. Two sides of a regular pentagon are extended to form angle x. Find the size of this angle x.

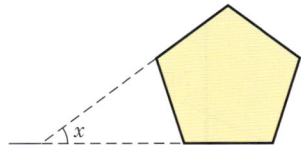

Angles formed within parallel lines

  i) $\hat{a} = \hat{c}$ (corresponding angles)

 ii) $\hat{c} = \hat{d}$ (alternate angles)

iii) $\hat{b} + \hat{c} = 180°$ (co-interior angles)

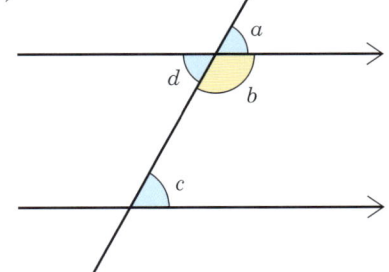

Tip

The acute angles (angles less than 90°) are the same and the obtuse angles (angles between 90° and 180°) are the same.

Exercise 7.1C

Find the size of the angles marked with letters. In each case, explain your reasoning using the correct geometric terminology.

1.

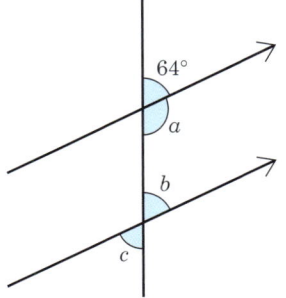

2.

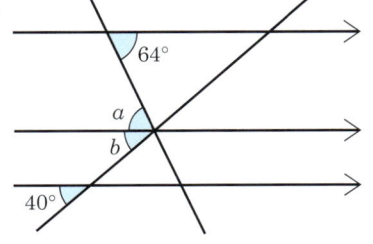

3.

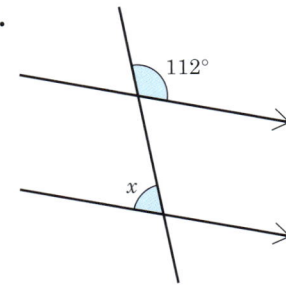

4.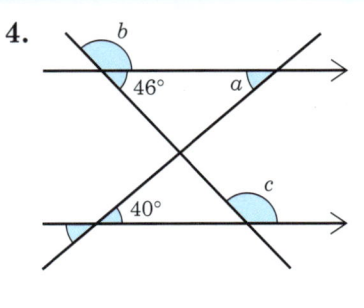

5.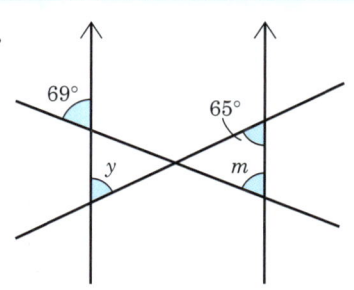

6.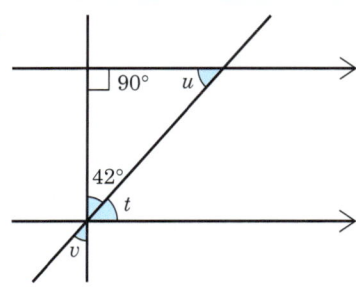

7.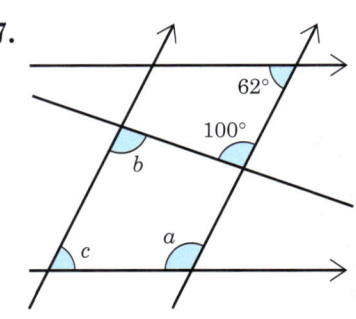

8.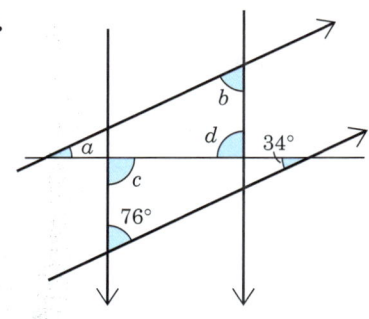

9.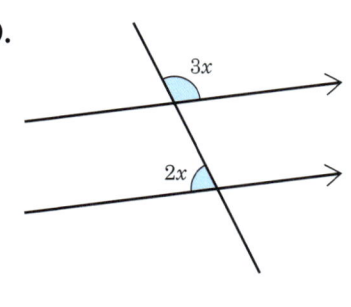

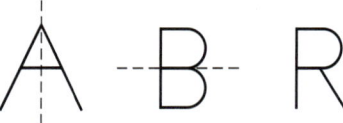

7.2 Symmetry

Line symmetry

A line of symmetry divides a shape or an object into two equal and symmetric parts. Here, the letter A has one line of symmetry, shown as a dashed line. The letter B is symmetric about the horizontal dashed line. The letter R has no line of symmetry.

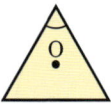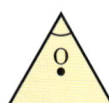

Rotational symmetry

The order of rotational symmetry that a shape has is the number of times it coincides with itself as you rotate it through 360°.

This equilateral triangle may be rotated about the point O into three identical positions. It has rotational symmetry of order 3.

Note that every shape looks the same as it did at the beginning when you have rotated it through a full 360°, since it is then back in its original position. Because of this, no shapes have rotational symmetry of an order less than 1. In this sense, every shape can be said to have rotational symmetry.

Consider the following quadrilaterals:

1. **Square**

   All sides are equal, all angles 90°, opposite sides parallel; diagonals bisect at right angles. Four lines of symmetry. Rotational symmetry of order of 4.

   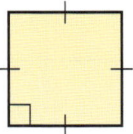

2. **Rectangle**

   Opposite sides parallel and equal, all angles 90°, diagonals bisect each other. Two lines of symmetry. Rotational symmetry of order 2.

   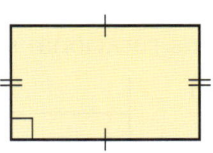

3. **Parallelogram**

   Opposite sides parallel and equal, opposite angles equal, diagonals bisect each other (but not equal). No lines of symmetry. Rotational symmetry of order 2.

   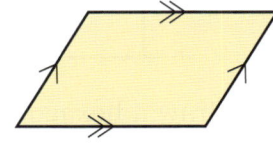

4. **Rhombus**

   A parallelogram with all sides equal, diagonals bisect each other at right angles and bisect angles. Two lines of symmetry. Rotational symmetry of order 2.

   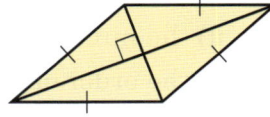

5. **Trapezium**

   One pair of sides is parallel. No line of symmetry. Rotational symmetry of order 1.

   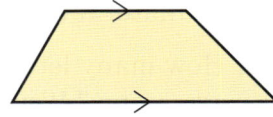

6. **Kite**

   Two pairs of adjacent sides equal, diagonals meet at right angles bisecting one of them. One line of symmetry. Rotational symmetry of order 1.

   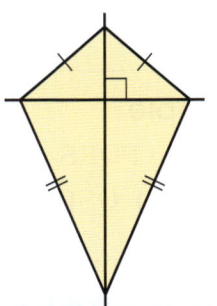

Exercise 7.2A

1. For each shape, state:

   i) the number of lines of symmetry

   ii) the order of rotational symmetry.

   a)    **b)** 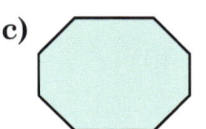   **c)** 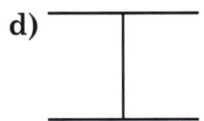   **d)**

   e) 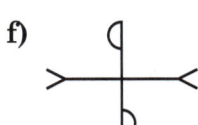   **f)**   **g)**    **h)**

i) 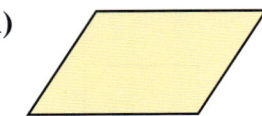   j)    k)    l)

2. Copy each of these diagrams and add one line segment so that the resulting figure has rotational symmetry but not line symmetry.

   a) 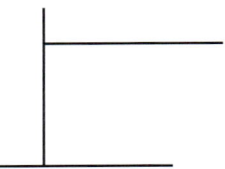   b)

3. Draw a hexagon with just two lines of symmetry.

4. For each of the following shapes, find:

   a) the number of lines of symmetry

   b) the order of rotational symmetry.

   Square; rectangle; parallelogram; rhombus; trapezium; kite; equilateral triangle; regular hexagon; scalene triangle.

5. How many letters of the alphabet can you write so that they have a line of symmetry? Write them down, drawing the axes of symmetry on them.

Problems can sometimes be solved by considering the symmetries within shapes.

Example

In a kite PQRS with PQ = PS and RQ = RS, $Q\hat{R}S = 40°$ and $Q\hat{P}S = 100°$

Find: **a)** $Q\hat{S}R$ **b)** $P\hat{S}Q$ **c)** $P\hat{Q}R$

Begin by drawing a diagram.

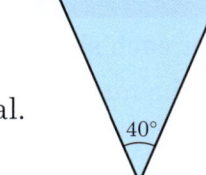

a) Triangle QSR is isosceles because of a kite's line of symmetry, which means angles QSR and SQR are equal.

$$Q\hat{S}R = \frac{180° - 40°}{2} = 70°$$

b) Triangle PSQ is isosceles meaning angles PQS and PSQ are equal.

$$P\hat{S}Q = \frac{180° - 100°}{2} = 40°$$

c) $P\hat{Q}R = P\hat{Q}S + S\hat{Q}R$

Because of the kite's line of symmetry

$P\hat{Q}S + S\hat{Q}R = P\hat{S}Q + Q\hat{S}R = 40° + 70° = 110°$

Exercise 7.2B

1. In a rectangle KLMN, $\hat{LNM} = 34°$

Calculate: **a)** $\hat{KLN}$

b) $\hat{KML}$

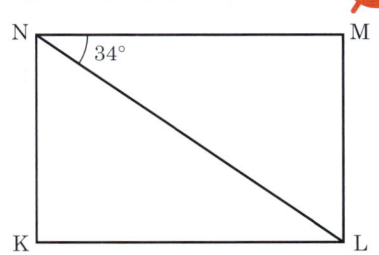

2. In a trapezium ABCD, $\hat{ABD} = 35°$, $\hat{BAD} = 110°$ and AB is parallel to DC.

Calculate: **a)** $\hat{ADB}$

b) $\hat{BDC}$

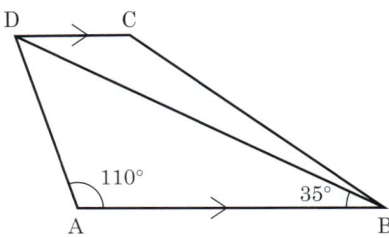

3. In a parallelogram WXYZ, $\hat{WXY} = 72°$, $\hat{ZWY} = 80°$

Calculate:

a) $\hat{WZY}$

b) $\hat{XWZ}$

c) $\hat{WYZ}$

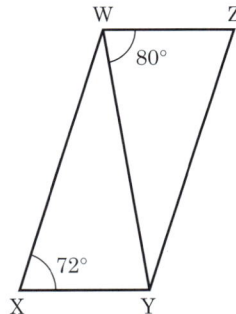

For Questions **4** to **8**, begin by drawing a diagram.

4. In a kite ABCD, AB = AD; BC = CD; $\hat{CAD} = 40°$ and $\hat{CBD} = 60°$. Calculate:

a) $\hat{BAC}$ **b)** $\hat{BCA}$ **c)** $\hat{ADC}$

5. In a rhombus ABCD, $\hat{ABC} = 64°$. Calculate:

a) $\hat{BCD}$ **b)** $\hat{ADB}$ **c)** $\hat{BAC}$

6. In a rectangle WXYZ, M is the midpoint of WX and $\hat{ZMY} = 70°$. Calculate:

a) $\hat{MZY}$ **b)** $\hat{YMX}$

7. In a trapezium ABCD, AB is parallel to DC, AB = AD, BD = DC and $\hat{BAD} = 128°$. Find:

a) $\hat{ABD}$ **b)** $\hat{BDC}$ **c)** $\hat{BCD}$

8. In a parallelogram KLMN, KL = KM and $\hat{KML} = 64°$. Find:

a) $\hat{MKL}$ **b)** $\hat{KNM}$ **c)** $\hat{LMN}$

Axes of symmetry

An axis of symmetry is a line in three-dimensional space around which a solid shape has rotational symmetry. This hexagonal prism, for example, has an axis of symmetry running through the middle of it.

The order of rotational symmetry is the number of times the shape coincides with itself as you rotate it through 360°. For a line to be an axis of symmetry, the solid must have rotational symmetry around it of an order greater than 1. This hexagonal prism has rotational symmetry of order 6 around the axis shown.

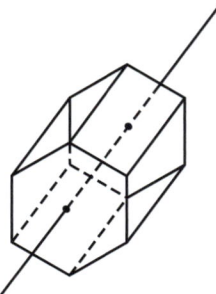

Exercise 7.2C

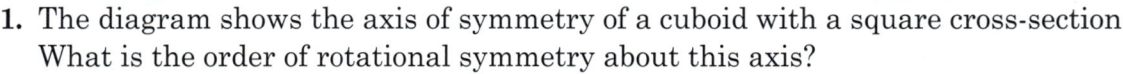

1. The diagram shows the axis of symmetry of a cuboid with a square cross-section. What is the order of rotational symmetry about this axis?

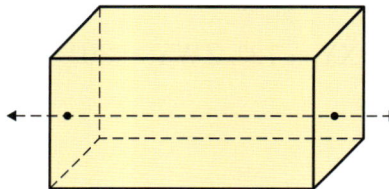

2. Four axes of symmetry for a cube are shown. For each axis, state the order of rotational symmetry.

a) 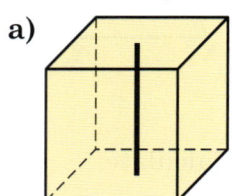   b) 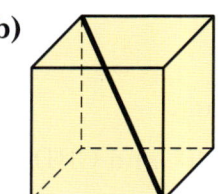   c) 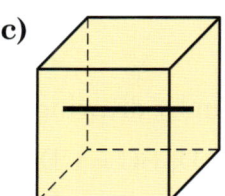   d)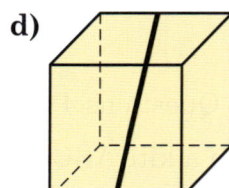

3. A cuboid has three axes of symmetry. Copy the cuboid below and draw on the axes of symmetry.

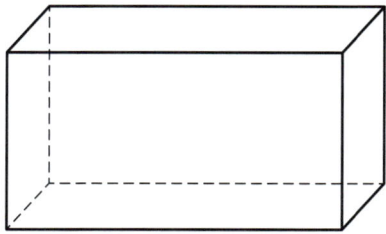

4. Angelique says that the line she has drawn is also an axis of symmetry. Is she correct?

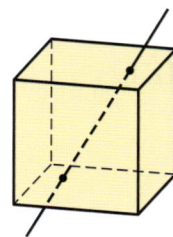

5. A cylinder has an axis of symmetry running through the middle of it, as shown in the diagram.

   Does it have any others and, if so, what is the order of rotational symmetry around each of these other axes?

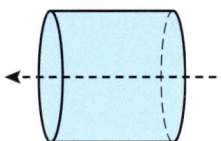

6. Name a shape that has an infinite number of axes of symmetry.

7. The cross-section of this prism is an equilateral triangle.

   How many axes of symmetry does it have?

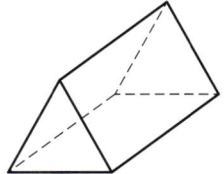

Planes of symmetry

Two shapes are **congruent** if they are exactly the same shape and size.

A **plane of symmetry** divides a 3D shape into two congruent shapes. One shape is a mirror image of the other.

The diagrams show two of the planes of symmetry of a cube.

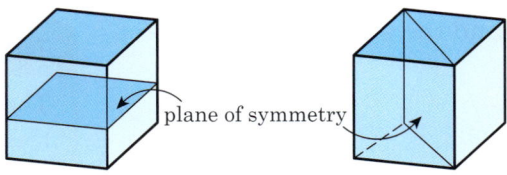

plane of symmetry

Exercise 7.2D

1. How many planes of symmetry does this cuboid with six rectangular faces have?

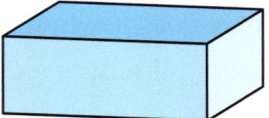

2. How many planes of symmetry do these prisms have?
   (The cross-section in part **(c)** is a semi-circle.)

   a) 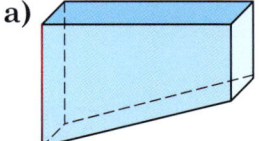   **b)** 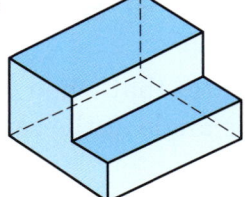   **c)**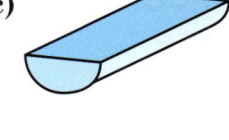

3. **a)** Draw a diagram of a cube like the one before this exercise and draw a different plane of symmetry.

   b) How many planes of symmetry does a cube have?

4. How many planes of symmetry does a hexagonal prism have?

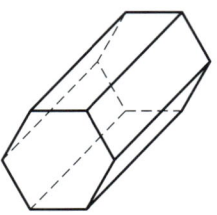

5. How many planes of symmetry does an octagonal prism have?

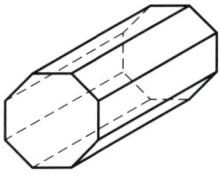

6. How many planes of symmetry does a prism have if its cross-section is a regular polygon with an even number of sides, n?

7. How many planes of symmetry does a prism have if its cross-section is a regular polygon with an odd number of sides, n?

8. Draw a pyramid with a square base so that the point of the pyramid is vertically above the centre of the square base. Show any planes of symmetry by shading.

9. The diagrams show the plan view and the side view of an object.

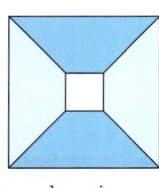

plan view

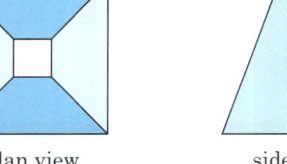

side view

> **Tip**
>
> The plan view is the view looking down on the object from above. The side view is the view from one side.

How many planes of symmetry does this object have?

10. a) How many planes of symmetry does a cylinder have?

   b) Describe the planes of symmetry, if any, of a cone.

7.3 Circle theorems

Angle at the centre is twice the angle at the circumference

The first circle theorem we will discuss states that when two angles are subtended by the same arc, the angle at the centre of a circle is twice the angle at the circumference.

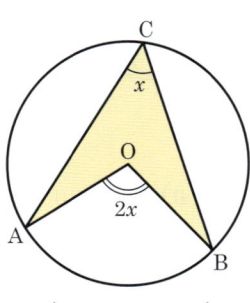

$$A\hat{O}B = 2 \times A\hat{C}B$$

Proof:

Draw the straight line COD. Let $A\hat{C}O = y$ and $B\hat{C}O = z$

In triangle AOC,

$\qquad$ AO = OC $\qquad$ (radii)

$\therefore \quad$ $O\hat{C}A = O\hat{A}C$ $\qquad$ (isosceles triangle)

$\therefore \quad$ $C\hat{O}A = 180° - 2y$ (angle sum of a triangle $= 180°$)

$\therefore \quad$ $A\hat{O}D = 2y$ $\qquad$ (sum of angles at a point on a straight line $= 180°$)

Similarly from triangle COB,

$\qquad$ $D\hat{O}B = 2z$

Now $\quad A\hat{C}B = y + z$

and $\quad A\hat{O}B = 2y + 2z$

$\therefore \qquad A\hat{O}B = 2 \times A\hat{C}B$ as required.

Example

Given that $A\hat{B}O = 50°$, find $B\hat{C}A$.

Triangle OBA is isosceles (OA = OB)

$\therefore \qquad O\hat{A}B = 50°$

$\therefore \qquad B\hat{O}A = 80°$ (angle sum of a triangle $= 180°$)

$\therefore \qquad B\hat{C}A = 40°$ (angle at the centre is twice the
$\qquad\qquad\qquad\qquad$ angle at the circumference)

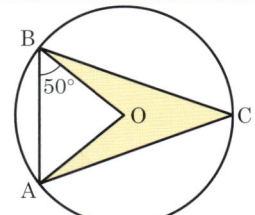

Angles in the same segment are equal

This theorem states that angles subtended by an arc in the same segment of a circle are equal. For arc AB in this diagram,

$$A\hat{X}B = A\hat{Y}B = A\hat{Z}B$$

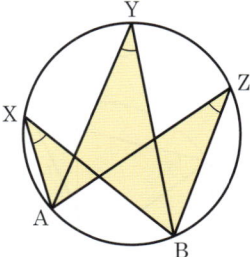

Example

Given that $B\hat{D}C = 62°$ and $D\hat{C}A = 44°$, find $B\hat{A}C$ and $A\hat{B}D$.

$\qquad B\hat{D}C = B\hat{A}C$ (angles in the same segment
$\qquad\qquad\qquad\quad$ are equal)

$\therefore \qquad B\hat{A}C = 62°$

$\qquad D\hat{C}A = A\hat{B}D$ (angles in the same segment
$\qquad\qquad\qquad\quad$ are equal)

$\therefore \qquad A\hat{B}D = 44°$

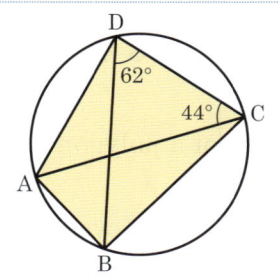

Exercise 7.3A

Find the angles marked with letters. A line passes through the centre only when point O is shown. Make sure you explain all of your reasoning.

1.

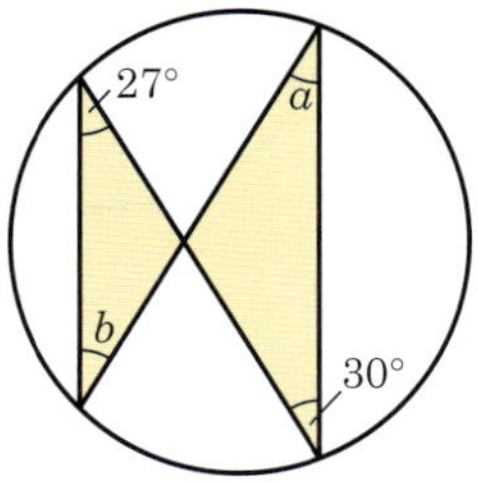

2.

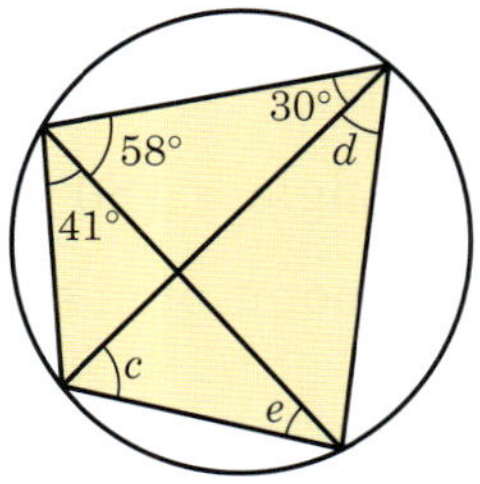

3.

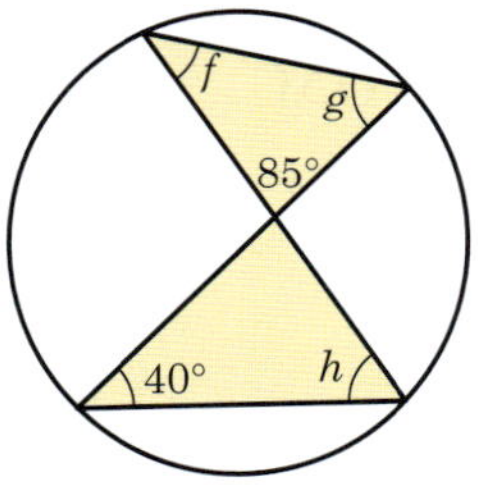

4.

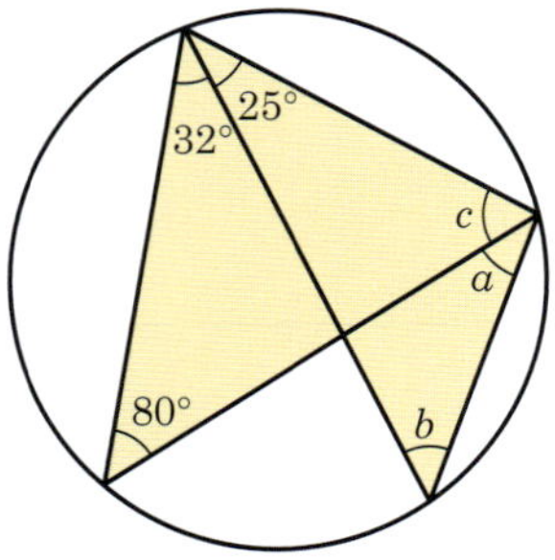

5.

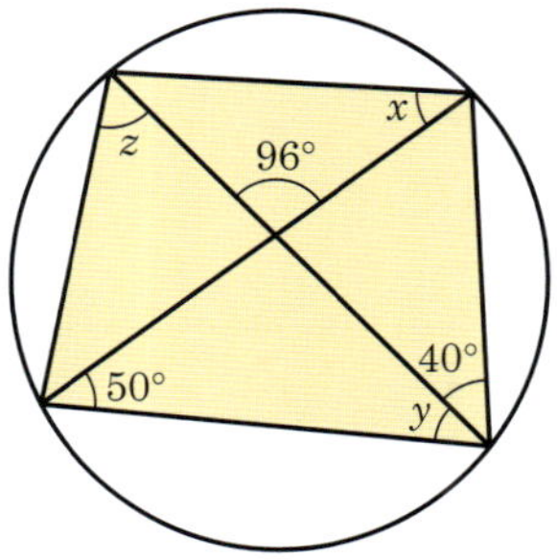

6.

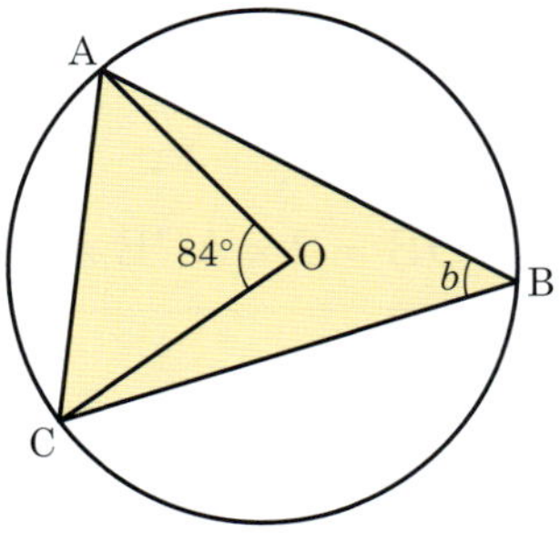

7.

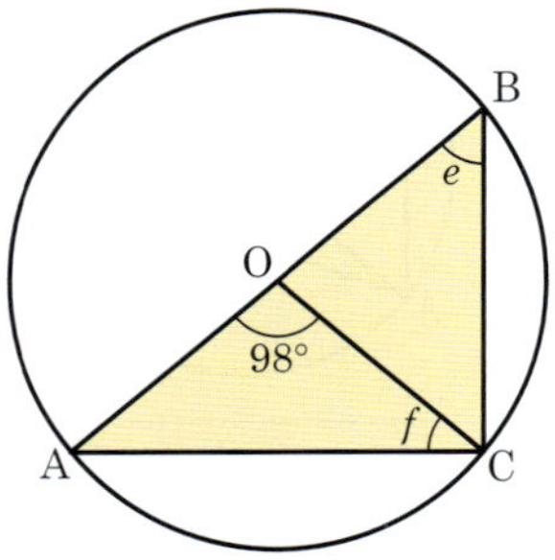

8.

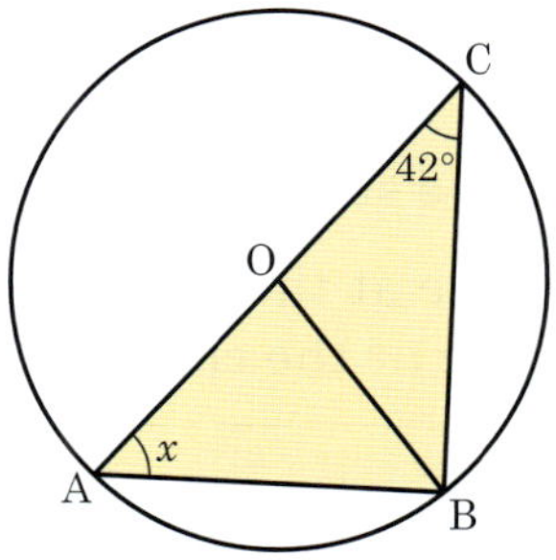

9.

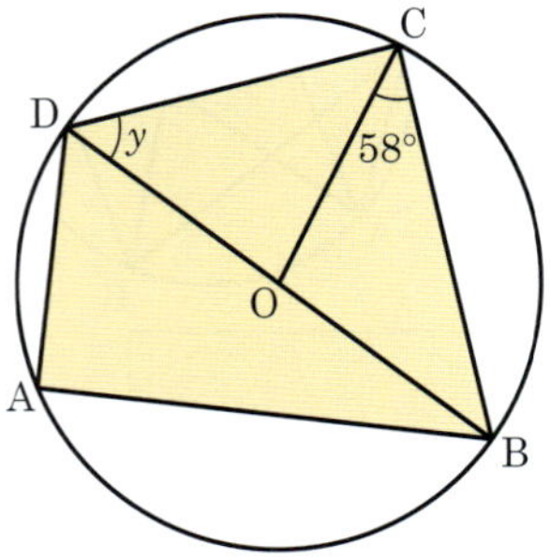

10.

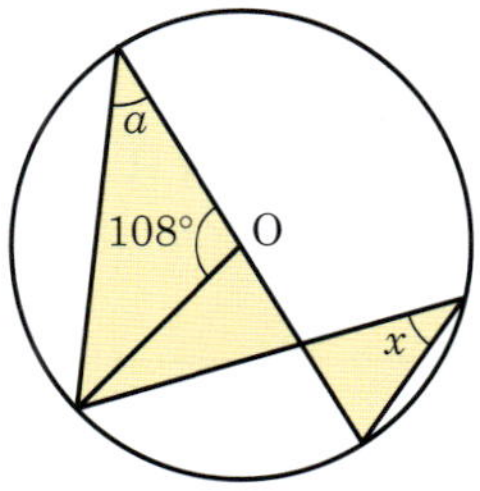

Opposite angles of a cyclic quadrilateral sum to 180°

If all the vertices of a polygon lie on the same circle, you say that the polygon is **cyclic**.

The opposite angles in a cyclic quadrilateral add up to 180°.

ABCD is a cyclic quadrilateral. All four vertices are on the circumference of the circle.

Proof:

Draw radii OA and OC.

Let $\hat{ADC} = x$ and $\hat{ABC} = y$.

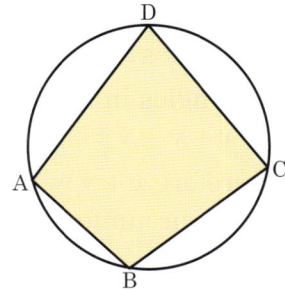

$\hat{AOC}$ obtuse $= 2x$ (angle at the centre is twice the angle at the circumference)

$\hat{AOC}$ reflex $= 2y$ (angle at the centre is twice the angle at the circumference)

$\therefore$ $2x + 2y = 360°$ (angles at a point add to 360°)

$\therefore$ $x + y = 180°$ as required

$\hat{A} + \hat{C} = 180°$
$\hat{B} + \hat{D} = 180°$

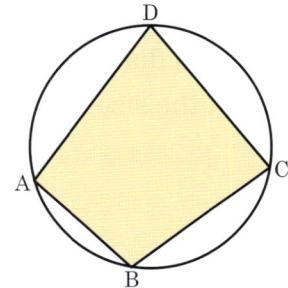

Example

Find the size of the angles labelled a and x.

$a = 180° - 81°$ (opposite angles of a cyclic quadrilateral add to 180°)

$\therefore$ $a = 99°$

$x + 2x = 180°$ (opposite angles of a cyclic quadrilateral add to 180°)

$3x = 180°$

$x = 60°$

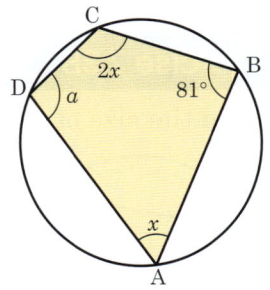

Angle in a semi-circle $= 90°$

This result is particularly interesting. It is sometimes known as Thale's theorem, after the ancient Greek mathematician Thales of Miletus.

In the diagram, points A, B and C lie on the circumference of the circle and AC is a diameter. The theorem states that no matter where on the circle point B is located, angle ABC will always be a right angle.

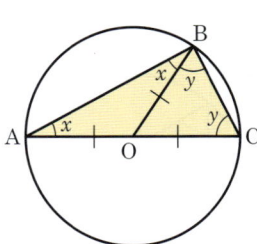

To see why this is true, notice that in the diagram OA, OB and OC are all radii of the circle, making triangles OAB and OBC isosceles.

Since the base angles of isosceles triangles are equal, you can label two angles x and two angles y.

The angles in the triangle ABC therefore add up to
$x + x + y + y = 2(x + y) = 180°$.

Therefore $x + y$ will always equal $90°$, no matter where point B lies on the circumference of the circle.

At this point, it is interesting to notice that this is also a special case of the theorem that says the angle at the centre is twice the angle at the circumference, when the angle at the centre is $180°$.

Example

AB is a diameter.

Find the size of angle b.

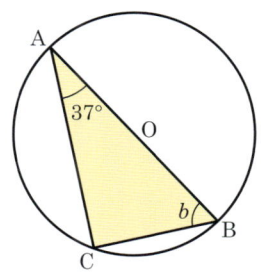

$A\hat{C}B = 90°$ (angle in a semi-circle = $90°$)

$\therefore \quad b = 180° - (90° + 37°)$

$\quad = 53°$

Exercise 7.3B

Find the size of angles marked with a letter. Explain your reasoning.

1.

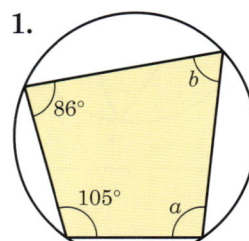

2.

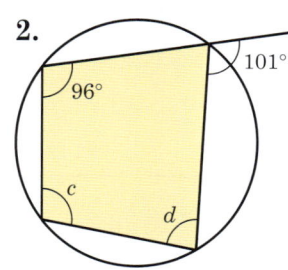

3.

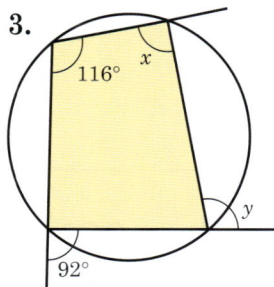

4.

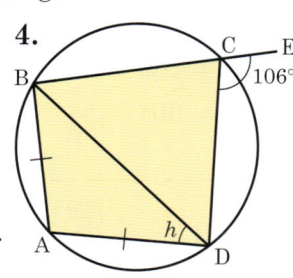

5. B

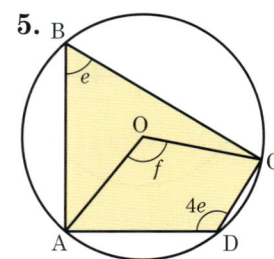

6.

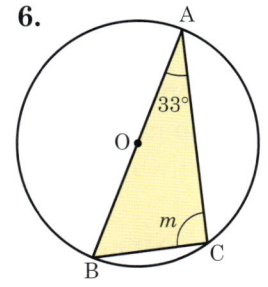

7.

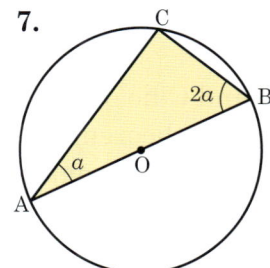

8.

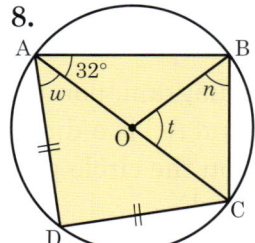

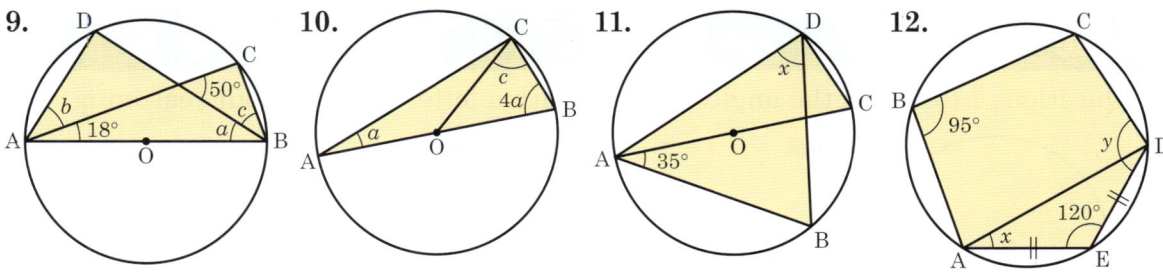

9.   10.   11.   12.

Angle between tangent and radius = 90°

The angle between a tangent of a circle and the radius drawn to the point of contact is 90°.

$\hat{ABO} = 90°$

> **Tip**
>
> A tangent to a circle is a straight line segment that touches the circle at one point only.

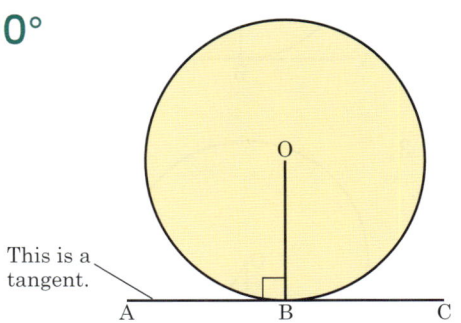

This is a tangent.

Tangents from an external point are equal in length

From any point outside a circle, just two tangents to the circle may be drawn and they are of equal length.

$TA = TB$

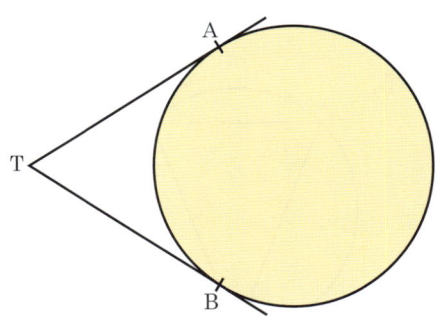

Example

TA and TB are tangents to the circle, centre O.

Given that $\hat{ATB} = 50°$, find

a) $\hat{ABT}$

b) $\hat{OBA}$

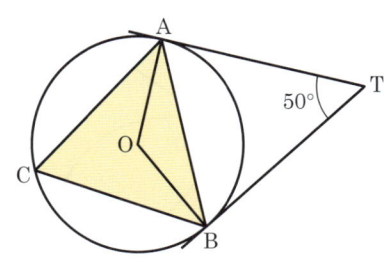

a) △TBA is isosceles (TA = TB)

∴ $\hat{ABT} = \frac{1}{2}(180° - 50°) = 65°$

b) $\hat{OBT} = 90°$ (angle between tangent and radius = 90°)

∴ $\hat{OBA} = 90° - 65°$

  $= 25°$

Exercise 7.3C

For Questions **1** to **8**, find the angles marked with a letter. Explain your reasoning.

1.

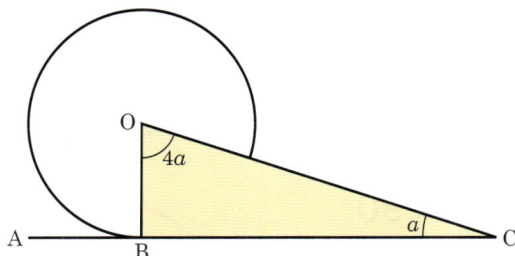

2.

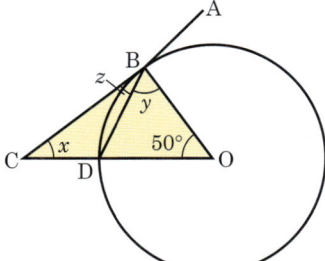

3.

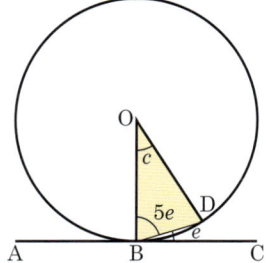

4.

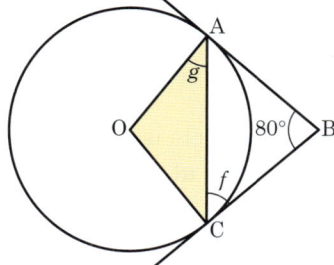

5.

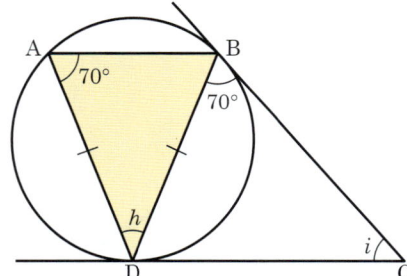

6.

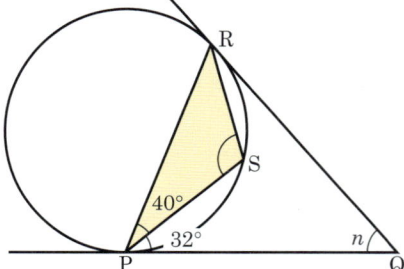

7.

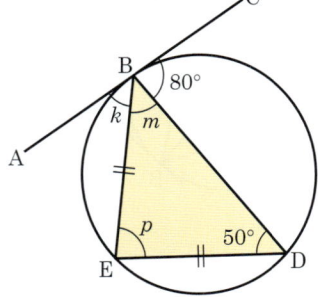

8.

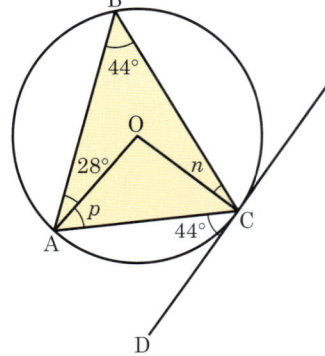

The alternate segment theorem

The angle that lies between a tangent and a chord is equal to the angle subtended by the same chord in the alternate segment.

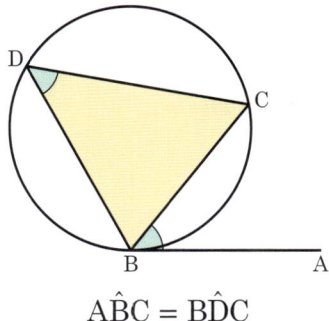

$$A\hat{B}C = B\hat{D}C$$

Proof:

EB is a diameter of the circle so $E\hat{C}B = 90°$

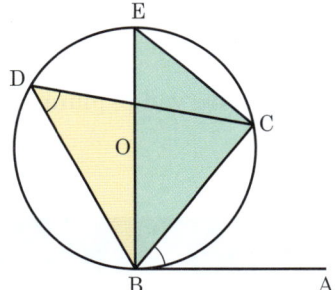

$B\hat{E}C + E\hat{B}C = 90°$ (angles in a triangle)

AB is a tangent so $A\hat{B}E = 90°$

Thus $A\hat{B}C + E\hat{B}C = 90°$

Hence $A\hat{B}C = B\hat{E}C$

$B\hat{E}C = B\hat{D}C$ (angles in the same segment)

$\therefore A\hat{B}C = B\hat{D}C$ as required.

It can similarly be shown that $D\hat{B}F = D\hat{C}B$:

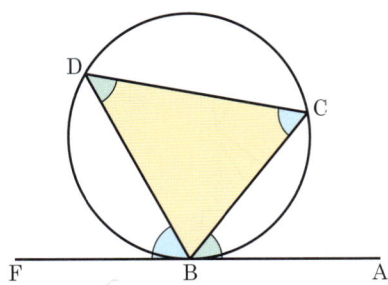

Example

O is the centre of the circle. AB is a tangent to the circle.

$B\hat{O}C = 114°$.

Find the size of $A\hat{B}C$.

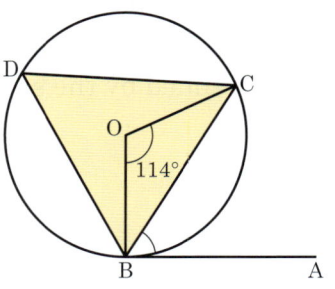

$B\hat{D}C = \dfrac{1}{2} B\hat{O}C = 57°$ (angle at the centre is twice the angle at the circumference)

$A\hat{B}C = B\hat{D}C = 57°$ (alternate segment theorem)

Hence $A\hat{B}C = 57°$

Tip

There might be several ways to work out an unknown angle. Make sure you explain your reasoning carefully.

Exercise 7.3D

For Questions **1** to **8**, find the angles marked with a letter.

1.

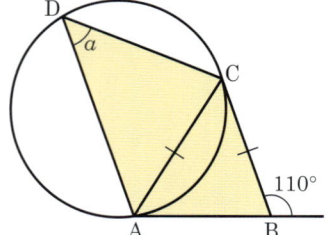

2.

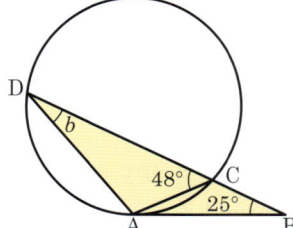

3.

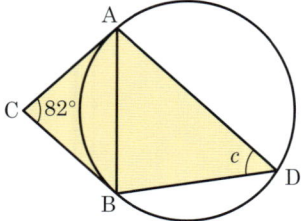

4.

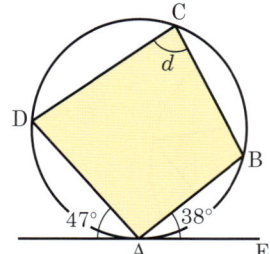

5.

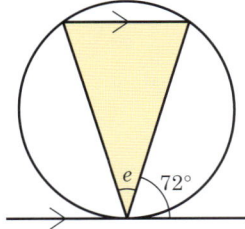

6.

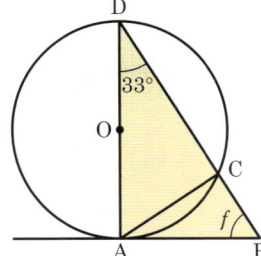

7.

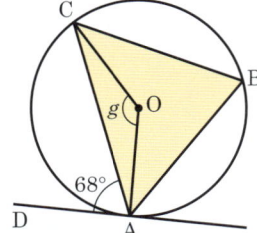

8.

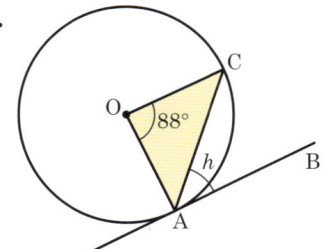

Equal chords are equidistant from the centre

If two chords in a circle are the same length, then their perpendicular distances from the centre of the circle will be equal.

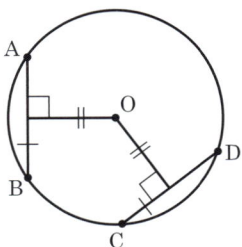

The perpendicular bisector of a chord passes through the centre

Another way to say this is that if a radius bisects a chord, it will do so at right-angles. The converse of this is also true: if a radius crosses a chord at right-angles, it will bisect the chord at that crossing point.

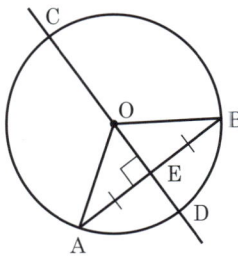

Exercise 7.3E

For Questions **1** to **5**, find the side lengths or angles marked with a letter.
For Question **6**, find the area of the quadrilateral.

1.

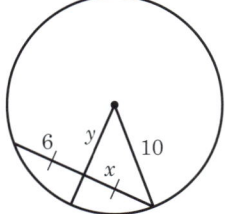

2.

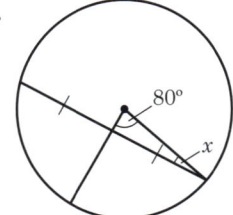

3.

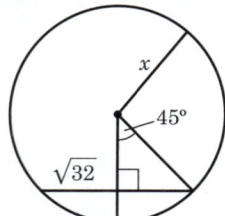

4.

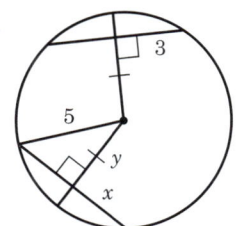

5.

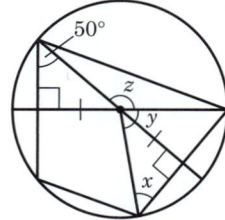

6.

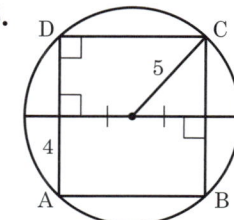

7.4 Constructions

When the word 'construct' is used, the diagram should be drawn using equipment such as a pair of compasses and a ruler.

You need to be able to construct different sized angles and shapes.

Here are some things to consider:

- Learn how to construct the perpendicular bisector of a line segment. This will enable you to construct a 90° angle.

- Learn how to construct an equilateral triangle. This will enable you to construct a 60° angle.

- Learn how to bisect an angle. Once you know how to construct a 90° angle and a 60° angle (using your equilateral triangle method) this will enable you to construct a 45° angle, a 30° angle and a 15° angle.

Some constructions, however, will not need these techniques. For example, if you are asked to construct a triangle, having been given the lengths of its sides, you will be able to do this simply by setting your compasses to the correct lengths, drawing arcs and joining points. See the following example.

Example

Construct the triangle ABC full size and measure the angle x.

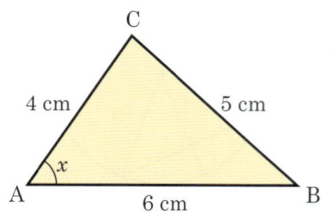

Construct a base line AB, exactly 6 cm long.

Open a pair of compasses to 4 cm and draw an arc centred on A above the base line.

Then, open the pair of compasses to 5 cm and draw another arc centred on B which intersects the first arc. Label the intersection as C.

Draw line segments connecting A to C, and B to C. The triangle is formed.

Use a protractor to measure the angle marked x.

$x = 56°$

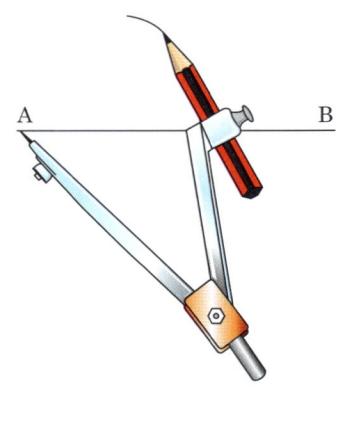

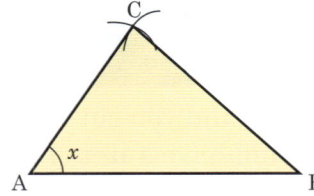

Exercise 7.4A

Use a ruler and pair of compasses to construct accurate drawings of these triangles and measure the angles labelled x.

1.

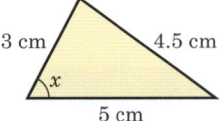

2.

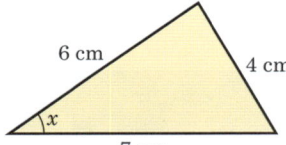

3.

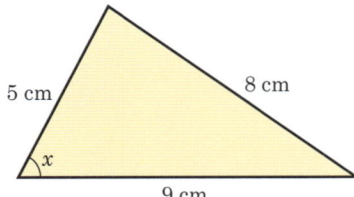

4.

5.

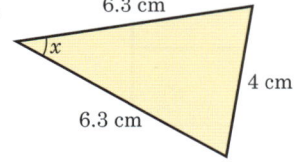

6.

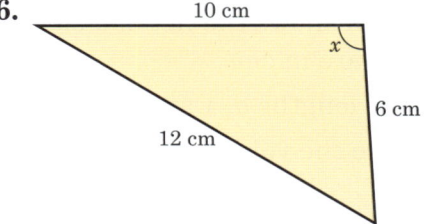

7. Construct a triangle ABC in which AB = 8 cm, AC = 6 cm and BC = 5 cm. Measure the angle $A\hat{C}B$.

8. Construct a triangle PQR in which PQ = 10 cm, PR = 7 cm and RQ = 6 cm. Measure the angle RP̂Q.

9. Construct an equilateral triangle of side length 7 cm, and then bisect one of the interior angles to construct a 30° angle.

10. Construct a 90° angle, and then bisect it to construct a 45° angle.

11. Construct an isosceles triangle that contains a right angle and two 45° angles.

12. Construct a rhombus with side length 8 cm.

7.5 Nets

If the cube below was made of cardboard, and you cut along some of the edges and laid it out flat, you would have a **net** of the cube. The diagram shows one such net of the cube, but it is not the only net possible.

Exercise 7.5A

1. Which of the nets below can be used to make a cube?

   a)
   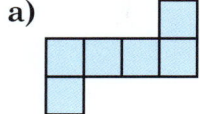

   b)
   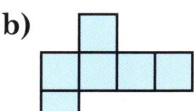

   c)
   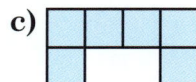

   d)
   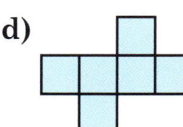

2. The diagram shows the net of a closed rectangular box. All lengths are in cm.

   a) Find the lengths a, x and y.

   b) Calculate the volume of the box.

   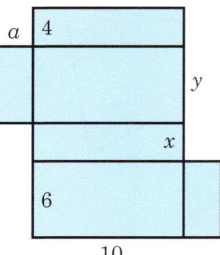

3. The diagram shows the net of a pyramid. The base is shaded. The lengths are in cm.

   a) Find the lengths a, b, c and d.

   b) Find the volume of the pyramid.

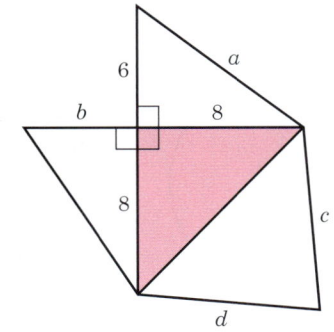

4. The diagram shows the net of a prism.

   a) Find the area of one of the triangular faces (shown shaded).

   b) Find the volume of the prism.

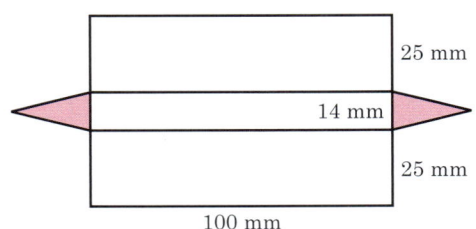

5. Sketch a net for each of the following shapes.

   a) A closed rectangular box: 7 cm × 9 cm × 5 cm

   b) A closed cylinder: length 10 cm, radius 6 cm

   c) A prism of length 12 cm, with a cross-section of an equilateral triangle with side length 4 cm.

Revision exercise 7

1. ABCD is a parallelogram. AE bisects angle A. Show that DE = BC.

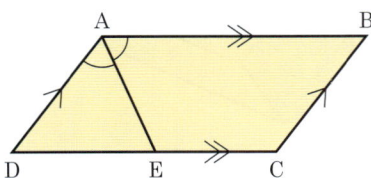

2. In a triangle PQR, $P\hat{Q}R = 50°$ and point X lies on PQ such that QX = XR. Calculate $Q\hat{X}R$.

3. a) ABCDEF is a regular hexagon. Calculate $F\hat{D}E$.

   b) ABCDEFGH is a regular octagon. Calculate $A\hat{G}H$.

4. Each interior angle of a regular polygon measures 160°. How many sides has the polygon?

5. In the quadrilateral PQRS, PQ = QS = QR. PS is parallel to QR and $Q\hat{R}S = 70°$. Calculate:

   a) $R\hat{Q}S$

   b) $P\hat{Q}S$

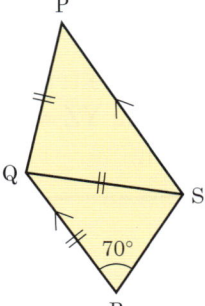

6. Find the size of the angles marked with letters. (O is the centre of the circle.)

a)

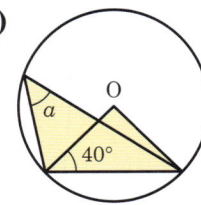

b)

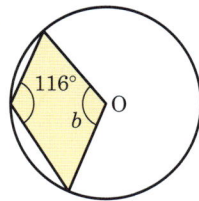

c)

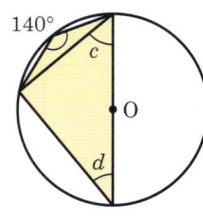

d)

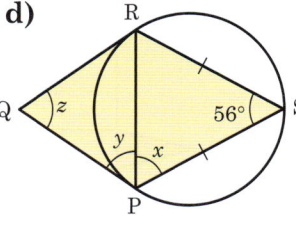

7. ABCD is a cyclic quadrilateral in which AB = BC and AB̂C = 70°.

AD extended meets BC extended at the point P, where AP̂B = 30°.

Calculate:

a) AD̂B

b) AB̂D

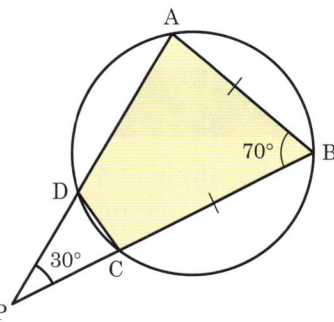

8. Using a ruler and pair of compasses only:

a) Construct the triangle ABC in which AB = 7 cm, BC = 5 cm and AC = 6 cm.

b) Construct the triangle XYZ in which XY = 10 cm, YZ = 11 cm and XZ = 9 cm.

9. The diagram shows a regular hexagon.

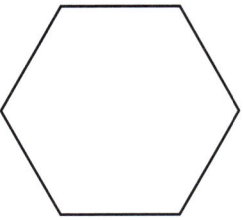

a) How many lines of symmetry does it have?

b) What is its order of rotational symmetry?

10. How many axes of symmetry does this cone have?

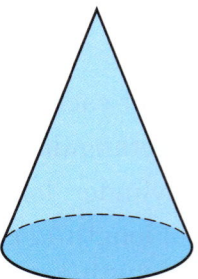

11. How many planes of symmetry does a prism with a regular pentagonal cross-section have?

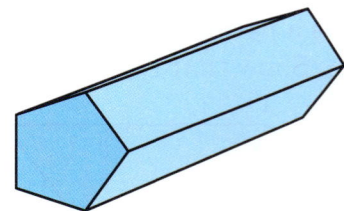

12. Which of these is a net of a cube?

a)

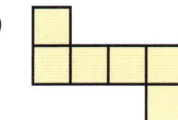

b)

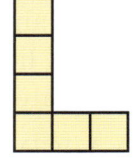

NON-CALCULATOR

1. *ABCDEFGHI* is a regular nonagon, with nine sides of equal length.

    HIJ is a straight line.

    Calculate:

    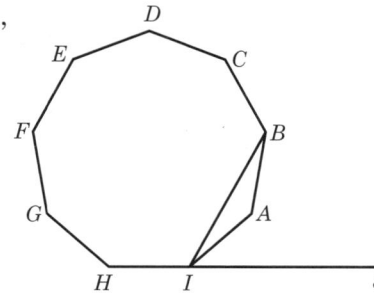

    a) angle *AIJ*　　　　　　　　　　　　　　　　　　　　　　　　[2]

    b) angle *ABI*.　　　　　　　　　　　　　　　　　　　　　　　[1]

2. *B*, *D*, *E* and *F* lie on a circle, centre *O*.

    DF is a diameter of the circle and *ABC* is the tangent to the circle at *B*.

    Angle *BDF* = 36°.

    Work out the sizes of the angles labelled *x*, *y* and *z*.

    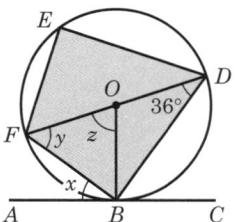

    　　　　　　　　　　　　　　　　　　　　　　　　　　　　　　[4]

3.

    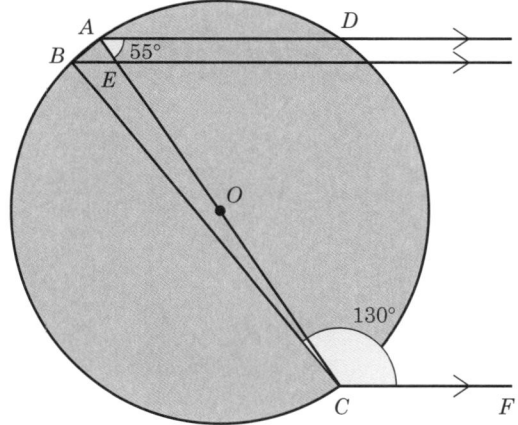

    Work out:

    a) angle *EBC*　　　　　　　　　　　　　　　　　　　　　　　[1]

    b) angle *OCF*　　　　　　　　　　　　　　　　　　　　　　　[1]

    c) angle *ABE*.　　　　　　　　　　　　　　　　　　　　　　　[1]

4. The points C, D and E lie on the circumference of a circle with centre O.
The line ABC is a tangent to the circle at point C.
Work out the values of x, y and z.

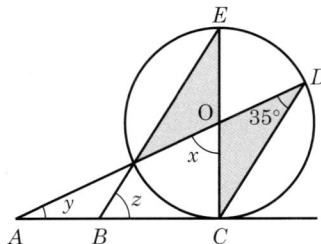

[3]

5. *ABCD* is a cyclic quadrilateral. *PQ* is a tangent to the circle at *A*.

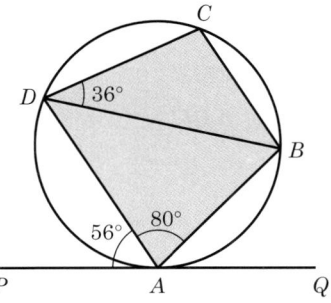

Given that $P\hat{A}D = 56°$, $D\hat{A}B = 80°$ and $C\hat{D}B = 36°$,

show that *AD* and *CB* are parallel.

[5]

Girolamo Cardano (1501–1576) was an Italian doctor who became a Professor of Mathematics at Milan. As well as being a distinguished academic, he was an astrologer, a physician and an enthusiastic chess player. In 1545 he published *Ars Magna*, the first Latin treatise devoted solely to algebra, in which he described methods for solving cubic and quartic equations. The treatise also contained the first calculation using complex numbers.

Terence Tao (1975–) was born to ethnic Chinese immigrant parents and raised in Australia. He is generally regarded as one of the greatest living mathematicians and has been called the 'Mozart of mathematics' by his colleagues. He has authored over 300 research papers on topics such as differential equations, probability, number theory and an area of mathematics called combinatorics, for which he won the prestigious Fields Medal in 2006.

- Work with algebraic fractions including using the four rules, factorising and simplifying.
- Change the subject of a formula.
- Use and understand linear inequalities including:
  - representing on a number line
  - constructing and solving
  - graphical representation of inequalities in two variables.
- Use and understand direct and inverse proportion including expressing algebraically and finding unknown quantitates.

8.1 Algebraic fractions

Simplifying fractions

As with numerical fractions, in order to simplify algebraic fractions you need to look for common factors in the numerator and denominator. You can then cancel the fraction by dividing both the numerator and denominator by these factors.

> **Example**
>
> Simplify: **a)** $\dfrac{32x^2}{56x}$ **b)** $\dfrac{3a}{5a^2}$ **c)** $\dfrac{3y + y^2}{6y}$
>
> **a)** $\dfrac{32x^2}{56x} = \dfrac{\cancel{8} \times 4 \times \cancel{x} \times x}{\cancel{8} \times 7 \times \cancel{x}} = \dfrac{4x}{7}$ **b)** $\dfrac{3a}{5a^2} = \dfrac{3 \times \cancel{a}}{5 \times a \times \cancel{a}} = \dfrac{3}{5a}$
>
> **c)** $\dfrac{3y + y^2}{6y} = \dfrac{\cancel{y}(3 + y)}{6\cancel{y}} = \dfrac{3 + y}{6}$

> **Tip**
>
> Always remember to factorise *before* simplifying when there are terms being added (or subtracted) in either the numerator or the denominator.

Exercise 8.1A

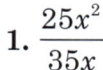

Simplify as far as possible, where you can:

1. $\dfrac{25x^2}{35x}$

2. $\dfrac{84y^2}{96y}$

3. $\dfrac{5y^2}{y}$

4. $\dfrac{y}{2y}$

5. $\dfrac{8x^2}{2x^2}$

6. $\dfrac{2x}{4y}$

7. $\dfrac{6y}{3y}$

8. $\dfrac{5ab}{10b}$

9. $\dfrac{8ab^2}{12ab}$

10. $\dfrac{7a^2b}{35ab^2}$

11. $\dfrac{(2a)^2}{4a}$

12. $\dfrac{7yx}{8xy}$

13. $\dfrac{5x + 2x^2}{3x}$

14. $\dfrac{9x + 3}{3x}$

15. $\dfrac{25 + 7x}{25}$

16. $\dfrac{4a + 5a^2}{5a}$

17. $\dfrac{3x}{4x - x^2}$

18. $\dfrac{5ab}{15a + 10a^2}$

19. $\dfrac{5x + 4}{8x}$

20. $\dfrac{12x + 6}{6y}$

21. $\dfrac{5x + 10y}{15xy}$

22. $\dfrac{18a - 3ab}{6a^2}$

23. $\dfrac{4ab + 8a^2}{2ab}$

24. $\dfrac{(2x)^2 - 8x}{4x}$

Factorising quadratic expressions will sometimes reveal common factors that can be cancelled.

Example

Simplify:

a) $\dfrac{x^2 + x - 6}{x^2 + 2x - 3}$ b) $\dfrac{x^2 + 3x - 10}{x^2 - 4}$ c) $\dfrac{3x^2 - 9x}{x^2 - 4x + 3}$

a) $\dfrac{x^2 + x - 6}{x^2 + 2x - 3} = \dfrac{(x - 2)\,\cancel{(x + 3)}}{\cancel{(x + 3)}\,(x - 1)} = \dfrac{x - 2}{x - 1}$

b) $\dfrac{x^2 + 3x - 10}{x^2 - 4} = \dfrac{\cancel{(x - 2)}\,(x + 5)}{\cancel{(x - 2)}\,(x + 2)} = \dfrac{x + 5}{x + 2}$

c) $\dfrac{3x^2 - 9x}{x^2 - 4x + 3} = \dfrac{3x\,\cancel{(x - 3)}}{(x - 1)\,\cancel{(x - 3)}} = \dfrac{3x}{x - 1}$

Exercise 8.1B

Write as a fraction in its simplest form:

1. $\dfrac{x^2 + 2x}{x^2 - 3x}$

2. $\dfrac{x^2 - 3x}{x^2 - 2x - 3}$

3. $\dfrac{x^2 + 4x}{2x^2 - 10x}$

4. $\dfrac{x^2 + 6x + 5}{x^2 - x - 2}$

5. $\dfrac{x^2 - 4x - 21}{x^2 - 5x - 14}$

6. $\dfrac{x^2 + 7x + 10}{x^2 - 4}$

7. $\dfrac{x^2 + x - 2}{x^2 - x}$

8. $\dfrac{3x^2 - 6x}{x^2 + 3x - 10}$

9. $\dfrac{6x^2 - 2x}{12x^2 - 4x}$

10. $\dfrac{3x^2 + 15x}{x^2 - 25}$

11. $\dfrac{12x^2 - 20x}{4x^2}$

12. $\dfrac{x^2 + x - 6}{x^2 + 2x - 3}$

Multiplication and division of algebraic fractions

Example

Write as a single fraction:

a) $\dfrac{2x}{3} \times \dfrac{x}{4}$ b) $\dfrac{x - 4}{6} \times \dfrac{3x}{2x - 8}$ c) $\dfrac{2x}{9} \div \dfrac{5}{3x}$ d) $\dfrac{5(x - 3)}{2} \div \dfrac{x + 1}{4x - 12}$

---

a) $\dfrac{2x}{3} \times \dfrac{x}{4} = \dfrac{2x^2}{12}$

$\qquad = \dfrac{x^2}{6}$

b) $\dfrac{x-4}{6} \times \dfrac{3x}{2x-8} = \dfrac{3x(x-4)}{6(2x-8)}$

$\qquad = \dfrac{\cancel{3}x(x\cancel{-4})}{\cancel{3} \times 2 \times 2(x\cancel{-4})}$

$\qquad = \dfrac{x}{4}$

c) $\dfrac{2x}{9} \div \dfrac{5}{3x} = \dfrac{2x}{9} \times \dfrac{3x}{5}$

$\qquad = \dfrac{6x^2}{45}$

$\qquad = \dfrac{\cancel{3} \times 2 \times x^2}{\cancel{3} \times 15}$

$\qquad = \dfrac{2x^2}{15}$

d) $\dfrac{5(x-3)}{2} \div \dfrac{x+1}{4x-12} = \dfrac{5(x-3)}{2} \times \dfrac{4x-12}{x+1}$

$\qquad = \dfrac{5(x-3)}{2} \times \dfrac{4(x-3)}{x+1}$

$\qquad = \dfrac{20(x-3)^2}{2(x+1)}$

$\qquad = \dfrac{10(x-3)^2}{x+1}$

> **Tip**
>
> Dividing by a fraction is equivalent to multiplying by its reciprocal.

Exercise 8.1C

Simplify the following:

1. $\dfrac{2x}{5} \times \dfrac{x}{3}$

2. $\dfrac{5x}{2} \times \dfrac{4}{3x}$

3. $\dfrac{2}{x} \times \dfrac{5}{x}$

4. $\dfrac{2x}{5} \times \dfrac{5}{2x}$

5. $\dfrac{3x}{7} \times \dfrac{7x}{3}$

6. $\dfrac{1}{7x} \times \dfrac{3}{7x}$

7. $\dfrac{x+1}{5} \times \dfrac{2x}{x+1}$

8. $\dfrac{x-3}{8} \times \dfrac{2x}{2x-6}$

9. $\dfrac{4(x+2)}{10x} \times \dfrac{x+3}{2x+4}$

10. $\dfrac{3x}{4} \div \dfrac{x}{2}$

11. $\dfrac{4x}{5} \div \dfrac{3}{2x}$

12. $\dfrac{3}{x} \div \dfrac{7}{x}$

13. $\dfrac{6x}{7} \sqrt{\dfrac{12}{14x}}$

14. $\dfrac{-5x}{9} \div \dfrac{9x}{5}$

15. $\dfrac{3}{4x} \div \dfrac{1}{8x}$

16. $\dfrac{x+4}{3} \div \dfrac{x+4}{6x}$

17. $\dfrac{4x-8}{3} \div \dfrac{4}{x-2}$

18. $\dfrac{5(x+1)}{2} \div \dfrac{x+1}{2x+2}$

Addition and subtraction of algebraic fractions

Example

Write as a single fraction:

a) $\dfrac{2x}{3} + \dfrac{3x}{4}$
b) $\dfrac{2}{x} + \dfrac{3}{y}$
c) $\dfrac{5x}{6} - \dfrac{2x}{9}$
d) $\dfrac{x+1}{4} + \dfrac{x-2}{5}$

a) $\dfrac{2x}{3} + \dfrac{3x}{4}$; the LCM of 3 and 4 is 12

$$\therefore \frac{2x}{3} + \frac{3x}{4} = \frac{8x}{12} + \frac{9x}{12}$$

$$= \frac{17x}{12}$$

b) $\dfrac{2}{x} + \dfrac{3}{y}$; the LCM of x and y is xy

$$\therefore \frac{2}{x} + \frac{3}{y} = \frac{2y}{xy} + \frac{3x}{xy}$$

$$= \frac{2y + 3x}{xy}$$

c) $\dfrac{5x}{6} - \dfrac{2x}{9}$; the LCM of 6 and 9 is 18

$$\therefore \frac{5x}{6} - \frac{2x}{9} = \frac{5x \times 3}{6 \times 3} - \frac{2x \times 2}{9 \times 2}$$

$$= \frac{15x}{18} - \frac{4x}{18}$$

$$= \frac{11x}{18}$$

d) $\dfrac{x+1}{4} + \dfrac{x-2}{5}$; the LCM of 4 and 5 is 20

$$\therefore \frac{x+1}{4} + \frac{x-2}{5} = \frac{(x+1) \times 5}{4 \times 5} + \frac{(x-2) \times 4}{5 \times 4}$$

$$= \frac{5x+5}{20} + \frac{4x-8}{20}$$

$$= \frac{9x-3}{20}$$

Exercise 8.1D

Simplify the following:

1. $\dfrac{2x}{5} + \dfrac{x}{5}$

2. $\dfrac{2}{x} + \dfrac{1}{x}$

3. $\dfrac{x}{7} + \dfrac{3x}{7}$

4. $\dfrac{1}{7x} + \dfrac{3}{7x}$

5. $\dfrac{5x}{8} + \dfrac{x}{4}$

6. $\dfrac{5}{8x} + \dfrac{1}{4x}$

7. $\dfrac{2x}{3} + \dfrac{x}{6}$

8. $\dfrac{2}{3x} + \dfrac{1}{6x}$

9. $\dfrac{3x}{4} + \dfrac{2x}{5}$

10. $\dfrac{3}{4x} + \dfrac{2}{5x}$

11. $\dfrac{3x}{4} - \dfrac{2x}{3}$

12. $\dfrac{3}{4x} - \dfrac{2}{3x}$

13. $\dfrac{x}{2} + \dfrac{x+1}{3}$

14. $\dfrac{x-1}{3} + \dfrac{x+2}{4}$

15. $\dfrac{2x-1}{5} + \dfrac{x+3}{2}$

16. $\dfrac{x+1}{3} - \dfrac{2x+1}{4}$

17. $\dfrac{x-3}{3} - \dfrac{x-2}{5}$

18. $\dfrac{2x+1}{7} - \dfrac{x+2}{2}$

19. $\dfrac{2x}{3} + \dfrac{3(x-5)}{2}$

20. $\dfrac{4x}{3} - \dfrac{2(x+1)}{5}$

21. $\dfrac{2(x+3)}{4} + \dfrac{4(x-2)}{7}$

22. $\dfrac{1}{x} + \dfrac{2}{x+1}$

23. $\dfrac{3}{x-2} + \dfrac{4}{x}$

24. $\dfrac{5}{x-2} + \dfrac{3}{x+3}$

25. $\dfrac{7}{x+1} - \dfrac{3}{x+2}$

26. $\dfrac{2}{x+3} - \dfrac{5}{x-1}$

27. $\dfrac{3}{x-2} - \dfrac{4}{x+1}$

Solving quadratics involving algebraic fractions

Example

A girl bought a certain number of golf balls for $20. If each ball had cost 20 cents less, she could have bought five more for the same money. How many golf balls did she buy?

Let the number of balls bought be x.

Cost of each ball $= \dfrac{2000}{x}$ cents

If five more balls had been bought:

Cost of each ball now $= \dfrac{2000}{(x+5)}$ cents

The new price is 20 cents less than the original price.

$\therefore \quad \dfrac{2000}{x} - \dfrac{2000}{(x+5)} = 20$

$$x\left(\frac{2000}{x}\right) - x\left(\frac{2000}{(x+5)}\right) = 20x \qquad \text{(Multiply by } x.\text{)}$$

$$2000(x+5) - x\,\frac{2000}{(x+5)}\,(x+5) = 20x(x+5) \qquad \text{(Multiply by } (x+5).\text{)}$$

$$2000x + 10\,000 - 2000x = 20x^2 + 100x$$

$$20x^2 + 100x - 10\,000 = 0$$

$$x^2 + 5x - 500 = 0$$

$$(x-20)(x+25) = 0$$

$$x = 20$$

$$\text{or} \qquad x = -25$$

Reject $x = -25$ as not relevant to this context.

The number of balls bought $= 20$

Exercise 8.1E

1. A number exceeds four times its reciprocal by 3. Find the number.

2. Two integers differ by 3. The sum of their reciprocals is $\frac{7}{10}$. Find the integers.

3. A cyclist travels 40 km at a speed of x km/h.

    a) Find the time taken in terms of x.

    b) Find the time taken when his speed is reduced by 2 km/h.

    c) If the difference between the times is 1 hour, find the original speed x.

4. An increase of speed of 4 km/h on a journey of 32 km reduces the time taken by 4 hours. Find the original speed.

5. A train normally travels 240 km at a certain speed. One day, due to bad weather, the train's speed is reduced by 20 km/h so that the journey takes two hours longer. Find the normal speed.

6. The speed of a sparrow is x km/h in still air. When the wind is blowing at 1 km/h, the sparrow takes 5 hours to fly 12 kilometres to her nest and 12 kilometres back again. She goes out directly into the wind and returns with the wind behind her. Find her speed in still air.

7. An aircraft flies a certain distance on a bearing of 135° and then twice the distance on a bearing of 225°. Its distance from the starting point is then 350 km. Find the length of the first part of the journey.

8. The numerator of a fraction is 1 less than the denominator. When both numerator and denominator are increased by 2, the new fraction is greater than the original fraction by $\frac{1}{12}$. Find the original fraction.

8.2 Changing the subject of a formula

The operations involved in solving ordinary linear equations are exactly the same as the operations required in changing the subject of a formula. Compare the two parts of the following example.

Example 1

a) Solve the equation $3x + 1 = 12$

b) Make x the subject of the formula $Mx + B = A$

---

a) $3x + 1 = 12$

$\qquad 3x = 12 - 1$ (Subtract 1 from both sides.)

$\qquad x = \dfrac{12 - 1}{3} = \dfrac{11}{3}$ (Divide both sides by 3.)

b) $Mx + B = A$

$\qquad Mx = A - B$ (Subtract B from both sides.)

$\qquad x = \dfrac{A - B}{M}$ (Divide both sides by M.)

Example 2

a) Solve the equation $3(y - 2) = 5$

b) Make y the subject of the formula $x(y - a) = e$

---

a) $3(y - 2) = 5$ (Expand the brackets.)

$\qquad 3y - 6 = 5$

$\qquad 3y = 11$ (Add 6 to both sides.)

$\qquad y = \dfrac{11}{3}$ (Divide both sides by 3.)

b) $x(y - a) = e$ (Expand the brackets.)

$\qquad xy - xa = e$

$\qquad xy = e + xa$ (Add xa to both sides.)

$\qquad y = \dfrac{e + xa}{x}$ (Divide both sides by x.)

Exercise 8.2A

Make x the subject of each formula.

1. $2x = 5$	**2.** $Ax = B$	**3.** $Mx = K$
4. $xy = 4$	**5.** $4x = D$	**6.** $9x = T + N$
7. $Ax = B - R$	**8.** $Lx = N - R^2$	**9.** $R - S^2 = Nx$
10. $x + A = T$	**11.** $M = x + B$	**12.** $L = x + D^2$
13. $N^2 + x = T$	**14.** $L + x = N + M$	**15.** $Z + x = R - S$
16. $x - 5 = 2$	**17.** $x - R = A$	**18.** $F = x - B$
19. $F^2 = x - B^2$	**20.** $x - D = A + B$	**21.** $x - E = A^2$

Make y the subject of the following formulae.

22. $L = y - B$	**23.** $Ay + C = N$	**24.** $Ny - F = H$
25. $Vy + m = Q$	**26.** $ty - m = n + a$	**27.** $qy + n = s - t$
28. $ny - s^2 = t$	**29.** $V^2y + b = c$	**30.** $r = ny - 6$
31. $s = my + d$	**32.** $t = my - b$	**33.** $2(y + 1) = 6$
34. $3(y - 1) = 5$	**35.** $A(y + B) = C$	**36.** $h(y + n) = a$
37. $b(y - d) = q$	**38.** $n = r(y + t)$	**39.** $t(y - 4) = b$

Example 1

a) Solve the equation $\dfrac{3a + 1}{2} = 4$

b) Make a the subject of the formula $\dfrac{na + b}{m} = n$

a) $\dfrac{3a + 1}{2} = 4$

$3a + 1 = 8$

$3a = 7$

$a = \dfrac{7}{3}$

b) $\dfrac{na + b}{m} = n$

$na + b = mn$

$na = mn - b$

$a = \dfrac{mn - b}{n}$

Example 2

Make a the subject of the formula $x - na = y$

Make the 'a' term positive.

$x = y + na$

$x - y = na$

$\dfrac{x - y}{n} = a$

Rearrange so that the subject a is on the left.

$a = \dfrac{x - y}{n}$

Exercise 8.2B

Make a the subject of each formula.

1. $\dfrac{a}{4} = 3$

2. $\dfrac{a}{D} = B$

3. $b = \dfrac{a}{m}$

4. $\dfrac{a - 2}{4} = 6$

5. $\dfrac{a - A}{B} = T$

6. $\dfrac{a + Q}{N} = B^2$

7. $g = \dfrac{a - r}{e}$

8. $\dfrac{2a + 1}{5} = 2$

9. $\dfrac{Aa + B}{C} = D$

10. $\dfrac{ra - t}{S} = v$

11. $\dfrac{za - m}{q} = t$

12. $\dfrac{m + Aa}{b} = c$

13. $A = \dfrac{Ba + D}{E}$

14. $n = \dfrac{ea - f}{h}$

15. $q = \dfrac{ga + b}{r}$

16. $6 - a = 2$

17. $7 - a = 9$

18. $5 = 7 - a$

19. $A - a = B$

20. $D - a = H$

21. $n - a = m$

22. $t = q - a$

23. $r = v^2 - ra$

24. $t^2 = w - na$

25. $n - qa = 2$

26. $\dfrac{3 - 4a}{2} = 1$

27. $\dfrac{D - Ea}{N} = B$

28. $\dfrac{h - fa}{b} = x$

29. $\dfrac{v^2 - ha}{C} = d$

30. $\dfrac{M(a + B)}{N} = T$

31. $\dfrac{f(Na - e)}{m} = B$

32. $\dfrac{T(M - a)}{E} = F$

33. $\dfrac{y(x - a)}{z} = t$

Example 1

a) Solve the equation $7 = \dfrac{4}{z}$

b) Make z the subject of the formula $k = \dfrac{n}{z}$

a) $7 = \dfrac{4}{z}$

$7z = 4$

$z = \dfrac{4}{7}$

b) $k = \dfrac{n}{z}$

$kz = n$

$z = \dfrac{n}{k}$

Example 2

Make t the subject of the formula $\dfrac{x}{t} + m = a$

$$\frac{x}{t} = a - m$$
$$x = (a - m)t$$
$$\frac{x}{(a - m)} = t$$

You can rearrange this so that t is on the left side:

$$t = \frac{x}{(a - m)}$$

Exercise 8.2C

Make a the subject of each formula.

1. $\dfrac{7}{a} = 14$

2. $\dfrac{B}{a} = C$

3. $m = \dfrac{n}{a}$

4. $\dfrac{B}{a} = x$

5. $\dfrac{5}{a} = \dfrac{3}{4}$

6. $\dfrac{N}{a} = \dfrac{B}{D}$

7. $\dfrac{5}{a + 1} = 2$

8. $\dfrac{7}{a - 1} = 3$

9. $\dfrac{B}{a + D} = C$

10. $\dfrac{Q}{a - C} = T$

11. $\dfrac{L}{Ma} = B$

12. $\dfrac{m}{ca} = d$

13. $x = \dfrac{z}{y - a}$

Make x the subject of each formula.

14. $\dfrac{2}{x} + 1 = 3$

15. $\dfrac{5}{x} - 2 = 4$

16. $\dfrac{A}{x} + B = C$

17. $\dfrac{r}{x} - t = n$

18. $h = d - \dfrac{b}{x}$

19. $C - \dfrac{d}{x} = e$

20. $r - \dfrac{m}{x} = e^2$

21. $t^2 = b - \dfrac{n}{x}$

22. $\dfrac{d}{x} + b = mn$

23. $\dfrac{M}{x + q} - N = 0$

24. $\dfrac{Y}{x - c} - T = 0$

25. $3M = M + \dfrac{N}{P + x}$

26. $A = \dfrac{B}{c + x} - 5A$

27. $\dfrac{K}{Mx} + B = C$

28. $\dfrac{z}{xy} - z = y$

29. $\dfrac{m^2}{x} - n = -p$

30. $t = w - \dfrac{q}{x}$

Example

Make x the subject of each formula.

a) $\sqrt{x^2 + A} = B$ **b)** $(Ax - B)^2 = M$ **c)** $\sqrt{R - x} = T$

a) $\sqrt{x^2 + A} = B$

$x^2 + A = B^2$ (square both sides)

$x^2 = B^2 - A$

$x = \pm\sqrt{B^2 - A}$

b) $(Ax - B)^2 = M$

$Ax - B = \pm\sqrt{M}$ (square root both sides)

$Ax = B \pm \sqrt{M}$

$x = \dfrac{B \pm \sqrt{M}}{A}$

c) $\sqrt{R - x} = T$

$R - x = T^2$

$R = T^2 + x$

$x = R - T^2$

Exercise 8.2D

Make x the subject of each formula.

1. $\sqrt{x} = 2$ **2.** $\sqrt{x - 2} = 3$ **3.** $\sqrt{x + a} = B$

4. $\sqrt{x - E} = H$ **5.** $\sqrt{ax + b} = c$ **6.** $\sqrt{x - m} = a$

7. $b = \sqrt{gx - t}$ **8.** $r = \sqrt{b - x}$ **9.** $b = \sqrt{x - d}$

10. $\sqrt{M - Nx} = P$ **11.** $\sqrt{Ax + B} = \sqrt{D}$ **12.** $\sqrt{x - D} = A^2$

13. $x^2 = g$ **14.** $x^2 + 1 = 17$ **15.** $x^2 - A = M$

16. $b = a + x^2$ **17.** $C - x^2 = m$ **18.** $N = d - x^2$

Make k the subject.

19. $\dfrac{kz}{a} = t$ **20.** $ak^2 - t = m$ **21.** $n = a - k^2$

22. $\sqrt{k^2 - A} = B$ **23.** $t = \sqrt{m + k^2}$ **24.** $2\sqrt{k + 1} = 6$

25. $A\sqrt{k} + B = M$

26. $\sqrt{\dfrac{M}{k}} = N$

27. $\sqrt{a - k} = b$

28. $\sqrt{a^2 - k^2} = t$

29. $\sqrt{m - k^2} = x$

30. $2\pi\sqrt{k + t} = 4$

31. $A\sqrt{k + 1} = B$

32. $\sqrt{ak^2 - b} = C$

33. $a\sqrt{k^2 - x} = b$

34. $k^2 + b = x^2$

35. $\dfrac{k^2}{a} + b = c$

36. $\sqrt{c^2 - ak} = b$

Rearranging when the subject appears twice

When the letter you want to make the subject appears twice in the equation, the way to make it appear only once is to collect all the terms that contain that letter, then factorise that letter out.

Example

Make x the subject of each formula.

a) $Ax - B = Cx + D$

b) $x + a = \dfrac{x + b}{c}$

a) $Ax - B = Cx + D$

$Ax - Cx = D + B$

$x(A - C) = D + B$ (factorise)

$x = \dfrac{D + B}{A - C}$

b) $x + a = \dfrac{x + b}{c}$

$c(x + a) = x + b$

$cx + ca = x + b$

$cx - x = b - ca$

$x(c - 1) = b - ca$ (factorise)

$x = \dfrac{b - ca}{c - 1}$

Exercise 8.2E

Make y the subject of each formula.

1. $5(y - 1) = 2(y + 3)$

2. $Ny + B = D - Ny$

3. $m(y + a) = n(y + b)$

4. $\dfrac{a - y}{a + y} = b$

5. $\dfrac{1 - y}{1 + y} = \dfrac{c}{d}$

6. $y + m = \dfrac{2y - 5}{m}$

7. $y - n = \dfrac{y + 2}{n}$

8. $\dfrac{ay + x}{x} = 4 - y$

9. $c - dy = e - ay$

10. $y(a - c) = by + d$

11. $\dfrac{y + x}{y - x} = 3$

12. $y(b - a) = a(y + b + c)$

13. $\sqrt{\dfrac{y + x}{y - x}} = 2$

14. $\sqrt{\dfrac{m(y + n)}{y}} = p$

15. $n - y = \dfrac{4y - n}{m}$

Example

Make w the subject of the formula $\sqrt{\dfrac{w}{w + a}} = c$

$$\dfrac{w}{w + a} = c^2$$

$$w = c^2(w + a) \quad \text{(Square both sides.)}$$

$$w = c^2 w + c^2 a$$

$$w - c^2 w = c^2 a$$

$$w(1 - c^2) = c^2 a$$

$$w = \dfrac{c^2 a}{1 - c^2}$$

Exercise 8.2F

Make the letter in square brackets the subject of each formula.

1. $ax + by + c = 0$ $[x]$

2. $\sqrt{a\left(y^2 - b\right)} = e$ $[y]$

3. $\dfrac{\sqrt{k - m}}{n} = \dfrac{1}{m}$ $[k]$

4. $\dfrac{x + y}{x - y} = 2$ $[x]$

5. $t = 2\pi\sqrt{\dfrac{d}{g}}$ $[d]$

6. $\sqrt{x^2 + a} = 2x$ $[x]$

7. $\sqrt{\dfrac{b\left(m^2 + a\right)}{e}} = t$ $[m]$

8. $\sqrt{\dfrac{x + 1}{x}} = a$ $[x]$

9. $\sqrt{a^2 + b^2} = x^2$ $[a]$

10. $\dfrac{a}{k} + b = \dfrac{c}{k}$ $[k]$

11. $a - y = \dfrac{b + y}{a}$ $[y]$

12. $G = 4\pi\sqrt{x^2 + T^2}$ $[x]$

13. $a\sqrt{\dfrac{x^2 - n}{m}} = \dfrac{a^2}{b}$ $[x]$

14. $\dfrac{M}{N} + E = \dfrac{P}{N}$ $[N]$

15. $\dfrac{Q}{P - x} = R$ $[x]$

16. $\sqrt{z - ax} = t$ $[a]$

17. $e + \sqrt{x + f} = g$ $[x]$

18. $\dfrac{m\left(ny - e^2\right)}{p} + n = 5n$ $[y]$

8.3 Proportion

Direct proportion

In Chapter 3, section 3.1, you looked at the ideas of direct and inverse proportion, and how they were closely related to the idea of ratio. In this section, you will approach it more algebraically.

If x is directly proportional to y, you write $x \propto y$, using the 'is proportional to' symbol $\propto$.

The '$\propto$' symbol can be replaced by '$= k$' where k is a constant, which means that $x = ky$.

Suppose you are told that $x = 3$ when $y = 12$.

Then $3 = k \times 12$ and $k = \dfrac{1}{4}$

You can then write $x = \dfrac{1}{4} y$, and this allows you to find the value

of x for any value of y, and vice versa.

Example 1

y is directly proportional to z.

When $z = 5$, $y = 2$.

Find:

a) the value of y when $z = 6$

b) the value of z when $y = 5$

Because $y \propto z$, then $y = kz$ where k is a constant.

$$y = 2 \text{ when } z = 5$$
$$2 = k \times 5$$
$$k = \frac{2}{5}$$

So $\quad y = \dfrac{2}{5} z$

a) When $z = 6$, $y = \dfrac{2}{5} \times 6 = 2\dfrac{2}{5}$

b) When $y = 5$, $5 = \dfrac{2}{5} z$

$$z = \frac{25}{2} = 12\frac{1}{2}$$

Example 2

The value in dollars, V, of a diamond is proportional to the square of its mass M.
If a diamond with a mass of 10 grams is worth \$200, find:

a) the value of a diamond with a mass of 30 grams

b) the mass of a diamond worth \$5000.

$$V \propto M^2$$

or $V = kM^2$ where k is a constant.

$V = 200$ when $M = 10$

$\therefore \quad 200 = k \times 10^2$

$k = 2$

So $V = 2M^2$

a) When $M = 30$,

$$V = 2 \times 30^2 = 2 \times 900$$
$$V = \$1800$$

A diamond with a mass of 30 grams is worth \$1800

b) When $V = 5000$,

$$5000 = 2 \times M^2$$
$$M^2 = \frac{5000}{2} = 2500$$
$$M = \sqrt{2500} = 50$$

A diamond of value \$5000 has a mass of 50 grams.

Exercise 8.3A

1. Rewrite the statement connecting each pair of variables using a constant k instead of '$\propto$'.

    a) $S \propto e$ **b)** $y \propto \sqrt{x}$ **c)** $T \propto \sqrt{L}$

    d) $C \propto r$ **e)** $A \propto r^2$ **f)** $V \propto r^3$

2. y is directly proportional to t. If $y = 6$ when $t = 4$, calculate:

    a) the value of y, when $t = 6$ **b)** the value of t, when $y = 4$

3. z is directly proportional to m. If $z = 20$ when $m = 4$, calculate:

    a) the value of z, when $m = 7$ **b)** the value of m, when $z = 55$

4. A is directly proportional to r^2. If $A = 12$, when $r = 2$, calculate:

    a) the value of A, when $r = 5$ **b)** the value of r, when $A = 48$

5. Given that $z \propto x$, copy and complete the table.

x	1	3		$5\frac{1}{2}$
z	4		16	

6. Given that $V \propto r^3$, copy and complete the table.

r	1	2		$1\frac{1}{2}$
V	4		256	

7. Given that $w \propto \sqrt{h}$, copy and complete the table.

h	4	9		$2\frac{1}{4}$
w	6		15	

8. The pressure of the water P at any point below the surface of the sea is directly proportional to the depth of the point below the surface d. If the pressure is 200 newtons/cm² at a depth of 3 m, calculate the pressure at a depth of 5 m.

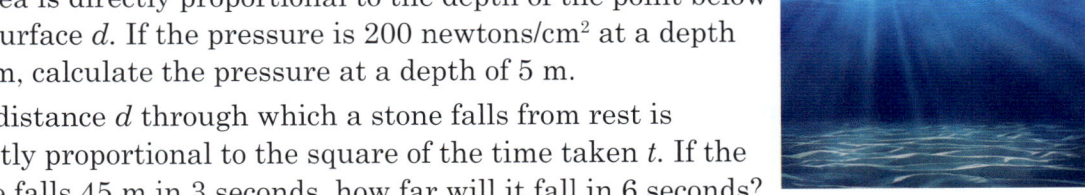

9. The distance d through which a stone falls from rest is directly proportional to the square of the time taken t. If the stone falls 45 m in 3 seconds, how far will it fall in 6 seconds? How long will it take to fall 20 m?

10. The energy E stored in an elastic band is directly proportional to the square of the extension x. When the elastic is extended by 3 cm, the energy stored is 243 joules. What is the energy stored when the extension is 5 cm? What is the extension when the stored energy is 36 joules?

11. In the first few days of its life, the length of an earthworm L is thought to be directly proportional to the square root of the number of hours n which have elapsed since its birth. If a worm is 2 cm long after 1 hour, how long will it be after 4 hours? How long will it take to grow to a length of 14 cm?

12. The number of eggs which a goose lays in a week is directly proportional to the cube root of the average number of hours of sleep she has. When she has 8 hours sleep, she lays 4 eggs. How long does she sleep when she lays 5 eggs?

13. The resistance to motion of a car is directly proportional to the square of the speed of the car. If the resistance is 4000 newtons at a speed of 20 m/s, what is the resistance at a speed of 30 m/s?

   At what speed is the resistance 6250 newtons?

14. A road research organisation recently claimed that the damage to road surfaces was directly proportional to the fourth power of the axle load. The axle load of a 44-tonne HGV is about 15 times that of a car. Calculate the ratio of the damage to road surfaces made by a 44-tonne HGV : damage to road surfaces made by a car.

Inverse proportion

If x is inversely proportional to y, you write $x \propto \dfrac{1}{y}$, again using the 'is proportional to' symbol $\propto$.

The '$\propto$' symbol can be replaced by '$= k$' where k is a constant, which means that $x = \dfrac{k}{y}$

Suppose you are told that $x = 4$ when $y = 5$.

Then $4 = \dfrac{k}{5}$

and $k = 20$

You can then write $x = \dfrac{20}{y}$, and this again allows you to find the value of x for any value of y and vice versa.

Example

z is inversely proportional to t^2, and $z = 4$ when $t = 1$. Calculate:

a) z when $t = 2$ **b)** t when $z = 16$.

Write $z \propto \dfrac{1}{t^2}$

or $z = k \times \dfrac{1}{t^2}$ (k is a constant)

$z = 4$ when $t = 1$,

$\therefore \quad 4 = k\left(\dfrac{1}{1^2}\right)$

so $k = 4$

$\therefore \quad z = 4 \times \dfrac{1}{t^2}$

a) When $t = 2$, $z = 4 \times \dfrac{1}{2^2} = 1$

b) When $z = 16$, $16 = 4 \times \dfrac{1}{t^2}$

$$16t^2 = 4$$

$$t^2 = \frac{1}{4}$$

$$t = \pm \frac{1}{2}$$

Exercise 8.3B

1. Rewrite the statements connecting the variables using a constant of variation, k.

   a) $x \propto \dfrac{1}{y}$ **b)** $s \propto \dfrac{1}{t^2}$ **c)** $t \propto \dfrac{1}{\sqrt{q}}$

   d) m is inversely proportional to w

   e) z is inversely proportional to t^2.

2. b is inversely proportional to e. If $b = 6$ when $e = 2$, calculate:

   a) the value of b when $e = 12$ **b)** the value of e when $b = 3$

3. q is inversely proportional to r. If $q = 5$ when $r = 2$, calculate:

   a) the value of q when $r = 4$ **b)** the value of r when $q = 20$

4. x is inversely proportional to y^2. If $x = 4$ when $y = 3$, calculate:

   a) the value of x when $y = 1$ **b)** the value of y when $x = 2\dfrac{1}{4}$.

5. R is inversely proportional to v^2. If $R = 120$ when $v = 1$, calculate:

   a) the value of R when $v = 10$ **b)** the value of v when $R = 30$

6. T is inversely proportional to x^2. If $T = 36$ when $x = 2$, calculate:

   a) the value of T when $x = 3$ **b)** the value of x when $T = 1.44$

7. p is inversely proportional to $\sqrt{y}$. If $p = 1.2$ when $y = 100$, calculate:

   a) the value of p when $y = 4$ **b)** the value of y when $p = 3$

8. y is inversely proportional to z. If $y = \dfrac{1}{8}$ when $z = 4$, calculate:

   a) the value of y when $z = 1$ **b)** the value of z when $y = 10$

9. Given that $z \propto \dfrac{1}{y}$, copy and complete the table.

y	2	4		$\dfrac{1}{4}$
z	8		16	

10. Given that $v \propto \dfrac{1}{t^2}$, copy and complete the table.

t	2	5		10
v	25		$\dfrac{1}{4}$	

11. Given that $r \propto \dfrac{1}{\sqrt{x}}$ copy and complete the table.

x	1	4		
r	12		$\dfrac{3}{4}$	2

12. M is inversely proportional to the square of l.

If $M = 9$ when $l = 2$, and if M and l are always positive, find:

a) M when $l = 10$ **b)** l when $M = 1$

13. Given $z = \dfrac{k}{x^n}$, find k and n, and then copy and complete the table.

x	1	2	4	
z	100	$12\dfrac{1}{2}$		$\dfrac{1}{10}$

14. Given $y = \dfrac{k}{\sqrt[n]{v}}$, find k and n, and then copy and complete the table.

v	1	4	36	
y	12	6		$\dfrac{3}{25}$

15. The volume V of a given mass of gas is inversely proportional to the pressure P. When $V = 2$ m^3, $P = 500$ N/m^2. Find the volume when the pressure is 400 N/m^2. Find the pressure when the volume is 5 m^3.

16. The number of hours N required to dig a certain hole is inversely proportional to the number of workers available, x. When 6 workers are digging, the hole takes 4 hours. Find the time taken when 8 workers are available. If it takes $\frac{1}{2}$ hour to dig the hole, how many workers are there?

17. The force of attraction F between two magnets is inversely proportional to the square of the distance d between them. When the magnets are 2 cm apart, the force of attraction is 18 newtons. How far apart are they if the attractive force is 2 newtons?

8.4 Indices 2

In Chapter 1 you learned how to use indices when dealing with numbers. The same rules for indices apply when working with algebra. Here are rules you need to remember.

1. $a^n \times a^m = a^{n+m}$ **2.** $a^n \div a^m = a^{n-m}$ **3.** $(a^n)^m = a^{nm}$

Also remember that:

- $a^{-n} = \dfrac{1}{a^n}$

- $a^{\frac{1}{n}}$ means 'the nth root of a'

- $a^{\frac{m}{n}}$ means 'the nth root of a raised to the power m'

- $a^0 = 1$ whenever $a \neq 0$, since $1 = \dfrac{a^n}{a^n} = a^{(n-n)} = a^0$

Example

Simplify:

a) $x^7 \times x^{13}$ **b)** $x^3 \div x^7$

c) $(x^4)^3$ **d)** $(3x^2)^3$

e) $(2x^{-1})^2 \div x^{-5}$ **f)** $3y^2 \times 4y^3$

---

a) $x^7 \times x^{13} = x^{7+13} = x^{20}$ **b)** $x^3 \div x^7 = x^{3-7} = x^{-4} = \dfrac{1}{x^4}$

c) $(x^4)^3 = x^{12}$ **d)** $(3x^2)^3 = 3^3 \times (x^2)^3 = 27x^6$

e) $\left(2x^{-1}\right)^2 \div x^{-5} = 4x^{-2} \div x^{-5}$ **f)** $3y^2 \times 4y^3 = 12y^5$

$$= 4x^{(-2--5)}$$
$$= 4x^3$$

Exercise 8.4A

Simplify:

1. $x^3 \times x^4$ **2.** $y^6 \times y^7$ **3.** $z^7 \div z^3$ **4.** $m^3 \div m^2$

5. $e^{-3} \times e^{-2}$ **6.** $y^{-2} \times y^4$ **7.** $w^4 \div w^{-2}$ **8.** $y^{\frac{1}{2}} \times y^{\frac{1}{2}}$

9. $(x^2)^5$ **10.** $x^{-2} \div x^{-2}$ **11.** $w^{-3} \times w^{-2}$ **12.** $w^{-7} \times w^2$

13. $x^3 \div x^{-4}$ **14.** $\left(k^{\frac{1}{2}}\right)^6$ **15.** $e^{-4} \times e^4$ **16.** $\left(y^4\right)^{\frac{1}{2}}$

17. $(x^{-3})^{-2}$ **18.** $t^{-3} \div t$ **19.** $(2x^3)^2$ **20.** $2x^2 \times 3x^2$

21. $5y^3 \times 2y^2$ **22.** $5a^3 \times 3a$ **23.** $(2a)^3$ **24.** $3x^3 \div x^3$

25. $8y^3 \div 2y$ **26.** $(2x)^2 \times (3x)^3$ **27.** $4z^4 \times z^{-7}$ **28.** $6x^{-2} \div 3x^2$

29. $5y^3 \div 2y^{-2}$ **30.** $(x^2)^{\frac{1}{2}} \div \left(x^{\frac{1}{3}}\right)^3$ **31.** $(2n)^4 \div 8n^0$ **32.** $x^{\frac{3}{2}} \div 2x^{\frac{1}{2}}$

33. $3x^{-4} \times \dfrac{2}{3} x^{\frac{1}{2}}$ **34.** $\dfrac{2}{7} x^{-\frac{1}{2}} \div 2x^{-3}$ **35.** $\left(\dfrac{3x^5}{4}\right)^3$ **36.** $5x^{-7} \div \dfrac{3}{10} x^{-\frac{1}{2}}$

37. $\dfrac{3}{5} x^{-\frac{1}{2}} \div 6x^{-4}$ **38.** $\left(\dfrac{3x^{\frac{1}{2}}}{2}\right)^4$ **39.** $\left(\dfrac{5x^{-\frac{1}{2}}}{-2}\right)^2$

Example

Simplify:

a) $\left(2a\right)^3 \div \left(9a^2\right)^{\frac{1}{2}}$ **b)** $(3ac^2)^3 \times 2a^{-2}$ **c)** $(2x)^2 \div 2x^2$

a) $\left(2a\right)^3 \div \left(9a^2\right)^{\frac{1}{2}} = 8a^3 \div 3a$ **b)** $(3ac^2)^3 \times 2a^{-2} = 27a^3c^6 \times 2a^{-2} = 54ac^6$

$$= \frac{8}{3} a^2$$

c) $\left(2x\right)^2 \div 2x^2 = 4x^2 \div 2x^2$

$$= 2$$

Exercise 8.4B

Rewrite without brackets:

1. $(5x^2)^2$ **2.** $(7y^3)^2$ **3.** $(10ab)^2$ **4.** $(2xy^2)^2$

5. $\left(4x^2\right)^{\frac{1}{2}}$ **6.** $(9y)^{-1}$ **7.** $(x^{-2})^{-1}$ **8.** $(2x^{-2})^{-1}$

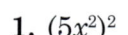

9. $(5x^2y)^0$

10. $\left(\dfrac{1}{2}x\right)^{-1}$

11. $(3x)^2 \times (2x)^2$

12. $(5y)^2 \div y$

13. $\left(2x^{\frac{1}{2}}\right)^4$

14. $\left(3y^{\frac{1}{3}}\right)^3$

15. $(5x^0)^2$

16. $((5x)^0)^2$

17. $(7y^0)^2$

18. $((7y)^0)^2$

19. $(2x^2y)^3$

20. $(10xy^3)^2$

Simplify:

21. $(3x^{-1})^2 \div 6x^{-3}$

22. $\left(4x\right)^{\frac{1}{2}} \div x^{\frac{3}{2}}$

23. $x^2y^2 \times xy^3$

24. $4xy \times 3x^2y$

25. $10x^{-1}\,y^3 \times xy$

26. $\left(3x\right)^2 \times \left(\dfrac{1}{9}x^2\right)^{\frac{1}{2}}$

27. $z^3yx \times x^2yz$

28. $(2x)^{-2} \times 4x^3$

29. $(3y)^{-1} \div (9y^2)^{-1}$

30. $(xy)^0 \times (9x)^{\frac{3}{2}}$

31. $(x^2y)(2xy)(5y^3)$

32. $\left(4x^{\frac{1}{2}}\right) \times \left(8x^{\frac{3}{2}}\right)$

33. $5x^{-3} \div 2x^{-5}$

34. $((3x^{-1})^{-2})^{-1}$

35. $(2a)^{-2} \times 8a^4$

36. $(abc^2)^3$

Evaluate, with $x = 16$ and $y = 8$:

37. $2x^{\frac{1}{2}} \times y^{\frac{1}{3}}$

38. $x^{\frac{1}{4}} \times y^{-1}$

39. $(y^2)^{\frac{1}{6}} \div (9x)^{\frac{1}{2}}$

40. $(x^2y^3)^0$

41. $x + y^{-1}$

42. $x^{-\frac{1}{2}} + y^{-1}$

43. $y^{\frac{1}{3}} \div x^{\frac{3}{4}}$

44. $\left(1000y\right)^{\frac{1}{3}} \times x^{-\frac{5}{2}}$

45. $\left(x^{\frac{1}{4}} + y^{-1}\right) \div x^{\frac{1}{4}}$

46. $x^{\frac{1}{2}} - y^{\frac{2}{3}}$

47. $\left(x^{\frac{3}{4}}y\right)^{-\frac{1}{3}}$

48. $\left(\dfrac{x}{y}\right)^{-2}$

It is sometimes useful to express one number as a power of another number.
To do this, use the rules of indices.

Example 1

Write $8 \times \dfrac{1}{16}$ in the form 2^p

$8 \times \dfrac{1}{16} = 2^3 \times 2^{-4} = 2^{3-4} = 2^{-1}$

You can then use your knowledge of indices to solve simple
equations where the variable is in the power.

Example 2

Solve the equations:

a) $4^{x-1} = 8^x$

b) $9^{x+2} = 3^{4x-2}$

a) $4^{x-1} = 8^x$

$\left(2^2\right)^{x-1} = \left(2^3\right)^x$ (Because 4 and 8 are both powers of 2.)

$2^{2(x-1)} = 2^{3x}$ (Using the rules of indices.)

$2(x-1) = 3x$

$2x - 2 = 3x$

$x = -2$

b) $9^{x+2} = 3^{4x-2}$

$\left(3^2\right)^{x+2} = 3^{4x-2}$ (Because 9 and 3 are both powers of 3.)

$3^{2(x+2)} = 3^{4x-2}$ (Using the rules of indices.)

$2(x+2) = 4x - 2$

$2x + 4 = 4x - 2$

$2x = 6$

$x = 3$

Exercise 8.4C

1. Write in the form 2^p (e.g. $4 = 2^2$).

   a) 32   **b)** 128   **c)** 64   **d)** 1

2. Write in the form 3^q.

   a) $\dfrac{1}{27}$ **b)** $\dfrac{1}{81}$ **c)** $\dfrac{1}{3}$ **d)** $9 \times \dfrac{1}{81}$

Make x the subject of each equation.

3. $2^x = 8$ **4.** $3^x = 81$ **5.** $5^x = \dfrac{1}{5}$

6. $10^x = \dfrac{1}{100}$ **7.** $3^{-x} = \dfrac{1}{27}$ **8.** $4^x = 64$

9. $6^{-x} = \dfrac{1}{6}$ **10.** $100\,000^x = 10$ **11.** $12^x = 1$

12. $10^x = 0.0001$ **13.** $2^x + 3^x = 13$ **14.** $\left(\dfrac{1}{2}\right)^x = 32$

15. $5^{2x} = 25$ **16.** $1\,000\,000^{3x} = 10$

17. These two are more difficult. Use a calculator to find solutions correct to three significant figures.

   a) $x^x = 100$ **b)** $x^x = 10\,000$

Make x the subject of each equation.

18. $3^{x+1} = 9^x$ **19.** $4^{x+1} = 2^{3x-1}$ **20.** $7^{3x} = 49^{4x}$

21. $25^{x+2} = 5^{x+3}$ **22.** $2^{2x} = 4^x$

8.5 Inequalities

When solving inequalities, you follow the same procedure used for solving equations except that when you multiply or divide by a *negative* number the inequality symbol is *reversed*.

e.g. $4 > -2$

but multiplying by -2,

$$-8 < 4$$

Example

Solve the inequalities:

a) $2x - 1 > 5$ **b)** $5 - 3x \leqslant 1$

---

a) $2x - 1 > 5$

$\qquad 2x > 5 + 1$

$\qquad x > \dfrac{6}{2}$

$\qquad x > 3$

b) $5 - 3x \leqslant 1$

$\qquad -3x \leqslant 1 - 5$

$\qquad -3x \leqslant -4$

$\qquad x \geqslant \dfrac{4}{3}$

Exercise 8.5A

Solve the inequalities:

1. $x - 3 > 10$ **2.** $x + 1 < 0$ **3.** $5 > x - 7$ **4.** $2x + 1 \leqslant 6$

5. $3x - 4 > 5$ **6.** $10 \leqslant 2x - 6$ **7.** $5x < x + 1$ **8.** $2x \geqslant x - 3$

9. $4 + x < -4$ **10.** $3x + 1 < 2x + 5$ **11.** $2(x + 1) > x - 7$ **12.** $7 < 15 - x$

13. $9 > 12 - x$ **14.** $4 - 2x \leqslant 2$ **15.** $3(x - 1) < 2(1 - x)$ **16.** $7 - 3x < 0$

Representing inequalities on a number line

The inequality $x < 4$ is represented on the number line as

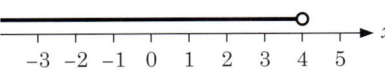

$x \geqslant -2$ is shown as

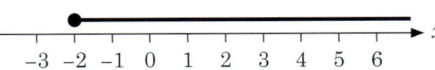

In the first case, 4 is *not* included so you use an unfilled circle ○

In the second case, -2 *is* included so you use a filled circle ●

$-1 \leqslant x < 3$ is shown as

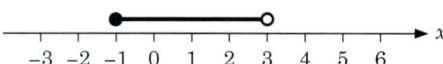

Sometimes you may have to solve a three-part inequality. Sometimes you solve one of these as one inequality, but sometimes you have to split it and solve it as though it were two inequalities. Consider the following examples.

Example

Solve the inequalities:

a) $-8 < 4(x - 3) < 16$ **b)** $9 \leqslant 2x - 1 \leqslant x + 9$

a) $-8 < 4(x - 3) < 16$ Divide each part by 4

$-2 < x - 3 < 4$ then add 3 to each part

$1 < x < 7$

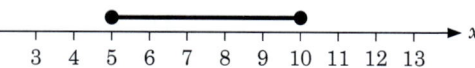

b) If you try to solve the three parts together you will not be able to get to the point where x is only in the middle part. Instead you need to solve two two-part inequalities.

The left-hand part: $9 \leqslant 2x - 1$

$10 \leqslant 2x$

$5 \leqslant x$

The right-hand part: $2x - 1 \leqslant x + 9$

$x \leqslant 10$

Putting these parts together gives the solution $5 \leqslant x \leqslant 10$

Exercise 8.5B

Solve each inequality and show the result on a number line.

1. $2x + 1 > 11$ **2.** $3x - 4 \leqslant 5$ **3.** $2 < x - 4$

4. $6 \geqslant 10 - x$ **5.** $8 < 9 - x$ **6.** $8x - 1 < 5x - 10$

7. $2x > 0$ **8.** $1 < 3x - 11$ **9.** $4 - x > 6 - 2x$

10. $\dfrac{x}{3} < -1$ **11.** $3 < x + 2 < 6$ **12.** $-5 \leqslant x - 3 \leqslant 2$

13. $3 \leqslant 3x < 18$ **14.** $0 \leqslant 2x < 10$ **15.** $-3 \leqslant 3x \leqslant 21$

16. $1 < 5x < 10$

17. $\frac{x}{4} > 20$

18. $3x - 1 > x + 19$

19. $7(x + 2) < 3x + 4$

20. $1 < 2x + 1 < 9$

21. $10 \leqslant 2x \leqslant x + 9$

22. $x < 3x + 2 < 2x + 6$

23. $10 \leqslant 2x - 1 \leqslant x + 5$

24. $x < 3x - 1 < 2x + 7$

25. $x - 10 < 2(x - 1) < x$

26. $18 - x < 5x \leqslant 7 + 4x$

27. $-4 \leqslant 4x \leqslant 12 + x$

28. $3x < 4x < 2(15 - x)$

29. $2(x - 9) < 8x < 2(x - 3)$

30. $11x - 20 \leqslant 15x < 5(20 - x)$

Exercise 8.5C

Find the solutions, subject to the given condition.

1. $3a + 1 < 20$; a is a positive integer

2. $b - 1 \geqslant 6$; b is a prime number less than 20

3. $2e - 3 < 21$; e is a positive even number

4. $1 < z < 50$; z is a square number

5. $0 < 3x < 40$; x is divisible by 5

6. $2x > -10$; x is a negative integer

7. $x + 1 < 2x < x + 13$; x is an integer

8. $x^2 < 100$; x is a positive square number

9. $0 \leqslant 2z - 3 \leqslant z + 8$; z is a prime number

10. $\frac{a}{2} + 10 > a$; a is a positive even number

11. State the smallest integer n for which $4n > 19$.

12. Find an integer value of x such that $2x - 7 < 8 < 3x - 11$.

13. Find an integer value of y such that $3y - 4 < 12 < 4y - 5$.

14. Find any value of z such that $9 < z + 5 < 10$.

15. Find any value of p such that $9 < 2p + 1 < 11$.

16. Find a simple fraction q such that $\frac{4}{9} < q < \frac{5}{9}$.

17. Find an integer value of a such that $a - 3 \leqslant 11 \leqslant 2a + 10$.

18. State the largest prime number z for which $3z < 66$.

19. Find the largest prime number p such that $p^2 < 400$.

20. Find the integer n such that $n < \sqrt{300} < n + 1$.

21. A youth club organiser is planning a day trip for the club members. The cost of the trip is \$330 and the club has already saved \$75. The price of a ticket for the trip is \$$x$ and there are 21 people going on the trip.

    a) Write down an inequality in terms of x to determine the price of each ticket if the cost of the trip is to be completely funded.

    b) What is the minimum ticket price that the youth club organiser must charge?

22. Chailai has $700 in her bank account. She wants to keep at least $300. She plans to withdraw $$y$ per week for the next 12 weeks to pay for entertainment and food.

a) Write down an inequality in terms of y to determine the amount of money Chailai can withdraw each week.

b) How much can Chailai withdraw per week?

23. A car rental firm charges $30 per day plus a flat fee of $240 to rent a car. Neema has no more than $470 to pay for the car rental.

a) Write down an inequality in terms of the number of days, d, that Neema rents the car for.

b) Solve the inequality to work out the maximum number of days for which Neema can rent the car.

Revision exercise 8

1. Write the following as single fractions.

a) $\dfrac{x}{4} + \dfrac{x}{5}$ **b)** $\dfrac{1}{2x} + \dfrac{2}{3x}$

c) $\dfrac{x+2}{2} + \dfrac{x-4}{3}$ **d)** $\dfrac{7}{x-1} - \dfrac{2}{x+3}$

2. a) Factorise $x^2 - 4$

   b) Simplify $\dfrac{3x-6}{x^2-4}$

3. Given that $s - 3t = rt$, express:

a) s in terms of r and t

b) r in terms of s and t

c) t in terms of s and r.

4. a) Given that $x - z = 5y$, express z in terms of x and y.

b) Given that $mk + 3m = 11$, express m in terms of k.

c) For the formula $T = C\sqrt{z}$, express z in terms of T and C.

5. It is given that $y = \dfrac{k}{x}$ and that $1 \leqslant x \leqslant 10$.

a) If the smallest possible value of y is 5, find the value of the constant k.

b) Find the largest possible value of y.

6. Given that y is directly proportional to x^2 and that $y = 36$ when $x = 3$, find:

a) the value of y when $x = 2$

b) the value of x when $y = 64$

7. Find x, given that:

a) $3^x = 81$ **b)** $7^x = 1$

8. Two integers differ by 6. The sum of their reciprocals is $\dfrac{5}{36}$. Find these numbers.

9. List the integer values of x which satisfy.

a) $2x - 1 < 20 < 3x - 5$

b) $5 < 3x + 1 < 17$

10. Given that $t = k\sqrt{x+5}$, express x in terms of t and k.

11. Given that $z = \dfrac{3y+2}{y-1}$, express y in terms of z.

12. Given that $y = \dfrac{k}{k+w}$

a) Find the value of y when $k = \dfrac{1}{2}$ and $w = \dfrac{1}{3}$

b) Express w in terms of y and k.

13. Calculate the value of:

a) $9^{-\frac{1}{2}} + \left(\dfrac{1}{8}\right)^{\frac{1}{3}} + (-3)^0$

b) $(1000)^{-\frac{1}{3}} - (0.1)^2$

14. It is given that $10^x = 3$ and $10^y = 7$. Find the value of 10^{x+y}

15. Make x the subject of the following formulae.

a) $x + a = \dfrac{2x - 5}{a}$

b) $cz + ax + b = 0$

c) $a = \sqrt{\dfrac{x + 1}{x - 1}}$

16. Write the following as single fractions.

a) $\dfrac{5x}{10} \times \dfrac{20}{15x}$

b) $\dfrac{x + 6}{4} \div \dfrac{2x + 12}{8x}$

c) $\dfrac{3}{x} + \dfrac{1}{2x}$

d) $\dfrac{3}{a - 2} + \dfrac{1}{a^2 - 4}$

e) $\dfrac{3}{x(x + 1)} - \dfrac{2}{x(x - 2)}$

17. p is directly proportional to the square of t, and inversely proportional to s. Given that $p = 5$ when $t = 1$ and $s = 2$, find a formula for s in terms of t.

18. In the diagram, the solution set $-1 \leqslant x < 2$ is shown on a number line.

Illustrate, on similar diagrams, the solution set of the following pairs of simultaneous inequalities.

a) $x > 2; x \leqslant 7$

b) $4 + x \geqslant 2; x + 4 < 10$

c) $2x + 1 \geqslant 3; x - 3 \leqslant 3$

NON-CALCULATOR

1. $\dfrac{x-2}{5} + \dfrac{5}{x-2} = \dfrac{x^2 - ax + b}{c(x-2)}$, where a, b and c are integers.

Work out a, b and c. [3]

2. Simplify $\left(64x^3\right)^{\frac{2}{3}}$ [2]

3. Work out the value of n in each of the following statements.

   a) $16^n = 1$ [1]

   b) $16^n = 2$ [1]

   c) $16^n = 8$ [1]

4. $(125)^{-\frac{2}{3}} = 25^p$. Determine p. [2]

5. Write $\dfrac{1}{a} + \dfrac{1}{b} - \dfrac{b}{ab}$ as a single fraction in its simplest form. [3]

6. Solve the inequality $\dfrac{3x-4}{7} < \dfrac{x+3}{4}$ [3]

7. Rearrange the formula to make b the subject: $a = \sqrt{\dfrac{b}{4}} - 2$ [3]

8. a) Factorise $cp^3 + dp^3$ [1]

   b) Make p the subject of the formula $cp^3 + dp^3 - a^2 = b^3$ [2]

9. The quantity x is inversely proportional to the square root of $(y + 1)$.
When $x = 20$, $y = 8$.

Work out y when $x = 12$. [3]

10. A torch is used to light up a wall.

The brightness of the light on the wall is b. The distance of the light from the wall is d. b is inversely proportional to the square of d.

What happens to b when d is doubled? [3]

11. Solve the equation $\dfrac{x}{x+1} - \dfrac{x+1}{3x-1} = \dfrac{1}{4}$

12. Aisha takes 2 hours 35 minutes to complete a walk.

   a) Show that the time of 2 hours 35 minutes can be written as $\dfrac{31}{12}$ hours. [1]

   b) Aisha walks $(x + 3)$ kilometres at $(x + 2)$ km/h and then a further $2x$ kilometres at 3 km/h.

   Show that the total time taken is $\dfrac{2x^2 + 7x + 9}{3x + 6}$ hours. [2]

   c) If the total time to complete the walk is 2 hours 35 minutes, work out x. [2]

   d) Calculate Aisha's average speed, in kilometres per hour, for the whole walk, giving your answer correct to 3 s.f. [3]

9 Graphs

René Descartes (1596–1650) was one of the greatest philosophers of his time. Strangely, his restless mind only found peace and quiet as a soldier and he apparently discovered the idea of 'Cartesian' geometry in a dream before the Battle of Prague. The word 'Cartesian' is derived from his name and his work formed the link between geometry and algebra which inevitably led to the discovery of calculus. In his book *Discourse on Method*, he said, 'It is not enough to have a good mind. The main thing is to use it well'.

- Use and understand real-life graphs such as travel graphs and conversion graphs.
- Understand and use Cartesian coordinates.
- Draw graphs of linear equations.
- For straight-line graphs, find, use and interpret:
  - the gradient from a graph
  - the gradient from the coordinates of two points
  - the length of a line segment
  - the midpoint of a line segment
  - the equation of a line
  - the gradient and equation of a parallel line
  - the gradient and equation of a perpendicular line.
- Understand and use the fact that the perpendicular distance from a point to a line is the shortest distance to the line.
- Understand and use distance–time and speed–time graphs, including finding speed, acceleration, deceleration and distance travelled as area under a speed–time graph.
- Draw, use and understand graphs including: functions of the form ax^n or, $ab^x + c$ where n is an integer between -2 and 3 or $\pm\frac{1}{2}$, and graphs representing exponential growth and decay.
- Solve associated equations graphically, e.g. find the intersection of a line and a curve.

- Sketch and interpret linear, quadratic, cubic, reciprocal and exponential graphs.
- Understand differentiation including:
  - the derivatives of functions of the form ax^n where n is a positive integer or 0
  - gradients and stationary points
  - maximum and minimum points
  - estimating the gradient of a curve by drawing a tangent.

9.1 Drawing linear graphs

You can draw an accurate graph by plotting points and then drawing a neat line through them.

Choose a value of x and substitute it into the function to obtain the value of y. This x, y pair can be plotted as the point with coordinates (x, y). Repeat this process until you have plotted enough points to be able to draw your graph.

These kind of coordinates are called Cartesian coordinates, after the mathematician and philosopher René Descartes, who showed how algebra could be used to solve problems in geometry.

Example 1

Draw the graph of $y = 2x - 3$ for values of x from -2 to $+4$.

Create a table to find the coordinates of some points on the line.

x	-2	-1	0	1	2	3	4
$2x$	-4	-2	0	2	4	6	8
-3	-3	-3	-3	-3	-3	-3	-3
y	-7	-5	-3	-1	1	3	5

Draw and label axes using suitable scales.

Plot the points and draw a pencil line through them. Label the line with its equation.

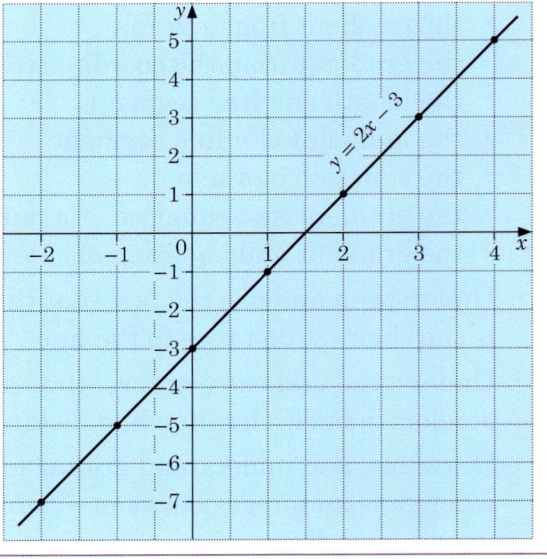

Sometimes the equation is given in a different form than $y = mx + c$.

Example 2

Draw the graph of $3x + 4y = 24$.

Because you only need two points to be able to draw a straight line, you can generate these by setting x and then y equal to zero, as shown in the table.

When $x = 0$, then $4y = 24$, so $y = 6$

When $y = 0$, then $3x = 24$, so $x = 8$

x	0	8
y	6	0

You can then draw a straight line through both of those points.

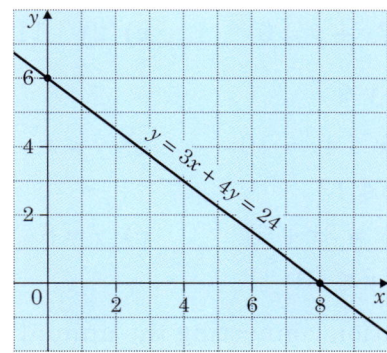

Finding a third point is always advisable as a check. If you have made a mistake in either of the other two points, then your three points will not lie on a straight line.

When $y = 3$, then $3x + 12 = 24$

$$3x = 12$$
$$x = 4$$

The point $(4, 3)$ lies on the line, so the graph is correct.

Exercise 9.1A

For Questions **1** to **10**, draw the graph, using a scale of 2 cm to 1 unit on the x-axis and 1 cm to 1 unit on the y-axis.

1. $y = 2x + 1$ for $-3 \leqslant x \leqslant 3$

2. $y = 3x - 4$ for $-3 \leqslant x \leqslant 3$

3. $y = 2x - 1$ for $-3 \leqslant x \leqslant 3$

4. $x + y = 8$ for $-2 \leqslant x \leqslant 4$

5. $y + 2x = 10$ for $-2 \leqslant x \leqslant 4$

6. $y = \dfrac{x + 5}{2}$ for $-3 \leqslant x \leqslant 3$

7. $y = 3(x - 2)$ for $-3 \leqslant x \leqslant 3$

8. $2y - x - 4 = 0$ for $-3 \leqslant x \leqslant 3$

9. $y = 2x - 3$ for $-2 \leqslant x \leqslant 4$

10. $y + 3x = 12$ for $-2 \leqslant x \leqslant 4$

For each Question from **11** to **16**, draw the graphs on the same set of axes and hence find the coordinates of the vertices of the polygon formed. Give the answers as accurately as your graph will allow.

11. a) $y = x$ **b)** $y = 6 - 2x$ **c)** $y = 4x$
Take $-1 \leqslant x \leqslant 3$ and $-4 \leqslant y \leqslant 14$

12. a) $y = 2x + 1$ **b)** $y = 4x - 6$ **c)** $y = \dfrac{1}{2}x + 1$
Take $0 \leqslant x \leqslant 5$ and $-8 \leqslant y \leqslant 12$

13. a) $y = 3x$ **b)** $y = 4 - x$ **c)** $y = x - 4$
Take $-2 \leqslant x \leqslant 5$ and $-9 \leqslant y \leqslant 8$

14. a) $y = \dfrac{1}{2}(x - 8)$ **b)** $2x + y = 6$ **c)** $2y - 11x = 12$
Take $-3 \leqslant x \leqslant 4$ and $-7 \leqslant y \leqslant 7$

15. a) $y = 2x + 7$ **b)** $x + 4y = 10$ **c)** $y = x$ **d)** $y = 10 - x$
Take $-2 \leqslant x \leqslant 4$ and $0 \leqslant y \leqslant 13$

16. a) $y = -x$ **b)** $y = 3x + 6$ **c)** $y = 8$ **d)** $x = 3\dfrac{1}{2}$
Take $-2 \leqslant x \leqslant 5$ and $-6 \leqslant y \leqslant 10$

17. For a certain car, the equation connecting the annual distance travelled M km, and the annual running cost, $\$C$ is $C = \dfrac{M}{20} + 200$
Draw the graph for $0 \leqslant M \leqslant 10\,000$ using scales of 1 cm = 1000 km for M, and 2 cm = \$100 for C.

From the graph find:

a) the cost when the annual distance travelled is 7200 km
b) the annual distance travelled corresponding to a cost of \$320.

18. The equation relating the cooking time t hours and the mass m kg
for a rainbow cake is $t = \dfrac{3m + 1}{4}$

Draw the graph for $0 \leqslant m \leqslant 5$. From the graph find:

a) the mass of a cake requiring a cooking time of 2.8 hours
b) the cooking time for a rainbow cake with a mass of 4.1 kg.

19. Some drivers try to estimate their annual cost of repairs $\$c$ in relation to their average speed of driving s km/h using the equation $c = 6s + 50$. Draw the graph for $0 \leqslant s \leqslant 160$. From the graph find:

a) the estimated repair bill for a man who drives at an average speed of 65 km/h
b) the average speed at which a motorist drives if his annual repair bill is \$300
c) the annual saving for a man who, on returning from a holiday, reduces his average speed of driving from 100 km/h to 65 km/h.

20. The value of a car $v is related to the number of kilometres n that it has travelled by the equation

$$v = 4500 - \frac{n}{20}$$

Draw the graph for $0 \leqslant n \leqslant 90\,000$. From the graph find:

a) the value of a car that has travelled 3700 km

b) the number of kilometres travelled by a car valued at $3200.

9.2 Coordinate geometry

Gradients of straight lines

The gradient of a straight line is a measure of how steep it is.

You can find the gradient of a line passing through the points (x_1, y_1) and (x_2, y_2) using the formula

$$\text{gradient} = \frac{y_2 - y_1}{x_2 - x_1} \qquad (1)$$

Example 1

Find the gradient of the line joining the points A(1, 2) and B(6, 5).

$$\text{gradient of AB} = \frac{BC}{AC} = \frac{5 - 2}{6 - 1} = \frac{3}{5}$$

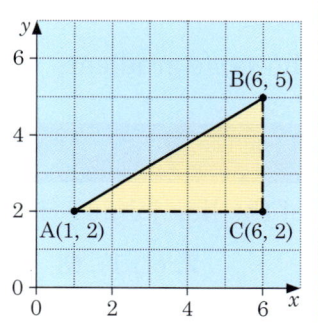

The gradient can also be calculated using the formula:

$$\text{gradient} = \frac{y_1 - y_2}{x_1 - x_2} \qquad (2)$$

Notice the order of the coordinates (x_1, y_1) and (x_2, y_2) used in both forms of the formula: the first number in the numerator and the first number in the denominator come from one of the points. The second numbers are from the other point.

When finding the gradient using either (1) or (2), just be sure that you are consistent when you do the subtractions.

Example 2

Find the gradient of the line joining the points D(1, 5) and E(5, 2).

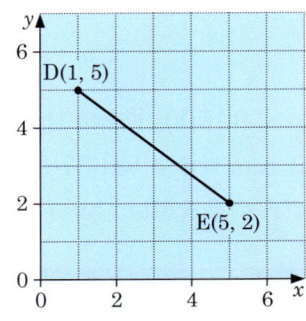

gradient of DE $= \dfrac{5-2}{1-5} = \dfrac{3}{-4} = -\dfrac{3}{4}$

Notice that:

- Lines which slope upward to the right have a *positive* gradient, and lines which slope downward to the right have a *negative* gradient.
- **Horizontal** lines have a gradient of zero because all the points they pass through will have the same *y*-coordinate, making the gradient $= \dfrac{y_1 - y_2}{x_1 - x_2} = \dfrac{0}{x_1 - x_2} = 0$
- **Vertical** lines do not have a gradient because all the points they pass through will have the same *x*-coordinate, making the gradient $= \dfrac{y_1 - y_2}{x_1 - x_2} = \dfrac{y_1 - y_2}{0}$. Since you cannot divide by zero the gradient is **undefined**.
- **Parallel lines** have the same gradient.

Exercise 9.2A

Calculate the gradient of the line joining the following pairs of points.

1. (3, 1), (5, 4)
2. (1, 1), (3, 5)
3. (−1, 3), (1, 6)
4. (−2, −1), (0, 0)
5. (7, 5), (1, 6)
6. (2, −3), (1, 4)
7. (0, −2), (−2, 0)
8. $\left(\dfrac{1}{2}, 1\right)$, $\left(\dfrac{3}{4}, 2\right)$
9. $\left(-\dfrac{1}{2}, 1\right)$, (0, −1)
10. (3.1, 2), (3.2, 2.5)
11. (−7, 10), (0, 0)
12. (3, 4), (−2, 4)
13. (2, 5), (1.3, 5)
14. (2.3, −2.2), (2.3, 1.8)
15. (0, 2), (0, 8)
16. (*m*, *n*), (*a*, −*b*)
17. (2*a*, *f*), (*a*, −*f*)
18. (2*k*, −*k*), (*k*, 3*k*)
19. (*m*, 3*n*), (−3*m*, 3*n*)
20. $\left(\dfrac{c}{2}, -d\right)$, $\left(\dfrac{c}{4}, \dfrac{d}{2}\right)$

In Questions **21** and **22**, find the gradient of each straight line.

21.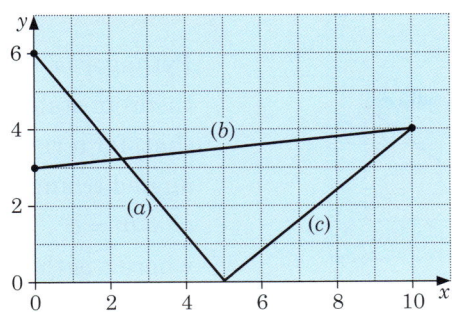

22.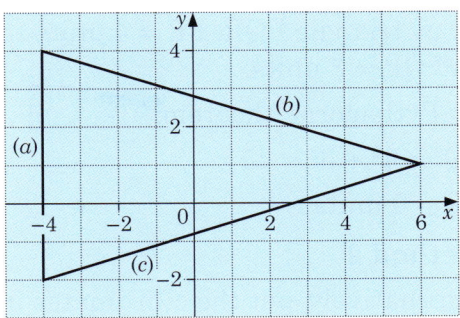

23. The line joining the points $(3a, 4)$ and $(a, -3)$ has a gradient of 1. Find the value of a.

24. a) Write down the gradient of the line joining the points $(2m, n)$ and $(3, -4)$.

b) Find the value of n if the line is parallel to the x-axis.

c) Find the value of m if the line is parallel to the y-axis.

Midpoints and lengths of line segments

The **midpoint** of the line segment joining the two points (x_1, y_1) and (x_2, y_2) can be found using the formula:

$$\text{midpoint} = \left(\frac{x_1 + x_2}{2}, \frac{y_1 + y_2}{2} \right)$$

The **length** of the line segment joining the two points (x_1, y_1) and (x_2, y_2) can be found using the formula:

$$\text{length of line segment} = \sqrt{(x_1 - x_2)^2 + (y_1 - y_2)^2}$$

Notice that this is an application of Pythagoras' theorem.

Example

a) Find the coordinates of the midpoint of the line segment joining point P(2, 1) to point Q(6, 4).

b) Find the length of the line segment PQ.

---

a) Add the x-coordinates of P and Q and then divide by 2.

Add the y-coordinates of P and Q and then divide by 2.

The midpoint has coordinates $= \left(\dfrac{(2 + 6)}{2}, \dfrac{(1 + 4)}{2} \right)$

$$= (4, 2.5)$$

b) Method 1

Draw triangle PQR. PR = 4 units and QR = 3 units.

By Pythagoras' theorem:

$PQ^2 = 4^2 + 3^2 = 25$

$PQ = 5$ units

Method 2

Alternatively, put the coordinates into the formula.

Length of $PQ = \sqrt{(6-2)^2 + (4-1)^2} = \sqrt{4^2 + 3^2}$

$$= \sqrt{16 + 9} = \sqrt{25} = 5 \text{ units}$$

> **Tip**
>
> Pythagoras' theorem states that, for a right-angled triangle, $a^2 + b^2 = c^2$ where c is the hypotenuse

Exercise 9.2B

For Questions **1** to **12**, find the midpoint and length of the line segment joining each pair of points. Leave lengths in simplified surd form wherever possible.

1. (3, 1), (5, 4)

2. (1, 1), (3, 5)

3. (3, 0), (4, 3)

4. (−1, 3), (1, 6)

5. (−2, −1), (0, 0)

6. (7, 5), (1, 6)

7. (2, −3), (1, 4)

8. (0, −2), (−2, 0)

9. $\left(\dfrac{1}{2}, 1\right), \left(\dfrac{3}{4}, 2\right)$

10. $\left(-\dfrac{1}{2}, 1\right)$, (0, −1)

11. (3.1, 2), (3.2, 2.5)

12. (−7, 10), (0, 0)

13. One end of a line segment is at (−2, 3). Its midpoint is at (3, 1). Find the coordinates of the point at the other end.

14. The distance between the points (x, x) and (10, −10) is $2\sqrt{122}$.

Find the two possible values of x.

9.3 Equations of straight lines

When the equation of a straight line is written in the form $y = mx + c$, the gradient of the line is m and the intercept on the y-axis is c.

If you know the gradient and y-intercept, you can quickly **sketch** the graph. On a sketch for a straight-line graph, you just need to draw the line with roughly the correct gradient, and then label the x- and y-intercepts. It does not need to be precise.

Example 1

Sketch the line $y = 2x + 3$.

The line $y = 2x + 3$ has a gradient of 2 and intercepts the y-axis at (0, 3).

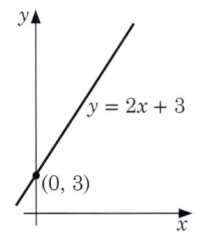

Example 2

Sketch the line $x + 2y - 6 = 0$.

Rearrange the equation to make y the subject.

$x + 2y - 6 = 0$

$2y = -x + 6$

$y = -\dfrac{1}{2}x + 3$

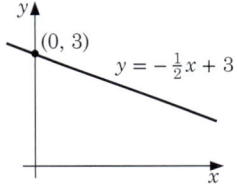

The line has a gradient of $-\dfrac{1}{2}$ and intercepts the y-axis at (0, 3).

You can recognise when two lines are parallel from their equations because they will have the same gradient.

Example 3

From the three straight lines represented by these equations, which two are parallel?

$\qquad y = 2x + 7 \qquad\qquad 2y - 2x = 10 \qquad\qquad 6x - 3y - 9 = 0$

Rearrange each equation so it is in the form $y = mx + c$, and then read off the value of m.

$\qquad y = 2x + 7 \qquad$ (is already in the required form with $m = 2$)

$\qquad 2y - 2x = 10$
$\qquad 2y = 2x + 10$
$\qquad y = x + 5 \qquad$ (is now in the required form with $m = 1$)

$\qquad 6x - 3y - 9 = 0$
$\qquad 3y = 6x - 9$
$\qquad y = 2x - 3 \qquad$ (is now in the required form with $m = 2$)

The lines $y = 2x + 7$ and $6x - 3y - 9 = 0$ have the same gradient, so they are parallel.

Exercise 9.3A

For Questions **1** to **10**, find the gradient of the line and the intercept on the *y*-axis, then sketch the graph.

1. $y = x + 3$

2. $y = x - 2$

3. $y = 2x + 1$

4. $y = 2x - 5$

5. $y = 3x + 4$

6. $y = \dfrac{1}{2}x + 6$

7. $y = 3x - 2$

8. $y = 2x$

9. $y = \dfrac{1}{4}x - 4$

10. $y = -x + 3$

For Questions **11** to **20**, find the gradient of the line and the intercept on the *y*-axis. Identify any pairs of lines that are parallel to each other.

11. $y = 6 - 2x$

12. $y = 2 - x$

13. $y + 2x = 3$

14. $x + 3y + 4 = 0$

15. $2y - 3x = 6$

16. $3y + x - 9 = 0$

17. $4x - y = 5$

18. $3x - 2y = 8$

19. $10x + 10y = 0$

20. $y - 4 = 0$

Finding an equation of a straight line

Equations of straight lines can be written in different forms. As well as the familiar $y = mx + c$ form, sometimes you may be asked to write the equation of the line in the form $ax + by = c$.

Example

Find an equation of the straight line which passes through (1, 3) and (3, 7)

a) in the form $y = mx + c$

b) in the form $ax + by = c$.

a) Let the equation of the line take the form $y = mx + c$.

The gradient $m = \dfrac{7 - 3}{3 - 1} = 2$

So, you can write the equation as $y = 2x + c$ \hfill (1)

Since the line passes through (1, 3), substitute 3 for y and 1 for x in (1).

$3 = 2 \times 1 + c$

$c = 1$

The equation of the line is therefore $y = 2x + 1$.

b) The equation of the line $y = 2x + 1$ can be rearranged and written as $-2x + y = 1$

Exercise 9.3B

For Questions **1** to **6**, find an equation of the line which passes through the given point with the given gradient. Give your equations in the form $y = mx + c$.

1. Passes through (0, 7), gradient of 3
2. Passes through (0, −9), gradient of 2
3. Passes through (0, 5), gradient of −1
4. Passes through (2, 3), gradient of 2
5. Passes through (2, 11), gradient of 3
6. Passes through (4, 3), gradient of −1

For Questions **7** to **11**, find an equation of the line as described. Give your equations in the form $ax + by = c$.

7. Passes through (6, 0), gradient of $\frac{1}{2}$
8. Passes through (2, 1) and (4, 5)
9. Passes through (5, 4) and (6, 7)
10. Passes through (0, 5) and (3, 2)
11. Passes through (3, −3) and (9, −1)
12. In lines of the form $y = mx + c$, the letter m represents the gradient.
    What expression represents the gradient if the line is in the form $ax + by = c$?
13. The only straight-line equations that cannot be written in the form $y = mx + c$ are vertical lines. Why is this?
14. Find an equation of a line that passes through the two points (1, −4) and (1, 6).
15. **a)** Find an equation of the line that passes through the two points (4, 3) and (7, 3).
    b) Is this line in the form $y = mx + c$? Explain your answer.

Parallel lines

You may be asked to find a line that passes through a certain point and is parallel to another line.

Example

Find an equation of the line which passes through (3, 4) and is parallel to the line $y = 2x - 7$.

The line $y = 2x - 7$ has a gradient of 2, and because parallel lines have the same gradient, the required line will also have a gradient of 2.

Let the equation of the line take the form $y = mx + c$, where $m = 2$.

You know the equation is $y = 2x + c$, where c is to be determined.

Since the line passes through (3, 4), substitute 4 for y and 3 for x into the equation.

$$4 = 2 \times 3 + c$$
$$c = -2$$

The equation of the line is therefore $y = 2x - 2$.

Exercise 9.3C

For Questions **1** to **5**, find an equation of the line passing through the given point, and which is parallel to the given line.

1. Through (1, 6) and parallel to $y = 2x - 5$

2. Through (3, 5) and parallel to $y = x - 1$

3. Through (12, –1) and parallel to $x + 3y = 12$

4. Through (4, –2) and parallel to $y = 8$

5. Through (–6, 9) and parallel to $x = 3$

6. **a)** Find equations of the lines A and B.

   b) Find an equation of the line which is parallel to line A and which passes through the point (0, 1).

   c) Find an equation of the line which is parallel to line B and which passes through the point (0, –2).

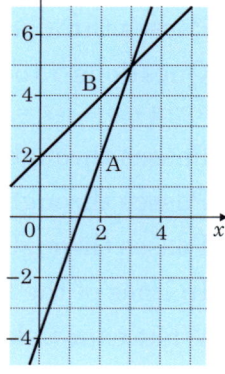

7. The graph shows intersecting lines A and B.

   a) Find an equation of the line parallel to line A, passing through (0, 5).

   b) Find an equation of the line parallel to line B, passing through (0, 3).

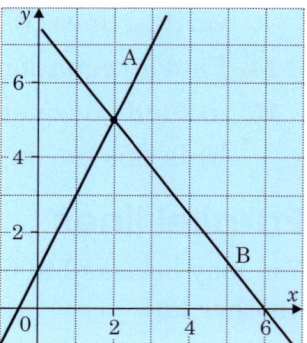

Perpendicular lines

If two lines are perpendicular, the product of their gradients is equal to –1. This is often written as $m_1 \times m_2 = -1$, where m_1 and m_2 are the gradients of the two perpendicular lines.

This means that if you know the gradient of one line, you can easily find the gradient of a line perpendicular to it.

Example 1

a) Find the gradient of lines A and B.

b) Show that lines A and B are perpendicular.

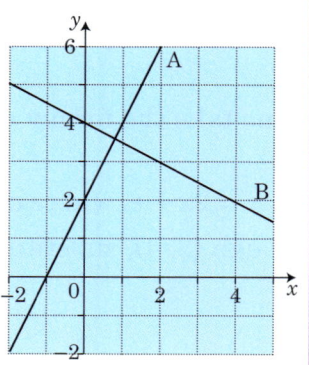

....

a) The gradient of line A: $m_1 = 2$, and the gradient of line B: $m_2 = -\dfrac{1}{2}$

b) $2 \times -\dfrac{1}{2} = -1$, and therefore the two lines are perpendicular.

Example 2

Find an equation of the line perpendicular to $y = 3x - 5$, passing through $(2, 2)$.

The gradient of line $y = 3x - 5$ is 3.

Therefore the gradient of any line perpendicular to it is $-\dfrac{1}{3}$

Let the equation of the line take the form $y = mx + c$, where $m = -\dfrac{1}{3}$

You know the equation is $y = -\dfrac{1}{3}x + c$, where c is to be determined.

Since the line passes through $(2, 2)$, substitute 2 for y and 2 for x into the equation.

$$2 = -\frac{1}{3} \times 2 + c$$

$$c = 2\frac{2}{3}$$

The equation of the line is therefore $y = -\dfrac{1}{3}x + 2\dfrac{2}{3}$

Alternatively, this could be written as $x + 3y = 8$.

> ### Tip
>
> $-\dfrac{1}{3}$ is sometimes called the negative reciprocal of 3.

The perpendicular bisector of a line segment is a line which is perpendicular to it and which passes through its midpoint.

Example 3

Find the perpendicular bisector of the line segment joining the points $(0, -4)$ and $(6, 4)$.

The line has a gradient of $\dfrac{4 - -4}{6 - 0} = \dfrac{8}{6} = \dfrac{4}{3}$

and therefore the gradient of the perpendicular is $-\dfrac{3}{4}$

The line has a midpoint of $\left(\dfrac{0 + 6}{2}, \dfrac{4 + -4}{2} \right) = (3, 0)$

You know the equation is $y = -\dfrac{3}{4}x + c$, where c is to be determined.

Since the line passes through $(3, 0)$, substitute 0 for y and 3 for x into the equation.

$$0 = -\frac{3}{4} \times 3 + c$$

$$c = \frac{9}{4} = 2\frac{1}{4}$$

The equation of the line is therefore $y = -\dfrac{3}{4}x + 2\dfrac{1}{4}$

The shortest distance from a point to a line is the perpendicular distance.

Example 4

Find the shortest distance from the point (1, –4) to the line $y = \dfrac{3}{4}x + 1\dfrac{1}{2}$

The line perpendicular to $y = \dfrac{3}{4}x + 1\dfrac{1}{2}$ has a gradient of $-\dfrac{4}{3}$

Now find the line with a gradient of $-\dfrac{4}{3}$ that passes through (1, –4):

$-4 = -\dfrac{4}{3} \times 1 + c$ which means $c = -4 + \dfrac{4}{3} = -\dfrac{8}{3}$ and the line is $y = -\dfrac{4}{3}x - \dfrac{8}{3}$

Now find the point where this line intersects the line $y = \dfrac{3}{4}x + 1\dfrac{1}{2}$:

$$\dfrac{3}{4}x + 1\dfrac{1}{2} = -\dfrac{4}{3}x - \dfrac{8}{3}$$

$$\dfrac{25}{12}x = -\dfrac{25}{6}$$

$$x = -2$$

and $y = \dfrac{3}{4} \times (-2) + 1\dfrac{1}{2} = 0$,

so the lines intersect at the point (–2, 0).

The distance between the points (1, –4) and (–2, 0) is

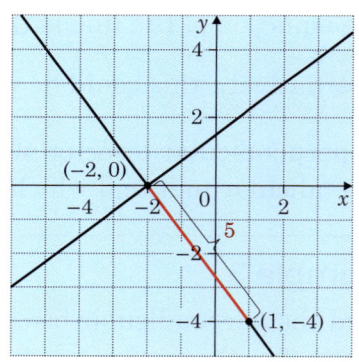

$$\sqrt{(1 - -2)^2 + (-4 - 0)^2} = \sqrt{3^2 + 4^2}$$

$$= \sqrt{9 + 16}$$

$$= \sqrt{25} = 5$$

Exercise 9.3D

In Questions **1** to **6**, find an equation of the line which:

1. passes through (3, 4) and is perpendicular to $y = x + 2$

2. passes through (2, –1) and is perpendicular to $x + 2y = 2$

3. passes through (–1, 6) and is perpendicular to $y = 4x - 3$

4. passes through (5, 0) and is perpendicular to $x + 6y = 24$

5. passes through (7, 2) and is perpendicular to $y = 5x - 2$

6. passes through (–1, 0) and is perpendicular to the line through (3, 1) and (5, 7).

7. Find the perpendicular bisector of the line segment joining the points (1, 4) and (5, 0). Give your answer in the form $y = mx + c$.

8. Find the perpendicular bisector of the line segment joining the points (0, 1) and (4, 9). Give your answer in the form $ax + by = c$.

9. Find the perpendicular bisector of the line segment joining the points (0.5, 6) and (7.5, 6).

10. **a)** Find an equation of the line which is perpendicular to the line $y = 0.5x + 3$ and passes through (1, −1).

    b) Hence, find the shortest distance from the line $y = 0.5x + 3$ to the point (1, −1). Give your answer correct to 2 d.p.

11. Find the shortest distance from the point (2, 3) to the line $y = -\dfrac{1}{3}x + 4$. Give your answer correct to 2 d.p.

12. Find the shortest distance from the point (4, −1) to the line $y = -5x - 3$. Give your answer correct to 2 d.p.

9.4 Plotting curves

Graphs of polynomial and reciprocal functions

Example

Draw the graph of the function $y = 2x^2 + x - 6$, for $-3 \leqslant x \leqslant 3$.

Create a table of integer values of x between −3 and 3, and find the value of y for each one.

x	−3	−2	−1	0	1	2	3
$2x^2$	18	8	2	0	2	8	18
x	−3	−2	−1	0	1	2	3
−6	−6	−6	−6	−6	−6	−6	−6
y	9	0	−5	−6	−3	4	15

Draw and label axes using suitable scales.

Plot the points and draw a smooth curve through them with a pencil.

Check any points which interrupt the smoothness of the curve.

Label the curve with its equation.

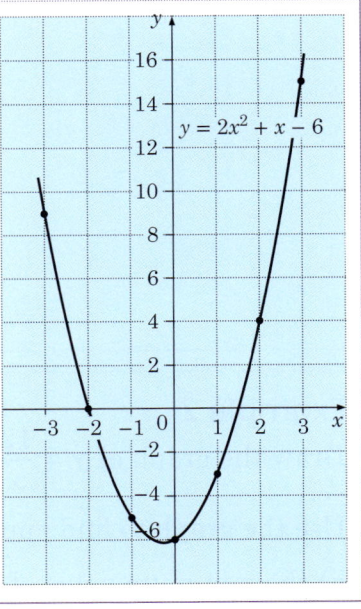

$y = 2x^2 + x - 6$

Exercise 9.4A

Draw the graphs of these functions using a scale of 2 cm for 1 unit on the x-axis, and 1 cm for 1 unit on the y-axis.

1. $y = x^2 + 2x$, for $-3 \leqslant x \leqslant 3$

2. $y = x^2 + 4x$, for $-3 \leqslant x \leqslant 3$

3. $y = x^2 - 3x$, for $-3 \leqslant x \leqslant 3$

4. $y = x^2 + 2$, for $-3 \leqslant x \leqslant 3$

5. $y = x^2 - 7$, for $-3 \leqslant x \leqslant 3$

6. $y = x^2 + x - 2$, for $-3 \leqslant x \leqslant 3$

7. $y = x^2 + 3x - 9$, for $-4 \leqslant x \leqslant 3$

8. $y = x^2 - 3x - 4$, for $-2 \leqslant x \leqslant 4$

9. $y = x^2 - 5x + 7$, for $0 \leqslant x \leqslant 6$

10. $y = 2x^2 - 6x$, for $-1 \leqslant x \leqslant 5$

11. $y = 2x^2 + 3x - 6$, for $-4 \leqslant x \leqslant 2$

12. $y = 3x^2 - 6x + 5$, for $-1 \leqslant x \leqslant 3$

13. $y = 2 + x - x^2$, for $-3 \leqslant x \leqslant 3$

14. $y = 1 - 3x - x^2$, for $-5 \leqslant x \leqslant 2$

15. $y = 3 + 3x - x^2$, for $-2 \leqslant x \leqslant 5$

16. $y = 7 - 3x - 2x^2$, for $-3 \leqslant x \leqslant 3$

17. $y = 6 + x - 2x^2$, for $-3 \leqslant x \leqslant 3$

18. $y = 8 + 2x - 3x^2$, for $-2 \leqslant x \leqslant 3$

19. $y = x(x - 4)$, for $-1 \leqslant x \leqslant 6$

20. $y = (x + 1)(2x - 5)$, for $-3 \leqslant x \leqslant 3$

Example 1

Draw the graph of $y = \dfrac{\sqrt{x}}{2}$, for $0 \leqslant x \leqslant 8$.

Here is the table of values. Non-integer values have been rounded to 2 d.p.

x	0	1	2	3	4	5	6	7	8
y	0	0.5	0.71	0.87	1	1.12	1.22	1.32	1.41

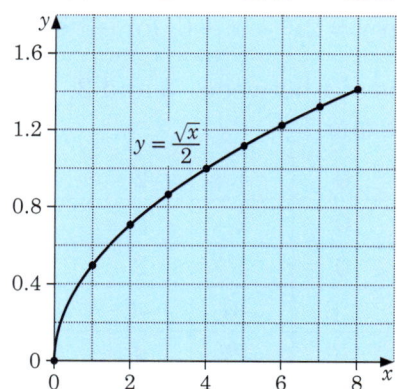

Example 2

Draw the graph of $y = \dfrac{12}{x} + x - 6$, for $1 \leqslant x \leqslant 8$.

Use the graph to find approximate values for:

a) the minimum value of $\dfrac{12}{x} + x - 6$

b) the value of x when $y = 5$

c) the gradient of the tangent to the curve drawn at the point where $x = 5$.

Here is the table of values. Non-integer values have been rounded to 1 d.p.

x	1	2	3	4	5	6	7	8	1.5
$\dfrac{12}{x}$	12	6	4	3	2.4	2	1.7	1.5	8
x	1	2	3	4	5	6	7	8	1.5
-6	-6	-6	-6	-6	-6	-6	-6	-6	-6
y	7	2	1	1	1.4	2	2.7	3.5	3.5

Notice that an extra value of y has been calculated at $x = 1.5$ because of the large difference between the y-values at $x = 1$ and $x = 2$.

a) From the graph, the minimum value of $\dfrac{12}{x} + x - 6$ (i.e. y) is approximately 0.9.

b) Draw a horizontal line from 5 on the y-axis until it meets the curve, then draw a vertical line down to the x-axis.

When $y = 5$, $x \approx 1.25$

c) The tangent AB is drawn to touch the curve at $x = 5$

The gradient of AB $= \dfrac{BC}{AC}$

gradient $= \dfrac{3}{8 - 2.4} = \dfrac{3}{5.6} \approx 0.54$

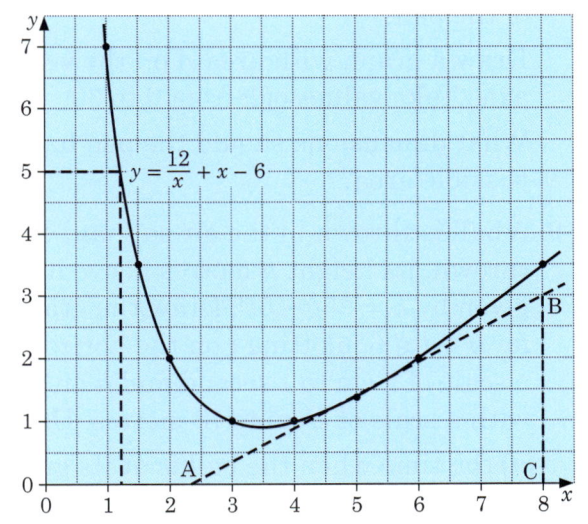

Exercise 9.4B

1. $y = x^2 - 3x$, for $-2 \leqslant x \leqslant 5$

Find:

a) the gradient of the tangent to the curve at $x = 3$

b) the gradient of the tangent to the curve at $x = -1$

c) the value of x where the gradient of the curve is zero.

2. $y = 5 + 3x - x^2$, for $-2 \leqslant x \leqslant 5$

Find:

a) the maximum value of the function $5 + 3x - x^2$

b) the gradient of the tangent to the curve at $x = 2.5$

c) the two values of x for which $y = 2$. Give your answers correct to 1 decimal place.

For Questions **3** to **7**, draw the curve. The scales given are for one unit of x and y.

3. $y = \dfrac{12}{x}$, for $1 \leqslant x \leqslant 10$

4. $y = \dfrac{10}{x^2} + x$, for $1 \leqslant x \leqslant 7$

5. $y = x^3 - 2x^2$, for $0 \leqslant x \leqslant 4$

6. $y = 3\sqrt{x}$, for $1 \leqslant x \leqslant 7$

7. $y = \dfrac{4}{\sqrt{x}}$, for $1 \leqslant x \leqslant 7$

8. A farmer has 60 m of wire fencing which he uses to make a rectangular pen for his sheep. He uses a stone wall as one side of the pen so the wire is used for only three sides of the pen.

If the width of the pen is x m, what is the length (in terms of x)? What is the area A of the pen?

Draw a graph with area A on the vertical axis and the width x on the horizontal axis. Take values of x from 0 to 30.

What dimensions should the pen have if the farmer wants to enclose the largest possible area?

9. A ball is thrown in the air so that t seconds after it is thrown, its height h metres above its starting point is given by $h = 25t - 5t^2$. Draw the graph of the function for $0 \leqslant t \leqslant 6$, plotting t on the horizontal axis with a scale of 2 cm to 1 second and h on the vertical axis with a scale of 2 cm to 10 metres. Use the graph to find:

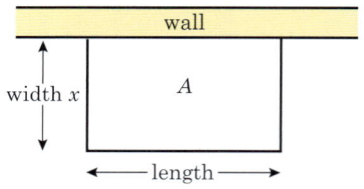

a) the time when the ball is at its greatest height

b) the greatest height reached by the ball

c) the time interval during which the ball is at a height of more than 30 m.

10. The velocity v m/s of a rocket t seconds after launching is given by the equation $v = 54t - 2t^3$. Draw a graph, plotting t on the horizontal axis with a scale of 2 cm to 1 second, and v on the vertical axis with a scale of 1 cm to 10 m/s. Take values of t from 0 to 5. Use the graph to find:

a) the maximum velocity reached

b) the time taken to accelerate to a velocity of 70 m/s

c) the interval of time during which the rocket is travelling at more than 100 m/s.

11. Draw the graph of $y = 3^x$, for $-3 \leqslant x \leqslant 3$. Find the gradient of the tangent to the curve at $x = 1$.

Graphs of exponential functions

You are used to functions like $y = x^2$, where a variable x is raised to the power of a constant, which in this case is 2. An exponential function is what you get if you raise a constant to the power of a variable, such as $y = 2^x$, for example.

The graph of $y = 2^x$ is shown on the right

Note that if a is an integer and $a > 1$, the curve $y = a^x$ will always have this shape and pass through the point (0, 1), since $a^0 = 1$ when $a \neq 0$.

The curve will also never meet the x-axis, since if $a \neq 0$, a^x cannot equal zero, for any value of x.

Because the graph approaches the x-axis but never meets it, we say that the x-axis is an **asymptote**.

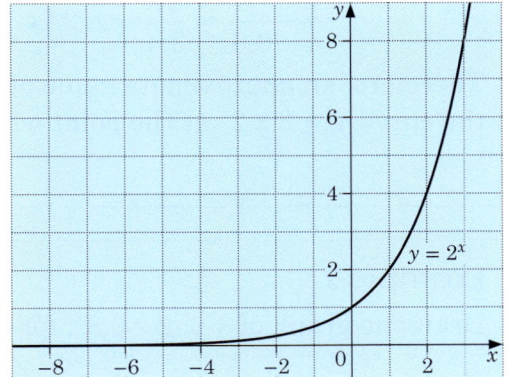

Many real processes can be modelled by exponential functions. If something is increasing exponentially, this is called exponential growth. If something is decreasing exponentially, this is called exponential decay.

If the number being raised to the power is greater than 1, then the model will show exponential growth. If it is strictly between 0 and 1, the model will show exponential decay.

Example 1

Draw the graph of $y = 3 \times 2^x$, for $-4 \leqslant x \leqslant 4$.

Use the graph to find approximate values for the gradient of the tangent to the curve drawn at the point where $x = 2$.

Here is the table of values:

x	-4	-3	-2	-1	0	1	2	3	4
2^x	$\dfrac{1}{16}$	$\dfrac{1}{8}$	$\dfrac{1}{4}$	$\dfrac{1}{2}$	1	2	4	8	16
3×2^x	$\dfrac{3}{16}$	$\dfrac{3}{8}$	$\dfrac{3}{4}$	$\dfrac{3}{2}$	3	6	12	24	48
y	0.19	0.38	0.75	1.5	3	6	12	24	48

Having drawn a tangent to the curve at the point where $x = 2$, you can see that this tangent passes through points very near to (0.6, 0) and (4, 28).

The gradient of a line that passes through those points is

$$\frac{28 - 0}{4 - 0.6} = \frac{28}{3.4} = 8.24$$

Therefore, an approximate value of the gradient of the curve $y = 3 \times 2^x$ at the point where $x = 2$ is 8.24.

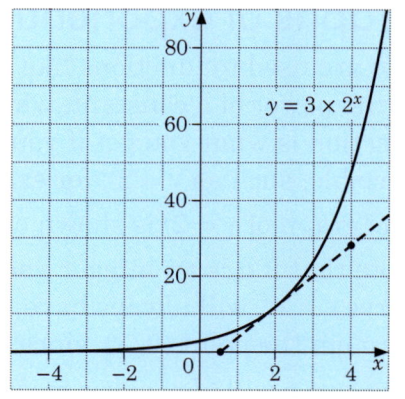

Example 2

Draw the graph of $y = 2 \times 0.8^x$, for $0 \leqslant x \leqslant 10$.

Here is the table of values:

x	0	1	2	3	4	5	6	7	8	9	10
y	2	1.6	1.28	1.02	0.82	0.66	0.52	0.42	0.34	0.27	0.21

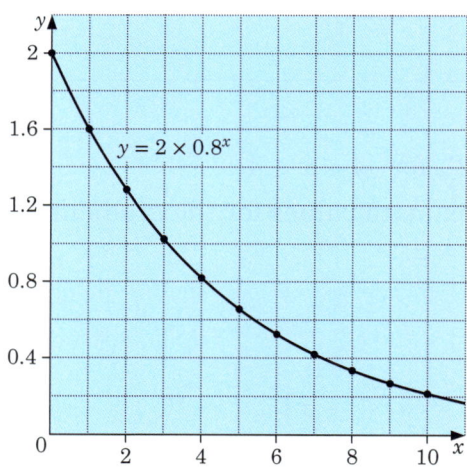

Exercise 9.4C

1. In a scientific experiment, the number of bacteria y in a colony can be modelled using the function $y = 4 \times 2^x$, where x is the time in minutes from the start of the experiment.

   a) How many bacteria were there at the start of the experiment?

b) Draw the graph for $0 \leqslant x \leqslant 8$.

c) At approximately what time were there 600 bacteria in the colony?

2. The number of molecules y of a chemical compound created by a reaction is modelled by the following function: $y = 600 \times 3^x$, where x is the number of hours after the start of the reaction.

   a) How many molecules were there at the start?

   b) Draw a graph for $0 \leqslant x \leqslant 4$.

   c) At approximately what time were there 30 000 molecules?

3. Draw the graph of the function $y = 3 \times 2^x + 1$ for $x = 0$, 1, 2, 3 and 4.

4. Draw the graph of $y = 2 \times 3^x + 5$ for $x = 0$, 1, 2, 3, 4 and 5.

5. A new drug is designed to kill dangerous bacteria. When treated with the drug, the number of bacteria at time t hours is modelled using the function $y = 1000 - 4 \times 2^t$.

   a) State the number of bacteria at the start.

   b) Draw the graph of the function for $0 \leqslant t \leqslant 7$.

   c) Use your graph to estimate the time when there are 800 bacteria.

   d) Estimate the number of bacteria after 3.5 hours.

   e) Explain why the function is not valid for $t = 9$ hours.

6. Draw the graph of $y = 4 \times 0.7^x + 1$ for $0 \leqslant x \leqslant 10$.

7. The value in dollars of a particular type of car when it is t years old can be modelled using the function $y = 80\,000 \times 0.9^t$.

   a) How much was the car worth when it was new?

   b) Draw the graph of the function for $0 \leqslant t \leqslant 10$, so that each unit on the vertical axis represents $10\,000.

   c) Estimate the value of the car after 4 and a half years.

   d) The owner wants to sell the car while it is still worth more than $30\,000. What is the maximum number of years they can keep the car for?

8. The temperature of a hot drink can be modelled by the function $T = 18 + 78 \times 0.85^t$, where T is the temperature of the drink in degrees Celsius t minutes after it was made.

   a) What was the temperature of the drink when it was made?

   b) Draw a graph showing how the temperature of the drink decreased in the first 15 minutes.

   c) After how many minutes did the temperature of the drink drop below $40\,°$ C?

   d) State one assumption being made by this model.

Recognising functions from sketches

There are several types of function you need to be able to recognise from sketches of their graphs.

1. Linear functions The graph of a linear function is always a straight line. The function will usually be of the form $y = mx + c$ or $ax + by = c$. When the gradient, m, is positive, the line will go up, from left to right. When m is negative, the line will go down from left to right.	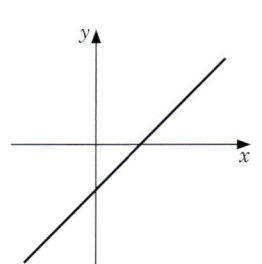
2. Quadratic functions These are functions where the highest power of x is 2. They will be of the form $y = ax^2 + bx + c$. If a is positive, the curve will have a minimum value, and will be $\cup$ –shaped. If a is negative, the curve will have a maximum value, and will be $\cap$ –shaped. A quadratic curve is symmetrical and it crosses the y-axis at $(0, c)$.	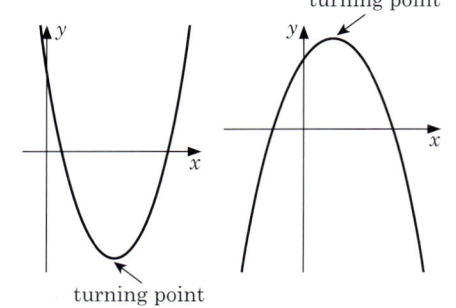

The lowest point in the first diagram and the highest point in the second diagram are called **turning points**. A quadratic graph will always have exactly one turning point.

3. Cubic functions These are functions where the highest power of x is 3. Cubic functions of the form $y = ax^3$ will look like the first graph, when a is positive. They pass through the origin $(0, 0)$. Cubic functions of the form $y = ax^3 + bx^2 + cx$ will often look more like the second graph.	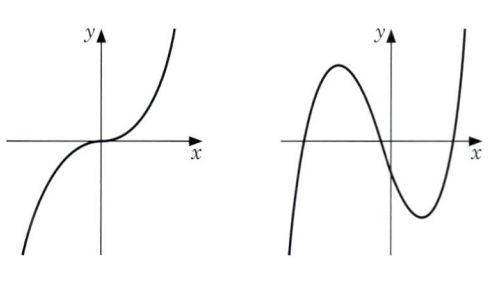

Note that the first cubic graph has no turning points and the second graph has two turning points, even though they are both cubic graphs.

4. Reciprocal functions

These are functions of the form $y = \dfrac{m}{x} + n$.

They are recognisable because they have two branches and two asymptotes, one horizontal and one vertical (shown here as dashed lines). The illustration shows the graph where m is positive. When m is negative the graph is reflected in the line $y = n$.

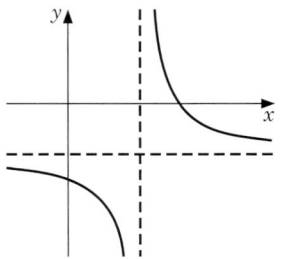

5. Exponential functions

These are functions of the form $y = m^x + n$. They have only one branch and one horizontal asymptote.

If m is a positive integer, the graph will increase in height as you move from left to right. The horizontal asymptote will be $y = n$.

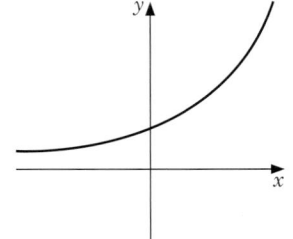

6. Functions based on the square root of x

These are functions of the form $a\sqrt{x}$.

Note that only the positive square root is plotted.

Also notice that negative values of x have no square root.

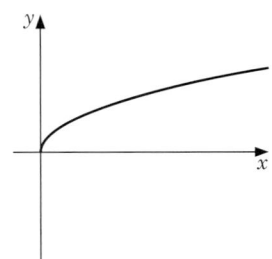

7. Functions based on the reciprocal of the square root of x.

These are functions of the form $\dfrac{a}{\sqrt{x}}$. They are similar to the graphs of reciprocal functions but they only have the one branch.

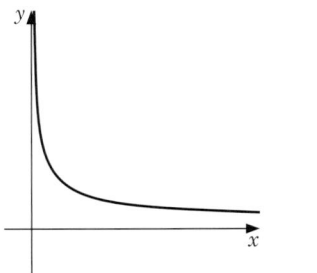

8. Functions based on the reciprocal of x^2.

These are functions of the form $\dfrac{a}{x^2}$. They have two branches, one on each side of the y-axis. The graph is also symmetrical in the y-axis.

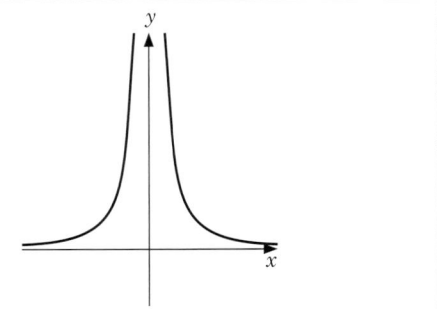

Exercise 9.4D

For Questions **1** to **12**, write down whether the function is linear, quadratic, cubic, reciprocal or exponential.

1. $y = 2x + 5$

2. $y = x^3 - 4$

3. $y = 2^x$

4. $y = x^2 + 3x - 4$

5. $y = 3^x - 1$

6. $y = \dfrac{2}{x}$

7. $3x + 4y = 10$

8. $y = \dfrac{4}{x} - 3$

9. $y = -x^2 + 3x - 1$

10. $y = 3x^3 + 9$

11. $y = 4$

12. $y = 2x^3 - 5x^2 + 6x$

For the graphs in **13** to **24**, identify the type of function from the sketch.

13.

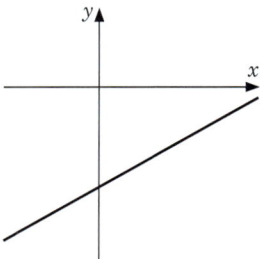

14.

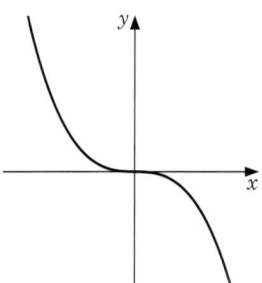

15.

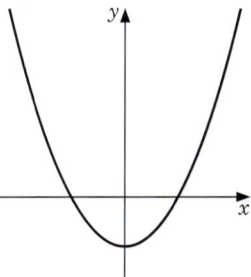

16.

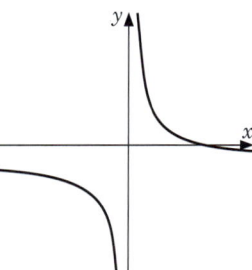

17.

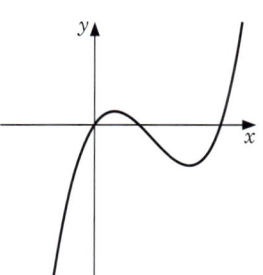

18.

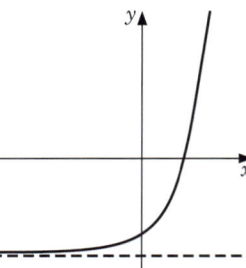

19.

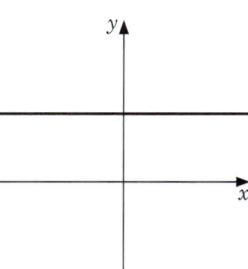

20.

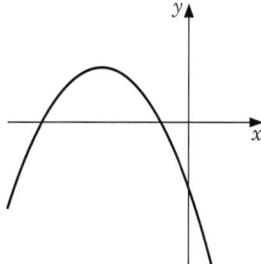

21.

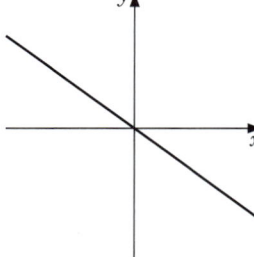

22.

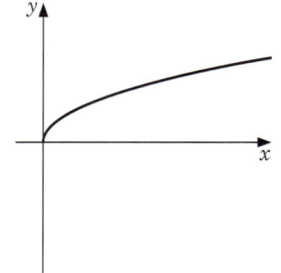

23.

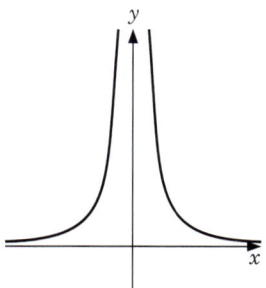

24.

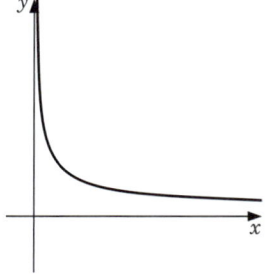

Sketching graphs

As well as being able to recognise types of functions from their sketches, you also need to be able to make your own sketches. Here are the main points you need to remember for the nine main graph types you need to know.

1. $ax + by = c$

   Find the x- and y-intercepts by letting the other variable equal zero and solving.

   Draw a straight line through the two intercepts.

2. $y = ax^2 + bx + c$

   Decide which way up the curve will be based on whether a is positive or negative.

   Mark the y-intercept on the vertical axis at $(0, c)$.

   Find the x-intercepts by solving the equation $ax^2 + bx + c = 0$.

   The x-intercepts of a function are also called its **roots**.

   The **turning point** is the lowest point on the graph if $a > 0$ or the highest point if $a < 0$. This can be found by writing the function in the form $y = (x - a)^2 + b$. The turning point is then the point (a, b). Alternatively, if the graph has two x-intercepts, the turning point can be found by finding the midpoint of the two x-intercepts and substituting that value of x into the function.

> **Tip**
>
> You will learn how to find the coordinates of the turning point in section 9.7.

   Then sketch the curve through those points, remembering that the graph of a quadratic function is always symmetrical along the vertical line which passes through the turning point.

3. $y = ax^3 + d$

   Take the basic $y = x^3$ graph and either raise it or lower it so that it passes through $(0, d)$.

   Then find the x-intercept by solving the equation $ax^3 + d = 0$.

4. $y = ax^3 + bx^2 + cx$

   This graph will pass through the origin.

   Factorise this so that it becomes $y = x(ax^2 + bx + c)$, then solve the equation $ax^2 + bx + c = 0$ to find any other x-intercepts.

   Sketch a cubic curve through the x-intercepts that you have found.

   If a is negative, the curve will have a negative gradient as it approaches the first x-intercept and as it passes through the final one.

5. $y = \dfrac{m}{x} + n$

   Take the basic $y = \dfrac{1}{x}$ graph and either raise it or lower it so that its horizontal asymptote is $y = n$.

6. $y = m^x + n$

Take the basic $y = m^x$ graph and either raise it or lower it so that its horizontal asymptote is $y = n$.

7. $y = ax^{\frac{1}{2}}$, which is another way to say $y = a\sqrt{x}$.

Take the basic $y = \sqrt{x}$ graph and stretch it appropriately in the vertical direction.

8. $y = ax^{-\frac{1}{2}}$, which is another way to say $y = \dfrac{a}{\sqrt{x}}$.

Take the basic $y = \dfrac{1}{\sqrt{x}}$ graph and stretch it appropriately in the vertical direction.

9. $y = ax^{-2}$, which is another way to say $y = \dfrac{a}{x^2}$.

Take the basic $y = \dfrac{1}{x^2}$ graph and stretch it appropriately in the vertical direction.

Exercise 9.4E

Sketch the following graphs, labelling any roots (intercepts on the x-axis) and y-intercepts. Also label any asymptotes.

1. $y = 3x - 4$ **2.** $y = x^2$ **3.** $y = 5^x$

4. $y = x^3$ **5.** $y = \dfrac{1}{x}$ **6.** $y = x^3 - 4$

7. $3x + 4y = 12$ **8.** $y = \dfrac{2}{x} + 1$ **9.** $y = (x + 1)(x - 3)$

10. $y = 3^x + 2$ **11.** $y = -1$ **12.** $y = x(x + 3)(x + 1)$

13. $y = x^3 + x^2 - 2x$ **14.** $y = -x^2 + 4$ **15.** $y = x^3 - 9x$

9.5 Interpreting graphs

Graphs in practical situations

Exercise 9.5A

1. The graph shows how to convert miles into kilometres.

    a) Use the graph to find approximately how many kilometres are the same as:

        i) 25 miles   **ii)** 15 miles

        iii) 45 miles   **iv)** 5 miles

    b) Use the graph to find approximately how many miles are the same as:

        i) 64 km   **ii)** 56 km

        iii) 16 km   **iv)** 32 km

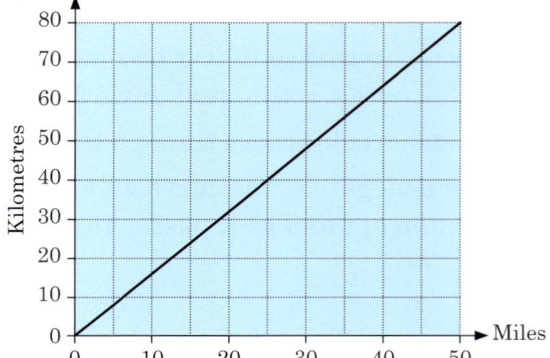

2. The first time Tim went to Paris, this graph showed him how to convert pounds (£) into euros (€).

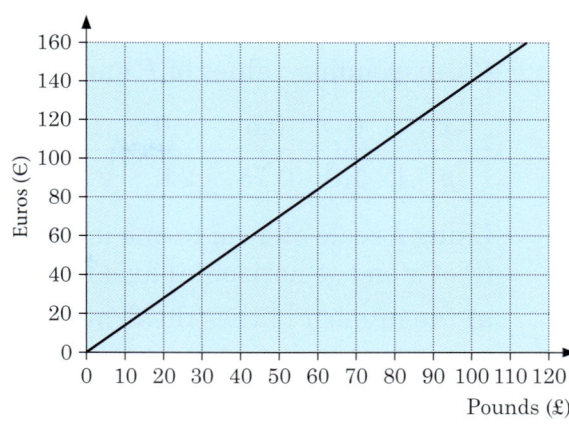

   a) Use the graph to find approximately how many euros were the same as:

   i) £20   ii) £80   iii) £50

   b) Use the graph to find approximately how many pounds were the same as:

   i) €56   ii) €84   iii) €140

   c) Tim spent €154 on clothes in Paris. How many pounds did he spend?

3. A company hires out vans at a basic charge of $35 plus a charge of 20c per km travelled. Copy and complete the table where x is the number of km travelled and C is the total cost in dollars.

x	0	50	100	150	200	250	300
C	35			65			95

Draw a graph of C against x, using scales of 2 cm to 50 km on the x-axis, and 1 cm to $10 on the C-axis.

   a) Use the graph to find the number of miles travelled when the total cost was $71.

   b) What is the formula connecting C and x?

4. A car travels along a motorway and the amount of fuel in its tank is monitored as shown on the graph.

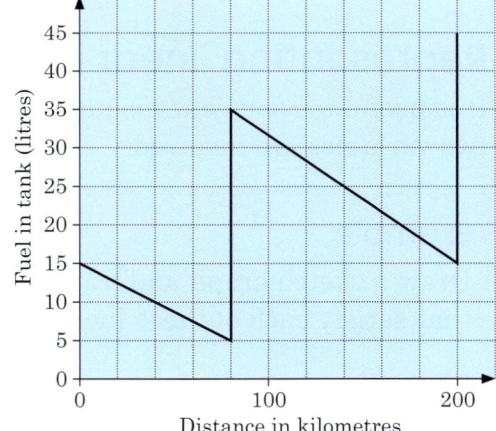

   a) How much fuel was bought at the first petrol station?

   b) What was the fuel consumption in km per litre:

   i) before the first stop

   ii) between the two stops?

   c) What was the average fuel consumption over the 200 km?

After it leaves the second fuel station, the car is stuck in slow traffic for the next 20 km. Its fuel consumption is reduced to 4 km per litre. After that, the road clears and the car travels a further 75 km during which time the consumption is 7.5 km/litre. Draw a copy of the graph and extend it to show the final 95 km of the journey.

   d) How much fuel is in the tank at the end of the journey?

5. A firm makes a profit of P thousand dollars from producing x thousand tiles. Corresponding values of P and x are given in the table:

x	0	0.5	1.0	1.5	2.0	2.5	3.0
p	−1.0	0.75	2.0	2.75	3.0	2.75	2.0

Using a scale of 4 cm to one unit on each axis, draw the graph of P against x. (Plot x on the horizontal axis.) Use your graph to find:

a) the number of tiles the firm should produce in order to make the maximum profit

b) the minimum number of tiles that should be produced to cover the cost of production

c) the range of values of x for which the profit is more than \$2850.

6. A small firm increases its monthly expenditure on advertising and records its monthly income from sales.

Month	1	2	3	4	5	6	7
Expenditure (\$)	100	200	300	400	500	600	700
Income (\$)	280	450	560	630	680	720	740

Draw a graph to display expenditure against income.

a) Is it wise to spend \$100 per month on advertising?

b) Is it wise to spend \$700 per month on advertising?

c) What is the most sensible level of expenditure on advertising?

Representing linear inequalities graphically

It is useful to represent inequalities on a graph, particularly where two variables are involved.

Example

Draw a sketch graph and leave unshaded the area which represents the set of points that satisfy each of these inequalities.

a) $x > 2$

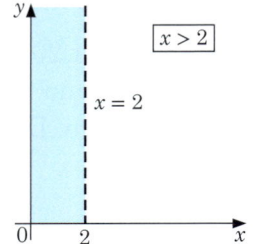

b) $1 \leqslant y \leqslant 5$

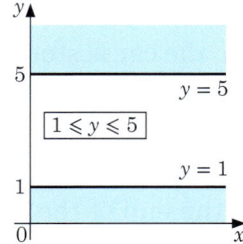

c) $x + y \leqslant 8$

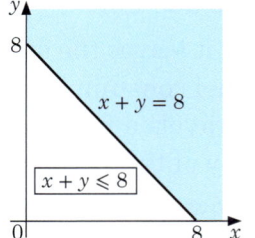

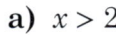

In each graph, the unwanted region is shaded so that the region representing the set of points is left clearly visible.

In **a)**, the line $x = 2$ is shown as a *broken* line to indicate that the points on the line are *not* included.

In **b)** and **c)**, the lines $y = 1$, $y = 5$ and $x + y = 8$ are shown as *solid* lines because points on the line *are* included in the solution set.

An inequality can thus be regarded as a set of points, for example, the unshaded region in part **c)** of the Example may be described as the set of points (x, y) such that $x + y \leqslant 8$.

Exercise 9.5B

For Questions **1** to **9**, describe the region left unshaded.

1.

2.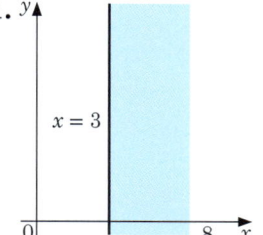

3.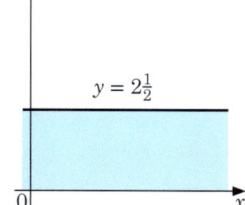

4.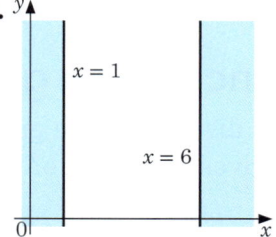

5.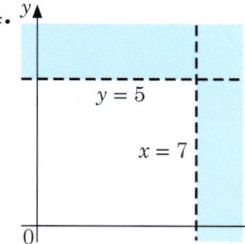

6.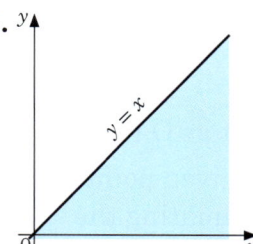

7.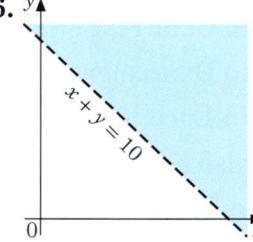

8.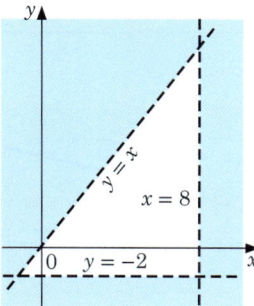

9.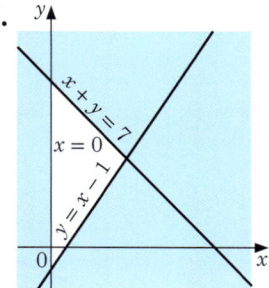

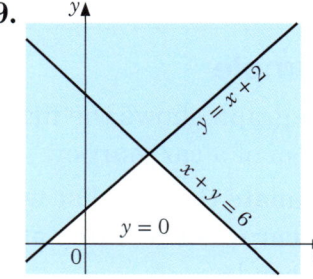

For Questions **10** to **27**, draw a sketch graph similar to those in Questions **1** to **9** and indicate the set of points which satisfy the inequalities by shading the unwanted regions.

10. $2 \leqslant x \leqslant 7$

11. $0 \leqslant y \leqslant 3\frac{1}{2}$

12. $-2 < x < 2$

13. $x < 6$ and $y \leqslant 4$

14. $0 < x < 5$ and $0 < y < 3$

15. $1 \leqslant x \leqslant 6$ and $2 \leqslant y \leqslant 8$

16. $-3 < x < 0$ and $-4 < y < 2$

17. $y \leqslant x$

18. $x + y < 5$

19. $y > x + 2$ and $y < 7$

20. $x \geqslant 0$ and $y \geqslant 0$ and $x + y \leqslant 7$

21. $x \geqslant 0$ and $x + y < 10$ and $y > x$

22. $8 \geqslant y \geqslant 0$ and $x + y > 3$

23. $x + 2y < 10$ and $x \geqslant 0$ and $y \geqslant 0$

24. $3x + 2y \leqslant 18$ and $x \geqslant 0$ and $y \geqslant 0$

25. $x \geqslant 0$, $y \geqslant x - 2$, $x + y \leqslant 10$

26. $3x + 5y \leqslant 30$ and $y > \dfrac{x}{2}$

27. $y \geqslant \dfrac{x}{2}$, $y \leqslant 2x$ and $x + y \leqslant 8$

Distance–time graphs

When a distance–time graph is drawn, the **gradient** of the graph gives the *speed* of the object.

From O to A: constant speed

     A to B: speed goes down to zero

     B to C: at rest

     C to D: accelerates

     D to E: constant speed (not as fast as O to A)

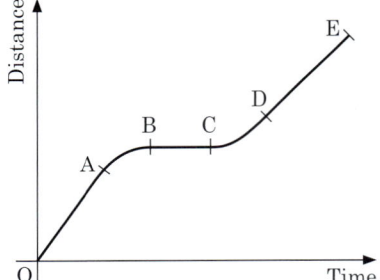

You can also estimate the speed at any given point by drawing a tangent at that point and estimating the gradient of the tangent.

Example

The graph shows the first 500 m of a car journey.

Estimate the speed at which the car was travelling after 4 seconds.

Draw a tangent to the curve at the point where $x = 4$.

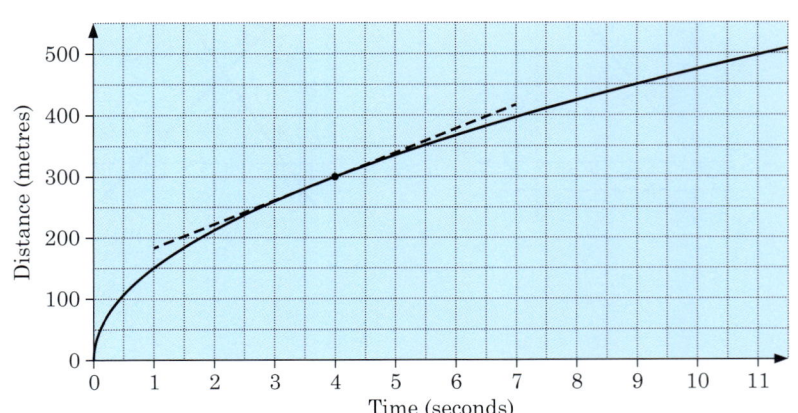

The endpoints of the tangent are (1, 180) and (7, 420), making the estimate of the gradient $\dfrac{420 - 180}{7 - 1} = \dfrac{240}{6} = 40$

This means the car was travelling at approximately 40 m/s after 4 seconds.

Exercise 9.5C

1. The graph shows the journeys made by a van and a car starting at Baden, travelling to St Gallen and returning to Baden.

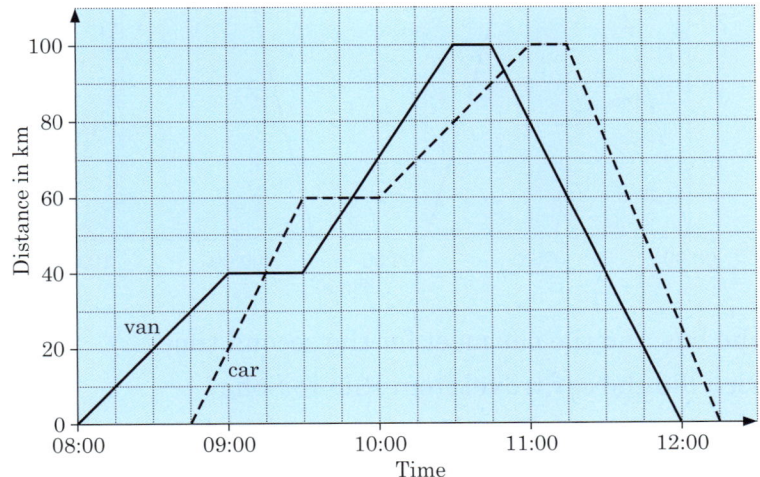

a) For how long was the van stationary during the journey?

b) At what time did the car first overtake the van?

c) At what speed was the van travelling between 09:30 and 10:00?

d) What was the greatest speed attained by the car during the entire journey?

e) What was the average speed of the car over its entire journey?

2. The graph on the next page shows the journeys of a bus and a car along the same road in Bulgaria. The bus goes from Sofia to Rila and back to Sofia. The car goes from Rila to Sofia and back to Rila.

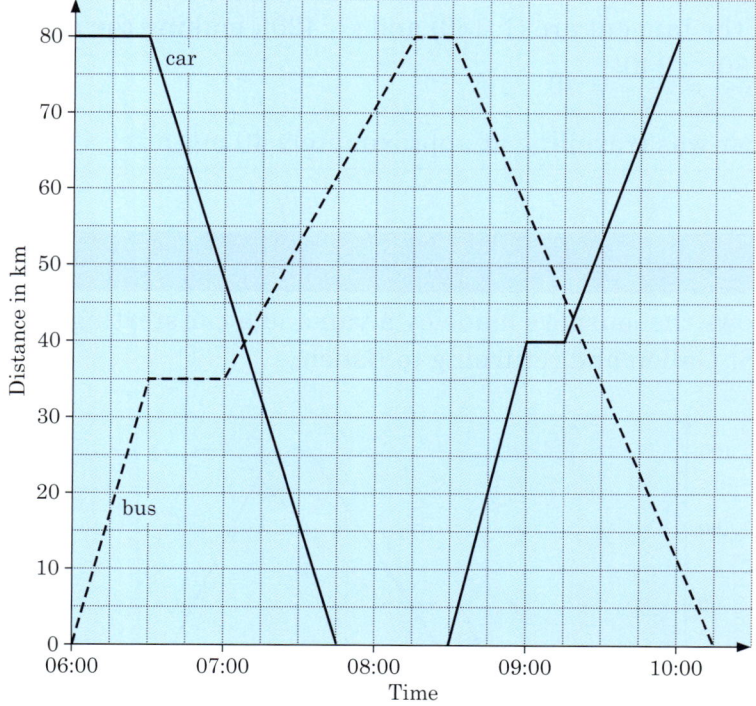

a) When did the bus and the car meet for the second time?

b) At what speed did the car travel from Rila to Sofia?

c) What was the average speed of the bus over its entire journey?

d) Approximately how far apart were the bus and the car at 09:45?

e) What was the greatest speed attained by the car during its entire journey?

3. The graph shows the motion of three cars A, B and C along the same road.

Answer the following questions giving estimates where necessary.

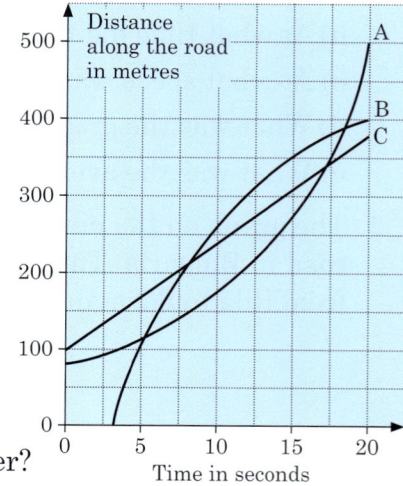

a) Which car is in front after

   i) 10 s   **ii)** 20 s?

b) When is B in the front?

c) When are B and C going at the same speed?

d) When are A and C going at the same speed?

e) Which car is going fastest after 5 s?

f) Which car starts slowly and then goes faster and faster?

g) Estimate the speed of car A after 10 s.

In Questions **4**, **5** and **6**, draw a travel graph to illustrate the journey described. Draw axes with similar scales to Question **2**.

4. Mrs Chuong leaves home at 08:00 and drives at a speed of 50 km/h. After $\frac{1}{2}$ hour she reduces her speed to 40 km/h and continues at this speed until 09:30. She stops from 09:30 until 10:00 and then returns home at a speed of 60 km/h.
   Use your graph to find the approximate time at which she arrives home.

5. Kemen leaves home at 09:00 and drives at a speed of 20 km/h. After $\frac{3}{4}$ hour he increases his speed to 45 km/h and continues at this speed until 10:45. He stops from 10:45 until 11:30 and then returns home at a speed of 50 km/h.
   Draw a graph and use it to find the approximate time at which he arrives home.

6. At 10:00 Akram leaves home and cycles to his grandparents' house which is 70 km away. He cycles at a speed of 20 km/h until 11:15, at which time he stops for $\frac{1}{2}$ hour.
   He then completes the journey at a speed of 30 km/h. At 11:45 Akram's sister, Hameeda, leaves home and drives her car at 60 km/h. Hameeda also goes to her grandparents' house and uses the same road as Akram.
   At approximately what time does Hameeda overtake Akram?

7. A boat can travel at a speed of 20 km/h in still water. The current in a river flows at 5 km/h so that downstream the boat travels at 25 km/h and upstream it travels at only 15 km/h.

The boat has only enough fuel to last 3 hours.
The boat leaves its base and travels downstream. Draw a distance–time graph and draw lines to indicate the outward and return journeys. How long after leaving must the boat turn round so that it can get back to base without running out of fuel?

8. The boat in Question **7** sails in a river where the current is 10 km/h and it has fuel for four hours.
   How long after leaving must the boat turn round this time if it is not to run out of fuel?

9. Three friends, Hanna, Fateema and Carrie took part in an egg and spoon race. A distance–time graph for the race is shown here. Describe what happened in the race, giving as many details as possible.

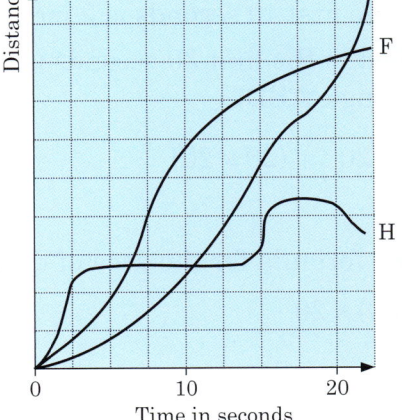

Speed–time graphs

For any speed–time graph:

- The **acceleration** at any point in the journey is the gradient of the speed–time graph at that point.

Note that **deceleration** is just negative acceleration.

If the graph is a curve, the acceleration can be estimated by drawing a tangent and estimating its gradient at the required point.

- The **distance travelled** during a section of the journey is the area under the graph for that part of the journey.

Note that when this is a trapezium it is quicker to use the formula for the area of a trapezium rather than breaking the area up into rectangles and triangles.

- The **average speed** for the whole journey is the total distance travelled divided by the total journey time.

Example

The diagram is the speed–time graph of the first 50 seconds of a car journey.

Calculate:

a) the acceleration during the first 10 seconds of the journey

b) the distance travelled in the first 30 seconds

c) the total distance travelled

d) the deceleration during the last 20 seconds of the journey

e) the average speed for the whole journey.

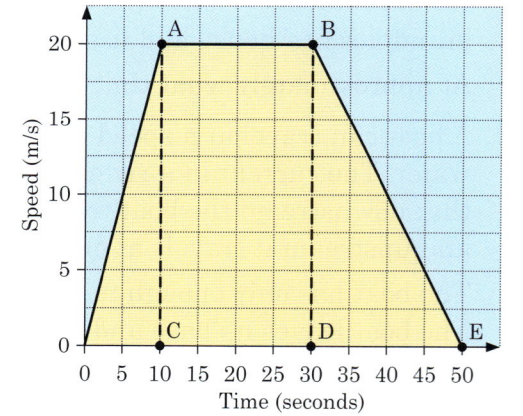

a) The gradient of line OA $= \dfrac{20}{10} = 2$

The acceleration in the first 10 seconds is 2 m/s².

b) The distance travelled in the first 30 seconds is given by the area of triangle OAC plus the area of rectangle ABDC.

Distance $= \left(\dfrac{1}{2} \times 10 \times 20 \right) + (20 \times 20)$

$\qquad = 500$ m

Alternatively, use the formula for the area of the trapezium OABD.

Distance $= \dfrac{1}{2} (20 + 30) \times 20$

$\qquad = 500$ m

c) The total area under the graph is a trapezium.

Distance $= \dfrac{1}{2}(20 + 50) \times 20$

$= 700$ m

d) The gradient of line BE $= \dfrac{-20}{20} = -1$

The deceleration in the last 20 seconds is 1 m/s².

e) Total distance travelled $= 700$ m.

Total time taken $= 50$ seconds.

Average speed for the whole journey is $\dfrac{700}{50} = 14\,\text{m/s}$

Exercise 9.5D

On the graphs in this exercise, the vertical axes represent speed, v m/s, and the horizontal axes represent time, t seconds.

1. Find:

   a) the acceleration between 0 and 10 seconds.

   b) the total distance travelled

   c) the average speed for the whole journey.

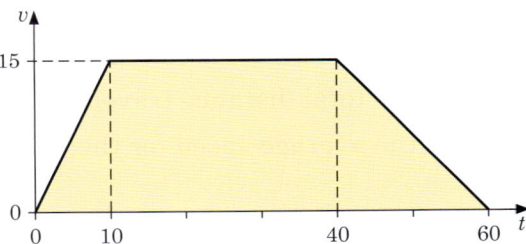

2. Find:

   a) the total distance travelled

   b) the average speed for the whole journey

   c) the distance travelled in the first 10 seconds

   d) the acceleration when $t = 20$.

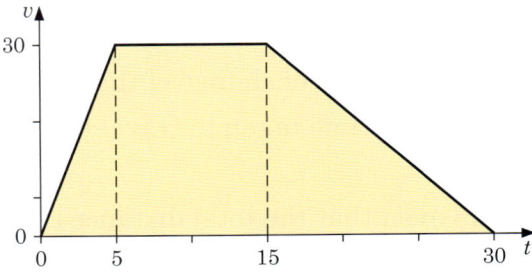

3. The graph shows the first 5 seconds of a journey.

   Estimate the acceleration after 1 second.

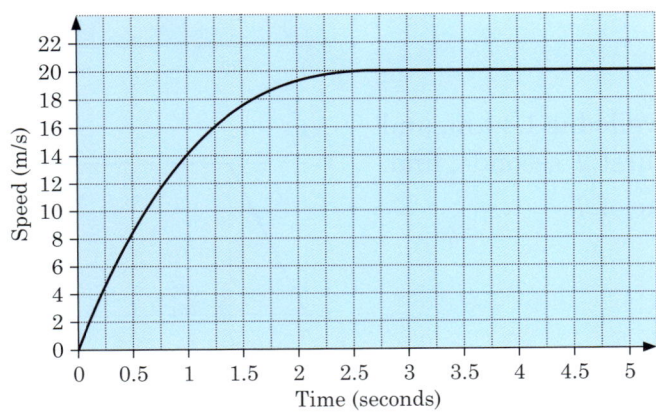

4. Find:

    a) the total distance travelled

    b) the distance travelled in the first 40 seconds

    c) the acceleration when $t = 15$.

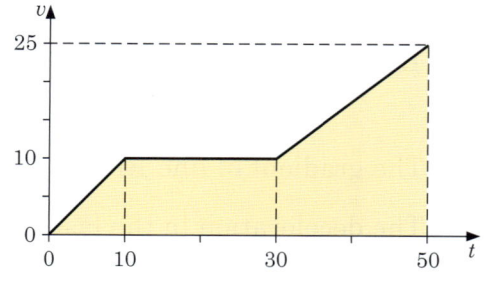

5. Find:

    a) V if the total distance travelled is 900 m

    b) the distance travelled in the first 60 seconds.

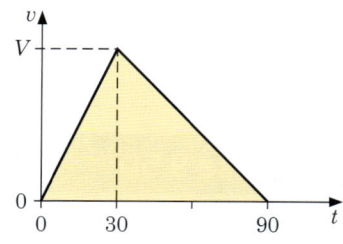

6. Find:

    a) T if the initial acceleration is 2 m/s²

    b) the total distance travelled

    c) the average speed for the whole journey.

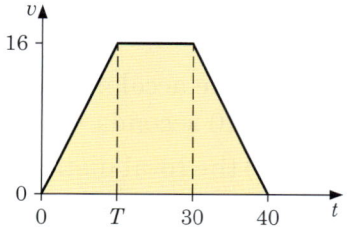

7. Given that the total distance travelled = 810 m, find:

    a) the value of V

    b) the rate of change of the speed when $t = 30$

    c) the time taken to travel the first 420 m of the journey.

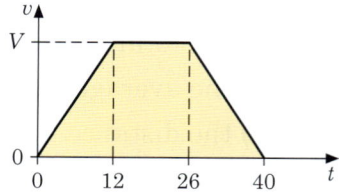

8. Given that the total distance travelled is 1.5 km, find:

    a) the value of V

    b) the rate of deceleration after 10 seconds.

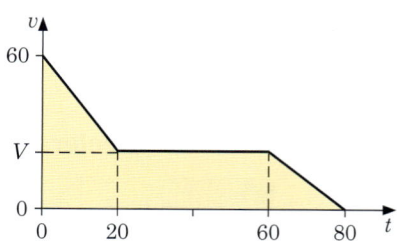

9. Given that the total distance travelled is 1.4 km, and the acceleration is 4 m/s² for the first T seconds, find:

    a) the value of V **b)** the value of T.

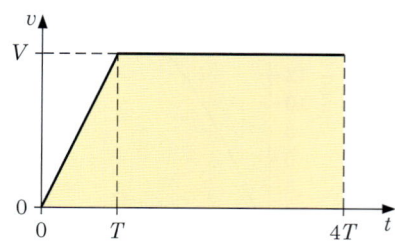

10. Given that the average speed for the whole journey is 37.5 m/s and that the deceleration between T and $2T$ is 2.5 m/s², find:

   a) the value of V b) the value of T.

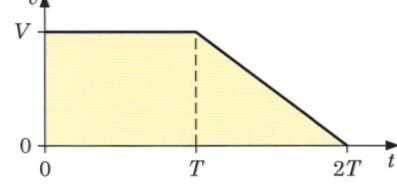

11. Given that the total distance travelled is 4 km and that the initial deceleration is 4 m/s², find:

   a) the value of V b) the value of T.

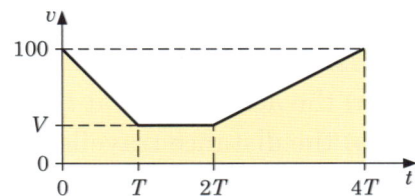

Exercise 9.5E

Sketch a speed–time graph for each question.

All accelerations are taken to be constant.

1. A car accelerated from 0 to 50 m/s in 9 s. How far did it travel in this time?

2. A motorcycle accelerated from 10 m/s to 30 m/s in 6 s. How far did it travel in this time?

3. A train slowed down from 50 km/h to 10 km/h in 2 minutes. How far did it travel in this time?

4. When taking off, an aircraft accelerates from 0 to 100 m/s in a distance of 500 m. How long did it take to travel this distance?

5. An earthworm accelerates from a speed of 0.01 m/s to 0.02 m/s over a distance of 0.9 m. How long did it take?

6. A car travelling at 60 km/h is stopped in 6 seconds. How far does it travel in this time?

7. A car accelerates from 15 km/h to 60 km/h in 3 seconds. How far does it travel in this time?

8. At lift-off, a rocket accelerates from 0 to 1000 km/h in just 10 s. How far does it travel in this time?

9. A coach accelerated from 0 to 60 km/h in 30 s. How many metres did it travel in this time?

10. Hamad was driving a car at 30 m/s when he saw an obstacle 45 m in front of him. It took a reaction time of 0.3 seconds before he could press the brakes and a further 2.5 seconds to stop the car. Did he hit the obstacle?

11. An aircraft is cruising at a speed of 200 m/s. When it lands, it must be travelling at a speed of 50 m/s. In the air it can slow down at a rate of 0.2 m/s². On the ground it slows down at a rate of 2 m/s². Draw a velocity–time graph for the aircraft as it reduces its speed from 200 m/s to 50 m/s and then to 0 m/s. How far does it travel in this time?

12. The speed of a train is measured at regular intervals of time from $t = 0$ to $t = 60$ s, as shown below.

t (s)	0	10	20	30	40	50	60
v (m/s)	0	10	16	19.7	22.2	23.8	24.7

Draw a speed–time graph to illustrate the motion. Plot t on the horizontal axis with a scale of 1 cm to 5 s and plot v on the vertical axis with a scale of 2 cm to 5 m/s.

Use the graph to estimate:

a) the acceleration at $t = 10$

b) the distance travelled by the train from $t = 30$ to $t = 60$.

(An approximate value for the area under a curve can be found by splitting the area into several trapeziums.)

13. The speed of a car is measured at regular intervals of time from $t = 0$ to $t = 60$ s, as shown below.

t (s)	0	10	20	30	40	50	60
v (m/s)	0	1.3	3.2	6	10.1	16.5	30

Draw a speed–time graph using the same scales as in Question **12**.

Use the graph to estimate:

a) the acceleration at $t = 30$

b) the distance travelled by the car from $t = 20$ to $t = 50$.

9.6 Graphical solutions of equations

Sometimes you can solve an equation by accurately plotting the left-hand side and the right-hand side as two different graphs and seeing where they intersect.

Example

Solve the equation $(x - 3)^2 = 5 - x$ graphically.

Plot the graphs of $y = (x - 3)^2$ and $y = 5 - x$.

The graphs intersect at the points (1, 4) and (4, 1).

The solutions to $(x - 3)^2 = 5 - x$ are $x = 1$ and $x = 4$.

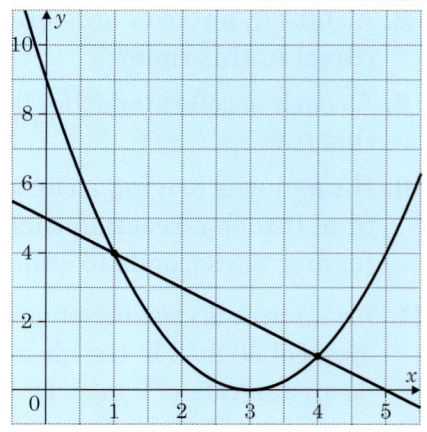

Exercise 9.6A

Solve the following equations by plotting appropriate graphs and finding their points of intersection.

1. $(x - 1)^2 = x + 1$

2. $(x - 3)^2 = 9 - x$

3. $7 - x^2 = x + 1$

4. $x + 1 = \dfrac{2}{x}$

5. $x^2 + 1 = 5 - (x - 2)^2$

6. $x^3 + 1 = x^2 - 1$

7. $x^2 - 2 = x^3 - 2x - 2$

8. $6 \times 3^x = 4x^2 + 8x + 6$

9. $3 \times 2^x = 7x + 3$

10. $30 - (x - 2)^2 = 3x^2 + 18$

The method in the previous exercise treated the two sides of each equation as though they were a pair of simultaneous equations.

Accurately drawing graphs is good way to obtain solutions to pairs of simultaneous equations. Sometimes these solutions may be only approximate, and sometimes they may be exact, depending on the equations.

To solve a pair of simultaneous equations graphically, draw both equations on the same axes. The coordinates of the point where the lines intersect give you the values of x and y that you are looking for.

Example

Solve the simultaneous equations: $y = 2x + 1$ and $y = 7 - x$

Draw both lines on the same diagram.

Notice that they cross at the point (2, 5).

Therefore, the solution to the simultaneous equations is $x = 2$ and $y = 5$

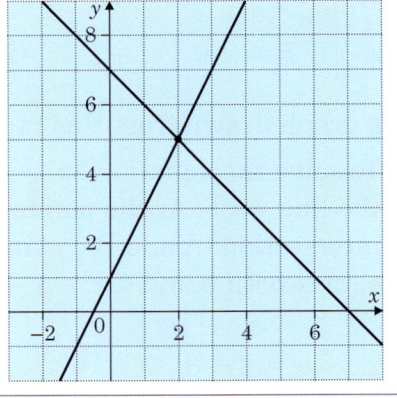

Exercise 9.6B

Find exact solutions to the following pairs of simultaneous equations by drawing their graphs and seeing where the lines intersect.

1. $y = 2x + 1$ and $y = 4x - 1$

2. $x + y = 4$ and $x + 3y = 6$

3. $y = x - 3$ and $y = -x - 1$

4. $y = x - 4$ and $6x - 10y = 16$

5. $y = x^2$ and $y = x + 2$

6. $y = 4 - x^2$ and $y = 2 - x$

315

Find approximate solutions to the following pairs of simultaneous equations by drawing their graphs and seeing where the lines intersect.

7. $y = x + 2$ and $y = 5 - x$ **8.** $y = 2x + 3$ and $y = 4 - 2x$

9. $3y = 2x + 9$ and $x + 2y = 5$ **10.** $y = x^2$ and $y = \dfrac{2}{3}x + 3$

This approach can be used to find the roots of even more complicated equations. Sometimes rearranging the equation first makes the process easier.

The next two examples illustrate this.

Example 1

Draw the graph of the function $y = 2x^2 - x - 3$ for $-2 \leqslant x \leqslant 3$.

Use the graph to find approximate solutions to the following equations.

a) $2x^2 - x - 3 = 6$ **b)** $2x^2 - x = x + 5$

The table of values for $y = 2x^2 - x - 3$ is found. Note the extra value at $x = \dfrac{1}{2}$.

x	-2	-1	0	1	2	3	$\dfrac{1}{2}$
$2x^2$	8	2	0	2	8	18	$\dfrac{1}{2}$
$-x$	2	1	0	-1	-2	-3	$-\dfrac{1}{2}$
-3	-3	-3	-3	-3	-3	-3	-3
y	7	0	-3	-2	3	12	-3

The graph drawn from this table is shown.

a) To solve the equation $2x^2 - x - 3 = 6$, draw the line $y = 6$. At the points of intersection (A and B), y simultaneously equals both 6 and $(2x^2 - x - 3)$.
So

$$2x^2 - x - 3 = 6$$

The solutions are the x-values of the points A and B.

i.e. $x = -1.9$ and $x = 2.4$ approx.

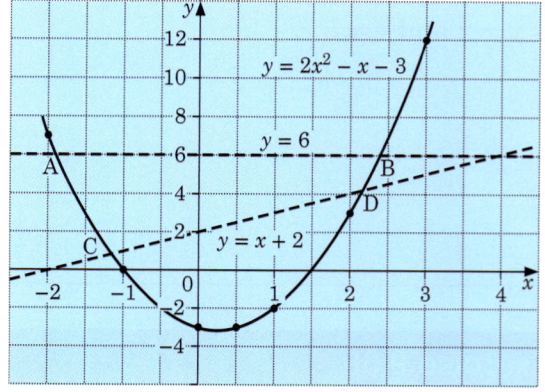

b) To solve the equation $2x^2 - x = x + 5$, rearrange the equation to obtain the function $(2x^2 - x - 3)$ on the left-hand side. In this case, subtract 3 from both sides.

$$2x^2 - x - 3 = x + 5 - 3$$

$$2x^2 - x - 3 = x + 2$$

If you now draw the line $y = x + 2$, the solutions of the equation are given by the x-values of C and D, the points of intersection, i.e. $x = -1.2$ and $x = 2.2$ approx.

It is important to rearrange the equation to be solved so that the function already plotted is on one side.

Example 2

Assuming that the graph of $y = x^2 - 3x + 1$ has been drawn, find the equation of the line which should be drawn to solve the equation $x^2 - 4x + 3 = 0$.

Rearrange $x^2 - 4x + 3 = 0$ in order to obtain $(x^2 - 3x + 1)$ on the left-hand side.

$$x^2 - 4x + 3 = 0$$
$$x^2 - 3x + 3 = x \qquad \text{(add } x\text{)}$$
$$x^2 - 3x + 1 = x - 2 \quad \text{(subtract 2)}$$

Therefore, draw the line $y = x - 2$ to solve the equation.

Exercise 9.6C

1. In the diagram, the graphs of $y = x^2 - 2x - 3$, $y = -2$ and $y = x$ have been drawn. Use the graphs to find approximate solutions to the following equations.

   a) $x^2 - 2x - 3 = -2$ **b)** $x^2 - 2x - 3 = x$

   c) $x^2 - 2x - 3 = 0$ **d)** $x^2 - 2x - 1 = 0$

   In Questions **2** to **4**, use a scale of 2 cm to 1 unit for x and 1 cm to 1 unit for y.

2. Draw the graphs of the functions $y = x^2 - 2x$ and $y = x + 1$ for $-1 \leqslant x \leqslant 4$. Hence find approximate solutions of the equation $x^2 - 2x = x + 1$.

3. Draw the graphs of the functions $y = x^2 - 3x + 5$ and $y = x + 3$ for $-1 \leqslant x \leqslant 5$. Hence find approximate solutions of the equation $x^2 - 3x + 5 = x + 3$.

4. Draw the graphs of the functions $y = 6x - x^2$ and $y = 2x + 1$ for $0 \leqslant x \leqslant 5$. Hence find approximate solutions of the equation $6x - x^2 = 2x + 1$.

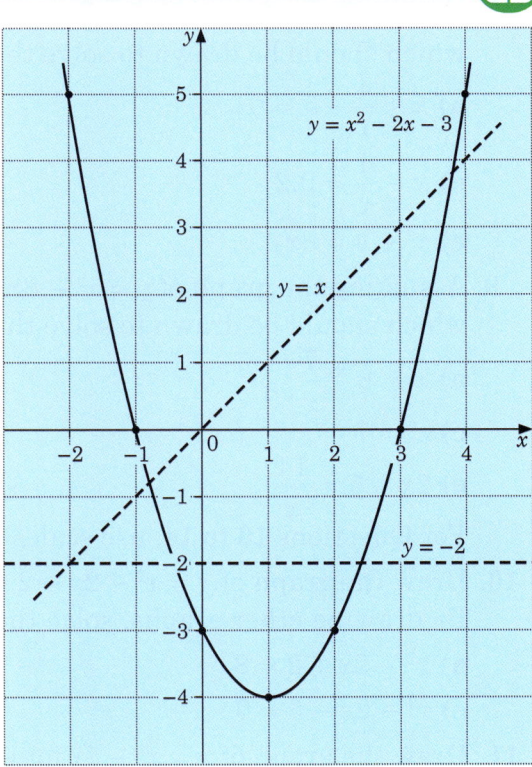

In Questions **5** to **9**, do *not* draw any graphs.

5. Assuming the graph of $y = x^2 - 5x$ has been drawn, find the equation of the line which should be drawn to solve the equations:

   a) $x^2 - 5x = 3$ **b)** $x^2 - 5x = -2$

   c) $x^2 - 5x = x + 4$ **d)** $x^2 - 6x = 0$

   e) $x^2 - 5x - 6 = 0$

6. Assuming the graph of $y = x^2 + x + 1$ has been drawn, find the equation of the line which should be drawn to solve the equations:

   a) $x^2 + x + 1 = 6$ **b)** $x^2 + x + 1 = 0$

   c) $x^2 + x - 3 = 0$ **d)** $x^2 - x + 1 = 0$

   e) $x^2 - x - 3 = 0$

7. Assuming the graph of $y = 6x - x^2$ has been drawn, find the equation of the line which should be drawn to solve the equations:

   a) $4 + 6x - x^2 = 0$ **b)** $4x - x^2 = 0$

   c) $2 + 5x - x^2 = 0$ **d)** $x^2 - 6x = 3$

   e) $x^2 - 6x = -2$

8. Assuming the graph of $y = x + \dfrac{4}{x}$ has been drawn, find the equation of the line which should be drawn to solve the equations:

   a) $x + \dfrac{4}{x} - 5 = 0$ **b)** $\dfrac{4}{x} - x = 0$

   c) $x + \dfrac{4}{x} = 0.2$ **d)** $2x + \dfrac{4}{x} - 3 = 0$

   e) $x^2 + 4 = 3x$

9. Assuming the graph of $y = x^2 - 8x - 7$ has been drawn, find the equation of the line which should be drawn to solve the equations:

   a) $x = 8 + \dfrac{7}{x}$ **b)** $2x^2 = 16x + 9$

   c) $x^2 = 7$ **d)** $x = \dfrac{4}{x - 8}$

   e) $2x - 5 = \dfrac{14}{x}$

   For Questions **10** to **14**, use scales of 2 cm = 1 unit for x and 1 cm = 1 unit for y.

10. Draw the graph of $y = x^2 - 2x + 2$ for $-2 \leqslant x \leqslant 4$.
    By drawing other graphs, solve the equations:

    a) $x^2 - 2x + 2 = 8$ **b)** $x^2 - 2x + 2 = 5 - x$

    c) $x^2 - 2x - 5 = 0$

11. Draw the graph of $y = x^2 - 7x$ for $0 \leqslant x \leqslant 7$.
    Draw suitable straight lines to solve the equations:

    a) $x^2 - 7x + 9 = 0$ **b)** $x^2 - 5x + 1 = 0$

12. Draw the graph of $y = x^2 + 4x + 5$ for $-6 \leqslant x \leqslant 1$.
    Draw suitable straight lines to find approximate solutions of the equations:
    a) $x^2 + 3x - 1 = 0$ **b)** $x^2 + 5x + 2 = 0$

13. Draw the graph of $y = 2x^2 + 3x - 9$ for $-3 \leqslant x \leqslant 2$.
    Draw suitable straight lines to find approximate solutions of the equations:
    a) $2x^2 + 3x - 4 = 0$ **b)** $2x^2 + 2x - 9 = 1$

14. Draw the graph of $y = 2 + 3x - 2x^2$ for $-2 \leqslant x \leqslant 4$.

    a) Draw suitable straight lines to find approximate solutions of the equations:
        i) $2 + 4x - 2x^2 = 0$ **ii)** $2x^2 - 3x - 2 = 0$

    b) Find the range of values of x for which $2 + 3x - 2x^2 \geqslant -5$.

15. Draw the graph of $y = \dfrac{18}{x}$ for $1 \leqslant x \leqslant 10$, using scales of 1 cm to one unit on both axes. Use the graph to solve approximately:

    a) $\dfrac{18}{x} = x + 2$ **b)** $\dfrac{18}{x} + x = 10$ **c)** $x^2 = 18$

16. Draw the graph of $y = \dfrac{1}{2}x^2 - 6$ for $-4 \leqslant x \leqslant 4$, taking 2 cm to 1 unit on each axis.

    a) Use your graph to solve approximately the equation $\dfrac{1}{2}x^2 - 6 = 1$.

    b) Using tables or a calculator confirm that your solutions are approximately $\pm\sqrt{14}$ and explain why this is so.

    c) Use your graph to find the square roots of 8.

17. Draw the graph of $y = 6 - 2x - \dfrac{1}{2}x^3$ for $x = \pm 2, \pm 1\dfrac{1}{2}, \pm 1, \pm\dfrac{1}{2}, 0$. Take 4 cm to 1 unit for x and 1 cm to 1 unit for y. Use your graph to find approximate solutions of the equations:

    a) $\dfrac{1}{2}x^3 + 2x - 6 = 0$ **b)** $x - \dfrac{1}{2}x^3 = 0$

    Using tables confirm that two of the solutions to the equation in part **b)** are $\pm\sqrt{2}$ and explain why this is so.

18. Draw the graph of $y = x + \dfrac{12}{x} - 5$ for $x = 1, 1\dfrac{1}{2}, 2, 3, 4, 5, 6, 7, 8$, taking 2 cm to 1 unit on each axis.

    a) From your graph find the range of values of x for which $x + \dfrac{12}{x} \leqslant 9$.

    b) Find an approximate solution of the equation $2x - \dfrac{12}{x} - 12 = 0$.

19. Draw the graph of $y = 2^x$ for $-4 \leqslant x \leqslant 4$, taking 2 cm to one unit for x and 1 cm to one unit for y. Find approximate solutions to the equations:

    a) $2^x = 6$ **b)** $2^x = 3x$ **c)** $x2^x = 1$

    d) Find also the approximate value of $2^{2.5}$.

20. Draw the graph of $y = \dfrac{1}{x}$ for $-4 \leqslant x \leqslant 4$ taking 2 cm to one unit on each axis. Find approximate solutions to the equations:

a) $\dfrac{1}{x} = x + 1$

b) $2x^2 - x - 1 = 0$

9.7 Differentiation

Completing the square

In Chapter 2, the method of completing the square was used to solve quadratic equations. Completing the square can also be used to find the coordinates of the minimum or maximum point on the graph of a quadratic function. Such points are called **turning points**.

When the quadratic function is written in the form $y = (x - a)^2 + b$, the coordinates of the turning point on the graph are (a, b).

Example

$y = x^2 - 4x + 1$

Find the coordinates of the turning point on the graph.

The function can be rewritten by completing the square:

$y = (x - 2)^2 - 2^2 + 1$

$y = (x - 2)^2 - 3$

The coordinates of the turning point are $(2, -3)$. This is because the bracket that is squared cannot be negative. Therefore the smallest value of y will be b, which will occur when the contents of the bracket equal zero, that is, when $x = a$.

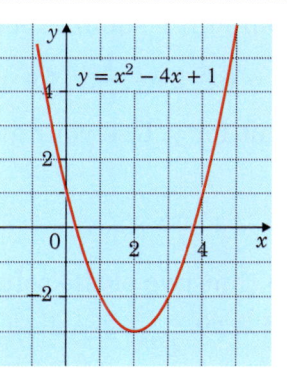

Exercise 9.7A

Find the coordinates of the turning points on the graphs of these quadratic functions. Give your answers as exact values.

1. $y = x^2 - 6x + 2$

2. $y = x^2 + 4x - 3$

3. $y = x^2 + 5x - 2$

4. $y = x^2 - 7x + 5$

5. $y = 6 - 4x - x^2$

6. $y = 4 - 3x - x^2$

7. $y = 2x^2 - 6x + 5$

8. $y = 3x^2 + 6x - 4$

9. $y = 4 - 3x - 2x^2$

10. $y = 7 - 5x - 4x^2$

Derivative functions

Completing the square to find the coordinates of the turning point is possible only if the function is quadratic.

In order to find the turning points on the graphs of other functions (cubic functions, for example), a different method is required.

The gradient of a curve at a particular point can be found by drawing a tangent to the curve at that point and finding the gradient of the tangent.

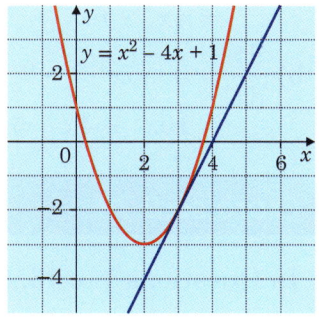

For example, the gradient of the curve $y = x^2 - 4x + 1$ at the point where $x = 3$ is 2.

It is possible to make a table for the values of the gradient at various points on the curve and hence plot the **gradient function**.

x	−1	0	1	2	3	4
gradient	−6	−4	−2	0	2	4

Plotting the graph of the gradient function, it is clear that it is a straight line.

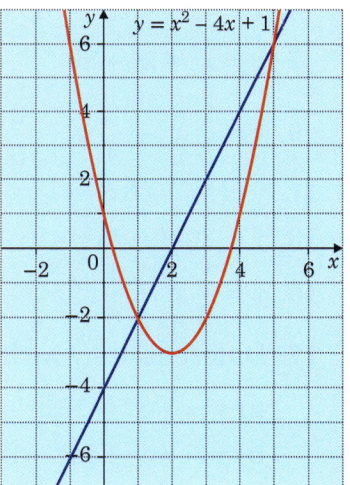

The gradient function is called the **derivative function** and, if y is written in terms of x, it is denoted using the notation $\dfrac{dy}{dx}$ (the derivative of y with respect to x, or 'dy by dx').

In this case, $\dfrac{dy}{dx} = 2x - 4$, as can be seen from the graph.

The rule for finding the derivative function for integer powers of x is:

$$y = x^n \rightarrow \frac{dy}{dx} = nx^{n-1}$$

('Multiply by the power, then reduce the power by 1.')

The process of finding the derivative function is called **differentiation**.

In the case of $y = x^2 - 4x + 1$, you differentiate each term one after the other.

$$\frac{dy}{dx} = 2 \times x^{2-1} - 1 \times 4x^{1-1} + 0 \times 1 = 2x - 4$$

Tip

Note that the constant term in y disappears since the power of x is zero and zero multiplied by anything is zero.

Example

Find the derivative of the functions:

a) $y = x^4 - 3x^2 + 2$ **b)** $y = 5x^3 - 2x^2 + 6x$

a) $\dfrac{dy}{dx} = 4 \times x^{4-1} - 2 \times 3x^{2-1} + 0$

      $= 4x^3 - 6x$

b) $\dfrac{dy}{dx} = 3 \times 5x^{3-1} - 2 \times 2x^{2-1} + 1 \times 6x^{1-1}$

      $= 15x^2 - 4x + 6$

Exercise 9.7B

In Questions **1** to **16**, find $\dfrac{dy}{dx}$.

1. $y = 3x^2$

2. $y = 2x^3 - 4x$

3. $y = 6x^4$

4. $y = 2x^5 - 4x^2 + 5$

5. $y = 4x^4 - 3x^3 + 5x^2$

6. $y = 5 - 3x^2 - 3x^4$

7. $y = x^7 + x^6 + x^5$

8. $y = \dfrac{1}{2}x^3 + \dfrac{2}{3}x^2$

9. $y = \dfrac{1}{5}x^4 + \dfrac{3}{4}x^3 - \dfrac{2}{5}x^2$

10. $y = \dfrac{1}{16}x^4 - \dfrac{1}{3}x^3 + \dfrac{17}{25}$

11. $y = 5x^3 - 6x^2$

12. $y = 6x^5 - 4x^4 + 3$

13. $y = 20x^2 - 5x^5 + 2x$

14. $y = 7x^8 - 13x$

15. $y = \dfrac{1}{8}x^7 - \dfrac{1}{6}x^5$

16. $y = \dfrac{8}{9}x^5 + \dfrac{1}{15}x^3 + \dfrac{1}{8}$

17. Differentiate y with respect to x.

     a) $y = 14x^5 - 16x^4 - 13x$

     b) $y = 8x^9 - 5x^2 - 18$

     c) $y = \dfrac{1}{14}x^7 - \dfrac{5}{6}x^6 + \dfrac{1}{4}x^3$

Tip

'Differentiate y with respect to x' just means 'find the derivative function'.

Finding gradients

To find the gradient of a curve at a particular point, substitute the given x-value into the derivative function.

Example

Find the gradient of the curve $y = 6x^2 - 3x^3 - 5x$ when $x = 6$.

$\dfrac{dy}{dx} = 12x - 9x^2 - 5$

When $x = 6$, $\dfrac{dy}{dx} = 12 \times 6 - 9 \times 6^2 - 5 = -257$

Exercise 9.7C

1. $y = 2x^2 - 3x^3$

   Find the gradient of the curve when:

   a) $x = 1$ **b)** $x = 4$ **c)** $x = -5$

2. $y = 4x^3 - 5x$

   Find the gradient of the curve when:

   a) $x = 2$ **b)** $x = -6$ **c)** $x = 0.5$

3. $y = 6x^2 + 8x^3 - 7x$

   Find the gradient of the curve when:

   a) $x = 3$ **b)** $x = -4$ **c)** $x = \dfrac{2}{3}$

4. The curve $y = x^2 - 4x + 3$ has a gradient of -1 at the point where $x = a$.
   Find the value of a.

5. The curve $y = 3x^2 - 2x + 7$ has a gradient of -20 at the point where $x = b$.
   Find the value of b.

6. Find the coordinates of the point on the curve $y = 7 - 3x - 2x^2$ where the gradient is 5.

7. The curve $y = x^3 + 2x^2 - 3x$ has a gradient of 4 at points **A** and **B**.
   Find the x-coordinates of **A** and **B**.

8. The curve $y = \dfrac{1}{3}x^3 + \dfrac{1}{2}x^2 - 5x$ has a gradient of -3 at points **P** and **Q**.
   Find the coordinates of **P** and **Q**.

9. The curve $y = \dfrac{1}{2}x^4 - 4x^2 - 3x$ has a gradient of -3 at three points.
   Find the coordinates of these points.

10. Find the coordinates of the points on the curve $y = x^3 - 5x^2 - 8x$ where the gradient is zero.

Turning points

At a **turning point** on a graph, the gradient is zero. A point at which the gradient is zero is called a **stationary point**. A turning point is an example of a stationary point. This means that all turning points are stationary points, but not all stationary points are turning points!

On the cubic graph here, there are two turning points: one at A and one at B.

Completing the square can be used to find the turning point on a quadratic graph, but for other graphs this does not work.

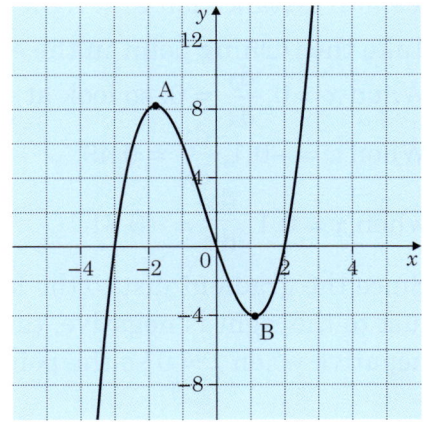

Turning points for other graphs (and for quadratic graphs) can be found by setting the derivative function equal to zero and solving the resulting equation.

Example

Find the coordinates of the turning points on the curve
$y = 3x^3 - 2x^2$

$\dfrac{dy}{dx} = 9x^2 - 4x$

Set $\dfrac{dy}{dx} = 0$: $9x^2 - 4x = 0$

                    $x(9x - 4) = 0$

Hence $x = 0$ or $x = \dfrac{4}{9}$

When $x = 0$, $y = 0$ so one turning point is at $(0, 0)$.

When $x = \dfrac{4}{9}$, $y = -\dfrac{32}{243}$ so the other turning point is at $\left(\dfrac{4}{9}, -\dfrac{32}{243}\right)$.

Unless the graph of a function is given, it may not be obvious whether a turning point is a maximum point or a minimum point. There are three ways to find this out:

Method 1

Investigate the gradient immediately to the left and to the right of the turning point. In other words, find the gradient on the curve at a small distance left and right of the turning point.

Take the turning point in the example above when $x = 0$:

When $x = 0$, $\dfrac{dy}{dx} = 0$, so look at $\dfrac{dy}{dx}$ when $x = -0.1$ and 0.1

When $x = -0.1$, $\dfrac{dy}{dx} = 0.49$

when $x = 0.1$, $\dfrac{dy}{dx} = -0.31$

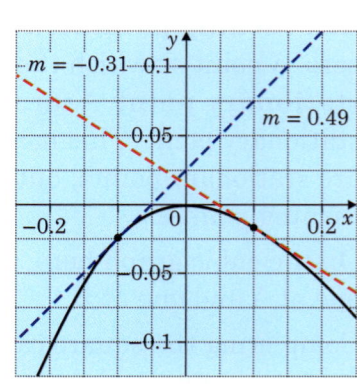

Since the gradient just to the left is positive and the gradient just to the right is negative, the curve turns from positive to negative when $x = 0$ so the point $(0, 0)$ is a **maximum** point.

Method 2

Find the **second derivative** $\dfrac{d^2y}{dx^2}$ and substitute in the coordinates of the turning point.

The **sign** of the second derivative determines whether the turning point is a maximum or a minimum.

Take the turning point in the example above when $x = \dfrac{4}{9}$:

The second derivative is found by differentiating $\dfrac{dy}{dx}$ again so $\dfrac{d^2y}{dx^2} = 18x - 4$.

When $x = \dfrac{4}{9}$, $\dfrac{d^2y}{dx^2} = 4$

If the second derivative is **positive**, the turning point is a **minimum** point.

If the second derivative is **negative**, the turning point is a **maximum** point.

Method 3

The third method is to accurately draw the graph. From this you will be able to see whether a turning point is a maximum or a minimum.

> **Tip**
>
> If you are asked to determine the nature of the turning points, you need to state whether each one is a maximum or a minimum.

Exercise 9.7D

1. Use differentiation to find the coordinates of the turning points of these graphs.

    a) $y = x^2 - 3x - 5$ **b)** $y = 4x^2 - 7x$ **c)** $y = 2 - 3x - 2x^2$

2. Determine the nature of the turning points in Question **1**.

3. $y = 5x^2 - 7x + 6$

    a) Find the coordinates of the turning point on the graph.

    b) Show that the turning point is a minimum point.

4. $y = 2x^3 - 2x^2 - 3$

    a) Find the exact coordinates of the turning points on the graph.

    b) Determine the nature of the turning points.

5. $y = 2x^3 - 6x - 5$

    a) Find the exact coordinates of the turning points on the graph.

    b) Determine the nature of the turning points.

6. $y = 3 + 12x - x^3$

    a) Find the exact coordinates of the turning points on the graph.

    b) Determine the nature of the turning points.

7. Show that the graph of $y = 4 - 2x - x^3$ has no turning points.

8. The graph of $y = kx + x^2 - x^3$ has no turning points. Find the range of values of k.

> **Tip**
>
> Turning points occur when $\dfrac{dy}{dx} = 0$. Show that the quadratic equation $\dfrac{dy}{dx} = 0$ has no solutions.

> **Tip**
>
> Find the values of k such that $\dfrac{dy}{dx} = 0$ has no solutions.

Revision exercise 9

1. Find the equation of the straight line satisfied by each set of points.

a)

x	2	7	10
y	−5	0	3

b)

x	1	2	3
y	7	9	11

c)

x	1	2	3
y	8	6	4

d)

x	3	4	5
y	2	$2\frac{1}{2}$	3

2. Find the gradient of the line joining each pair of points.

a) $(3, 3)$, $(5, 7)$

b) $(3, -1)$, $(7, 3)$

c) $(-1, 4)$, $(1, -3)$

d) $(2, 4)$, $(-3, 4)$

e) $(0.5, -3)$, $(0.4, -4)$

3. Find the gradient and the intercept on the y-axis for the following lines. Draw a *sketch* graph of each line.

a) $y = 2x - 7$

b) $y = 5 - 4x$

c) $2y = x + 8$

d) $2y = 10 - x$

e) $y + 2x = 12$

f) $2x + 3y = 24$

4. In the diagram, the equations of the lines are $y = 3x$, $y = 6$, $y = 10 - x$ and $y = \frac{1}{2}x - 3$.

Match each line A to D with its equation.

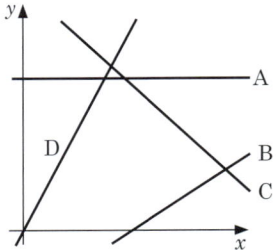

5. In the diagram, the equations of the lines are $2y = x - 8$, $2y + x = 8$, $4y = 3x - 16$ and $4y + 3x = 16$.

Match each line A to D with its equation.

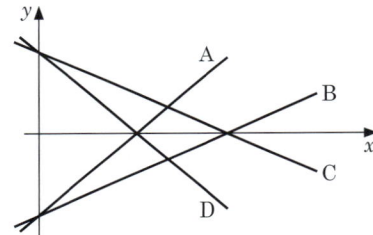

6. Find the equations of the lines which pass through the following pairs of points.

a) $(2, 1)$, $(4, 5)$ **b)** $(0, 4)$, $(-1, 1)$

c) $(2, 8)$, $(-2, 12)$ **d)** $(0, 7)$, $(-3, 7)$

7. The sketch represents a section of the curve $y = x^2 - 2x - 8$.

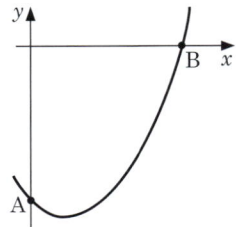

Calculate:

a) the coordinates of A and of B

b) the gradient of the line AB

c) the equation of the straight line AB.

8. Find the area of the triangle formed by the intersection of the lines $y = x$, $x + y = 10$ and $x = 0$.

 9. Find, correct to two decimal places, the shortest distance from the point $(-1, 2)$ to the line $y = 2x - 3$.

10. Draw the graph of $y = 7 - 3x - 2x^2$ for $-4 \leqslant x \leqslant 2$.

Find the gradient of the tangent to the curve at the point where the curve intercepts the y-axis.

 11. Draw the graph of $y = \dfrac{4000}{x} + 3x$ for $10 \leqslant x \leqslant 80$. Find the minimum value of y.

12. Draw the graph of $y = \dfrac{1}{x} + 2^x$ for
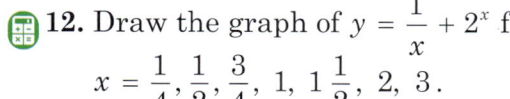
$x = \dfrac{1}{4}, \dfrac{1}{2}, \dfrac{3}{4}, 1, 1\dfrac{1}{2}, 2, 3$.

13. Assuming that the graph of $y = 4 - x^2$ has been drawn, find the equation of the straight line which should be drawn in order to solve the following equations:

a) $4 - 3x - x^2 = 0$ **b)** $\dfrac{1}{2}(4 - x^2) = 0$

c) $x^2 - x + 7 = 0$ **d)** $\dfrac{4}{x} - x = 5$

14. Draw the graph of $y = 5 - x^2$ for $-3 \leqslant x \leqslant 3$, taking 2 cm to one unit for x and 1 cm to one unit for y.

Use the graph to find:

a) approximate solutions to the equation $4 - x - x^2 = 0$

b) the square roots of 5

c) the square roots of 7.

15. Draw the graph of $y = \dfrac{5}{x} + 2x - 3$, for $\dfrac{1}{2} \leqslant x \leqslant 7$, taking 2 cm to one unit for x and 1 cm to one unit for y. Use the graph to find:

a) approximate solutions to the equation $2x^2 - 10x + 7 = 0$

b) the range of values of x for which $\dfrac{5}{x} + 2x - 3 < 6$.

c) the minimum value of y.

16. Draw the graph of $y = 4^x$ for $-2 \leqslant x \leqslant 2$.

Use the graph to find:

a) the approximate value of $4^{1.6}$

b) the approximate value of $4^{-\frac{1}{3}}$,

c) the gradient of the curve at $x = 0$

d) an approximate solution to the equation $4^x = 10$.

17. The shaded region A is formed by the lines $y = 2$, $y = 3x$ and $x + y = 6$. Write down the three inequalities which define A.

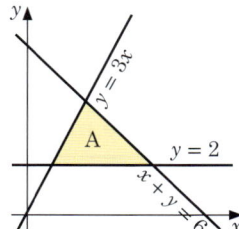

18. The shaded region B is formed by the lines $x = 0$, $y = x - 2$ and $x + y = 7$.

Write down the four inequalities which define B.

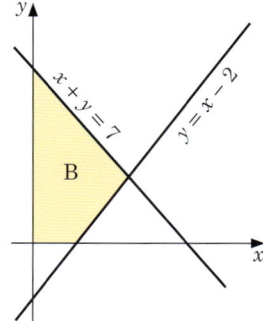

19. The diagram is the speed–time graph of a bus. Calculate:

a) the acceleration during the first 50 seconds

b) the total distance travelled

c) how long it takes before it is moving at 12 m/s for the first time.

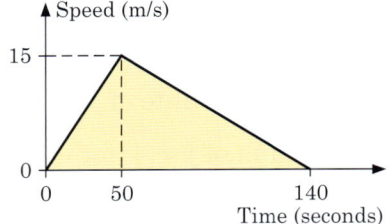

20. The diagram is the speed–time graph of a car.

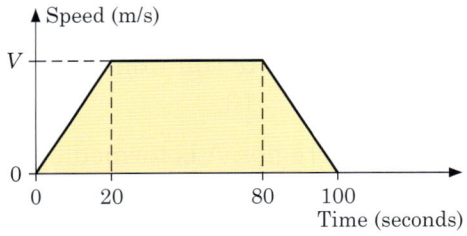

Given that the total distance travelled is 2.4 km, calculate:

a) the value of the maximum speed V

b) the distance travelled in the first 30 seconds of the motion.

21. $y = 3x^4 - 6x^2 + 7$

Find $\dfrac{dy}{dx}$.

22. $y = \dfrac{1}{4}x^6 - \dfrac{2}{5}x^3 + \dfrac{7}{8}x^2$

a) Find $\dfrac{dy}{dx}$.

b) Find the gradient of the curve when $x = 2$.

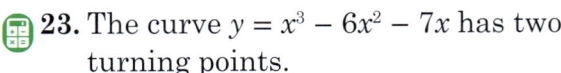 **23.** The curve $y = x^3 - 6x^2 - 7x$ has two turning points.

Find, correct to two decimal places, the x-coordinates of the turning points and determine their nature.

NON-CALCULATOR SECTION

1. The diagram shows two lines, one of which is the graph of $y = -2x + 3$.

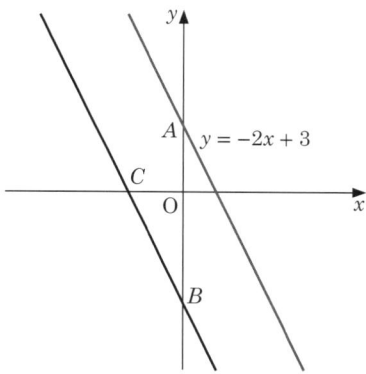

The distance AB is 8 units.

   a) Write down the equation of the line through B which is parallel to
      $y = -2x + 3$.   [1]

   b) Work out the coordinates of the point C where this line crosses the x-axis.   [2]

2. The equation of a straight line can be written in the form $5x + 2y + 10 = 0$.

   a) Rearrange this equation to make y the subject.   [2]

   b) Write down the gradient of the line.   [1]

   c) Write down the coordinates of the point where the line crosses the y-axis.   [1]

3. A straight line passes through two points with coordinates (2, 11) and (5, 23).

   Work out the equation of the line.   [3]

4. The curve $y = 2x^3 - 3x^2 - 12x + 1$ has two turning points.

   Work out the x-coordinates of the turning points and determine their nature.   [4]

5. The diagram shows a graph that has been accurately drawn.

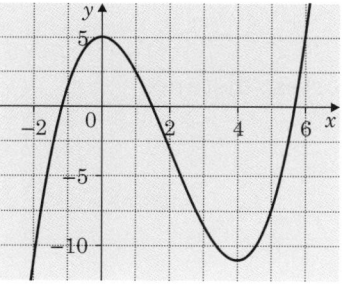

a) Use the graph to write down
   i) the value of y when $x = 2$ [1]
   ii) the value of y when $x = 2.5$. [1]

b) Write down the values of x when $y = 0$. [2]

c) k is an integer for which the equation $y = k$ has exactly two solutions. Use the graph to write down the two values of k. [2]

d) Write down the range of values of x for which the graph has a negative gradient. [2]

CALCULATOR SECTION

6. The graph shows a train journey between two cities.

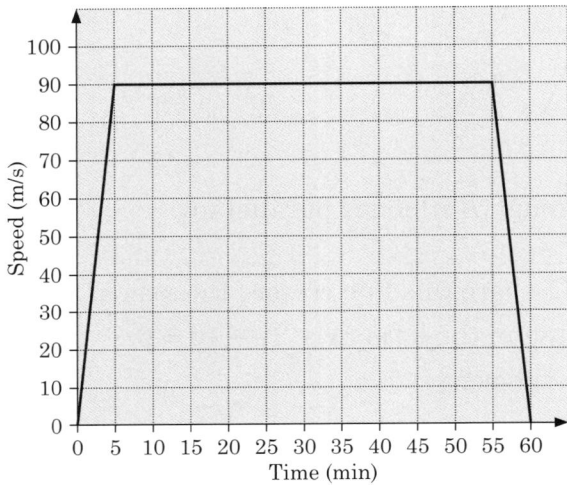

Work out

a) the acceleration in m/s² of the train during the first 5 minutes of its journey [2]

b) the distance between the two cities [3]

c) the average speed of the train for the journey. Give your answer in km/h. [1]

7. a) Work out the equation of the straight line that passes through the point (6, 5) that is perpendicular to the line $y = \dfrac{1}{2}x + 1$. [3]

b) Hence calculate, correct to three decimal places, the shortest distance from the point (6, 5) to the line $y = \dfrac{1}{2}x + 1$. [4]

8. The diagram shows the graph of $y = x^3 - 2x^2 - 4x$.

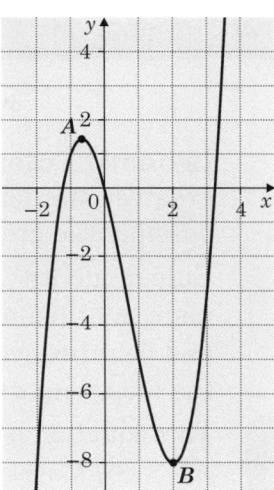

   a) Work out $\dfrac{dy}{dx}$. [3]

   b) Determine the exact coordinates of the points marked A and B. [4]

   c) Show mathematically that point A is a maximum point. [2]

9. A curve C has equation $y = 2x^3 - 4x^2 + 5x$.

   a) Work out $\dfrac{dy}{dx}$. [3]

   b) Calculate the value of the gradient of the curve at the point where $x = 0.5$. [2]

   c) Explain, with a reason, whether curve C has any turning points. [2]

Leonard Euler (1707–1783) was arguably the greatest mathematician of the 18th century; possibly the greatest of all time.

Euler's identity, $e^{i\pi} + 1 = 0$, is considered by many mathematicians to be the most elegant and beautiful equation of all time, linking five of the most important numbers in mathematics.

This equation is a special case of Euler's formula $e^{i\theta} = \cos\theta + i\sin\theta$, which links complex numbers with trigonometry. Euler spent considerable time on the particularly troublesome 'three-body problem' – trying to predict the interactions of the Sun, Moon and Earth. The problem remains unsolved to this day.

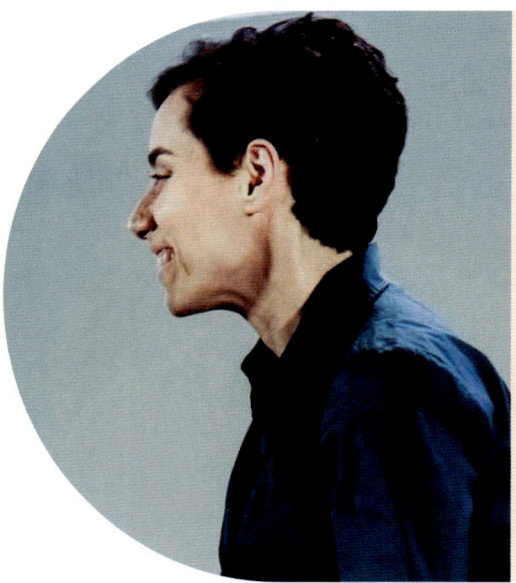

Maryam Mirzakhani (1977 – 2017) was the first woman ever to be awarded the Fields Medal, the most prestigious award in mathematics, for outstanding work on the geometry of curved surfaces. On a curved surface, the shortest distance between two points is not a straight line but is part of a curve called a geodesic. Mirzakhani became fascinated with surfaces which are saddle shaped, and in 2004 she solved a problem related to how many geodesics these kinds of surfaces have.

- Sketch and interpret the graphs of $\sin x$, $\cos x$, and $\tan x$. Solve trigonometric equations.
- Use the sine rule and the cosine rules to find lengths and angles for non-right-angled triangles.

10.1 Sine, cosine and tangent for any angle

So far, you have used sine, cosine and tangent only in right-angled triangles. For angles greater than 90°, there is a close connection between trigonometric ratios and circles.

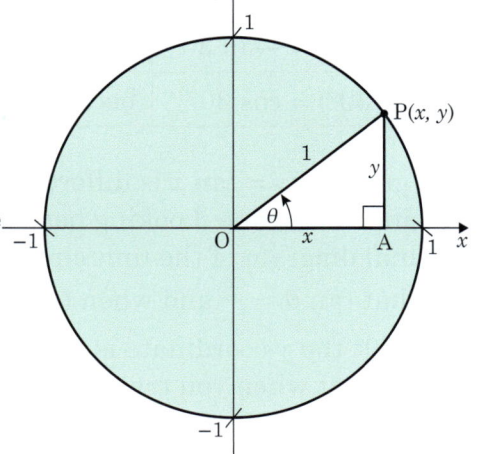

The circle in the diagram is called a 'unit circle'. Its centre is at (0, 0) and it has a radius of 1 unit. Imagine that a point P, with coordinates (x, y), moves around the circumference of the circle. The angle that OP makes with the positive x-axis as it turns in an anticlockwise direction is θ.

In triangle OAP, $\cos \theta = \dfrac{x}{1}$ and $\sin \theta = \dfrac{y}{1}$

The x-coordinate of P is $\cos \theta$

The y-coordinate of P is $\sin \theta$

This idea is used to define the cosine and the sine of any angle, including angles greater than 90°.

The diagram on the right shows an angle that is greater than 90°, along with its cosine and sine values, cos 120° and sin 120°.

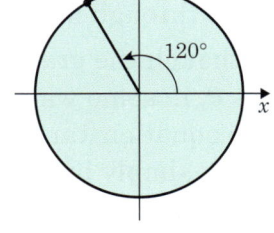

$$\cos 120° = -0.5$$
$$\sin 120° = 0.866$$

A graphical calculator can be used to show the graph of $y = \sin x$ for any range of angles. The graphs below show:

- $y = \sin x$ for x from 0° to 360°. The sine curve above the x-axis has reflective symmetry about $x = 90°$ and rotational symmetry about the origin.

- $y = \cos x$ for x from 0° to 360°. The cosine curve has rotational symmetry about $x = 90°$ and reflective symmetry about the y-axis.

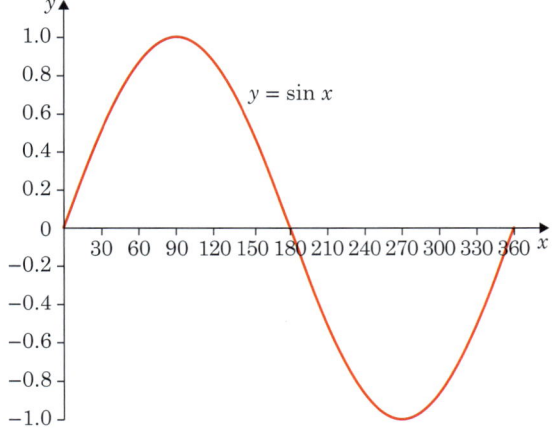

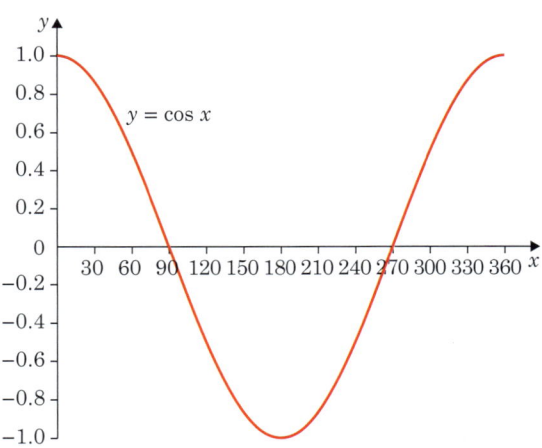

Note the following:

sin 150° = sin 30°	because of the general rule	sin x = sin (180° − x)
cos 150° = cos 210°	because of the general rule	cos x = cos (360° − x)
sin (−30°) = −sin 30°	because of the general rule	sin (−x) = −sin x
cos (−30°) = cos 30°	because of the general rule	cos (−x) = cos x

The graph of $y = \tan x$ is different from those for sine and cosine. Looking back at the original diagram of the unit circle, you can see that $\tan \theta = \dfrac{x}{y}$ and when $\theta = 90°$ or $\theta = 270°$ the y-coordinate is zero. This means that when you try to calculate $\tan \theta$ for $\theta = 90°$ or $\theta = 270°$, you would be dividing by zero. Hence, $\tan \theta$ is *undefined* when $\theta = 90°$ or $\theta = 270°$. This is shown on the graph as vertical dotted

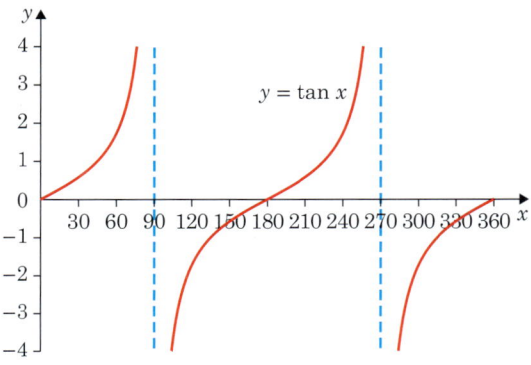

lines through 90° and 270°. These lines are called **asymptotes**.

Although the graph of $\tan \theta$ initially looks more complicated than the graphs of $\sin \theta$ and $\cos \theta$, in some ways it is the simplest one to work with. Once you have found a solution to the equation $\tan \theta = x$ for some value of x, you can find as many other solutions as you need, simply by adding or subtracting multiples of 180° from θ.

You can write that fact as a formula by saying that $\tan (x + 180°) = \tan x$.

An example of this would be $\tan 240° = \tan (60° + 180°) = \tan 60° = \sqrt{3}$.

Example 1

If sin 35° = 0.574, find another angle whose sine is 0.574.

Note that the graph of $y = \sin x$ is symmetrical along the line $x = 90°$.

Therefore, by symmetry,

sin 35° = sin (180 − 35)° = sin 145°.

An answer is therefore 145°.

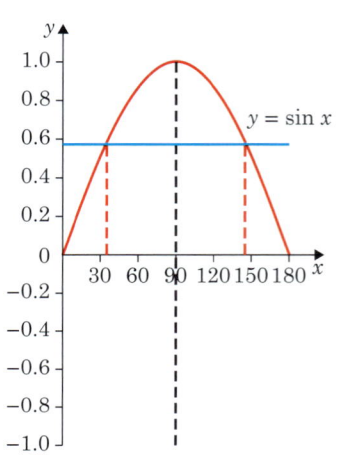

Example 2

Solve the equation $\cos x = 0.8$.

Give your answers in the interval $0° \leqslant x \leqslant 360°$.

$\cos^{-1}(0.8) = 36.9°$

Note that the graph of $y = \cos x$ is symmetrical along the line $x = 180°$.

Also note that $\cos x° = \cos(360 - x)°$.

Therefore
$\cos 36.9° = \cos(360 - 36.9)° = \cos 323.1°$.

The answers, therefore, are $36.9°$ and $323.1°$.

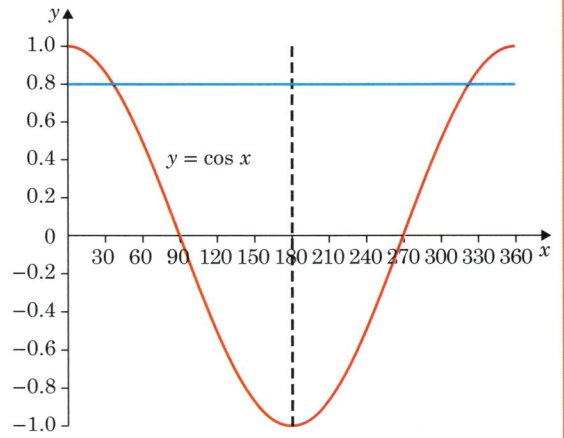

Example 3

Solve the equation $1 + 4\tan x = 0$.

Give your answers in the interval $0° \leqslant x \leqslant 360°$.

$1 + 4\tan x = 0$

$\tan x = -0.25$

$\tan^{-1}(-0.25) = -14.0°$

Note, though, that $-14.0°$ is not in the range $0° \leqslant x \leqslant 360°$.

To find more solutions, add $180°$ because $\tan(x + 180°) = \tan x$.

$-14.0° + 180° = 166°$ and $166° + 180° = 346°$

Therefore, the answers are $166°$ and $346°$.

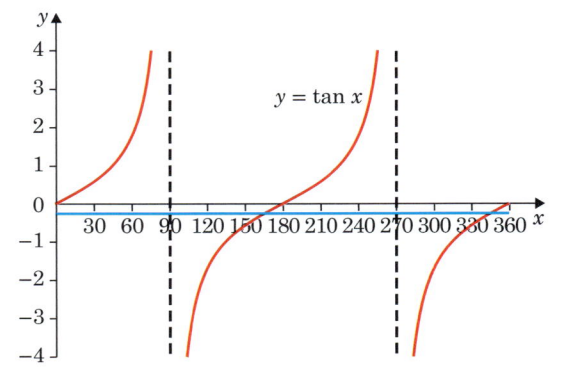

Exercise 10.1A

1. **a)** Use a calculator to create a table of values for the cosine of all angles $0°$, $30°$, $60°$, ... , $360°$. Give answers correct to two decimal places, where necessary.

   b) Use your table to draw a graph of $y = \cos x$ for $0° \leqslant x \leqslant 360°$. Use a scale of 1 cm to $30°$ on the x-axis and 5 cm to 1 unit on the y-axis.

2. Draw the graph of $y = \sin x$ using the same angles and scales as in Question **1**.

3. Draw the graph of $y = \tan x$ for $0° \leqslant x \leqslant 360°$. Choose the angles you use to calculate the tangent and your scales carefully. Check your graph using a graphical calculator if possible.

In Questions **4** to **12** do not use a calculator. Use the symmetries of the graphs $y = \sin x$, $y = \cos x$ and $y = \tan x$. Give your answers in the interval $0° \leqslant x \leqslant 360°$.

4. If $\sin 18° = 0.309$, find another angle whose sine is 0.309.

5. If $\sin 27° = 0.454$, find another angle whose sine is 0.454.

6. If $\sin 230° = -0.766$, find another angle whose sine is -0.766.

7. Find another angle which has the same sine as:

   a) $40°$ **b)** $130°$ **c)** $300°$

8. If $\cos 70° = 0.342$, find another angle whose cosine is 0.342.

9. If $\cos 105° = -0.259$, find another angle whose cosine is -0.259.

10. If $\cos 20° = 0.940$, find two angles whose cosine is -0.940.

11. If $\tan 36° = 0.727$, find another angle whose tangent is 0.727.

12. If $\tan 112° = -2.475$, find another angle whose tangent is -2.475.

13. Solve the following equations. Give your answers in the interval $0° \leqslant x \leqslant 360°$.

   a) $\sin x = \dfrac{\sqrt{3}}{2}$ **b)** $\cos x = 0.9$ **c)** $\tan x = 0.5$

   d) $\cos x = -\dfrac{\sqrt{2}}{2}$ **e)** $\sin x = -0.75$ **f)** $\tan x = -6$

14. Solve the following equations. Give your answers in the interval $0° \leqslant x \leqslant 360°$.

   a) $2 \sin x = 1$ **b)** $3 \cos x = 2$ **c)** $2 \tan x = 7$ **d)** $1 + 3 \sin x = 0$

   e) $5 \cos x + 4 = 0$ **f)** $4 + 3 \tan x = 0$ **g)** $\sin(x + 30°) = \dfrac{1}{\sqrt{2}}$ **h)** $\tan(x - 45°) = 1$

In Chapter 4, Section 4.2 you learned how to calculate exact values of trigonometric functions for certain angles. You can now add this knowledge to what you know about the trigonometric graphs to find the exact values of sin, cos and tan of some other angles outside the range $0°$ to $90°$.

> **Tip**
>
> See the table of exact trigonometric values on page 135.

Example

Find the value of:

a) $\sin 150°$ **b)** $\cos 330°$ **c)** $\tan 225°$

$\rightarrow$

a) $\sin 150° = \sin(180° - 150°)$ since $\sin(180° - x) = \sin x$
$\qquad = \sin 30°$
$\qquad = 0.5$

b) $\cos 330° = \cos(360° - 330°)$ since $\cos(360° - x) = \cos x$
$\qquad = \cos 30°$
$\qquad = \dfrac{\sqrt{3}}{2}$

c) $\tan 225° = \tan(225° - 180°)$ since $\tan(x - 180°) = \tan x$
$\qquad = \tan 45°$
$\qquad = 1$

Exercise 10.1B

Work out the exact values of:

1. $\sin 210°$ **2.** $\cos 300°$ **3.** $\sin 120°$ **4.** $\cos 120°$

5. $\sin 330°$ **6.** $\cos 135°$ **7.** $\sin 135°$ **8.** $\cos 150°$

9. $\sin(-30°)$ **10.** $\cos 240°$ **11.** $\tan 210°$ **12.** $\sin(-60°)$

13. $\cos 225°$ **14.** $\sin(-45°)$ **15.** $\cos 210°$ **16.** $\sin 315°$

17. $\cos(-30°)$ **18.** $\sin 225°$ **19.** $\tan(-135°)$ **20.** $\sin 240°$

21. $\tan 240°$

10.2 The sine rule

The sine rule enables you to calculate sides and angles in triangles that do not include a right angle.

In $\triangle ABC$, you use the convention that:

a is the side opposite angle A

b is the side opposite angle B.

c is the side opposite angle C

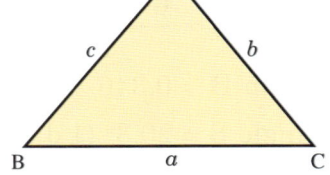

The sine rule states:

Either $\dfrac{a}{\sin A} = \dfrac{b}{\sin B} = \dfrac{c}{\sin C}$ $\qquad$ (1)

or $\qquad \dfrac{\sin A}{a} = \dfrac{\sin B}{b} = \dfrac{\sin C}{c}$ $\qquad$ (2)

Use (1) when finding a **side**, and (2) when finding an **angle**.

Example 1

Find the length of side c.

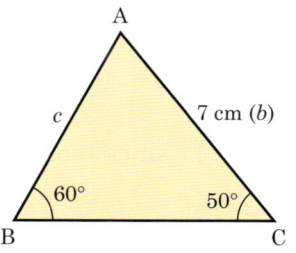

$$\frac{c}{\sin C} = \frac{b}{\sin B}$$

$$\frac{c}{\sin 50°} = \frac{7}{\sin 60°}$$

$$c = \frac{7 \times \sin 50°}{\sin 60°} = 6.19 \text{ cm (3 s.f.)}$$

Although you cannot have an angle of more than 90° in a right-angled triangle, you can still calculate the sine, cosine and tangent of these angles. A useful rule to remember is that, for an obtuse angle x, $\sin x = \sin(180 - x)$.

You can also use a calculator to find the sine of an obtuse angle.

Example 2

Find the size of angle B.

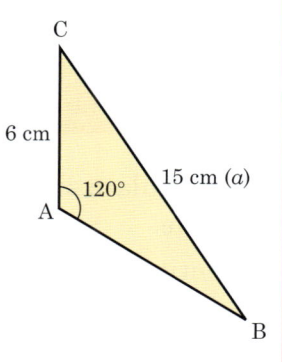

$$\frac{\sin B}{b} = \frac{\sin A}{a}$$

$$\frac{\sin B}{6} = \frac{\sin 120°}{15} \quad (\sin 120° = \sin 60°)$$

$$\sin B = \frac{6 \times \sin 60°}{15}$$

$$\sin B = 0.346...$$

angle B = 20.3° (1 d.p.)

Exercise 10.2A

For Questions **1** to **5**, find the length of each side marked with a letter. Give your answers correct to 3 significant figures.

1.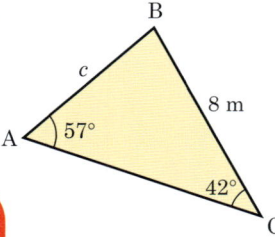

2.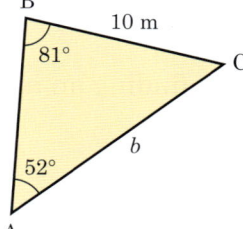

3.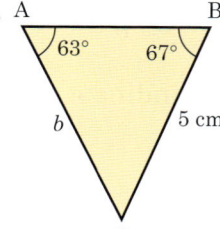

4.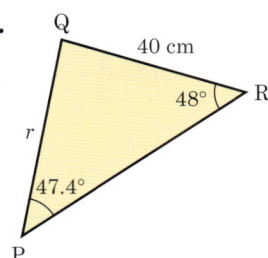

5.

> **Tip**
>
> Â means angle A, and so on.

6. In △ABC, Â = 61°, B̂ = 47°, AC = 7.2 cm. Find BC.

7. In △XYZ, Ẑ = 32°, Ŷ = 78°, XY = 54 cm. Find XZ.

8. In △PQR, Q̂ = 100°, R̂ = 21°, PQ = 3.1 cm. Find PR.

9. In △LMN, L̂ = 21°, N̂ = 30°, MN = 7 cm. Find LN.

> **Tip**
>
> For Questions **6** to **9**, sketch each triangle and label the measurements you know.

In Questions **10** to **16**, find each angle marked with an asterisk,*.

10.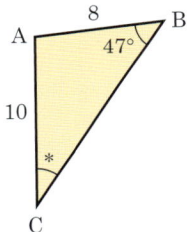

11.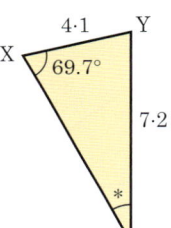

12.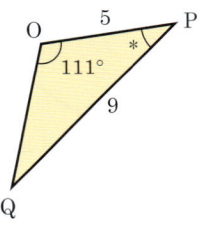

13.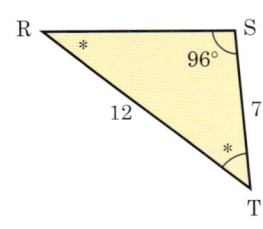

14.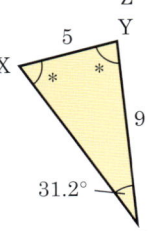

15.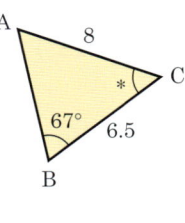

16.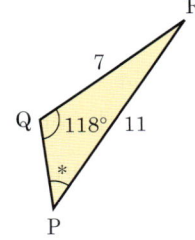

17. In △ABC, Â = 62°, BC = 8, AB = 7. Find Ĉ.

18. In △XYZ, Ŷ = 97.3°, XZ = 22, XY = 14. Find Ẑ.

19. In △DEF, D̂ = 58°, EF = 7.2, DE = 5.4. Find F̂.

20. In △LMN, M̂ = 127.1°, LN = 11.2, LM = 7.3. Find L̂.

10.3 The cosine rule

You use the cosine rule when you know either

- two sides and the included angle or
- all three sides.

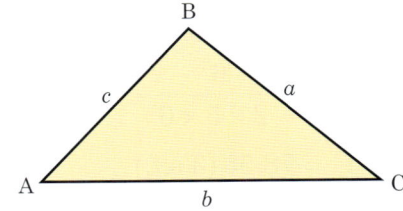

There are two forms of the cosine rule. Choose the form as follows.

To find the length of a side:

$$a^2 = b^2 + c^2 - (2bc \cos A)$$

or $\quad b^2 = c^2 + a^2 - (2ac \cos B)$

or $\quad c^2 = a^2 + b^2 - (2ab \cos C)$

To find an angle when given all three sides:

$$\cos A = \frac{b^2 + c^2 - a^2}{2bc}$$

or $\quad \cos B = \dfrac{a^2 + c^2 - b^2}{2ac}$

or $\quad \cos C = \dfrac{a^2 + b^2 - c^2}{2ab}$

For an obtuse angle x you can use $\cos x = -\cos(180 - x)$.

Examples: $\quad \cos 120° = -\cos 60°$

$\qquad\qquad \cos 142° = -\cos 38°$

Example 1

Find the length of side b.

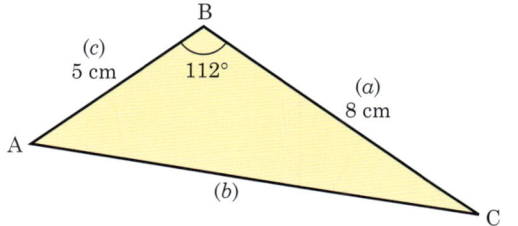

$b^2 = a^2 + c^2 - (2ac \cos B)$

$b^2 = 8^2 + 5^2 - (2 \times 8 \times 5 \times \cos 112°)$

$b^2 = 64 + 25 + 29.968$

(Notice the change of sign for the obtuse angle.)

$b = \sqrt{118.968} = 10.9$ cm (3 s.f.)

Example 2

Find the size of angle C.

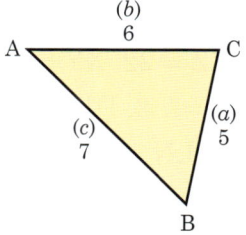

$\cos C = \dfrac{a^2 + b^2 - c^2}{2ab}$

$\cos C = \dfrac{5^2 + 6^2 - 7^2}{2 \times 5 \times 6} = \dfrac{12}{60} = 0.2$

$\hat{C} = 78.5°$ (3 s.f.)

Exercise 10.3A

For Questions **1** to **5**, find the sides marked with an asterisk,*.

1.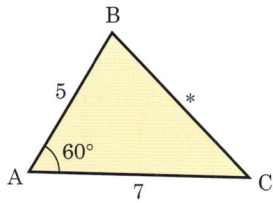

2.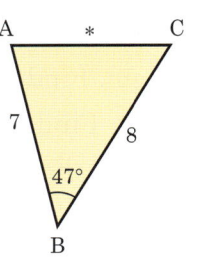

3.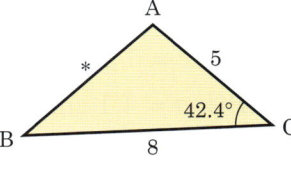

4.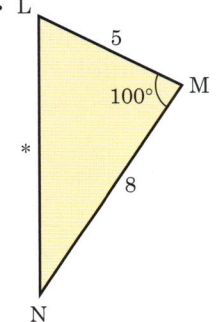

5.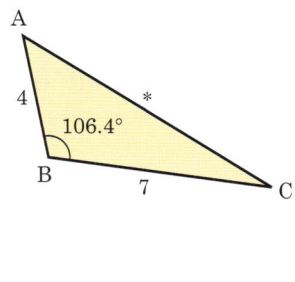

Tip

For Questions **6** to **9**, sketch each triangle and label the measurements you know.

6. In $\triangle$ABC, AB = 4 cm, AC = 7 cm, $\hat{A}$ = 57°. Find BC.

7. In $\triangle$XYZ, XY = 3 cm, YZ = 3 cm, $\hat{Y}$ = 90°. Find XZ.

8. In $\triangle$LMN, LM = 5.3 cm, MN = 7.9 cm, $\hat{M}$ = 127°. Find LN.

9. In $\triangle$PQR, $\hat{Q}$ = 117°, PQ = 80 cm, QR = 100 cm. Find PR.

In Questions **10** to **14**, find each angle marked with an asterisk, *.

10.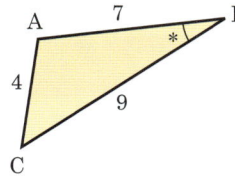

11.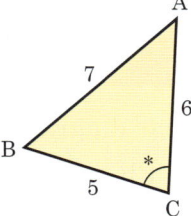

12.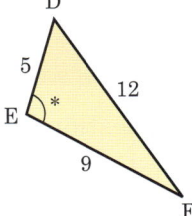

13.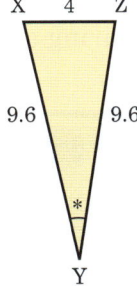

14.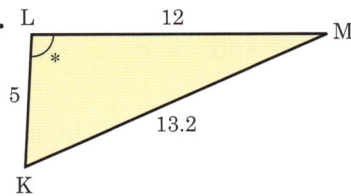

15. In $\triangle$ABC, $a = 4.3$ cm, $b = 7.2$ cm, $c = 9$ cm. Find $\hat{C}$.

16. In $\triangle$DEF, $d = 30$ cm, $e = 50$ cm, $f = 70$ cm. Find $\hat{E}$.

17. In $\triangle$PQR, $p = 8$ cm, $q = 14$ cm, $r = 7$ cm. Find $\hat{Q}$.

18. In $\triangle$LMN, $l = 7$ cm, $m = 5$ cm, $n = 4$ cm. Find $\hat{N}$.

19. In $\triangle$XYZ, $x = 5.3$ cm, $y = 6.7$ cm, $z = 6.14$ cm. Find $\hat{Z}$.

20. In $\triangle$ABC, $a = 4.1$ cm, $c = 6.3$ cm, $\hat{B} = 112.2°$. Find b.

21. In $\triangle$PQR, $r = 0.72$ cm, $p = 1.14$ cm, $\hat{Q} = 94.6°$. Find q.

22. In $\triangle$LMN, $n = 7.206$ cm, $l = 6.3$ cm, $\hat{L} = 51.2°, \hat{N} = 63°$. Find m.

> ### Tip
> For Questions **15** to **22**, sketch each triangle and label the measurements you know.

Sometimes you will be required to solve trigonometry problems that include bearings. When solving these problems, you will need to combine all your knowledge of angles with all your knowledge of triangles. Remember that all north lines are parallel.

Example

A ship sails from a port P for a distance of 7 km on a bearing of 306° and then a further 11 km on a bearing of 070° to arrive at X. Calculate the direct distance from P to X.

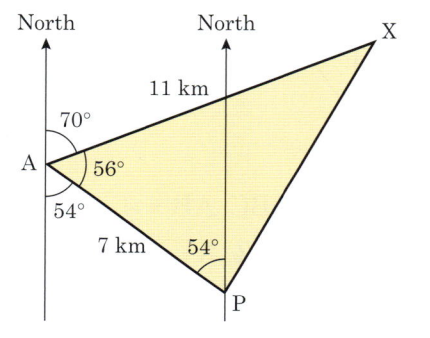

$$PX^2 = 7^2 + 11^2 - (2 \times 7 \times 11 \times \cos 56°)$$
$$= 49 + 121 - 86.12$$
$$= 83.88$$
$$PX = 9.16 \text{ km (to 3 s.f.)}$$

The distance from P to X is 9.16 km

Exercise 10.3B

Start each question by drawing a large, clear diagram.

1. In triangle PQR, $\hat{Q} = 72°$, $\hat{R} = 32°$, and PR = 12 cm. Find PQ.

2. In triangle LMN, $\hat{M} = 84°$, LM = 7 m and MN = 9 m. Find LN.

3. A fishing boat F and a cargo ship C leave port P at the same time. The fishing boat sails 25 km on a bearing of 040° and the cargo ship sails 30 km on a bearing of 320°. How far apart are the ships?

4. Two honeybees, A and B, leave the hive H at the same time.

   Bee A flies 27 m due south and bee B flies 9 m on a bearing of 111°.

   How far apart are they now?

5. Find the three angles of a triangle in which the sides are in the ratio $5:6:8$.

6. On the last hole of a golf course, the distance from the tee to the hole is 195 m.

   A golfer hits his ball from the tee a distance of 170 m, but his shot is directed 10° away from the true line to the hole. Find the distance between the hole and his ball where it lands.

7. From point A, point B lies 11 km away on a bearing of 041° and point C lies 8 km away on a bearing of 341°. Find:

   a) the distance between B and C

   b) the bearing of B from C.

8. From a lighthouse L, a yacht Y is 15 km away on a bearing of 112° and a submarine S is 26 km away on a bearing of 200°. Find:

   a) the distance between Y and S

   b) the bearing of Y from S.

9. If the line BCD is horizontal find:

   a) the length of AE

   b) EÂC

   c) the angle of elevation of E from A.

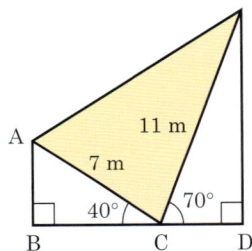

10. An aircraft flies from its base 200 km on a bearing of 162°, then 350 km on a bearing of 260°, and then returns directly to base. Calculate the length and bearing of the return journey.

11. Town Y is 9 km due north of town Z. Town X is 8 km from Y, 5 km from Z and somewhere to the west of the line YZ.

    a) Draw triangle XYZ and find angle YZX.

    b) During an earthquake, town X moves due south until it is due west of Z. Find how far it has moved.

12. Calculate WX, given YZ = 15 m.

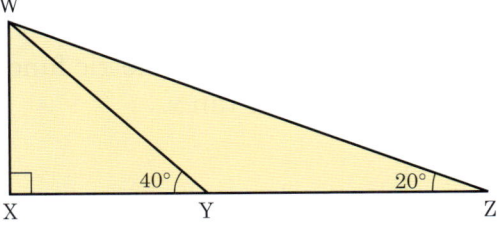

13. A golfer hits her ball a distance of 127 m so that it finishes 31 m from the hole. If the straight-line distance to the hole is 150 m, calculate the angle between the line of her shot and the direct line to the hole.

Revision exercise 10

1. Solve the following equations for $0 \leqslant x \leqslant 360°$, giving your answers correct to 1 d.p.

   a) $\sin x = 0.2$ b) $\tan(x - 10°) = 0.6$

2. Find the length of side a.

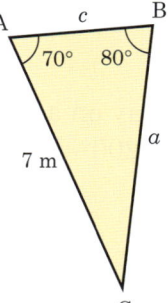

3. Find the size of $\hat{C}$.

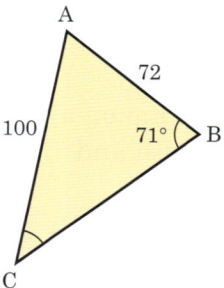

4. Find the length of the side PQ.

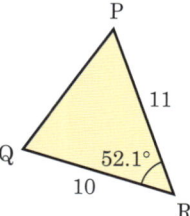

5. Find the size of $\hat{M}$.

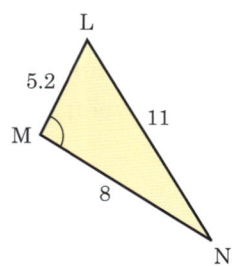

6. Two lighthouses, A and B, are 25 km apart and A is due west of B. A submarine S is on a bearing of 137° from A and on a bearing of 170° from B. Find the distance of S from A and the distance of S from B.

7. In triangle PQR, PQ = 7 cm, PR = 8 cm and QR = 9 cm. Find angle $R\hat{P}Q$.

8. In triangle XYZ, XY = 8 m, $\hat{X} = 57°$ and $\hat{Z} = 50°$. Find the lengths YZ and XZ.

9. In triangle ABC, $\hat{A} = 22°$ and $\hat{C} = 44°$. Find the ratio $\dfrac{BC}{AB}$. Give your answer as a decimal.

10. Given that $\cos A\hat{C}B = 0.6$, AC = 4 cm, BC = 5 cm and CD = 7 cm, find the length of AB and AD.

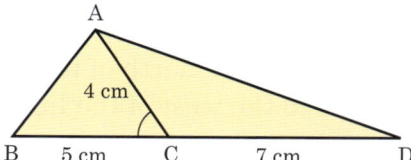

11. Find the smallest angle in a triangle whose sides are of length $3x$, $4x$ and $6x$.

12. Part of the graph of one of the trigonometric functions is shown below. Identify which trigonometric function it is: $\sin x$, $\cos x$ or $\tan x$.

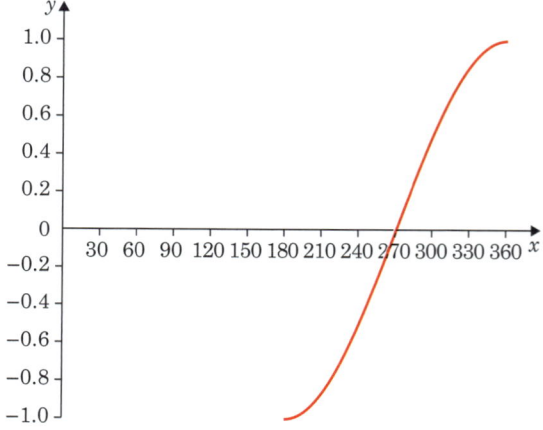

NON-CALCULATOR SECTION

1. $\sin x° = -\dfrac{1}{2}$ and $0 \leqslant x \leqslant 360°$.

    Determine the two values of x. [2]

2.

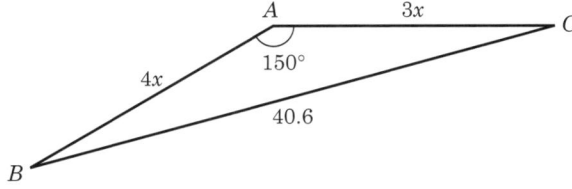

In triangle ABC, $AB = 4x$, $AC = 3x$ and $BC = 40.6$ units.

Calculate the value of x correct to 2 decimal places. [3]

CALCULATOR SECTION

3.

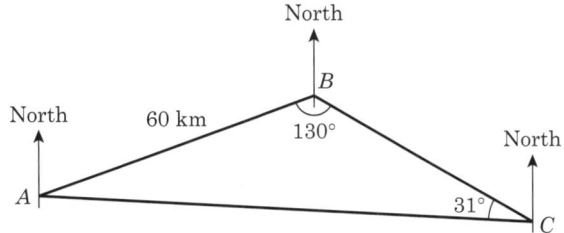

The diagram shows three straight horizontal roads in a town, connecting points A, B and C.

$AB = 60$ km, angle $ABC = 130°$ and angle $ACB = 31°$.

a) Calculate the length of the road BC. [3]

b) The bearing of B from C is $306°$.

  Work out the bearing of

   i) A from C [2]

   ii) C from A. [1]

4. A plane flies from Fresno (*F*) to Las Vegas (*L*) on a bearing of 100°.
   The plane then flies on to San Diego (*S*). Angle *FLS* = 75°.

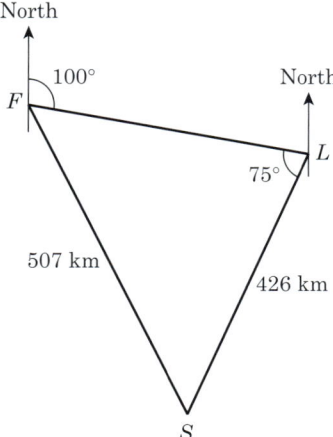

a) Calculate the bearing of San Diego from Las Vegas. [2]

b) The distance from San Diego to Las Vegas is 426 kilometres.

The distance from Fresno to San Diego is 507 kilometres.

Calculate the bearing of San Diego from Fresno. [4]

5.

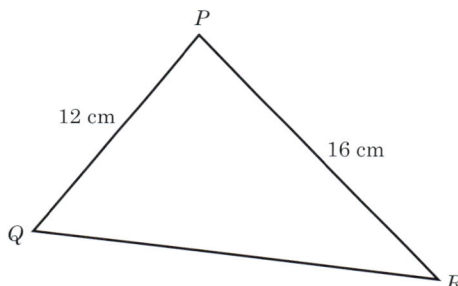

In triangle *PQR*, angle *QPR* is acute, *PQ* = 12 cm and *PR* = 16 cm.
The area of triangle *PQR* is 93 cm².

a) Calculate angle *QPR* and show that it rounds to 75.6°, correct to 1 decimal place.
   You must show all your working. [3]

b) Calculate the length of the side *QR*. [4]

> **Tip**
>
> You used the formula for the area of a triangle in
> Chapter 5 on page 155.

6.

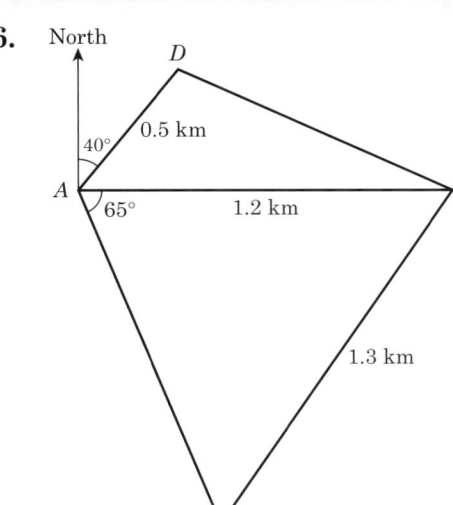

The quadrilateral *ABCD* shows the boundary of a park. A straight 1.2 kilometre road goes due east from *A* to *C*.

a) The bearing of *D* from *A* is 040° and *AD* = 0.5 km.

   i) Write down the size of the angle *DAC*. [1]

   ii) Calculate the length of *CD*. [4]

b) Angle *CAB* = 65° and *BC* = 1.3 km.

   i) Write down the bearing of *B* from *A*. [1]

   ii) Calculate the acute angle *ABC*. [3]

   iii) Calculate the length of *AB*. [3]

c) Calculate the area of the park, correct to the nearest square kilometre. [4]

Bertrand Russell (1872–1970) was a British mathematician and philosopher who co-wrote the book *Principia Mathematica,* in which the authors tried to reduce all mathematics to formal logic. In 1901, he discovered what became known as Russell's paradox, based on an abstract question about sets. This inspired mathematicians in the early 20th century to search for a consistent, contradiction-free, version of set theory.

Georg Cantor (1845–1918) was a German mathematician who played a big role in the development of set theory. He is also responsible for proving several surprising mathematical ideas, one of which is that even though there are an infinite number of real numbers on the number line, and an infinite number of fractions, there are actually infinitely more real numbers than there are fractions. In proving this, Cantor showed that there are in fact an infinite number of different infinities.

- Understand and use Venn diagrams and set notation.
- Functions including notation, domain, range, inverse functions and composite functions.

11.1 Sets

In mathematics, a **set** is a collection of well defined and distinct items that share a particular property. Members of a set are called **elements**. Sets are often displayed graphically in a **Venn diagram**. You need to understand the following language and notation for dealing with sets.

1. The symbol $\cap$ means 'intersection'.
   In this diagram, this means A **and** B.
   $A \cap B$ is shaded.

   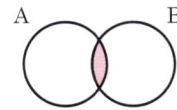

2. The symbol $\cup$ means 'union'.
   Here, this means A **or** B **or both**.
   $A \cup B$ is shaded.

   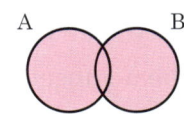

3. The symbol $\subseteq$ means 'is a subset of'.
   The symbol $\nsubseteq$ means 'is not a subset of'.
   $A \subseteq B$ means A lies completely inside B.

   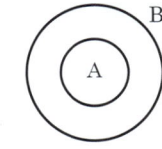

   A can actually equal B, which means every set is a subset of itself.

   Set A might lie completely outside B (having no elements in common) or may only partly overlap B (having only some elements in common).

   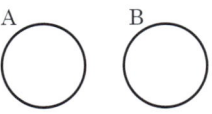 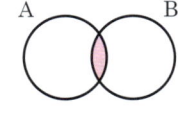

4. The symbol $\in$ means 'is an element of'.
   You can also think of it as meaning 'belongs to' or 'is a member of'.
   The symbol $\notin$ means 'is not an element of'.
   $b \in X$ (the element b is a member of set X)
   $e \notin X$ (the element e is not an element of set X)

   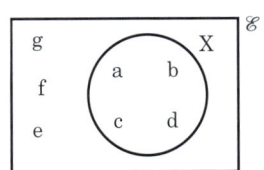

5. The symbol $\mathscr{E}$ means the 'universal set'.
   The universal set is the set of all things being considered at the time. In a Venn diagram such as this one, everything inside the rectangle makes up the universal set.
   $\mathscr{E} = \{a, b, c, d, e\}$

   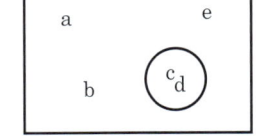

6. The symbol A' means 'the complement of set A'.
   This means all elements that are *not* in set A.
   A' is shaded.
   Note that $A \cup A' = \mathscr{E}$

   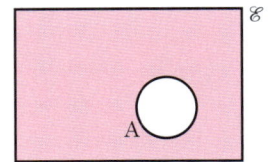

7. The symbol n(A) means 'the number of elements in set A'.

   In the set A here, n(A) = 3, as set A has 3 elements.

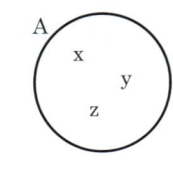

It is not always possible to list all the elements in a set; sometimes because the set contains an infinite number of elements, and sometimes because it is just not practical to do so if the set has a lot of elements.

8. Set notation

   A = {x: x is an integer, $2 \leqslant x < 9$}

   This reads, 'A is the set of all elements x, such that x is an integer, and $2 \leqslant x < 9$'.

   The set A is {2, 3, 4, 5, 6, 7, 8}.

9. The symbol ∅ means 'the empty set'. This is the set that contains no elements.

   Note that ∅ is considered to be a subset of every set.

Exercise 11.1A

1. In the Venn diagram:

   ℰ = {people eating breakfast at a hotel}

   T = {people who like toast}

   E = {people who like eggs}

   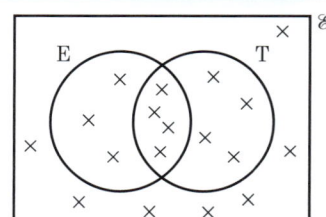

   a) How many people like toast?

   b) How many people like eggs but not toast?

   c) How many people like toast and eggs?

   d) How many people are in the hotel?

   e) How many people like neither toast nor eggs?

2. In the Venn diagram:

   ℰ = {students in form group 10ARO}

   R = {members of the robotics club}

   C = {members of the chess club}

   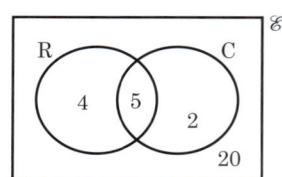

   a) How many students are in the robotics club?

   b) How many students are in both clubs?

   c) How many are in the robotics club but not in the chess club?

   d) How many are in neither club?

   e) How many students are there in 10ARO?

3. In the Venn diagram:

$\mathscr{E}$ = {cars parked on a street}

B = {blue cars}

L = {cars with left-hand drive}

F = {cars with four doors}

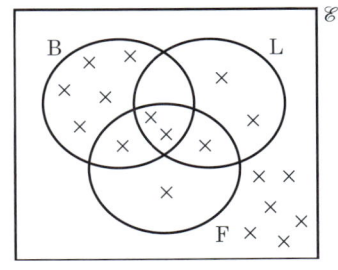

Each cross represents one car.

   a) How many cars are blue?

   b) How many blue cars have four doors?

   c) How many cars with left-hand drive have four doors?

   d) How many blue cars have left-hand drive?

   e) How many cars are in the street?

   f) How many blue cars with left-hand drive do not have four doors?

4. In the Venn diagram:

$\mathscr{E}$ = {houses on Abbey Road}

C = {houses with a rooftop chimney}

D = {houses with a driveway}

G = {houses with a garden}

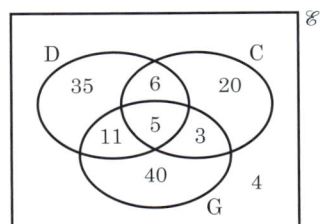

   a) How many houses have a garden?

   b) How many houses have a driveway and a chimney?

   c) How many houses have a driveway and a chimney and a garden?

   d) How many houses have a garden, but not a driveway or a chimney?

   e) How many houses have a driveway and a garden, but not a chimney?

   f) How many houses are there on Abbey Road?

5. In the Venn diagram:

$\mathscr{E}$ = {children in a school}

G = {girls}

S = {children who can swim}

L = {children who are left-handed}

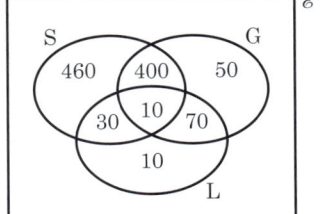

   a) How many left-handed children are there?

   b) How many girls cannot swim?

   c) How many boys can swim?

   d) How many girls are left-handed?

   e) How many boys are left-handed?

   f) How many left-handed girls can swim?

   g) How many boys are there in the school?

Set notation

You need to be able to use and understand set notation. Sometimes sets will be defined directly and sometimes you will be given them in a Venn diagram.

Example 1

$A = \{x: x$ is a natural number$\}$ and $B = \{x: x$ is a prime number$\}$

State whether true or false:

a) $5 \in A \cap B$ **b)** $8 \in A \cup B$

c) $B \subseteq A$ **d)** $2 \in A \cap B'$

Set A is the set of natural numbers, which are the counting numbers 1, 2, 3, 4, …

Set B are the prime numbers.

a) 5 is a natural number and it is prime, so the statement is true.

b) 8 is a natural number, so the statement is true.

c) All prime numbers are natural numbers, so the statement is true.

d) 2 is a natural number but it is prime, so the statement is false.

Example 2

$P = \{(x, y): y = 2x + 3\}$ and $Q = \{(x, y): y = -2x - 1\}$

State whether true or false:

a) $(1, 5) \in P \cup Q$ **b)** $(-1, 1) \in P \cap Q$

c) $(3, 10) \in P' \cap Q$ **d)** $\{(0, -1), (1, -3), (2, -4)\} \subseteq Q$

a) $(1, 5)$ belongs to set P because $5 = 2 \times 1 + 3$. Therefore the statement is true.

b) $(-1, 1)$ belongs to both sets. Therefore the statement is true.

c) $(3, 10)$ does not belong to set P, but it also does not belong to set Q.
Therefore the statement is false.

d) $(0, -1)$ and $(1, -3)$ are members of set Q, but $(2, -4)$ is not.
Therefore the statement is false.

Example 3

$\mathscr{E} = \{1, 2, 3, \ldots, 12\}$, $A = \{2, 3, 4, 5, 6\}$ and $B = \{2, 4, 6, 8, 10\}$

a) Draw a Venn diagram to represent these sets.

b) Use your diagram to find:

    i) $A \cup B$ **ii)** $A \cap B$ **iii)** A' **iv)** $n(A \cup B) = 7$ **v)** $B' \cap A$

a)

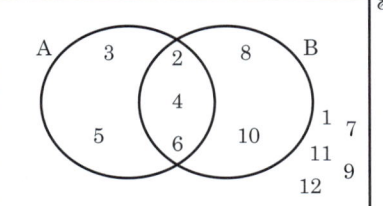

b) i) $A \cup B = \{2, 3, 4, 5, 6, 8, 10\}$ **ii)** $A \cap B = \{2, 4, 6\}$

iii) $A' = \{1, 7, 8, 9, 10, 11, 12\}$ **iv)** $n(A \cup B) = 7$ **v)** $B' \cap A = \{3, 5\}$

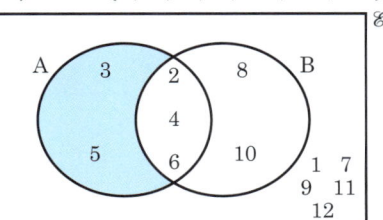

Exercise 11.1B

In this exercise, be careful to use set notation only when the answer *is* a set.

1. If $M = \{1, 2, 3, 4, 5, 6, 7, 8\}$, $N = \{5, 7, 9, 11, 13\}$, find:

   a) $M \cap N$ **b)** $M \cup N$ **c)** $n(N)$ **d)** $n(M \cup N)$

   State whether true or false:

   e) $5 \in M$ **f)** $7 \in (M \cup N)$ **g)** $N \subseteq M$ **h)** $\{5, 6, 7\} \subseteq M$

2. If $A = \{2, 3, 5, 7\}$, $B = \{1, 2, 3, \ldots, 9\}$, find:

   a) $A \cap B$ **b)** $A \cup B$ **c)** $n(A \cap B)$ **d)** $\{1, 4\} \cap A$

   State whether true or false:

   e) $A \in B$ **f)** $A \subseteq B$ **g)** $9 \subseteq B$ **h)** $3 \in (A \cap B)$

3. $A = \{x: x \text{ is a natural number}\}$ and $B = \{x: x \text{ is an even number}\}$

   State whether true or false:

   a) $21 \in A \cap B$ **b)** $7 \in A \cup B$ **c)** $A \subseteq B$ **d)** $6 \in A' \cap B$

4. $P = \{(x, y): y = x + 5\}$ and $Q = \{(x, y): y = 1 - x\}$

   State whether true or false:

   a) $(-2, 3) \in P \cup Q$ **b)** $(-2, 3) \in P \cap Q$

   c) $(-1, 2) \in P' \cap Q$ **d)** $\{(2, -1), (-4, 1), (-2, 3)\} \subseteq P \cup Q$

5. If X = {1, 2, 3,..., 10}, Y = {2, 4, 6,..., 20} and Z = {$x : x$ is an integer, $15 \leqslant x \leqslant 25$}, find:

a) X ∩ Y **b)** Y ∩ Z **c)** X ∩ Z

d) n(X ∪ Y) **e)** n(Z) **f)** n(X ∪ Z)

State whether true or false:

g) 5 ∈ Y **h)** 20 ∈ X

i) n(X ∩ Y) = 5 **j)** {15, 20, 25} ⊆ Z

6. If D = {1, 3, 5}, E = {3, 4, 5}, F = {1, 5, 10}, find:

a) D ∪ E **b)** D ∩ F **c)** n(E ∩ F)

d) (D ∪ E) ∩ F **e)** (D ∩ E) ∪ F **f)** n(D ∪ F)

State whether true or false:

g) D ⊆ (E ∪ F) **h)** 3 ∈ (E ∩ F) **i)** 4 ∉ (D ∩ E)

7. Find:

a) n(E) **b)** n(F) **c)** E ∩ F

d) E ∪ F **e)** n(E ∪ F) **f)** n(E ∩ F)

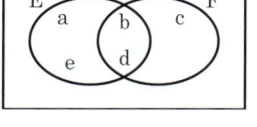

8. Find:

a) n(M ∩ N) **b)** n(N) **c)** M ∪ N

d) M′ ∩ N **e)** N′ ∩ M **f)** (M ∩ N)′

g) M ∪ N′ **h)** N ∪ M′ **i)** M′ ∪ N′

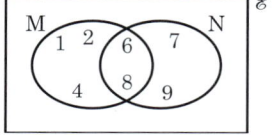

Shading Venn diagrams

You need to know how to shade areas on a Venn diagram that have been described using set notation.

To shade the union of two sets, for example, A ∪ B, first shade the whole of the first set, and then shade the whole of the second set.

To shade the intersection of two sets, for example, A ∩ B, lightly shade the whole of the first set using diagonal lines in one direction, and then lightly shade the whole of the second set using diagonal lines in the other direction. The intersection that you need to shade properly is the part that has been shaded twice.

Example

On a Venn diagram, shade the regions:

a) A ∪ B **b)** A ∩ C **c)** (B ∩ C) ∩ A′

where A, B, C are intersecting sets.

---

a) $A \cup B$

Shading set A then set B gives this diagram.

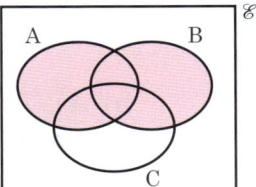

b) $A \cap C$

'A intersection C' contains only those elements common to both sets.

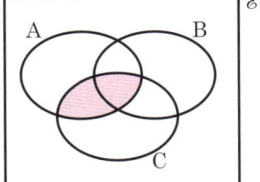

c) $(B \cap C) \cap A'$

First identify the intersection of sets B and C, then remove the part that is also in set A.

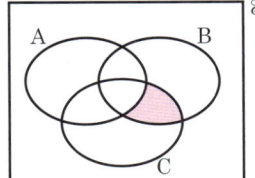

Exercise 11.1C

1. Draw six diagrams similar to Figure 1 and shade the following sets:

   a) $A \cap B$　　　**b)** $A \cup B$　　　**c)** A'

   d) $A' \cap B$　　　**e)** $B' \cap A$　　　**f)** $(B \cup A)'$

Figure 1

2. Draw four diagrams similar to Figure 2 and shade the following sets:

   a) $A \cap B$　　　**b)** $A \cup B$　　　**c)** $B' \cap A$

   d) $(B \cup A)'$

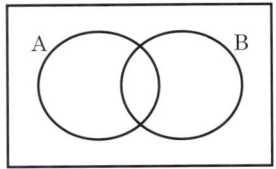

Figure 2

3. Draw four diagrams similar to Figure 3 and shade the following sets:

   a) $A \cup B$　　　**b)** $A \cap B$　　　**c)** $A \cap B'$

   d) $(B \cup A)'$

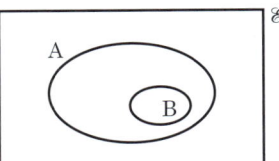

Figure 3

4. Draw nine diagrams similar to Figure 4 and shade the following sets:

a) $A \cap B$ b) $A \cup C$ c) $A \cap (B \cap C)$

d) $(A \cup B) \cap C$ e) $A \cap B'$ f) $A \cap (B \cup C)'$

g) $C' \cap (A \cap B)$ h) $(A \cup C) \cup B'$ i) $(A \cup C) \cap (B \cap C)$

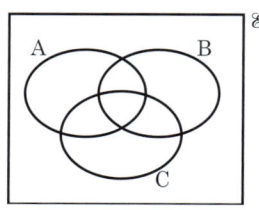

Figure 4

5. Draw nine diagrams similar to Figure 5 and shade the following sets:

a) $(A \cup B) \cap C$ b) $(A \cap B) \cup C$ c) $(A \cup B) \cup C$

d) $A \cap (B \cup C)$ e) $A' \cap C$ f) $C' \cap (A \cup B)$

g) $(A \cap B) \cap C$ h) $(A \cap C) \cup (B \cap C)$ i) $(A \cup B \cup C)'$

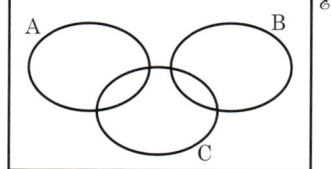

Figure 5

6. Copy each diagram and shade the region indicated.

a)
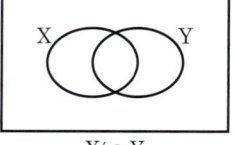
$X' \cap Y$

b)
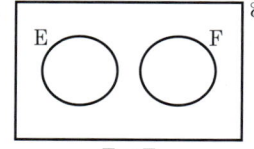
$E \cup F$

c)
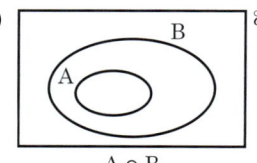
$A \cap B$

d)
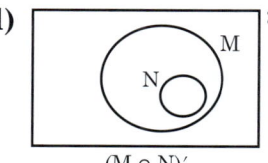
$(M \cap N)'$

7. Describe the shaded region in each Venn diagram using set notation.

a)
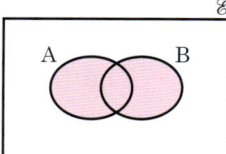

b)
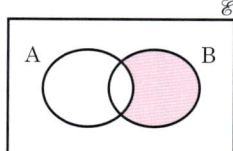

c)
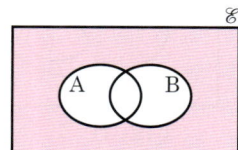

d)
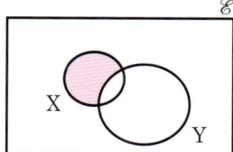

11.2 Logical problems

Example 1

In a form of 30 students, 18 play basketball and 14 play hockey, while 5 students play neither sport. Find the number who play both basketball and hockey.

Let $\mathscr{E}$ = {students in the form}

      B = {students who play basketball}

      H = {students who play hockey}

and x = the number of students who play both basketball and hockey

The number of students in each portion of the universal set is shown in the Venn diagram.

Since $n(\mathscr{E}) = 30$

$$18 - x + x + 14 - x + 5 = 30$$

$$37 - x = 30$$

$$x = 7$$

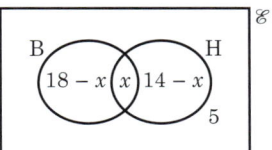

Seven students play both basketball and hockey.

Example 2

Sets A to D are defined as follows:

   A = {sheep}   C = {'intelligent' animals}

   B = {horses}   D = {animals that make good pets}

a) Express the following sentences in set language:

   i) No sheep are 'intelligent' animals.   **ii)** All horses make good pets.

   iii) Some sheep make good pets.

b) Interpret the following statements:

   i) B ⊆ C   **ii)** B ∪ C = D

a) i) $A \cap C = \varnothing$ **ii)** $B \subseteq D$ **iii)** $A \cap D \neq \varnothing$

b) i) All horses are intelligent animals.

   ii) Animals that make good pets are either horses or 'intelligent' animals (or both).

Exercise 11.2A

1. In the Venn diagram, $n(A) = 10$, $n(B) = 13$, $n(A \cap B) = x$ and $n(A \cup B) = 18$.

   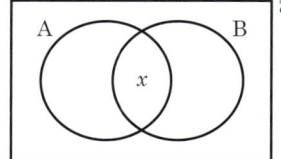

   a) Write in terms of x the number of elements in A but not in B.

   b) Write in terms of x the number of elements in B but not in A.

   c) Add together the number of elements in the three parts of the diagram to obtain the equation $10 - x + x + 13 - x = 18$.

   d) Hence find the number of elements that are in both A and B.

2. In the Venn diagram, $n(A) = 21$, $n(B) = 17$, $n(A \cap B) = x$ and $n(A \cup B) = 29$.

   a) Write down in terms of x the number of elements in each part of the diagram.

   b) Form an equation and hence find x.

3. The sets M and N intersect such that $n(M) = 31$, $n(N) = 18$ and $n(M \cup N) = 35$. Find the number of elements in both M and N.

4. The sets P and Q intersect such that $n(P) = 11$, $n(Q) = 29$ and $n(P \cup Q) = 37$. Find the number of elements in both P and Q.

5. The sets A and B intersect such that $n(A \cap B) = 7$, $n(A) = 20$ and $n(B) = 23$. Find $n(A \cup B)$.

6. Twenty students all play either pickle ball or table tennis (or both). If thirteen play pickle ball and ten play table tennis, how many play both sports?

7. Of the 53 staff at a school, 36 drink tea, 18 drink coffee and 10 drink neither tea nor coffee. How many staff members drink both tea and coffee?

8. Of the 32 students in a class, 18 play golf, 16 play the piano and 7 play both. How many students play neither sport?

9. Of the students in a class, 15 can correctly spell the word 'parallel', 14 can correctly spell 'asymptote', 5 can spell both words correctly, and 4 can spell neither. How many students are there in the class?

10. In a school, students must take at least one of these subjects: Maths, Physics or Chemistry. Here is information about a group of 50 students:
    - 7 take all three subjects
    - 9 take Physics and Chemistry only
    - 8 take Maths and Physics only
    - 5 take Maths and Chemistry only
    - x take Maths only
    - x take Physics only
    - $x + 3$ take Chemistry only.

    Draw a Venn diagram, find x, and hence find the number taking Maths.

11. All of 60 different vitamin pills contain at least one of the vitamins A, B and C.

    - 12 contain A only
    - 7 contain B only
    - 11 contain C only
    - 6 pills contain all three vitamins
    - x contain A and B only
    - x contain B and C only
    - x contain A and C only

    How many pills contain vitamin A?

12. The IGCSE results of the 30 members of a badminton team were as follows: all 30 players passed at least two subjects, 18 players passed at least three subjects, and 3 players passed four subjects or more. Calculate:

    a) how many passed exactly two subjects

    b) the fraction of the team who passed exactly three subjects.

13. In a group of 59 people, some are wearing hats, gloves or scarves (or a combination of these) as follows:

    - 4 people are wearing all three items
    - 7 people are wearing just a hat and gloves
    - 3 are wearing just gloves and a scarf
    - 9 are wearing just a hat and scarf
    - x are wearing only a hat
    - x are wearing only gloves
    - $(x - 2)$ are wearing only a scarf
    - $(x - 2)$ are wearing none of the three items.

    Find x and hence the number of people wearing a hat.

14. In a street of 150 houses, three different newspapers are delivered: the Tribune, the Herald and the Chronicle, as follows:

    - 40 receive the Tribune
    - 35 receive the Herald
    - 60 receive the Chronicle
    - 7 receive the Tribune and the Herald
    - 10 receive the Herald and the Chronicle
    - 4 receive the Tribune and the Chronicle
    - 34 receive no newspaper at all.

    How many receive all three newspapers?

    Note: If '7 receive Tribune and the Herald', this information does not mean that 7 people receive the Tribune and the Herald *only*.

15. If S = {skydivers}, G = {good swimmers}, express the following statements in words:

a) G ⊆ S   **b)** G ∩ S = ∅   **c)** G ∩ S ≠ ∅

(Ignore the truth or otherwise of the statements.)

16. Given that $\mathscr{E}$ = {students in a school}, G = {girls}, I = {ice skaters}, S = {surfers}, express the following possible situations in words:

a) S ⊆ G   **b)** I ⊆ G′   **c)** S ∩ I ≠ ∅   **d)** G ∩ I = ∅

Express in set notation:

e) No girls are surfers.   **f)** All students either surf or ice skate.

17. $\mathscr{E}$ = {living creatures}, S = {spiders}, F = {animals that fly}, C = {animals that are cute} Express in set notation:

a) No spiders are cute.   **b)** All animals that fly are cute.

c) Some spiders can fly.

Express in words:

d) S ∪ F ∪ C = $\mathscr{E}$ **e)** C ⊆ S

11.3 Functions

The idea of a function is used in almost every branch of mathematics.
The two common forms of notation used are:

- $f(x) = x^2 + 4$
- $f : x \mapsto x^2 + 4$

In this course, however, only the first notation is used.
You interpret the second form as: 'function f such that x is mapped onto $x^2 + 4$'.

Example 1

If $f(x) = 3x - 1$ and $g(x) = 1 - x^2$ find:

a) $f(2)$ **b)** $f(-2)$ **c)** $g(1)$ **d)** $g(3)$ **e)** x if $f(x) = 1$

a) $f(2) = 3 \times 2 - 1 = 5$ **b)** $f(-2) = 3 \times (-2) - 1 = -7$

c) $g(1) = 1 - 1^2 = 0$ **d)** $g(3) = 1 - 3^2 = -8$

e) If $f(x) = 1$

Then $3x - 1 = 1$

$3x = 2$

$x = \dfrac{2}{3}$

Flow diagrams

The function f in Example 1 consisted of two simpler functions as illustrated by a flow diagram.

$x \longrightarrow \boxed{\text{multiply by 3}} \xrightarrow{3x} \boxed{\text{subtract 1}} \longrightarrow 3x - 1$

The input is x, and the output is $3x - 1$.

It is important to 'multiply by 3' and 'subtract 1' in the correct order.

Example 2

Draw flow diagrams for the functions:

a) $f(x) = (2x + 5)^2$ **b)** $g(x) = \dfrac{5 - 7x}{3}$

Find:

c) $f(2)$ **d)** $g(-4)$

---

a) $x \longrightarrow \boxed{\text{multiply by 2}} \xrightarrow{2x} \boxed{\text{add 5}} \xrightarrow{2x + 5} \boxed{\text{square}} \longrightarrow (2x + 5)^2$

b) $x \longrightarrow \boxed{\text{multiply by } (-7)} \xrightarrow{-7x} \boxed{\text{add 5}} \xrightarrow{5 - 7x} \boxed{\text{divide by 3}} \longrightarrow \dfrac{5 - 7x}{3}$

c) $f(2) = \left(2 \times 2 + 5\right)^2$

$\qquad = 9^2$

$\qquad = 81$

d) $-4 \longrightarrow \boxed{\text{multiply by } (-7)} \xrightarrow{28} \boxed{\text{add 5}} \xrightarrow{33} \boxed{\text{divide by 3}} \longrightarrow 11$

Therefore, $g(-4) = 11$

Exercise 11.3A

1. Given the functions $h(x) = x^2 + 1$ and $g(x) = 10x + 1$. Find:

   a) $h(2), h(-3), h(0)$ **b)** $g(2), g(10), g(-3)$

For Questions **2** to **15**, draw a flow diagram for each function.

2. $f(x) = 5x + 4$ **3.** $f(x) = 3(x - 4)$ **4.** $f(x) = (2x + 7)^2$

5. $f(x) = \dfrac{9 + 5x}{4}$ **6.** $f(x) = \dfrac{4 - 3x}{5}$ **7.** $f(x) = 2x^2 + 1$

8. $f(x) = \dfrac{3x^2}{2} + 5$ **9.** $f(x) = \sqrt{4x - 5}$ **10.** $f(x) = 4\sqrt{x^2 + 10}$

11. $f(x) = (7 - 3x)^2$ **12.** $f(x) = 4(3x + 1)^2 + 5$ **13.** $f(x) = 5 - x^2$

14. $f(x) = \dfrac{10\sqrt{x^2 + 1} + 6}{4}$ **15.** $f(x) = \left(\dfrac{x^3}{4} + 1\right)^2 - 6$

For Questions **16**, **17** and **18**, the functions f, g and h are defined as follows:

$$f(x) = 1 - 2x \qquad g(x) = \frac{x^3}{10} \qquad h(x) = \frac{12}{x}$$

16. Find:

    a) f(5), f(−5), f$\left(\dfrac{1}{4}\right)$ **b)** g(2), g(−3), g$\left(\dfrac{1}{2}\right)$ **c)** h(3), h(10), h$\left(\dfrac{1}{3}\right)$

17. Find:

    a) x if f(x) = 1   **b)** x if f(x) = −11   **c)** x if h(x) = 1

18. Find:

    a) y if g(y) = 100   **b)** z if h(z) = 24   **c)** w if g(w) = 0.8

For Questions **19** and **20**, the functions f, g and h are defined as follows:

$$f(x) = \frac{2x^2}{3} \qquad g(x) = \sqrt{(y-1)(y-2)} \qquad h(x) = 10 - x^2$$

19. Find:

    a) f(3), f(6), f(−3)   **b)** g(2), g(0), g(4)   **c)** h(4), h(−2), h$\left(\dfrac{1}{2}\right)$

20. Find:

    a) x if f(x) = 6   **b)** x if h(x) = 1   **c)** y if f(y) = $2\dfrac{2}{3}$ **d)** p if h(p) = −26

21. If $g(x) = 2^x + 1$, find:

    a) g(2)   **b)** g(4)   **c)** g(−1)   **d)** the value of x if g(x) = 9

22. The function f is defined as $f(x) = ax + b$ where a and b are constants.

    If f(1) = 8 and f(4) =17, find the values of a and b.

23. The function g is defined as $g(x) = ax^2 + b$ where a and b are constants.

    If g(2) = 3 and g(−3) = 13, find the values of a and b.

24. Functions h and k are defined as follows:

    $h(x) = x^2 + 1$, $k(x) = ax + b$, where a and b are constants.

    If h(0) = k(0), and k(2) = 15, find the values of a and b.

Domain and range

The numbers that are allowed to go into a function are called its **domain**. The numbers that come out of the function are called its **range**.

A function's domain and range can be illustrated using a **mapping diagram**.

Here is a mapping diagram for the function $f(x) = 2x + 1$.

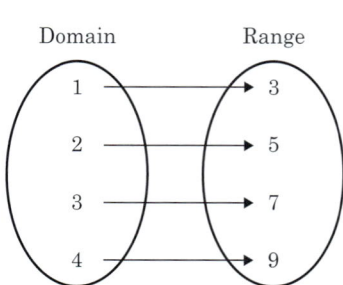

In the diagram on the previous page, the domain has been defined to be the set of integers {1, 2, 3, 4}.

The range is therefore the set {3, 5, 7, 9}.

Note that it is not the function itself that has restricted the domain to just these four numbers. Normally, there would be nothing to stop you evaluating f(5), for example. In this example, restricting the domain to just the numbers 1, 2, 3 and 4 is a choice that has been made.

Example 1

Use the mapping diagram to find the values of a, b and c for the function $f(x) = 3x - 2$.

$a = 3 \times 3 - 2 = 7$

$3b - 2 = 22$

$3b = 24$

$b = 8$

$c = 3 \times 15 - 2 = 43$

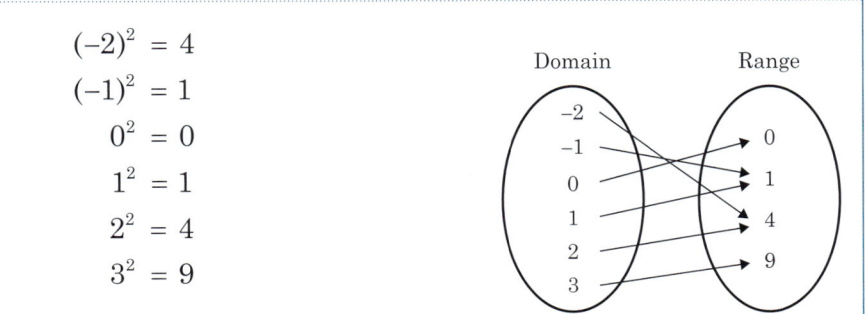

So far, you have looked at mapping diagrams for functions that are one-to-one. This means that every input value in the domain has a unique output value in the range.

However, a function does not have to be one-to-one. It can also be many-to-one, which means that more than one different input value in the domain can have the same output value in the range.

Example 2

Draw a mapping diagram for the function $f(x) = x^2$ with domain {–2, –1, 0, 1, 2, 3}.

$(-2)^2 = 4$

$(-1)^2 = 1$

$0^2 = 0$

$1^2 = 1$

$2^2 = 4$

$3^2 = 9$

Tip

Functions are not allowed to be one-to-many (which would imply that one value in the domain would give more than one value in the range).

Exercise 11.3B

1. Copy and complete the mapping diagram shown for the function $f(x) = 5x + 2$.

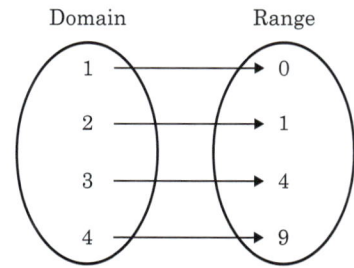

2. Draw a mapping diagram for:

   a) the function $f(x) = 6x - 5$, with domain {2, 4, 6, 8}

   b) the function $f(x) = 2x + 12$, with domain {1, 3, 5, 7}.

3. Draw a mapping diagram for:

   a) the function $f(x) = x^2 + 1$, with domain {1, 2, 3, 4}

   b) the function $f(x) = x^2 - 4$, with domain {−3, −1, 1, 4}.

4. Draw a mapping diagram for:

   a) the function $f(x) = 4x + 10$, with range {14, 18, 22, 26}

   b) the function $f(x) = 3x - 9$, with range {−9, 3, 15, 21}.

5. Identify the functions represented by the following mapping diagrams.

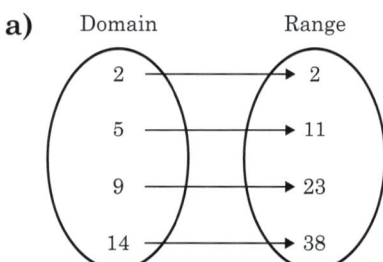

6. If the domain of the function $y = 2x^2 + 7$ is {1, 2, 5, 11}, write down the range of the function.

7. If the range of the function $y = 3x^2 - 2$ is { 1, 10, 73, 241}, write down the domain of the function, if all the numbers in the domain are positive.

8. Can you think of a function, other than $y = x$, whose domain and range are the same sets?

11.4 Composite and inverse functions

Composite functions

If $f(x) = 3x + 2$ and $g(x) = x^2$ then $f[g(x)]$ is a composite function where g is performed first and then f is performed on the result of g. $f[g(x)]$ is usually abbreviated to $fg(x)$.

The function fg may be found using a flow diagram:

$$x \longrightarrow \boxed{\text{square}} \xrightarrow{x^2} \boxed{\text{multiply by 3}} \xrightarrow{3x^2} \boxed{\text{add 2}} \longrightarrow 3x^2 + 2$$

$$\underbrace{\phantom{\boxed{\text{square}}}}_{g} \qquad \underbrace{\phantom{\boxed{\text{multiply by 3}}\boxed{\text{add 2}}}}_{f}$$

$fg(x) = 3x^2 + 2$

Sometimes, once you have found the composite function, it may need simplifying. Look at the following example.

Example 1

If $f(x) = 3x + 1$ and $g(x) = 2x^2 - 3$, find:

    a) $fg(x)$ **b)** $gf(x)$

    a) $3(2x^2 - 3) + 1$ **b)** $2(3x + 1)^2 - 3$

        $= 6x^2 - 9 + 1$ $= 2(9x^2 + 6x + 1) - 3$

        $= 6x^2 - 8$ $= 18x^2 + 12x + 2 - 3$

                                                 $= 18x^2 + 12x - 1$

To evaluate a composite function, you do not necessarily need to find the composite function first.

Example 2

If $f(x) = 2x^3 + 4x^2 + 7x + 1$ and $g(x) = 7x^2 - 25$, find $fg(2)$.

Evaluate the function g when $x = 2$, then use the output as the input to function f:

$g(2) = 7 \times 2^2 - 25 = 3$

$f(3) = 2 \times 3^3 + 4 \times 3^2 + 7 \times 3 + 1$

       $= 2 \times 27 + 4 \times 9 + 21 + 1$

       $= 54 + 36 + 21 + 1$

       $= 112$

Inverse functions

If a function f maps a number n onto m, then the inverse function f^{-1} maps m onto n. The inverse of a given function can be found in two main ways.

Example

Find the inverse of the function f, where $f(x) = \dfrac{5x - 2}{3}$

Method 1

a) Draw a flow diagram for f.

$$x \longrightarrow \boxed{\text{multiply by 5}} \xrightarrow{5x} \boxed{\text{subtract 2}} \xrightarrow{5x - 2} \boxed{\text{divide by 3}} \longrightarrow \frac{5x - 2}{3}$$

---

b) Draw a new flow diagram with each operation replaced by its inverse. Start with x on the right.

$$\frac{3x+2}{5} \longleftarrow \boxed{\text{divide by 5}} \xleftarrow{3x+2} \boxed{\text{add 2}} \xleftarrow{3x} \boxed{\text{multiply by 3}} \longleftarrow x$$

So, the inverse of the function f is given by $f^{-1}(x) = \dfrac{3x+2}{5}$

Method 2

Let $y = \dfrac{5x-2}{3}$, then interchange x and y.

$$x = \frac{5y-2}{3}$$

Now rearrange this equation to make y the subject again:

$$3x = 5y - 2$$
$$3x + 2 = 5y$$
$$y = \frac{3x+2}{5}$$

So, the inverse function is $\dfrac{3x+2}{5}$

> **Tip**
>
> Many people prefer this algebraic method. You should use the method which you find easier.

> **Tip**
>
> Because a function cannot be one-to-many, a many-to-one function does not have an inverse.

Exercise 11.4A

For Questions **1** and **2**, the functions f, g and h are as follows:

$f(x) = 4x$ $\qquad$ $g(x) = x + 5$ $\qquad$ $h(x) = x^2$

1. Find the following:

a) fg $\qquad$ **b)** gf $\qquad$ **c)** hf $\qquad$ **d)** fh $\qquad$ **e)** gh

2. Find:

a) x if $hg(x) = h(x)$ $\qquad$ **b)** x if $fh(x) = gh(x)$

For Questions **3** to **8**, find the inverse of each function.

3. $f(x) = 5x - 2$ $\qquad$ **4.** $f(x) = 5(x - 2)$ $\qquad$ **5.** $f(x) = 3(2x + 4)$

6. $g(x) = \dfrac{2x+1}{3}$ $\qquad$ **7.** $f(x) = \dfrac{3(x-1)}{4}$ $\qquad$ **8.** $g(x) = 2(3x + 4) - 6$

For Questions **9**, **10** and **11**, the functions p, q and r are as follows:

$$p(x) = 2x + 1 \qquad q(x) = 3x - 1 \qquad r(x) = x^2$$

9. Find:

   a) pq   **b)** qp   **c)** pr   **d)** rq

10. Find:

   a) pq(2)   **b)** rp(1)   **c)** qp(−2)   **d)** qq(2)

11. If $p(x) = 2x + 1$, $q(x) = 3x - 1$ and $r(x) = x^2$, find:

   a) x if $p(x) = q(x)$ **b)** two values of x if $rp(x) = rq(x)$ **c)** x if $pr(x) = qr(x)$

12. If $f(x) = 2x^2$, $g(x) = x^2 + 5x - 3$, $h(x) = \sqrt[3]{x}$, evaluate

   a) fg(2)   **b)** gf(−1)   **c)** gh(27)

For Questions **13** to **19**, find the inverse of each function.

13. $h(x) = \dfrac{1}{2}\left(4 + 5x\right) + 10$ **14.** $k(x) = -7x + 3$ **15.** $j(x) = \dfrac{12 - 5x}{3}$

16. $n(x) = \dfrac{4 - x}{3} + 2$ **17.** $m(x) = \dfrac{\left(\dfrac{2x - 1}{4} - 3\right)}{5}$ **18.** $f(x) = \dfrac{3(10 - 2x)}{7}$

19. $g(x) = \dfrac{\left(\dfrac{x}{4} + 6\right)}{5} + 7$

20. Explain why the function $y = 3x^2 + 4$ does not have an inverse.

Revision exercise 11

1. Given that $\mathscr{E} = \{1, 2, 3, 4, 5, 6, 7, 8\}$, $A = \{1, 3, 5\}$ and $B = \{5, 6, 7\}$, list the members of the sets:

   a) $A \cap B$ **b)** $A \cup B$

   c) A' **d)** $A' \cap B'$

   e) $A \cup B'$

2. The sets P and Q are such that $n(P \cup Q) = 50$, $n(P \cap Q) = 9$ and $n(P) = 27$. Find the value of $n(Q)$.

3. Draw three diagrams similar to Figure 1, and shade the following:

   a) $Q \cap R'$ **b)** $(P \cup Q) \cap R$

   c) $(P \cap Q) \cap R'$

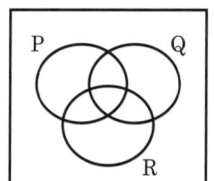

Figure 1

4. Describe the shaded regions in Figures 2 and 3 using set notation.

   a)
   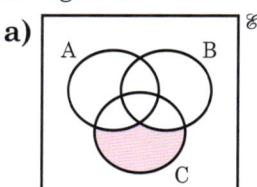
   Figure 2

   b)
   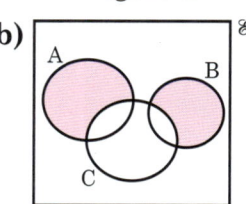
   Figure 3

5. Given are: $\mathscr{E} = \{$people on a train$\}$, $M = \{$males$\}$, $T = \{$people over 25 years old$\}$ and $S = \{$Spanish speakers$\}$

   a) Express in set notation:

     i) all the Spanish speakers are over 25

     ii) some Spanish speakers are women.

   b) Express in words: $T \cap M' = \varnothing$

6. The figures in the diagram indicate the number of elements in each subset of E.

   Find:

   a) $n(P \cap R)$

   b) $n(Q \cup R)'$

   c) $n(P' \cap Q')$

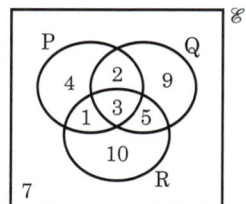

Figure 4

7. Given $f(x) = 2x - 3$ and $g(x) = x^2 - 1$, find:

   a) $f(-1)$ **b)** $g(-1)$

   c) $fg(-1)$ **d)** $gf(3)$

8. Given $f(x) = 3x + 4$, find the inverse function f^{-1}, and then find:

   a) $f^{-1}(13)$ **b)** the value of z if $f(z) = 20$

9. Find the inverse of the function

   $$f(x) = \frac{x + 1}{x - 1}$$

   What do you notice?

10. If $f(x) = 4x - 1$, find:

   a) $f^{-1}(x)$ **b)** $ff^{-1}(10)$

Examination-style exercise 11

NON-CALCULATOR SECTION

For Question **1**, make three copies of this Venn diagram in your notebook, one for each question part:

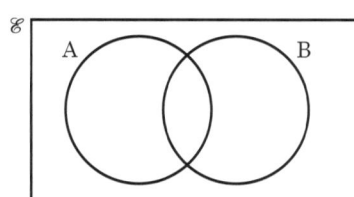

1. **a)** Shade the region $A \cup B$. [1]

   b) Shade the region $(A \cap B)'$. [1]

   c) Shade the complement of set A. [1]

2. $\mathscr{E} = \{1, \ 3, \ 5, \ 7, \ 9, \ 10, \ 12, \ 14, \ 16\}$

   $A = \{1, \ 5, \ 9, \ 12, \ 14\}$

   $B = \{1, \ 3, \ 9, \ 16\}$

   $C = \{1, \ 5, \ 9, \ 16\}$

   a) Draw a Venn diagram to show this information. [2]

   b) Write down the value of $n(B' \cap C)$. [1]

3. A and B are sets.

   Write the following sets in their simplest form.

   a) $A \cup A'$ [1]

   b) $A \cap A'$ [1]

   c) $(A \cup B) \cap (A \cup B)'$ [1]

CALCULATOR SECTION

4. $f(x) = x^3 - 2x^2 + 5x - 1$ and $g(x) = 3x + 1$

   Work out:

   a) $f(-2)$ [1]

   b) $gf(x)$ [2]

   c) $g^{-1}(x)$ [2]

5. $f(x) = 7 - 2x$

Work out:

a) $f(-2)$ [1]

b) $f^{-1}(x)$ [2]

c) $ff^{-1}(4)$ [1]

6. $f(x) = \sin x$, $g(x) = 3x + 6$

Work out:

a) $f(30)$ [1]

b) $fg(58)$ [2]

c) $g^{-1}(f(x))$ [2]

7. $f(x) = 4x - 1$, $g(x) = \dfrac{2}{x} + 1$, $h(x) = 3^x$

a) Work out the value of $fg(3)$ [1]

b) Write, as a single fraction, $gf(x)$ in terms of x. [3]

c) Work out $g^{-1}(x)$ [3]

d) Work out $hh(2)$ [2]

e) Calculate x when $h(x) = g\left(-\dfrac{9}{4}\right)$ [2]

12 Vectors and transformations

William Rowan Hamilton (1805–1865) was an Irish mathematician, astronomer, and physicist. He is famous for inventing quaternions, which are four-dimensional numbers, useful for describing the rotation of vectors in three-dimensional space. Hamilton introduced many new mathematical terms, including 'scalar' and 'vector', as he developed his new theory of quaternions. There is a plaque on a bridge over the canal in Dublin where Hamilton had the idea for quaternions that can still be seen today.

Katherine Johnson (1918–2020) was an American mathematician who worked for NASA. Her orbital calculations were critical to the success of many spaceflights, including the Apollo missions to the moon in the 1960s. She was one of the first black American women to work as a scientist at NASA. The story of her life was made into a film called Hidden Figures and, in 2015, President Barack Obama awarded her the Presidential Medal of Freedom.

- Draw and describe reflections, rotations, enlargements and translations.
- Understand and use vectors including describing a translation, adding and subtracting vectors and multiplying a vector by a scalar.
- Find the magnitude of a vector.
- Understand and use vector geometry including representing vectors by directed line segments, position vectors and vector geometry problems including using the sum and difference of vectors to express given vectors in terms of other vectors.

12.1 Vectors

A vector quantity has both magnitude and direction. Problems involving forces, velocities and displacements are often made easier when vectors are used. The magnitude of a vector means its size if, for example, you are dealing with a force, or its length if you are representing a vector on a diagram.

Addition of vectors

Vectors **a** and **b** represented by line segments with arrows can be added using the parallelogram rule or the 'tip-to-tail' method.

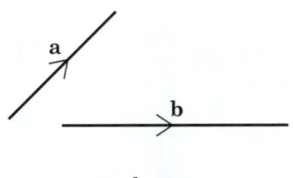

The 'tail' of vector **b** is joined to the 'tip' of vector **a**.

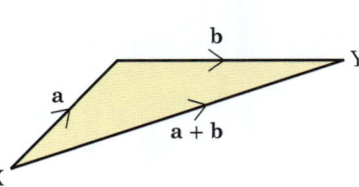

Alternatively, the 'tail' of **a** can be joined to the 'tip' of vector **b**.

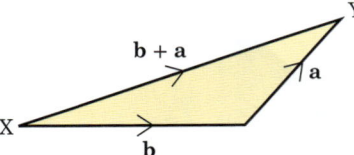

In both cases the vector $\overrightarrow{XY}$ has the same magnitude and direction, and therefore **a** + **b** = **b** + **a**

Note that when lower-case letters are used in textbooks to represent vectors, they are printed using bold type. When you write them in your notes, you should underline the letters, rather than attempting to write them in bold. Vectors between two locations labelled using upper-case letters are written with an arrow above the letters. The arrow goes from left to right, with the letter at the tail end of the vector written first.

Multiplication by a scalar

A scalar quantity has a magnitude but no direction. Mass, volume and temperature are all examples of scalar quantities. Ordinary numbers are also scalars.

When vector **x** is multiplied by 2, the result is 2**x**.

When **x** is multiplied by −3 the result is −3**x**.

Note:

1. The negative sign reverses the direction of the vector.
2. The result of **a** − **b** is **a** + −**b**.

   Subtracting **b** is equivalent to adding the negative of **b**.

The **position vector** of a point P is the vector whose tip is at P and whose tail is at the origin. Position vectors are instantly recognisable as they begin with the letter O.

The position vector of the point P is $\overrightarrow{OP}$.

On a coordinate grid the position vector of a point with coordinates (x, y), is written as a column vector $\begin{pmatrix} x \\ y \end{pmatrix}$.

Example

The diagram shows vectors **a** and **b**.
$\overrightarrow{OP}$ and $\overrightarrow{OQ}$ are the position vectors of points P and Q.
If $\overrightarrow{OP} = 3\mathbf{a} + \mathbf{b}$ and $\overrightarrow{OQ} = -2\mathbf{a} - 3\mathbf{b}$, illustrate the vectors $\overrightarrow{OP}$ and $\overrightarrow{OQ}$ on a diagram.

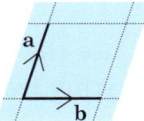

For $\overrightarrow{OP}$, the vector **a** is multiplied by the scalar value 3. Add the tail of **b** to the tip of 3**a** to get the vector 3**a** + **b**, as shown in the diagram.

For $\overrightarrow{OQ}$, the vector **a** is multiplied by the scalar value −2 and the vector **b** is multiplied by the scalar value −3. Add the tail of −3**b** to the tip of −2**a** to get the vector −2**a** − 3**b**, as shown in the diagram.

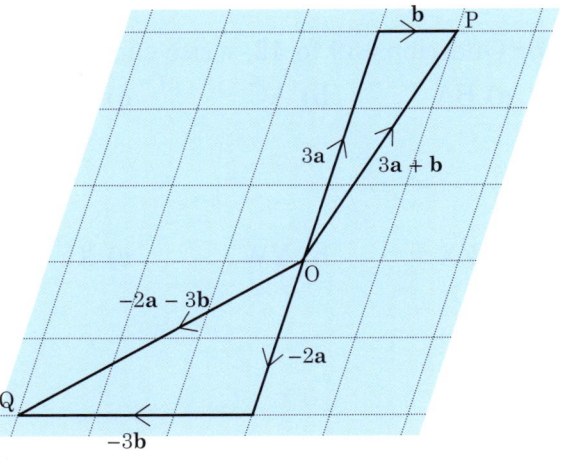

Exercise 12.1A

For Questions **1** to **26**, use the diagram below to describe the vectors given in terms of **c** and **d** where $\mathbf{c} = \overrightarrow{QN}$ and $\mathbf{d} = \overrightarrow{QR}$.

For example: $\overrightarrow{QS} = 2\mathbf{d}$, $\overrightarrow{TD} = \mathbf{c} + \mathbf{d}$

1. $\overrightarrow{AB}$
2. $\overrightarrow{SG}$
3. $\overrightarrow{VK}$
4. $\overrightarrow{KH}$
5. $\overrightarrow{OT}$
6. $\overrightarrow{WJ}$
7. $\overrightarrow{FH}$
8. $\overrightarrow{FT}$
9. $\overrightarrow{KV}$
10. $\overrightarrow{NQ}$
11. $\overrightarrow{OM}$
12. $\overrightarrow{SD}$
13. $\overrightarrow{PI}$
14. $\overrightarrow{YG}$
15. $\overrightarrow{OI}$
16. $\overrightarrow{RE}$
17. $\overrightarrow{XM}$
18. $\overrightarrow{ZH}$
19. $\overrightarrow{MR}$
20. $\overrightarrow{KA}$
21. $\overrightarrow{RZ}$
22. $\overrightarrow{CR}$
23. $\overrightarrow{NV}$
24. $\overrightarrow{EV}$
25. $\overrightarrow{JS}$
26. $\overrightarrow{LE}$

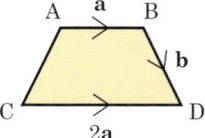

For Questions **27** to **38**, use the same diagram to find vectors for the following in terms of the capital letters, starting from **Q** each time.

For example: $3\mathbf{d} = \overrightarrow{QT}$, $\mathbf{c} + \mathbf{d} = \overrightarrow{QA}$

27. $2\mathbf{c}$
28. $4\mathbf{d}$
29. $2\mathbf{c} + \mathbf{d}$
30. $2\mathbf{d} + \mathbf{c}$
31. $3\mathbf{d} + 2\mathbf{c}$
32. $2\mathbf{c} - \mathbf{d}$
33. $-\mathbf{c} + 2\mathbf{d}$
34. $\mathbf{c} - 2\mathbf{d}$
35. $2\mathbf{c} + 4\mathbf{d}$
36. $-\mathbf{c}$
37. $-\mathbf{c} - \mathbf{d}$
38. $2\mathbf{c} - 2\mathbf{d}$

For Questions **39** to **42**, write each vector in terms of **a** and/or **b**.

39. a) $\overrightarrow{BA}$ b) $\overrightarrow{AC}$ c) $\overrightarrow{DB}$ d) $\overrightarrow{AD}$

40. a) $\overrightarrow{ZX}$ b) $\overrightarrow{YW}$ c) $\overrightarrow{XY}$ d) $\overrightarrow{XZ}$

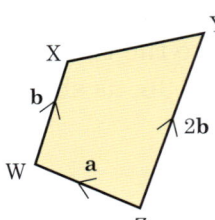

41. a) $\overrightarrow{MK}$ **b)** $\overrightarrow{NL}$ **c)** $\overrightarrow{NK}$ **d)** $\overrightarrow{KN}$

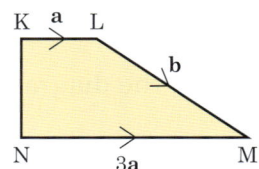

42. a) $\overrightarrow{FE}$ **b)** $\overrightarrow{BC}$ **c)** $\overrightarrow{FC}$ **d)** $\overrightarrow{DA}$

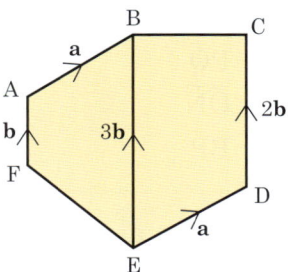

For Questions **43** to **45**, write each vector in terms of **a**, **b** and **c**.

43. a) $\overrightarrow{FC}$ **b)** $\overrightarrow{GB}$ **c)** $\overrightarrow{AB}$ **d)** $\overrightarrow{HE}$ **e)** $\overrightarrow{CA}$

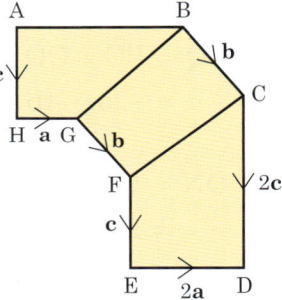

44. a) $\overrightarrow{OF}$ **b)** $\overrightarrow{OC}$ **c)** $\overrightarrow{BC}$ **d)** $\overrightarrow{EB}$ **e)** $\overrightarrow{FB}$

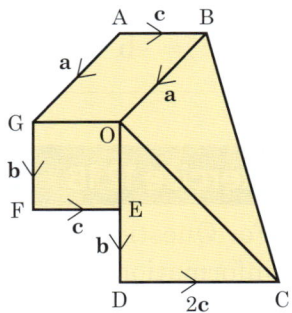

45. a) $\overrightarrow{GD}$ **b)** $\overrightarrow{GE}$ **c)** $\overrightarrow{AD}$ **d)** $\overrightarrow{AF}$ **e)** $\overrightarrow{FE}$

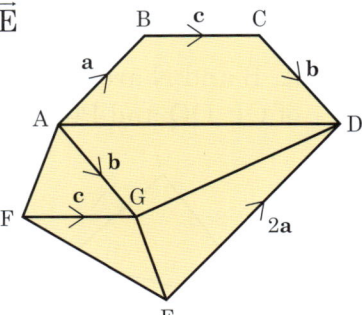

Example

Using the diagram, express each of the following vectors in terms of **a** and/or **b**.

a) $\overrightarrow{AP}$

b) $\overrightarrow{AB}$

c) $\overrightarrow{OQ}$

d) $\overrightarrow{PO}$

e) $\overrightarrow{PQ}$

f) $\overrightarrow{PN}$

g) $\overrightarrow{ON}$

h) $\overrightarrow{AN}$

i) $\overrightarrow{BP}$

j) $\overrightarrow{QA}$

OA = AP

BQ = 3OB

N is the midpoint of PQ

$\overrightarrow{OA}$ = **a**, $\overrightarrow{OB}$ = **b**

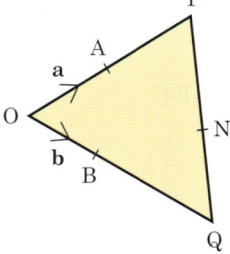

a) $\overrightarrow{AP}$ = **a**

b) $\overrightarrow{AB}$ = −**a** + **b**

c) $\overrightarrow{OQ}$ = 4**b**

d) $\overrightarrow{PO}$ = −2**a**

e) $\overrightarrow{PQ}$ = $\overrightarrow{PO}$ + $\overrightarrow{OQ}$
   = −2**a** + 4**b**

f) $\overrightarrow{PN}$ = $\frac{1}{2}$ $\overrightarrow{PQ}$
   = −**a** + 2**b**

g) $\overrightarrow{ON}$ = $\overrightarrow{OP}$ + $\overrightarrow{PN}$
   = 2**a** + (−**a** + 2**b**)
   = **a** + 2**b**

h) $\overrightarrow{AN}$ = $\overrightarrow{AP}$ + $\overrightarrow{PN}$
   = **a** + (−**a** + 2**b**)
   = 2**b**

i) $\overrightarrow{BP}$ = $\overrightarrow{BO}$ + $\overrightarrow{OP}$
   = −**b** + 2**a**

j) $\overrightarrow{QA}$ = $\overrightarrow{QO}$ + $\overrightarrow{OA}$
   = −4**b** + **a**

Exercise 12.1B

For Questions **1** to **6**, $\overrightarrow{OA}$ = **a** and $\overrightarrow{OB}$ = **b**. Copy each diagram and use the information given to express the following vectors in terms of **a** and/or **b**.

a) $\overrightarrow{AP}$

b) $\overrightarrow{AB}$

c) $\overrightarrow{OQ}$

d) $\overrightarrow{PO}$

e) $\overrightarrow{PQ}$

f) $\overrightarrow{PN}$

g) $\overrightarrow{ON}$

h) $\overrightarrow{AN}$

i) $\overrightarrow{BP}$

j) $\overrightarrow{QA}$

1. A, B and N are midpoints of OP, OQ and PQ respectively.

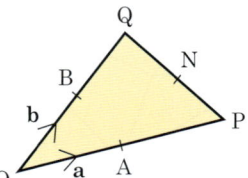

2. A and N are midpoints of OP and PQ and BQ = 2OB.

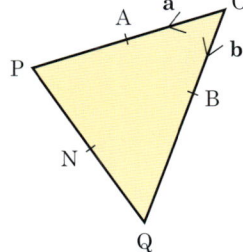

3. AP = 2OA, BQ = OB, PN = NQ.

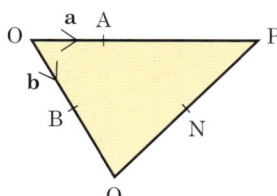

4. OA = 2AP, BQ = 3OB, PN = 2NQ.

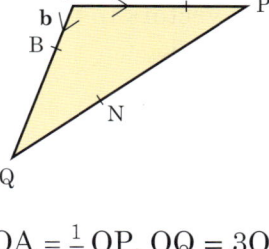

5. AP = 5OA, OB = 2BQ, NP = 2QN.

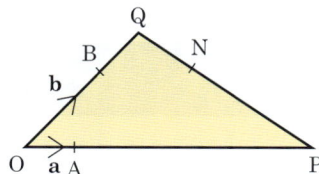

6. OA = $\frac{1}{5}$OP, OQ = 3OB, N is $\frac{1}{4}$ of the way along PQ.

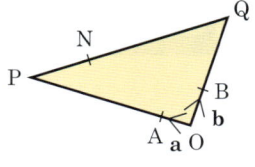

7. In △XYZ, the midpoint of YZ is M.
   If $\overrightarrow{XY}$ = **s** and $\overrightarrow{ZX}$ = **t**,
   find $\overrightarrow{XM}$ in terms of **s** and **t**.

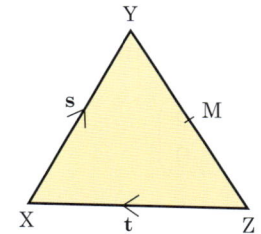

8. In △AOB, AM : MB = 2 : 1.
   If $\overrightarrow{OA}$ = **a** and $\overrightarrow{OB}$ = **b**,
   find $\overrightarrow{OM}$ in term of **a** and **b**.

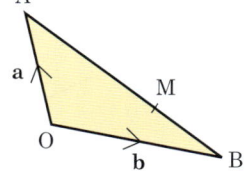

9. O is any point in the plane of the square ABCD.
   The vectors $\overrightarrow{OA}$, $\overrightarrow{OB}$ and $\overrightarrow{OC}$ are **a**, **b** and **c** respectively.
   Find the vector $\overrightarrow{OD}$ in terms of **a**, **b** and **c**.

10. ABCDEF is a regular hexagon with $\overrightarrow{AB}$ representing
    the vector **m**, and $\overrightarrow{AF}$ representing the vector **n**.
    Find the vector representing $\overrightarrow{AD}$.

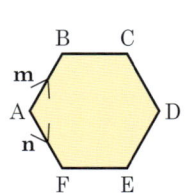

11. ABCDEF is a regular hexagon with centre O.
    $\overrightarrow{FA}$ = **a** and $\overrightarrow{FB}$ = **b**.

    Express the following vectors in terms of **a** and/or **b**.

    a) $\overrightarrow{AB}$ b) $\overrightarrow{FO}$ c) $\overrightarrow{FC}$

    d) $\overrightarrow{BC}$ e) $\overrightarrow{AO}$ f) $\overrightarrow{FD}$

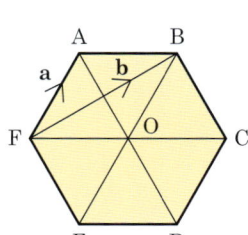

12. In the diagram, M is the midpoint of CD,
BP:PM = 2:1, $\overrightarrow{AB}$ = **x**, $\overrightarrow{AC}$ = **y** and $\overrightarrow{AD}$ = **z**.

Express the following vectors in terms of **x**, **y** and **z**.

a) $\overrightarrow{DC}$ b) $\overrightarrow{DM}$ c) $\overrightarrow{AM}$

d) $\overrightarrow{BM}$ e) $\overrightarrow{BP}$ f) $\overrightarrow{AP}$

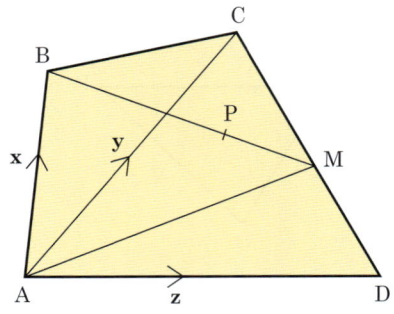

12.2 Column vectors

The vector $\overrightarrow{AB}$ may be written as a **column vector**: $\overrightarrow{AB} = \begin{pmatrix} 5 \\ 3 \end{pmatrix}$

The top number, 5, is the horizontal component of $\overrightarrow{AB}$
and the bottom number, 3, is the vertical component.

The diagram shows each of the following vectors:

$\overrightarrow{AB} = \begin{pmatrix} 5 \\ 3 \end{pmatrix}$ $\overrightarrow{CD} = \begin{pmatrix} 4 \\ -2 \end{pmatrix}$ $\overrightarrow{EF} = \begin{pmatrix} -5 \\ 0 \end{pmatrix}$

$\overrightarrow{GH} = \begin{pmatrix} 0 \\ 7 \end{pmatrix}$ $\overrightarrow{IJ} = \begin{pmatrix} 2 \\ -7 \end{pmatrix}$ $\overrightarrow{KL} = \begin{pmatrix} -4 \\ -2 \end{pmatrix}$

$\overrightarrow{MN} = \begin{pmatrix} -4 \\ 6 \end{pmatrix}$ $\overrightarrow{OP} = \begin{pmatrix} 3 \\ 0 \end{pmatrix}$ $\overrightarrow{QR} = \begin{pmatrix} 0 \\ -3 \end{pmatrix}$

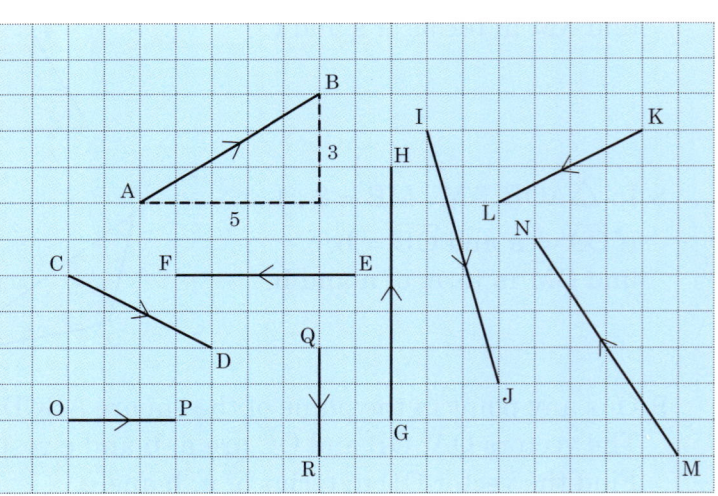

Addition of vectors

Suppose you want to add vectors $\overrightarrow{AB}$ and $\overrightarrow{CD}$ in Figure 1, where $\overrightarrow{AB} = \begin{pmatrix} 5 \\ 2 \end{pmatrix}$ and $\overrightarrow{CD} = \begin{pmatrix} 2 \\ -3 \end{pmatrix}$.

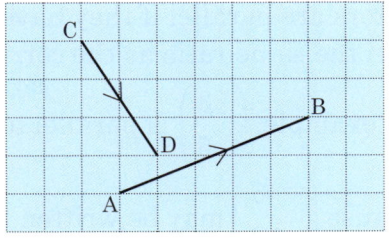

Figure 1

First move $\overrightarrow{CD}$ so that $\overrightarrow{AB}$ and $\overrightarrow{CD}$ join 'tip to tail' as in Figure 2. Remember that changing the **position** of a vector does not change the vector. A vector is described by its magnitude and direction.

The dashed line shows the result of adding $\overrightarrow{AB}$ and $\overrightarrow{CD}$.

Using column vectors,

$$\overrightarrow{AB} + \overrightarrow{CD} = \begin{pmatrix} 5 \\ 2 \end{pmatrix} + \begin{pmatrix} 2 \\ -3 \end{pmatrix}$$

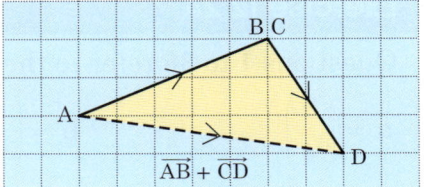

Figure 2

The column vector for the dashed line is $\begin{pmatrix} 7 \\ -1 \end{pmatrix}$.

You perform addition with vectors by adding together the corresponding components of the vectors.

Subtraction of vectors

Figure 3 shows $\overrightarrow{AB} - \overrightarrow{CD}$.

To subtract vector $\overrightarrow{CD}$ from $\overrightarrow{AB}$, first reverse the direction of $\overrightarrow{CD}$ to give vector $\overrightarrow{DC}$, and then join the tail of $\overrightarrow{DC}$ to the tip of $\overrightarrow{AB}$.

Again, $\overrightarrow{AB} = \begin{pmatrix} 5 \\ 2 \end{pmatrix}$ and $\overrightarrow{CD} = \begin{pmatrix} 2 \\ -3 \end{pmatrix}$, so $\overrightarrow{DC} = \begin{pmatrix} -2 \\ 3 \end{pmatrix}$

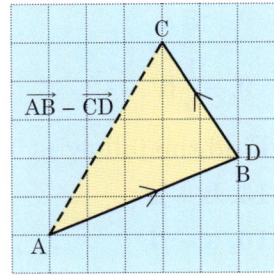

Figure 3

$$\overrightarrow{AB} - \overrightarrow{CD} = \overrightarrow{AB} + \left(-\overrightarrow{CD} \right)$$

In column vectors,

$$\overrightarrow{AB} + \left(-\overrightarrow{CD} \right) = \begin{pmatrix} 5 \\ 2 \end{pmatrix} + \begin{pmatrix} -2 \\ 3 \end{pmatrix} = \begin{pmatrix} 3 \\ 5 \end{pmatrix}$$

Multiplication by a scalar

If $\mathbf{a} = \begin{pmatrix} 3 \\ -4 \end{pmatrix}$ then $2\mathbf{a} = 2 \begin{pmatrix} 3 \\ -4 \end{pmatrix} = \begin{pmatrix} 6 \\ -8 \end{pmatrix}$ 　　If $\mathbf{a} = \begin{pmatrix} 0 \\ 7 \end{pmatrix}$ then $2\mathbf{a} = 2 \begin{pmatrix} 0 \\ 7 \end{pmatrix} = \begin{pmatrix} 0 \\ 14 \end{pmatrix}$

Each component is multiplied by the number 2.

Parallel vectors

Vectors are parallel if they have the same direction. Both components of one vector must be in the same ratio as the corresponding components of the parallel vector.

For example, $\begin{pmatrix} 3 \\ -5 \end{pmatrix}$ is parallel to $\begin{pmatrix} 6 \\ -10 \end{pmatrix}$,

because $\begin{pmatrix} 6 \\ -10 \end{pmatrix}$ may be written $2\begin{pmatrix} 3 \\ -5 \end{pmatrix}$.

In general, the vector $k\begin{pmatrix} a \\ b \end{pmatrix}$ is parallel to $\begin{pmatrix} a \\ b \end{pmatrix}$.

Exercise 12.2A

Questions **1** to **36** refer to the following vectors.

$$\mathbf{a} = \begin{pmatrix} 3 \\ 4 \end{pmatrix} \qquad \mathbf{b} = \begin{pmatrix} 1 \\ 4 \end{pmatrix} \qquad \mathbf{c} = \begin{pmatrix} 4 \\ -3 \end{pmatrix} \qquad \mathbf{d} = \begin{pmatrix} -1 \\ 1 \end{pmatrix}$$

$$\mathbf{e} = \begin{pmatrix} 5 \\ 12 \end{pmatrix} \qquad \mathbf{f} = \begin{pmatrix} 3 \\ -2 \end{pmatrix} \qquad \mathbf{g} = \begin{pmatrix} -4 \\ -2 \end{pmatrix} \qquad \mathbf{h} = \begin{pmatrix} -12 \\ 5 \end{pmatrix}$$

Draw and label the following vectors on graph paper (use 1 cm to 1 unit).

1. **c**	2. **f**	3. 2**b**	4. −**a**
5. −**g**	6. 3**a**	7. $\frac{1}{2}\mathbf{e}$	8. 5**d**
9. $-\frac{1}{2}\mathbf{h}$	10. $\frac{3}{2}\mathbf{g}$	11. $\frac{1}{5}\mathbf{h}$	12. −3**b**

Find the following vectors in component form.

13. **b** + **h**	14. **f** + **g**	15. **e** − **b**
16. **a** − **d**	17. **g** − **h**	18. 2**a** + 3**c**
19. 3**f** + 2**d**	20. 4**g** − 2**b**	21. $5\mathbf{a} + \frac{1}{2}\mathbf{g}$
22. **a** + **b** + **c**	23. 3**f** − **a** + **c**	24. **c** + 2**d** + 3**e**

In each of the following, find **x** in component form.

25. **x** + **b** = **e**	26. **x** + **d** = **a**	27. **c** + **x** = **f**
28. **x** − **g** = **h**	29. 2**x** + **b** = **g**	30. 2**x** − 3**d** = **g**
31. 2**b** = **d** − **x**	32. **f** − **g** = **e** − **x**	33. 2**x** + **b** = **x** + **e**
34. 3**x** − **b** = **x** + **h**	35. **a** + **b** + **x** = **b** + **a**	36. 2**x** + **e** = **0** (zero vector)

37. a) Draw and label each of the following vectors on graph paper.

$$\mathbf{l} = \begin{pmatrix} -3 \\ -3 \end{pmatrix}; \mathbf{m} = \begin{pmatrix} 2 \\ 0 \end{pmatrix}; \mathbf{n} = \begin{pmatrix} 3 \\ 2 \end{pmatrix}; \mathbf{p} = \begin{pmatrix} 1 \\ -2 \end{pmatrix}; \mathbf{q} = \begin{pmatrix} 3 \\ 0 \end{pmatrix};$$

$$\mathbf{r} = \begin{pmatrix} 6 \\ 4 \end{pmatrix}; \mathbf{s} = \begin{pmatrix} 2 \\ 2 \end{pmatrix}; \mathbf{t} = \begin{pmatrix} 2 \\ -4 \end{pmatrix}; \mathbf{u} = \begin{pmatrix} -1 \\ -3 \end{pmatrix}; \mathbf{v} = \begin{pmatrix} 0 \\ 3 \end{pmatrix};$$

b) Find four pairs of parallel vectors among the ten vectors.

38. State whether each statement is true or false.

a) $\begin{pmatrix} 3 \\ -1 \end{pmatrix}$ is parallel to $\begin{pmatrix} 9 \\ -3 \end{pmatrix}$ **b)** $\begin{pmatrix} -2 \\ 0 \end{pmatrix}$ is parallel to $\begin{pmatrix} 4 \\ 0 \end{pmatrix}$

c) $\begin{pmatrix} -1 \\ 1 \end{pmatrix}$ is parallel to $\begin{pmatrix} -1 \\ 1 \end{pmatrix}$ **d)** $\begin{pmatrix} 5 \\ -15 \end{pmatrix} = 5 \begin{pmatrix} 1 \\ -3 \end{pmatrix}$

e) $\begin{pmatrix} 4 \\ 0 \end{pmatrix}$ is parallel to $\begin{pmatrix} 0 \\ 6 \end{pmatrix}$ **f)** $\begin{pmatrix} 3 \\ -1 \end{pmatrix} + \begin{pmatrix} -4 \\ -2 \end{pmatrix} = \begin{pmatrix} -1 \\ 1 \end{pmatrix}$

39. a) Draw a diagram to illustrate the vector addition $\overrightarrow{AB} + \overrightarrow{CD}$.

b) Draw a separate diagram to illustrate $\overrightarrow{AB} - \overrightarrow{CD}$.

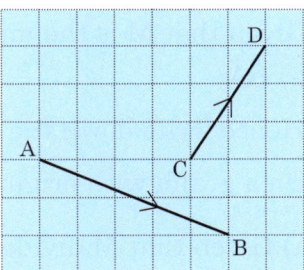

40. Draw separate diagrams to illustrate the following.

a) $\overrightarrow{FE} + \overrightarrow{JI}$

b) $\overrightarrow{HG} + \overrightarrow{FE}$

c) $\overrightarrow{JI} - \overrightarrow{FE}$

d) $\overrightarrow{HG} + \overrightarrow{JI}$

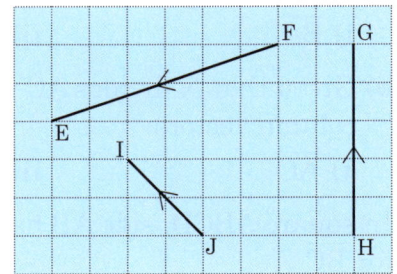

Exercise 12.2B

1. If D has coordinates (7, 2) and E has coordinates (9, 0), find the column vector for $\overrightarrow{DE}$.

2. Find the column vector $\overrightarrow{XY}$, where X and Y have coordinates (−1, 4) and (5, 2) respectively.

3. In the diagram, $\overrightarrow{AB}$ represents the vector $\begin{pmatrix} 5 \\ 2 \end{pmatrix}$ and $\overrightarrow{BC}$ represents the vector $\begin{pmatrix} 0 \\ 3 \end{pmatrix}$.

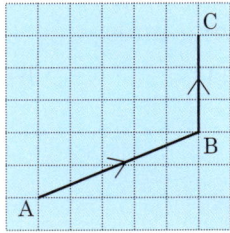

a) Copy the diagram and mark point D such that ABCD is a parallelogram.

b) Write $\overrightarrow{AD}$ and $\overrightarrow{CA}$ as column vectors.

4. a) On squared paper, draw $\overrightarrow{AB} = \begin{pmatrix} 3 \\ -2 \end{pmatrix}$ and $\overrightarrow{BC} = \begin{pmatrix} 4 \\ 2 \end{pmatrix}$ and mark point D such that ABCD is a parallelogram.

b) Write $\overrightarrow{AD}$ and $\overrightarrow{CA}$ as column vectors.

5. Copy the diagram in which $\overrightarrow{OA} = \begin{pmatrix} 5 \\ 2 \end{pmatrix}$ and $\overrightarrow{OB} = \begin{pmatrix} 2 \\ 5 \end{pmatrix}$.

M is the midpoint of AB. Express the following as column vectors:

a) $\overrightarrow{BA}$ **b)** $\overrightarrow{BM}$

c) $\overrightarrow{OM}$ (use $\overrightarrow{OM} = \overrightarrow{OB} + \overrightarrow{BM}$)

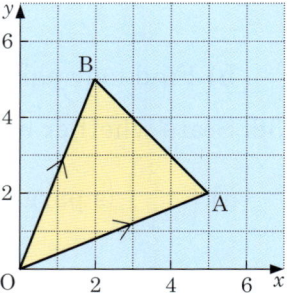

Hence write down the coordinates of M.

6. On a graph with origin at O, draw the position vectors $\overrightarrow{OA} = \begin{pmatrix} 5 \\ -1 \end{pmatrix}$ and $\overrightarrow{OB} = \begin{pmatrix} 6 \\ -7 \end{pmatrix}$.

Given that M is the midpoint of AB express the following as column vectors:

a) $\overrightarrow{BA}$ **b)** $\overrightarrow{BM}$ **c)** $\overrightarrow{OM}$

Hence write down the coordinates of M.

7. On a graph with origin at O, draw $\overrightarrow{OA} = \begin{pmatrix} -2 \\ 5 \end{pmatrix}$, $\overrightarrow{OB} = \begin{pmatrix} 4 \\ 2 \end{pmatrix}$ and $\overrightarrow{OC} = \begin{pmatrix} -2 \\ -4 \end{pmatrix}$.

a) Given that M divides AB such that $AM:MB = 2:1$, express the following as column vectors:

i) $\overrightarrow{BA}$ **ii)** $\overrightarrow{BM}$ **iii)** $\overrightarrow{OM}$

b) Given that N divides AC such that $AN:NC = 1:2$, express the following as column vectors:

i) $\overrightarrow{AC}$ **ii)** $\overrightarrow{AN}$ **iii)** $\overrightarrow{ON}$

8. In square ABCD, side AB has column vector $\begin{pmatrix} 2 \\ 1 \end{pmatrix}$. Find two possible column vectors for $\overrightarrow{BC}$.

9. Rectangle KLMN has an area of 10 square units and $\overrightarrow{KL}$ has column vector $\begin{pmatrix} 5 \\ 0 \end{pmatrix}$. Find two possible column vectors for $\overrightarrow{LM}$.

10. In the diagram, ABCD is a trapezium in which $\overrightarrow{DC} = 2\overrightarrow{AB}$. If $\overrightarrow{AB} = \mathbf{p}$ and $\overrightarrow{AD} = \mathbf{q}$ express in terms of $\mathbf{p}$ and $\mathbf{q}$:

a) $\overrightarrow{BD}$ **b)** $\overrightarrow{AC}$ **c)** $\overrightarrow{BC}$

11. Find the image of the vector $\begin{pmatrix} 1 \\ 3 \end{pmatrix}$ after reflection in the following lines:

a) $y = 0$ **b)** $x = 0$ **c)** $y = x$ **d)** $y = -x$

Magnitude of a vector

The magnitude (or length) of **a** vector a is written as $|\mathbf{a}|$.
This is also called the modulus of **a**.

In the diagram, $\mathbf{a} = \begin{pmatrix} 5 \\ 3 \end{pmatrix}$

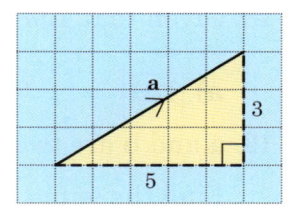

By Pythagoras' theorem, $|\mathbf{a}| = \sqrt{5^2 + 3^2}$

$$|\mathbf{a}| = \sqrt{34} \text{ units}$$

In general if $\mathbf{x} = \begin{pmatrix} m \\ n \end{pmatrix}, |\mathbf{x}| = \sqrt{m^2 + n^2}$

Exercise 12.2C

Questions **1** to **12** refer to the following vectors:

$$\mathbf{a} = \begin{pmatrix} 3 \\ 4 \end{pmatrix} \qquad \mathbf{b} = \begin{pmatrix} 4 \\ 1 \end{pmatrix} \qquad \mathbf{c} = \begin{pmatrix} 5 \\ 12 \end{pmatrix}$$

$$\mathbf{d} = \begin{pmatrix} -3 \\ 0 \end{pmatrix} \qquad \mathbf{e} = \begin{pmatrix} -4 \\ -3 \end{pmatrix} \qquad \mathbf{f} = \begin{pmatrix} -3 \\ 6 \end{pmatrix}$$

Find the following, leaving the answer in surd form where necessary.

1. $|\mathbf{a}|$ 2. $|\mathbf{b}|$ 3. $|\mathbf{c}|$ 4. $|\mathbf{d}|$ 5. $|\mathbf{e}|$
6. $|\mathbf{f}|$ 7. $|\mathbf{a} + \mathbf{b}|$ 8. $|\mathbf{c} - \mathbf{d}|$ 9. $|2\mathbf{e}|$ 10. $|\mathbf{f} + 2\mathbf{b}|$
11. **a)** Find $|\mathbf{a} + \mathbf{c}|$ **b)** Is $|\mathbf{a} + \mathbf{c}|$ equal to $|\mathbf{a}| + |\mathbf{c}|$?
12. **a)** Find $|\mathbf{c} + \mathbf{d}|$ **b)** Is $|\mathbf{c} + \mathbf{d}|$ equal to $|\mathbf{c}| + |\mathbf{d}|$?

13. If $\overrightarrow{AB} = \begin{pmatrix} 3 \\ -1 \end{pmatrix}$ and $\overrightarrow{BC} = \begin{pmatrix} 2 \\ 3 \end{pmatrix}$, find the magnitude of $\overrightarrow{AC}$.

14. If $\overrightarrow{PQ} = \begin{pmatrix} 5 \\ -2 \end{pmatrix}$ and $\overrightarrow{QR} = \begin{pmatrix} 0 \\ 1 \end{pmatrix}$, find the magnitude of $\overrightarrow{PR}$.

15. If $\overrightarrow{WX} = \begin{pmatrix} 1 \\ 3 \end{pmatrix}$, $\overrightarrow{XY} = \begin{pmatrix} -2 \\ 1 \end{pmatrix}$ and $\overrightarrow{YZ} = \begin{pmatrix} 2 \\ -1 \end{pmatrix}$ find $|\overrightarrow{WZ}|$.

16. Given that $\overrightarrow{OP} = \begin{pmatrix} 0 \\ 5 \end{pmatrix}$ and $\overrightarrow{OQ} = \begin{pmatrix} n \\ 3 \end{pmatrix}$, find:

   a) the magnitude of $\overrightarrow{OP}$ **b)** a value for n if $|\overrightarrow{OP}| = |\overrightarrow{OQ}|$

17. Given that $\overrightarrow{OA} = \begin{pmatrix} 5 \\ 12 \end{pmatrix}$ and $\overrightarrow{OB} = \begin{pmatrix} 0 \\ m \end{pmatrix}$, find:

   a) $|\overrightarrow{OA}|$ **b)** a value for m if $|\overrightarrow{OA}| = |\overrightarrow{OB}|$

18. Given that $\overrightarrow{LM} = \begin{pmatrix} -3 \\ 4 \end{pmatrix}$ and $\overrightarrow{MN} = \begin{pmatrix} -15 \\ p \end{pmatrix}$, find:

    a) $\left|\overrightarrow{LM}\right|$ **b)** a value for p if $\left|\overrightarrow{MN}\right| = 3\left|\overrightarrow{LM}\right|$

19. **a** and **b** are two vectors and $|\mathbf{a}| = 3$.

    Find the value of $|\mathbf{a} + \mathbf{b}|$ when:

    a) $\mathbf{b} = 2\mathbf{a}$ **b)** $\mathbf{b} = -3\mathbf{a}$

    c) **b** is perpendicular to **a** and the magnitude of **b** is 4

20. **r** and **s** are two vectors and $|\mathbf{r}| = 5$.

    Find the value of $|\mathbf{r} + \mathbf{s}|$ when:

    a) $\mathbf{s} = 5\mathbf{r}$ **b)** $\mathbf{s} = -2\mathbf{r}$

    c) **r** is perpendicular to **s** and $|\mathbf{s}| = 5$ **d)** **s** is perpendicular to $(\mathbf{r} + \mathbf{s})$ and $|\mathbf{s}| = 3$

12.3 Vector geometry

Sometimes vectors can be used to solve problems in geometry.

Points are called **collinear** if they lie on the same straight line.

Example

In the diagram, $\overrightarrow{OD} = 2\overrightarrow{OA}$, $\overrightarrow{OE} = 4\overrightarrow{OB}$, $\overrightarrow{OA} = \mathbf{a}$ and $\overrightarrow{OB} = \mathbf{b}$

a) Express $\overrightarrow{OD}$ and $\overrightarrow{OE}$ in terms of **a** and **b** respectively.

b) Express $\overrightarrow{BA}$ in terms of **a** and **b**.

c) Express $\overrightarrow{ED}$ in terms of **a** and **b**.

d) Given that $\overrightarrow{BC} = 3\overrightarrow{BA}$, express $\overrightarrow{OC}$ in terms of **a** and **b**.

e) Express $\overrightarrow{EC}$ in terms of **a** and **b**.

f) Hence show that the points E, D and C are collinear.

a) $\overrightarrow{OD} = 2\mathbf{a}$

    $\overrightarrow{OE} = 4\mathbf{b}$

b) $\overrightarrow{BA} = -\mathbf{b} + \mathbf{a}$

c) $\overrightarrow{ED} = -4\mathbf{b} + 2\mathbf{a}$

d) $\overrightarrow{OC} = \overrightarrow{OB} + \overrightarrow{BC}$

    $\overrightarrow{OC} = \mathbf{b} + 3(-\mathbf{b} + \mathbf{a})$

    $\overrightarrow{OC} = -2\mathbf{b} + 3\mathbf{a}$

e) $\overrightarrow{EC} = \overrightarrow{EO} + \overrightarrow{OC}$

    $\overrightarrow{EC} = -4\mathbf{b} + (-2\mathbf{b} + 3\mathbf{a})$

    $\overrightarrow{EC} = -6\mathbf{b} + 3\mathbf{a}$

f) $\overrightarrow{EC} = \dfrac{3}{2}(-4\mathbf{b} + 2\mathbf{a})$, so $\overrightarrow{EC} = \dfrac{3}{2}\overrightarrow{ED}$.

    Since $\overrightarrow{EC}$ and $\overrightarrow{ED}$ are parallel vectors which both pass through the point E, the points E, D and C must be collinear.

Exercise 12.3A

1. $\overrightarrow{OD} = 2\overrightarrow{OA}$ $\quad$ $\overrightarrow{OE} = 3\overrightarrow{OB}$ $\quad$ $\overrightarrow{OA} = \mathbf{a}$ $\quad$ $\overrightarrow{OB} = \mathbf{b}$

   a) Express $\overrightarrow{OD}$ and $\overrightarrow{OE}$ in terms of **a** and **b** respectively.

   b) Express $\overrightarrow{BA}$ in terms of **a** and **b**.

   c) Express $\overrightarrow{ED}$ in terms of **a** and **b**.

   d) Given that $\overrightarrow{BC} = 4\overrightarrow{BA}$, express $\overrightarrow{OC}$ in terms of **a** and **b**.

   e) Express $\overrightarrow{EC}$ in terms of **a** and **b**.

   f) Use the results for $\overrightarrow{ED}$ and $\overrightarrow{EC}$ to show that points E, D and C are collinear.

2. $\overrightarrow{OY} = 2\overrightarrow{OB}$ $\quad$ $\overrightarrow{OX} = \dfrac{5}{2}\overrightarrow{OA}$ $\quad$ $\overrightarrow{OA} = \mathbf{a}$ $\quad$ $\overrightarrow{OB} = \mathbf{b}$

   a) Express the position vectors of X and Y in terms of **a** and **b**.

   b) Express $\overrightarrow{AB}$ in terms of **a** and **b**.

   c) Express $\overrightarrow{XY}$ in terms of **a** and **b**.

   d) Given that $\overrightarrow{AC} = 6\overrightarrow{AB}$, express $\overrightarrow{OC}$ in terms of **a** and **b**.

   e) Express $\overrightarrow{XC}$ in terms of **a** and **b**.

   f) Use the results for $\overrightarrow{XY}$ and $\overrightarrow{XC}$ to show that points X, Y and C are collinear.

3. $\overrightarrow{OA} = \mathbf{a}$ $\quad$ $\overrightarrow{OB} = \mathbf{b}$ $\quad$ $\overrightarrow{AQ} = \dfrac{1}{2}\mathbf{a}$ $\quad$ $\overrightarrow{BR} = \mathbf{b}$ $\quad$ $\overrightarrow{AP} = 2\overrightarrow{BA}$

   a) Express $\overrightarrow{BA}$ and $\overrightarrow{BP}$ in terms of **a** and **b**.

   b) Express $\overrightarrow{RQ}$ in terms of **a** and **b**.

   c) Express $\overrightarrow{QA}$ and $\overrightarrow{QP}$ in terms of **a** and **b**.

   d) Using the vectors for $\overrightarrow{RQ}$ and $\overrightarrow{QP}$, show that R, Q and P are collinear.

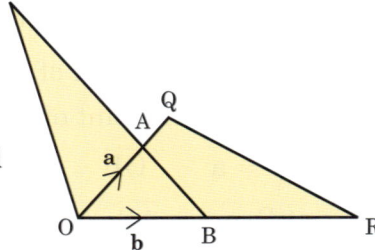

4. M is the midpoint of OA and P lies on AB such that $\overrightarrow{AP} = \dfrac{2}{3}\overrightarrow{AB}$.

   a) Express $\overrightarrow{AB}$ and $\overrightarrow{AP}$ in terms of **a** and **b**.

   b) Express $\overrightarrow{MA}$ and $\overrightarrow{MP}$ in terms of **a** and **b**.

   c) If X lies on OB produced such that OB = BX, express $\overrightarrow{MX}$ in terms of **a** and **b**.

   d) Show that MPX is a straight line.

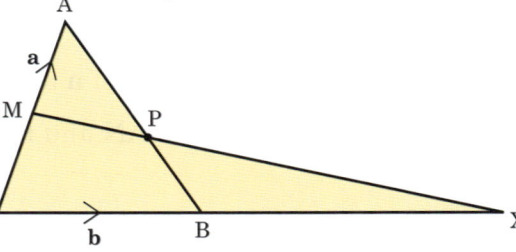

5. $\overrightarrow{OP} = \mathbf{a}$ $\overrightarrow{OA} = 3\mathbf{a}$ $\overrightarrow{OB} = \mathbf{b}$ M is the midpoint of AB.

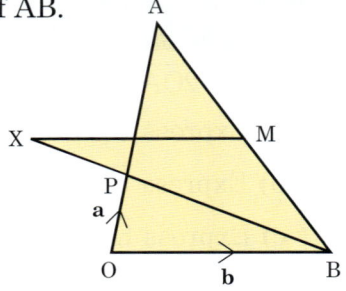

a) Express $\overrightarrow{BP}$ and $\overrightarrow{AB}$ in terms of $\mathbf{a}$ and $\mathbf{b}$.

b) Express $\overrightarrow{MB}$ in terms of $\mathbf{a}$ and $\mathbf{b}$.

c) If X lies on BP produced so that $\overrightarrow{BX} = k\overrightarrow{BP}$, express $\overrightarrow{MX}$ in terms of $\mathbf{a}$, $\mathbf{b}$ and k.

d) Find the value of k if MX is parallel to BO.

6. AC is parallel to OB

$$\overrightarrow{AX} = \frac{1}{4}\overrightarrow{AB} \qquad \overrightarrow{OA} = \mathbf{a} \qquad \overrightarrow{OB} = \mathbf{b} \qquad \overrightarrow{AC} = m\mathbf{b}$$

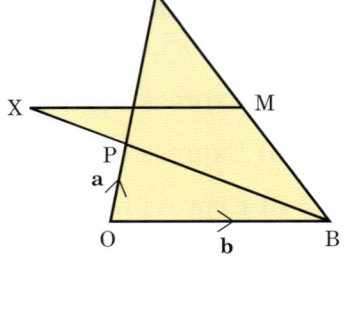

a) Express $\overrightarrow{AB}$ in terms of $\mathbf{a}$ and $\mathbf{b}$.

b) Express $\overrightarrow{AX}$ in terms of $\mathbf{a}$ and $\mathbf{b}$.

c) Express $\overrightarrow{BC}$ in terms of $\mathbf{a}$, $\mathbf{b}$ and m.

d) Given that OX is parallel to BC, find the value of m.

7. CY is parallel to OD

$$\overrightarrow{CX} = \frac{1}{5}\overrightarrow{CD} \qquad \overrightarrow{OC} = \mathbf{c} \qquad \overrightarrow{OD} = \mathbf{d} \qquad \overrightarrow{CY} = n\mathbf{d}$$

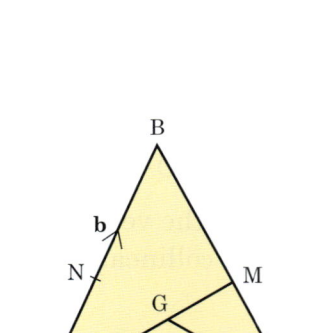

a) Express $\overrightarrow{CD}$ in terms of $\mathbf{c}$ and $\mathbf{d}$.

b) Express $\overrightarrow{CX}$ in terms of $\mathbf{c}$ and $\mathbf{d}$.

c) Express $\overrightarrow{OX}$ in terms of $\mathbf{c}$ and $\mathbf{d}$.

d) Express $\overrightarrow{DY}$ in terms of $\mathbf{c}$, $\mathbf{d}$ and n.

e) Given that OX is parallel to DY, find the value of n.

8. M is the midpoint of AB.

N is the midpoint of OB.

$$\overrightarrow{OA} = \mathbf{a} \qquad \overrightarrow{OB} = \mathbf{b}$$

a) Express $\overrightarrow{AB}$, $\overrightarrow{AM}$ and $\overrightarrow{OM}$ in terms of $\mathbf{a}$ and $\mathbf{b}$.

b) Given that G lies on OM such that OG:GM = 2:1, express $\overrightarrow{OG}$ in terms of $\mathbf{a}$ and $\mathbf{b}$.

c) Express $\overrightarrow{AG}$ in terms of $\mathbf{a}$ and $\mathbf{b}$.

d) Express $\overrightarrow{AN}$ in terms of $\mathbf{a}$ and $\mathbf{b}$.

e) Show that $\overrightarrow{AG} = m\overrightarrow{AN}$ and find the value of m.

9. M is the midpoint of AC and N is the midpoint of OB.

$$\overrightarrow{OA} = \mathbf{a} \qquad \overrightarrow{OB} = \mathbf{b} \qquad \overrightarrow{OC} = \mathbf{c}$$

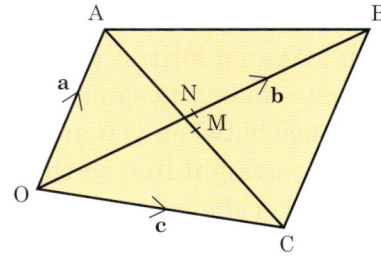

a) Express $\overrightarrow{AB}$ in terms of $\mathbf{a}$ and $\mathbf{b}$.

b) Express $\overrightarrow{ON}$ in terms of $\mathbf{b}$.

c) Express $\overrightarrow{AC}$ in terms of $\mathbf{a}$ and $\mathbf{c}$.

d) Express $\overrightarrow{AM}$ in terms of $\mathbf{a}$ and $\mathbf{c}$.

e) Express $\overrightarrow{OM}$ in terms of $\mathbf{a}$ and $\mathbf{c}$.

f) Express $\overrightarrow{NM}$ in terms of $\mathbf{a}$, $\mathbf{b}$ and $\mathbf{c}$.

g) If N and M coincide, write down an equation connecting $\mathbf{a}$, $\mathbf{b}$ and $\mathbf{c}$.

10. $\overrightarrow{OA} = \mathbf{a} \qquad \overrightarrow{OB} = \mathbf{b}$

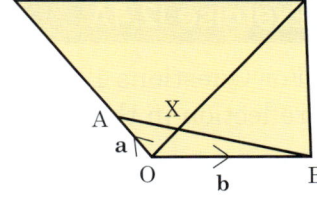

a) Express $\overrightarrow{BA}$ in terms of $\mathbf{a}$ and $\mathbf{b}$.

b) Given that $\overrightarrow{BX} = m\overrightarrow{BA}$, show that $\overrightarrow{OX} = m\mathbf{a} + (1 - m)\mathbf{b}$.

c) Given that $OP = 4\mathbf{a}$ and $\overrightarrow{PQ} = 2\mathbf{b}$, express $\overrightarrow{OQ}$ in terms of $\mathbf{a}$ and $\mathbf{b}$.

d) Given that $\overrightarrow{OX} = n\overrightarrow{OQ}$ use the results for $\overrightarrow{OX}$ and $\overrightarrow{OQ}$ to find the values of m and n.

11. X is the midpoint of OD, Y lies on CD such that:

$$\overrightarrow{CY} = \frac{1}{4}\overrightarrow{CD} \qquad \overrightarrow{OC} = \mathbf{c} \qquad \overrightarrow{OD} = \mathbf{d}$$

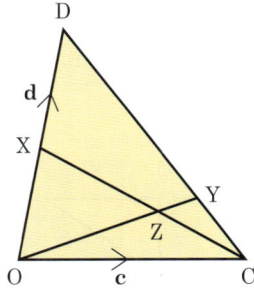

a) Express $\overrightarrow{CD}$, $\overrightarrow{CY}$ and $\overrightarrow{OY}$ in terms of $\mathbf{c}$ and $\mathbf{d}$.

b) Express $\overrightarrow{CX}$ in terms of $\mathbf{c}$ and $\mathbf{d}$.

c) Given that $\overrightarrow{CZ} = h\overrightarrow{CX}$, express $\overrightarrow{OZ}$ in terms of $\mathbf{c}$, $\mathbf{d}$ and h.

d) If $\overrightarrow{OZ} = k\overrightarrow{OY}$, form an equation and hence find the values of h and k.

12.4 Simple transformations

A transformation changes the size or position of a shape. You need to learn about four types of transformation: reflection, rotation, translation and enlargement.

Reflection

A mirror line acts very much like a real mirror. When you look in a mirror, you see your reflection, which appears to be the same distance behind the mirror as the distance between you and the mirror. A mirror line can be any straight line on the coordinate plane. An **object** (usually a shape) on one side of the mirror line will have an **image** on the other side of the line.

For all kinds of transformations, you say that an object **maps** onto its image.

$\triangle 2$ is the image of $\triangle 1$ after reflection in the x-axis.

$\triangle 3$ is the image of $\triangle 1$ after reflection in the line $y = x$.

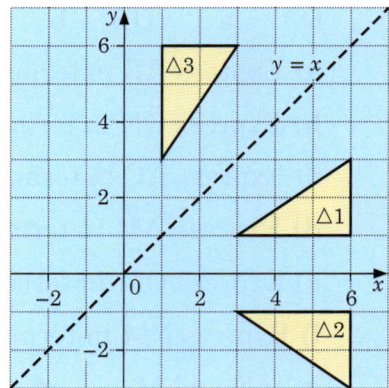

Exercise 12.4A

For Questions **1** to **6**, use squared paper to draw the object and its image after reflection in the mirror line.

1.

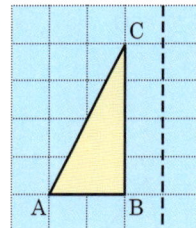

2.

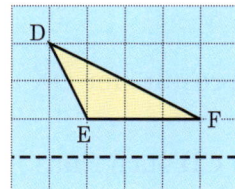

3.

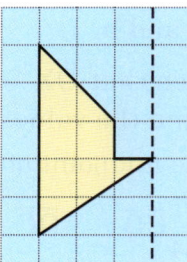

4.

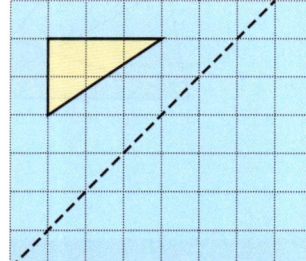

5.

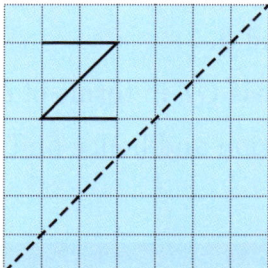

6.

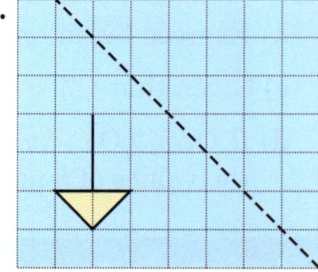

For Questions **7** to **12**, write down the equation of the line in which the shape has been reflected.

7.

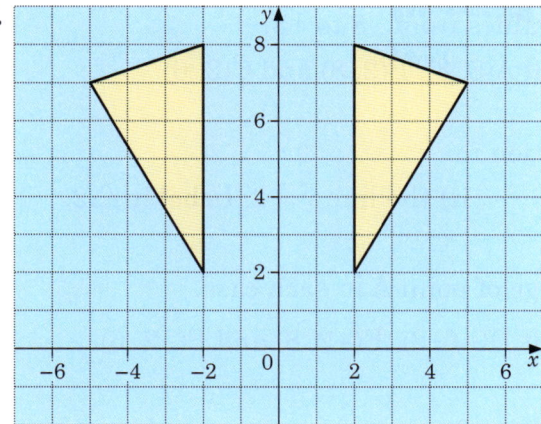

8.

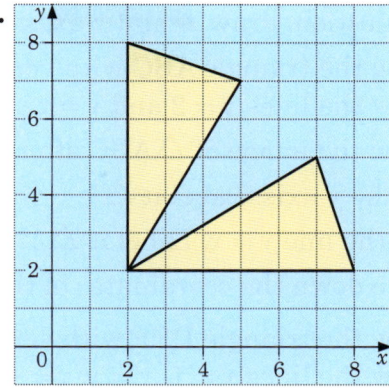

9.

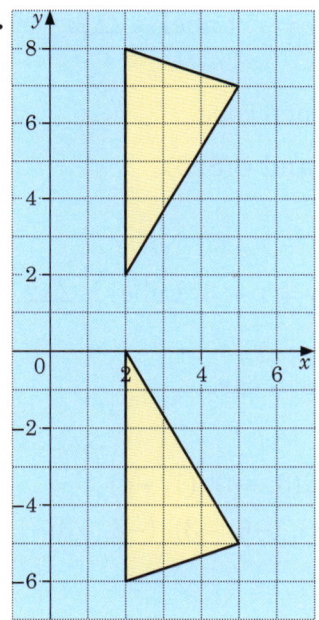

10.

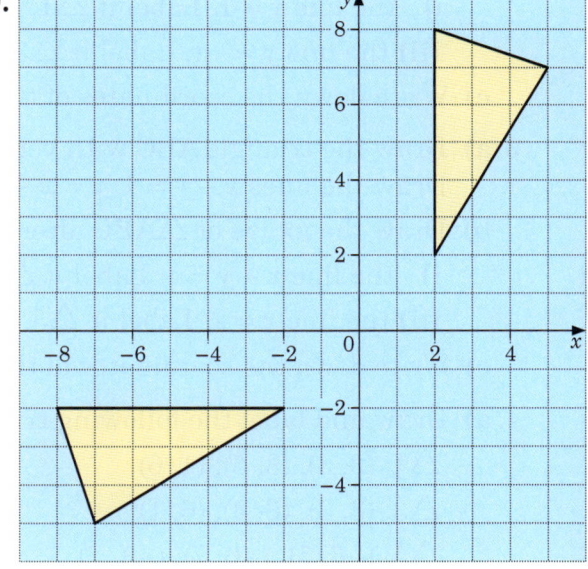

11.

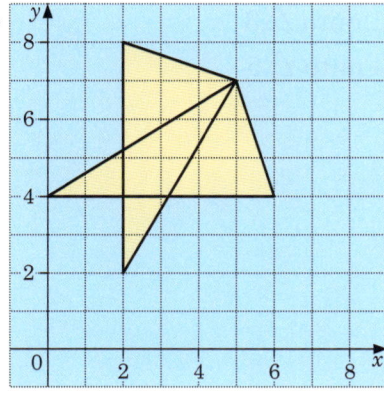

12.

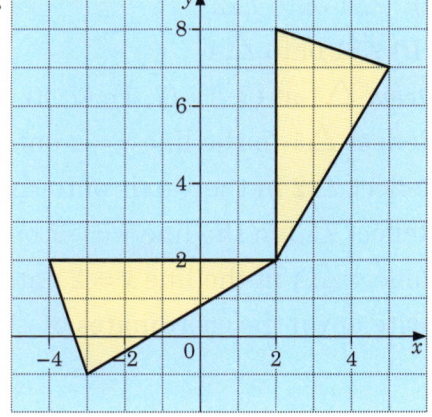

Exercise 12.4B

For each question, draw x- and y-axes with values from -8 to $+8$.

1. a) Draw the triangle ABC with vertices at A(6, 8), B(2, 8) and C(2, 6).
   Draw the lines $y = 2$ and $y = x$.

   b) Draw the image of $\triangle$ABC after reflection in:

   i) the y-axis. Label it $\triangle$1.   **ii)** the line $y = 2$. Label it $\triangle$2.

   iii) the line $y = x$. Label it $\triangle$3.

   c) Write down the coordinates of the image of point A in each case.

2. a) Draw the triangle DEF with vertices at D(−6, 8), E(−2, 8) and F(−2, 6).
   Draw the lines $x = 1$, $y = x$, $y = -x$.

   b) Draw the image of $\triangle$DEF after reflection in:

   i) the line $x = 1$. Label it $\triangle$1.   **ii)** the line $y = x$. Label it $\triangle$2.

   iii) the line $y = -x$. Label it $\triangle$3.

   c) Write down the coordinates of the image of point D in each case.

3. a) Draw the triangle ABC with vertices at A(5, 1), B(8, 1) and C(8, 3).
   Draw the lines $x + y = 4$, $y = x - 3$, $x = 2$.

   b) Draw the image of $\triangle$ABC after reflection in:

   i) the line $x + y = 4$. Label it $\triangle$1.   **ii)** the line $y = x - 3$. Label it $\triangle$2.

   iii) the line $x = 2$. Label it $\triangle$3.

   c) Write down the coordinates of the image of point A in each case.

4. a) Draw and label the following triangles:

   $\triangle$1: (3, 3), (3, 6), (1, 6) $\triangle$2: (3, −1), (3, −4), (1, −4)

   $\triangle$3: (3, 3), (6, 3), (6, 1) $\triangle$4: (−6, −1), (−6, −3), (−3, −3)

   $\triangle$5: (−6, 5), (−6, 7), (−3, 7)

   b) Find the equation of the mirror line for the reflection:

   i) $\triangle$1 onto $\triangle$2   **ii)** $\triangle$1 onto $\triangle$3

   iii) $\triangle$1 onto $\triangle$4   **iv)** $\triangle$4 onto $\triangle$5

5. a) Draw $\triangle$1 at (3, 1), (7, 1), (7, 3).

   b) Reflect $\triangle$1 in the line $y = x$ onto $\triangle$2.

   c) Reflect $\triangle$2 in the x-axis onto $\triangle$3.

   d) Reflect $\triangle$3 in the line $y = -x$ onto $\triangle$4.

   e) Reflect $\triangle$4 in the line $x = 2$ onto $\triangle$5.

   f) Write down the coordinates of $\triangle$5.

6. a) Draw △1 at (2, 6), (2, 8), (6, 6).

   b) Reflect △1 in the line $x + y = 6$ onto △2.

   c) Reflect △2 in the line $x = 3$ onto △3.

   d) Reflect △3 in the line $x + y = 6$ onto △4.

   e) Reflect △4 in the line $y = x - 8$ onto △5.

   f) Write down the coordinates of △5.

Rotation

In the diagram, the letter L, with endpoints X, Y and Z, has been rotated through 90° clockwise about the centre O, to give the image of L, with endpoints X′, Y′ and Z′.

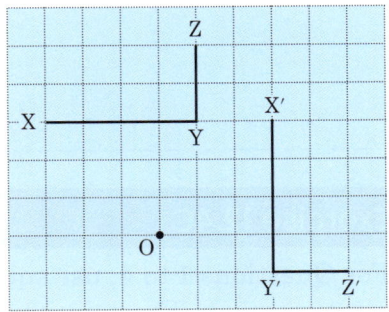

To fully describe a rotation, you need to state the angle, the direction (clockwise or anticlockwise), and the centre of rotation.

As well as saying that an object maps onto its image, you can say that individual points map onto their images. In this example, X maps onto X′, Y maps onto Y′ and Z maps onto Z′.

The centre of rotation is the part of the diagram around which the object rotates. Often, the best way to find the centre of rotation is to use tracing paper. Trace the original object onto the paper, place a sharp pencil where you think the centre of rotation might be, then rotate the paper to see if it moves onto the image. If it does not, move the centre of rotation slightly and try again until you succeed.

If this method fails, draw the perpendicular bisectors of the lines joining two pairs of corresponding points, for example X and X′, and Y and Y′. The centre of rotation is at the intersection of the two perpendicular bisectors.

Example

Rotate the blue L shape:

a) anticlockwise through 90° about centre (0, 1) and label the image (a).

b) clockwise through 90° about centre (0, 1) and label the image (b).

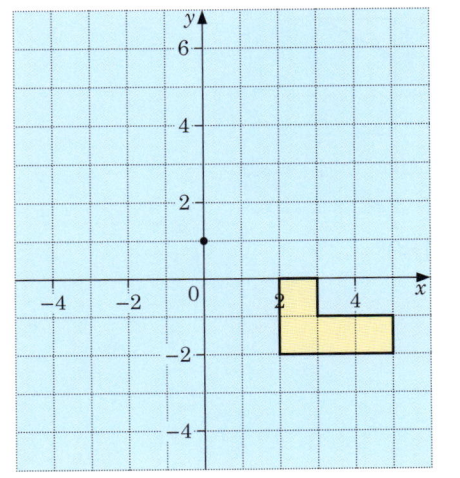

Trace the unlabelled L onto a piece of tracing paper.

Place a sharp pencil at the point (0, 1).

Rotate the shape 90° anticlockwise and draw the image, labelling it (a).

Rotate the unlabelled L shape 90° clockwise and draw the image, labelling it (b).

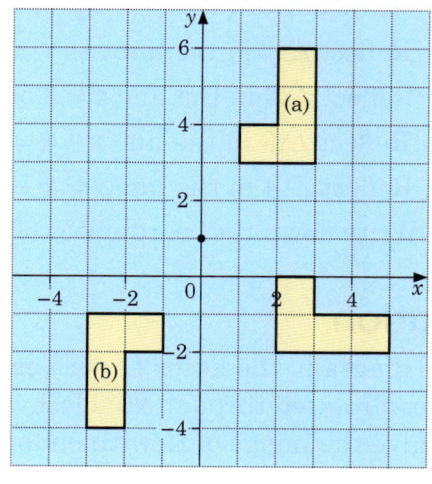

Exercise 12.4C

For Questions **1** to **4**, use squared paper to draw the object and its image under the rotation given. The point O is the centre of rotation in each case.

1.

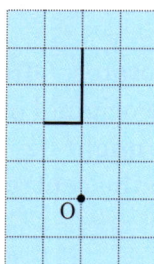

90° clockwise

2.

90° anticlockwise

3.

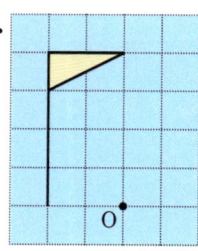

180°

4.

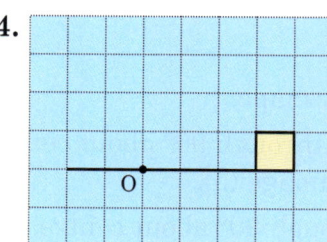

90° clockwise

For Questions **5** to **8**, copy the diagram on squared paper and find the angle, the direction, and the centre of the rotation.

5.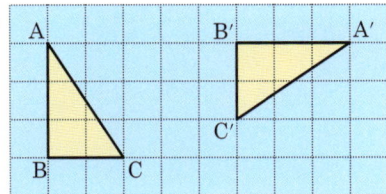

6.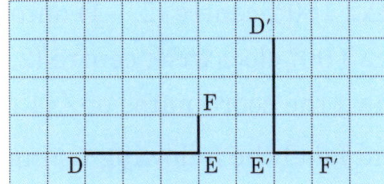

7.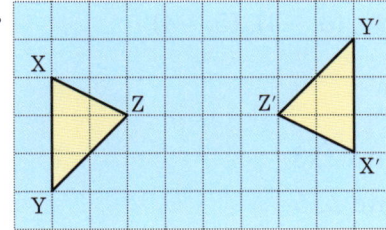

8.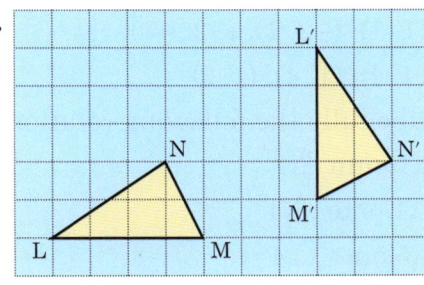

Exercise 12.4D

For all questions, draw x- and y-axes for values from -8 to $+8$.

1. **a)** Draw the object triangle ABC at A(1, 3), B(1, 6) and C(3, 6). Rotate ABC through 90° clockwise about (0, 0), mark A′B′C′.

   b) Draw the object triangle DEF at D(3, 3), E(6, 3) and F(6, 1). Rotate DEF through 90° clockwise about (0, 0), mark D′E′F′.

   c) Draw the object triangle PQR at P(−4, 7), Q(−4, 5) and R(−1, 5). Rotate PQR through 90° anticlockwise about (0, 0), mark P′Q′R′.

2. **a)** Draw △1 at (1, 4), (1, 7) and (3, 7).

   b) Draw the images of △1 under the following rotations:

   i) 90° clockwise, centre (0, 0). Label it △2.

   ii) 180°, centre (0, 0). Label it △3.

   iii) 90° anticlockwise, centre (0, 0). Label it △4.

3. **a)** Draw triangle PQR at P(1, 2), Q(3, 5) and R(6, 2).

   b) Find the image of PQR under the following rotations:

   i) 90° anticlockwise, centre (0, 0); label the image P′Q′R′

   ii) 90° clockwise, centre (−2, 2); label the image P″Q″R″

   iii) 180°, centre (1, 0); label the image P*Q*R*.

   c) Write down the coordinates of P′, P″, P*.

4. a) Draw $\triangle 1$ at (1, 2), (1, 6) and (3, 5).

  b) Rotate $\triangle 1$ 90° clockwise, centre (1, 2) onto $\triangle 2$.

  c) Rotate $\triangle 2$ 180°, centre (2, −1) onto $\triangle 3$.

  d) Rotate $\triangle 3$ 90° clockwise, centre (2, 3) onto $\triangle 4$.

  e) Write down the coordinates of $\triangle 4$.

5. a) Draw and label the following triangles:

  $\triangle 1$: (3, 1), (6, 1), (6, 3) $\triangle 2$: (−1, 3), (−1, 6), (−3, 6)

  $\triangle 3$: (1, 1), (−2, 1), (−2, −1) $\triangle 4$: (3, −1), (3, −4), (5, −4)

  $\triangle 5$: (4, 4), (1, 4), (1, 2)

  b) Describe fully the following rotations:

  i) $\triangle 1$ onto $\triangle 2$ **ii)** $\triangle 1$ onto $\triangle 3$

  iii) $\triangle 1$ onto $\triangle 4$ **iv)** $\triangle 1$ onto $\triangle 5$

  v) $\triangle 5$ onto $\triangle 4$ **vi)** $\triangle 3$ onto $\triangle 2$

6. a) Draw $\triangle 1$ at (4, 7), (8, 5) and (8, 7).

  b) Rotate $\triangle 1$ 90° clockwise, centre (4, 3) onto $\triangle 2$.

  c) Rotate $\triangle 2$ 180°, centre (5, −1) onto $\triangle 3$.

  d) Rotate $\triangle 3$ 90° anticlockwise, centre (0, −8) onto $\triangle 4$.

  e) Describe fully the following rotations:

  i) $\triangle 4$ onto $\triangle 1$ **ii)** $\triangle 4$ onto $\triangle 2$

Translation

A **translation** is a transformation that moves every point of an object by the same distance in a given direction.

The triangle ABC has been transformed onto the triangle A′B′C′ by a translation.

Here the translation is 7 squares to the right and 2 squares up. Translations can be described using a column vector.

In this case, the translation is $\begin{pmatrix} 7 \\ 2 \end{pmatrix}$.

The top number in the vector represents how far left or right the object has moved. Positive numbers represent a movement to the right, and negative numbers represent a movement to the left.

The bottom number in the vector represents how far up or down the object has moved. Positive numbers represent a movement upward, and negative numbers represent a movement downward.

Exercise 12.4E

1. Make a copy of the diagram below and write down the column vector for each of the following translations:

   a) D onto A   **b)** B onto F   **c)** E onto A   **d)** A onto C

   e) E onto C   **f)** C onto B   **g)** F onto E   **h)** B onto C.

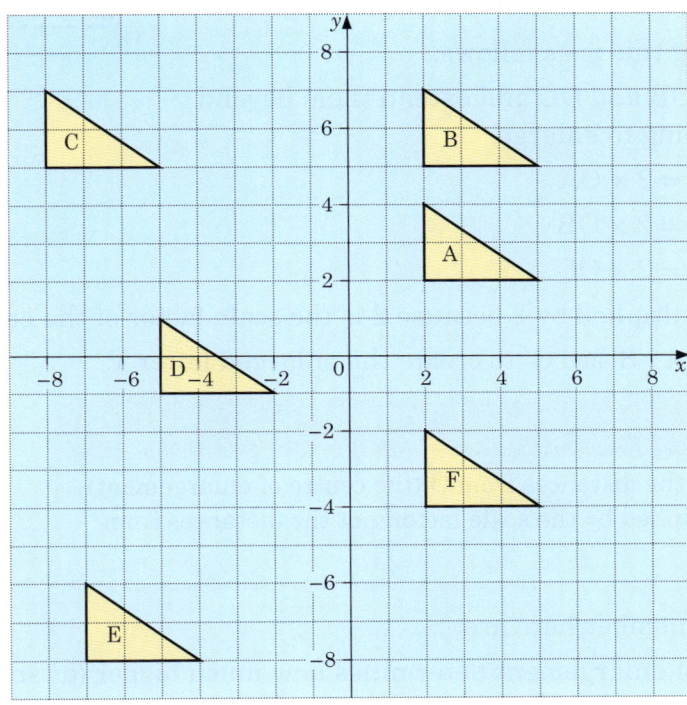

For Questions **2** to **11**, draw x- and y-axes with values from -8 to $+8$.
Draw object triangle ABC at A$(-4, -1)$, B$(-4, 1)$ and C$(-1, -1)$, and shade it.

Draw the image of ABC under the translations described by the vectors. For each question, write down the new coordinates of point C.

2. $\begin{pmatrix} 6 \\ 3 \end{pmatrix}$ 3. $\begin{pmatrix} 6 \\ 7 \end{pmatrix}$ 4. $\begin{pmatrix} 9 \\ -4 \end{pmatrix}$ 5. $\begin{pmatrix} 1 \\ 7 \end{pmatrix}$

6. $\begin{pmatrix} 5 \\ -6 \end{pmatrix}$ 7. $\begin{pmatrix} -2 \\ 5 \end{pmatrix}$ 8. $\begin{pmatrix} -2 \\ -4 \end{pmatrix}$ 9. $\begin{pmatrix} 0 \\ -7 \end{pmatrix}$

10. $\begin{pmatrix} 3 \\ 1 \end{pmatrix}$ followed by $\begin{pmatrix} 3 \\ 2 \end{pmatrix}$ 11. $\begin{pmatrix} -2 \\ 0 \end{pmatrix}$ followed by $\begin{pmatrix} 0 \\ 3 \end{pmatrix}$ followed by $\begin{pmatrix} 1 \\ -1 \end{pmatrix}$

Enlargement

An **enlargement** is a type of transformation that takes an object and creates an image using a scale factor and a centre of enlargement.

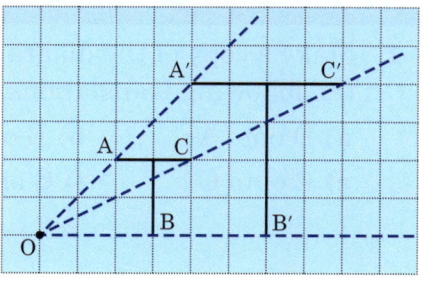

In this diagram, the letter T has been enlarged by a scale factor of 2 using the point O as the centre of the enlargement.

The method for doing this is as follows:

Draw the lines OA, OB and OC and extend them beyond the object you are going to enlarge.

Mark A′ so that OA′ = 2 × OA

Mark B′ so that OB′ = 2 × OB

Mark C′ so that OC′ = 2 × OC

The distances are multiplied by 2 because 2 is the scale factor of the enlargement.

Then join the points A′, B′ and C′ to create the enlarged letter T.

> ### Tip
> Remember that it is the distances from O (the centre of enlargement) that have been multiplied by the scale factor, not the distances from A, B and C.

General points to remember here are:

- The scale factor of enlargement determines how much bigger (or smaller) than the original object the image will be.

- The centre of enlargement determines where, relative to the original object, the image will be located.

When the image is smaller than the original object, it is still called an enlargement. Here the size of the scale factor will be a number strictly between 0 and 1.

Example 1

Draw the image of triangle ABC after an enlargement with a scale factor of $\frac{1}{2}$ using O as centre of enlargement.

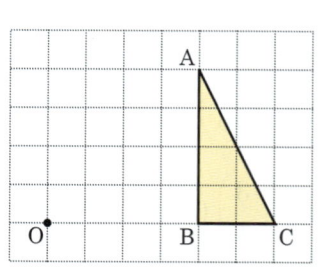

Draw the lines OA, OB and OC.

Mark A′ so that $OA' = \frac{1}{2}OA$

Mark B′ so that $OB' = \frac{1}{2}OB$

Mark C′ so that $OC' = \frac{1}{2}OC$

Join A′B′C′ as shown.

Note that because the scale factor is between 0 and 1, the image lies between the original object and the centre of enlargement.

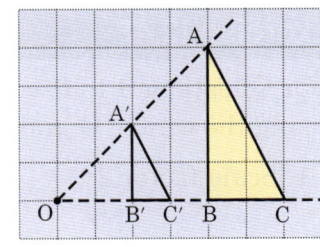

When the scale factor of enlargement is a negative number, the image is on the other side of the centre of enlargement.

Example 2

Draw the image of triangle PQR under an enlargement with a scale factor of −2 using O as centre of enlargement.

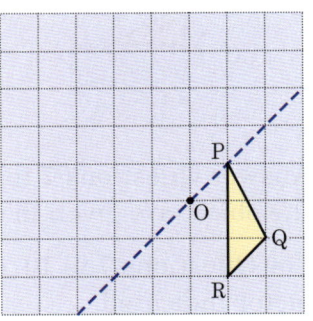

Draw the lines OP, OQ and OR, and extend them backwards through the centre of enlargement.

Mark P′ so that OP′ is on the other side of the centre of enlargement and OP′ = 2OP

Do the same thing with OQ and OR.

Join P′, Q′ and R′ to form a triangle.

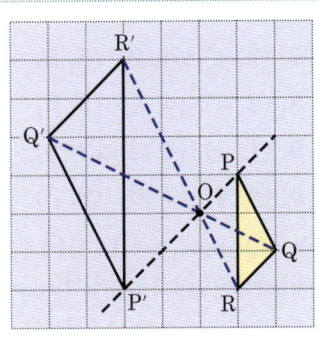

To find the centre of enlargement, join corresponding vertices with straight lines.

Extend the lines until they meet at a point.

To find the scale factor, work out $\dfrac{\text{length of image}}{\text{corresponding length of object}}$.

Exercise 12.4F

For Questions **1** to **6**, copy the diagram on squared paper and draw an enlargement using the centre O and the scale factor given.

1. Scale factor 2

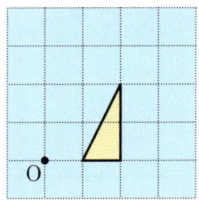

2. Scale factor 3

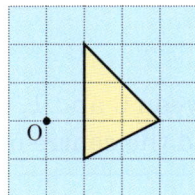

3. Scale factor 3

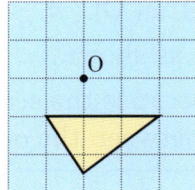

4. Scale factor −2

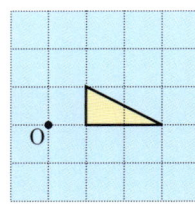

5. Scale factor −3

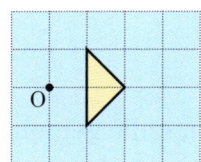

6. Scale factor $1\frac{1}{2}$

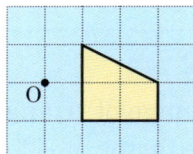

Answer Questions **7** to **19** on graph paper taking x and y from 0 to 15. The vertices of the object are given in coordinate form.

For Questions **7** to **10**, enlarge the object with the centre of enlargement and scale factor indicated.

	Object	Centre	Scale factor
7.	(2, 4), (4, 2), (5, 5)	(0, 0)	+2
8.	(2, 4), (4, 2), (5, 5)	(1, 2)	+2
9.	(1, 1), (4, 2), (2, 3)	(1, 1)	+3
10.	(4, 4), (7, 6), (9, 3)	(7, 4)	+2

For Questions **11** to **14**, plot the object and its image, and then find the centre of enlargement and the scale factor.

11. Object A(2, 1), B(5, 1), C(3, 3)

Image A′(2, 1), B′(11, 1), C′(5, 7)

12. Object A(2, 5), B(9, 3), C(5, 9)

Image A′$\left(6\frac{1}{2}, 7 \right)$, B′(10, 6), C′(8, 9)

13. Object A(2, 2), B(4, 4), C(2, 6)

Image A′(11, 8), B′(7, 4), C′(11, 0)

14. Object A(0, 6), B(4, 6), C(3, 0)

Image A′(12, 6), B′(8, 6), C′(9, 12)

For Questions **15** to **19**, enlarge the object using the centre of enlargement and scale factor indicated.

Object	Centre	Scale factor
15. (1, 2), (13, 2), (1, 10)	(0, 0)	$+\dfrac{1}{2}$
16. (5, 10), (5, 7), (11, 7)	(2, 1)	$+\dfrac{1}{3}$
17. (7, 3), (9, 3), (7, 8)	(5, 5)	-1
18. (1, 1), (3, 1), (3, 2)	(4, 3)	-2
19. (9, 2), (14, 2), (14, 6)	(7, 4)	$-\dfrac{1}{2}$

The next exercise contains questions involving the four basic transformations: reflection, rotation, translation, enlargement.

Exercise 12.4G

1. Refer to the diagram to fully describe the following transformations.

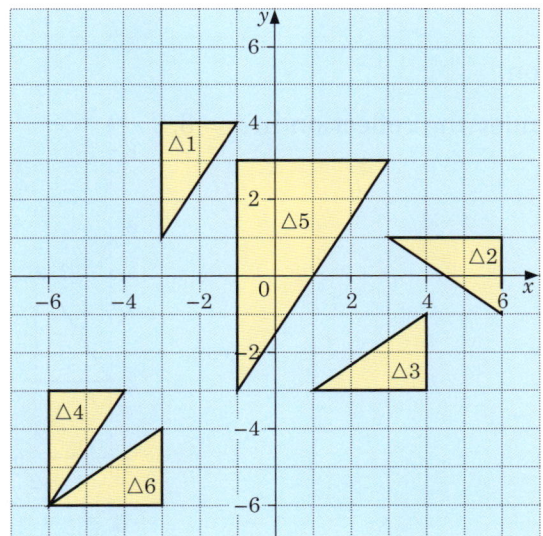

    a) △1 → △2   **b)** △1 → △3   **c)** △4 → △1

    d) △1 → △5   **e)** △3 → △6   **f)** △6 → △4

2. On squared paper, plot and label the following triangles.

    △1: (−5, −5), (−1, −5), (−1, −3)   △2: (1, 7), (1, 3), (3, 3)

    △3: (3, −3), (7, −3), (7, −1)   △4: (−5, −5), (−5, −1), (−3, −1)

    △5: (1, −6), (3, −6), (3, −5)   △6: (−3, 3), (−3, 7), (−5, 7)

    Describe fully the following transformations.

    a) △1 → △2   **b)** △1 → △3   **c)** △1 → △4   **d)** △1 → △5

    e) △1 → △6   **f)** △5 → △3   **g)** △2 → △3

3. On squared paper, plot and label the following triangles.

△1: (−3, −6), (−3, −2), (−5, −2)   △2: (−5, −1), (−5, −7), (−8, −1)

△3: (−2, −1), (2, −1), (2, 1)   △4: (6, 3), (2, 3), (2, 5)

△5: (8, 4), (8, 8), (6, 8)   △6: (−3, 1), (−3, 3), (−4, 3)

Describe fully the following transformations.

a) △1 → △2   b) △1 → △3   c) △1 → △4   d) △1 → △5

e) △1 → △6   f) △3 → △5   g) △6 → △2

12.5 Combined transformations

Sometimes you will be required to perform one transformation followed by another.

Example

Reflect the triangle with vertices at (0, 2), (2, 2) and (2, 5) in the line $x = 3$,

and then translate it by the vector $\begin{pmatrix} 2 \\ 1 \end{pmatrix}$.

First perform the reflection.

△2 is the image of △1 under the reflection in $x = 3$.

Then translate △2 by the vector $\begin{pmatrix} 2 \\ 1 \end{pmatrix}$.

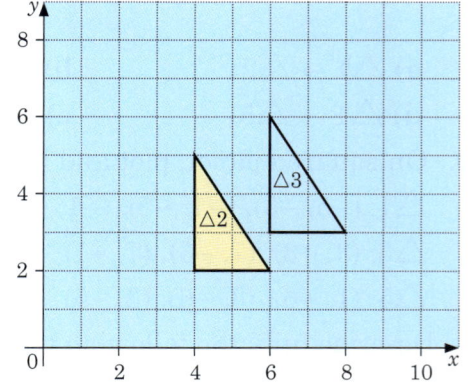

Exercise 12.5A

1. Draw x- and y-axes with values from -8 to $+8$ and plot the point P(3, 2).
   Write down the coordinates of the final image of P if it is:
   a) rotated 90° clockwise about (0, 0), then translated by the vector $\begin{pmatrix} 3 \\ 2 \end{pmatrix}$
   b) translated by the vector $\begin{pmatrix} 3 \\ 2 \end{pmatrix}$, then rotated 90° clockwise about (0, 0)
   c) rotated 180° clockwise about (0, 0), then translated by the vector $\begin{pmatrix} 3 \\ 2 \end{pmatrix}$
   d) translated by the vector $\begin{pmatrix} 3 \\ 2 \end{pmatrix}$, then reflected in the line $x = 0$
   e) reflected in the line $x = 0$, then rotated 180° clockwise about (0, 0)
   f) reflected in the line $x = 0$, then reflected again in the line $x = 0$
   g) reflected in the line $y = x$, then translated by the vector $\begin{pmatrix} 1 \\ 3 \end{pmatrix}$
   h) rotated 90° clockwise about (0, 0), then reflected in the line $y = x$
   i) reflected in the line $y = 0$, then reflected in the line $y = x$
   j) rotated 90° anticlockwise about (0, 0), then translated by the vector $\begin{pmatrix} -2 \\ -1 \end{pmatrix}$
   k) reflected in the line $y = x$, then reflected in the line $y = -x$
   l) translated by the vector $\begin{pmatrix} 4 \\ 4 \end{pmatrix}$, then reflected in the line $y = 1$
   m) reflected in the line $y = 3$, then reflected in the line $x = 2$
   n) reflected in the line $x = 3$, then translated by the vector $\begin{pmatrix} -10 \\ -5 \end{pmatrix}$
   o) reflected in the line $y = x - 2$, then rotated 180° anticlockwise about (0, 0).

Exercise 12.5B

Draw x- and y-axes with values from -8 to $+8$.

1. Draw triangle LMN at L(2, 2), M(6, 2), N(6, 4).

   Find the image of LMN under the following combinations of transformations.
   Write down the coordinates of the image of point L in each case:
   a) reflection in the line $x = 2$, then a translation by $\begin{pmatrix} -6 \\ 2 \end{pmatrix}$
   b) reflection in the line $y = x$, then a reflection in the line $y = 0$
   c) rotation 180° clockwise, centre (1, 1), then a reflection in the line $y = x$
   d) reflection in $y = 0$, then a rotation 180° anticlockwise, centre (1, 1)
   e) rotation 180° clockwise, centre (1, 1), then a reflection in the line $y = 0$.

2. Draw triangle PQR at P(2, 2), Q(6, 2) and R(6, 4). Find the image of PQR under the following combinations of transformations. Write down the coordinates of the image of point P in each case:

a) translation by $\begin{pmatrix} 4 \\ 3 \end{pmatrix}$, then a reflection in the line $x = 2$

b) rotation 90° clockwise, centre (0, 0), then a translation by $\begin{pmatrix} -6 \\ 2 \end{pmatrix}$

c) rotation 90° clockwise, centre (0, 0), then a reflection in the line $x = 2$

d) reflection in the line $y = 0$, then an enlargement, scale factor $+\dfrac{1}{2}$, centre (0, 0).

3. Draw triangle XYZ at X(−2, 4), Y(−2, 1) and Z(−4, 1). Find the image of XYZ under the following combinations of transformations and state the equivalent single transformation in each case:

a) reflection in $y = 0$, then a 90° rotation clockwise, centre (0, 0), then another 90° rotation clockwise, centre (0, 0)

b) 180° rotation, centre (1, 1), then a translation $\begin{pmatrix} -6 \\ 2 \end{pmatrix}$

c) reflection in $x = 2$, then a reflection in $y = x$.

4. Draw triangle OPQ at O(0, 0), P(0, 2) and Q(3, 2).

Find the image of OPQ under the following combinations of transformations and state the equivalent single transformation in each case:

a) reflection in the line $y = 0$, then a reflection in the line $y = x$

b) translation by $\begin{pmatrix} -6 \\ 2 \end{pmatrix}$, then a translation by $\begin{pmatrix} 4 \\ 3 \end{pmatrix}$

c) translation by $\begin{pmatrix} -6 \\ 2 \end{pmatrix}$, then a reflection in the line $y = 0$, then a reflection in the line $y = x$

d) reflection in the line $y = 0$, then a translation by $\begin{pmatrix} 4 \\ 3 \end{pmatrix}$, then a reflection in the line $y = x$.

5. Draw triangle RST at R(−4, −1), S$\left(-2\dfrac{1}{2}, -2 \right)$ and T(−4, −4). Find the image of RST under the following combinations of transformations and state the equivalent single transformation in each case:

a) rotation 90° clockwise, centre (0, 0), then a reflection in the line $x = 2$, then a reflection in the line $y = 0$

b) enlargement, scale factor $\dfrac{1}{2}$, centre (0, 0), then a translation by $\begin{pmatrix} 4 \\ 3 \end{pmatrix}$

c) translation by $\begin{pmatrix} 4 \\ 3 \end{pmatrix}$, then a rotation 90° clockwise, centre (0, 0).

Revision exercise 12

1. In $\triangle$OPR, the midpoint of PR is M.

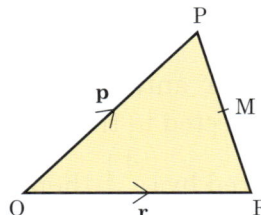

If $\overrightarrow{OP} = \mathbf{p}$ and $\overrightarrow{OR} = \mathbf{r}$,
find in terms of $\mathbf{p}$ and $\mathbf{r}$:

a) $\overrightarrow{PR}$ **b)** $\overrightarrow{PM}$ **c)** $\overrightarrow{OM}$

2. If $\mathbf{a} = \begin{pmatrix} 1 \\ 4 \end{pmatrix}$ and $\mathbf{b} = \begin{pmatrix} -3 \\ 4 \end{pmatrix}$, find:

a) $|\mathbf{b}|$ **b)** $|\mathbf{a} + \mathbf{b}|$ **c)** $|2\mathbf{a} - \mathbf{b}|$

3. If $4\begin{pmatrix} 1 \\ 3 \end{pmatrix} + 2\begin{pmatrix} 1 \\ m \end{pmatrix} = 3\begin{pmatrix} n \\ -6 \end{pmatrix}$ find the values of m and n.

4. The points O, A and B have coordinates
(0, 0), (5, 0) and (−1, 4) respectively.
Write as column vectors:

a) $\overrightarrow{OB}$ **b)** $\overrightarrow{OA} + \overrightarrow{OB}$ **c)** $\overrightarrow{OA} - \overrightarrow{OB}$

d) $\overrightarrow{OM}$ where M is the midpoint of AB.

5. In the parallelogram OABC, M is the
midpoint of AB and N is the midpoint
of BC.
If $\overrightarrow{OA} = \mathbf{a}$ and $\overrightarrow{OC} = \mathbf{c}$,
express in terms of $\mathbf{a}$ and $\mathbf{c}$:

a) $\overrightarrow{CA}$ **b)** $\overrightarrow{ON}$ **c)** $\overrightarrow{NM}$

Describe the relationship between
CA and NM.

6. The vectors $\mathbf{a}$, $\mathbf{b}$ and $\mathbf{c}$ are:

$$\mathbf{a} = \begin{pmatrix} 1 \\ 5 \end{pmatrix}, \mathbf{b} = \begin{pmatrix} -2 \\ 1 \end{pmatrix} \text{ and } \mathbf{c} = \begin{pmatrix} -1 \\ 17 \end{pmatrix}$$

Find numbers m and n so that $m\mathbf{a} + n\mathbf{b} = \mathbf{c}$.

7. Given that $\overrightarrow{OP} = \begin{pmatrix} 3 \\ 2 \end{pmatrix}$, $\overrightarrow{OQ} = \begin{pmatrix} 0 \\ 4 \end{pmatrix}$ and
that M is the midpoint of PQ, express
as column vectors:

a) $\overrightarrow{PQ}$ **b)** $\overrightarrow{PM}$ **c)** $\overrightarrow{OM}$

8. Find the coordinates of the image of
(1, 4) under:

a) a clockwise rotation of 90° about (0, 0)

b) a reflection in the line $y = x$

c) a translation which maps (5, 3)
onto (1, 1).

9. Draw x- and y-axes with values from
−8 to +8. Draw triangle ABC with
vertices at A(1, −1), B(3, −1) and
C(1, −4). Find the image of ABC under
the following enlargements:

a) scale factor 2, centre (5, −1)

b) scale factor 2, centre (0, 0)

c) scale factor $\dfrac{1}{2}$, centre (1, 3)

d) scale factor $-\dfrac{1}{2}$, centre (3, 1)

e) scale factor −2, centre (0, 0).

10. Using the diagram, describe the transformations for the following:

a) $T_1 \to T_6$ **b)** $T_4 \to T_5$

c) $T_8 \to T_2$ **d)** $T_4 \to T_1$

e) $T_8 \to T_4$ **f)** $T_6 \to T_8$

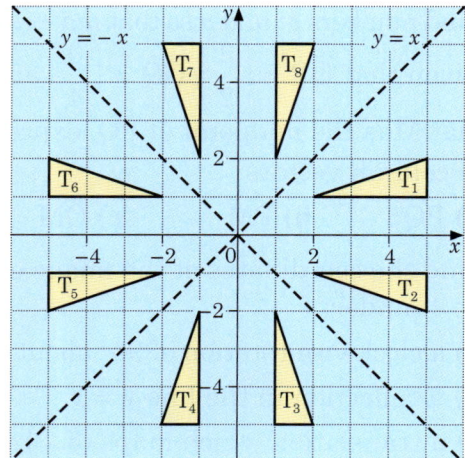

11. Describe the single transformation which maps:

a) $\triangle ABC$ onto $\triangle DEF$

b) $\triangle ABC$ onto $\triangle PQR$

c) $\triangle ABC$ onto $\triangle XYZ$

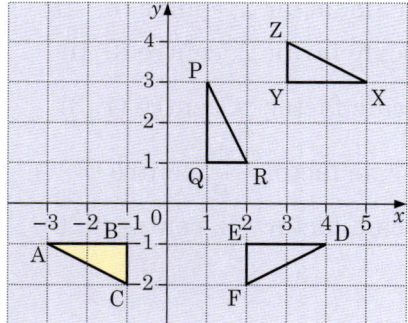

12. Find the image of the point $(3, 1)$ if it is:

a) reflected in the line $x + y = 0$

b) rotated 90° anticlockwise about $(0, 0)$

c) translated by $\begin{pmatrix} 3 \\ 1 \end{pmatrix}$

d) rotated 90° anticlockwise about $(0, 0)$, then reflected in the line $x + y = 0$

e) translated by $\begin{pmatrix} 3 \\ 1 \end{pmatrix}$, then rotated 90° anticlockwise about $(0, 0)$

f) rotated 90° anticlockwise about $(0, 0)$, then reflected in the line $x + y = 0$, then translated by $\begin{pmatrix} 3 \\ 1 \end{pmatrix}$.

Examination-style exercise 12

NON-CALCULATOR

1.

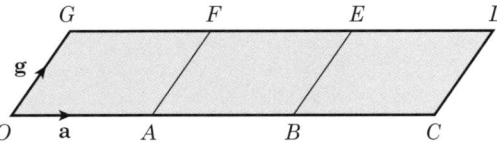

The diagram is made from three identical parallelograms.

O is the origin. $\overrightarrow{OA} = \mathbf{a}$ and $\overrightarrow{OG} = \mathbf{g}$.

Write down in terms of $\mathbf{a}$ and $\mathbf{g}$

a) $\overrightarrow{AD}$ [1]

b) the position vector of the centre of the parallelogram $ABEF$. [1]

2.

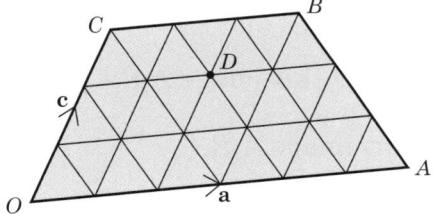

O is the origin. $\overrightarrow{OA} = \mathbf{a}$ and $\overrightarrow{OC} = \mathbf{c}$.

a) D has position vector $\dfrac{1}{3}\,\mathbf{a} + \dfrac{2}{3}\,\mathbf{c}$

  Mark the point D on the diagram. [1]

b) Write down, in terms of $\mathbf{a}$ and $\mathbf{c}$, the position vector of the point B. [1]

c) Work out, in terms of $\mathbf{a}$ and $\mathbf{c}$, the vector $\overrightarrow{DB}$. [2]

3.

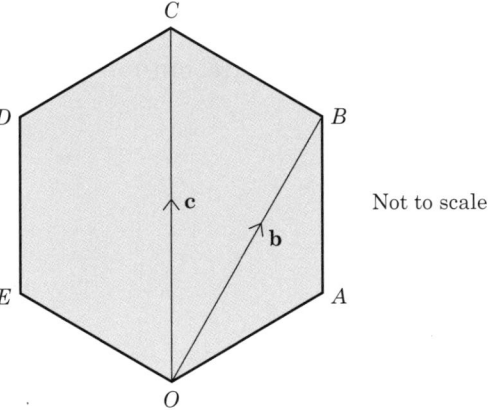

Not to scale

$OABCDE$ is a regular hexagon.

With O as origin the position vector of C is $\mathbf{c}$ and the position vector of B is $\mathbf{b}$.

a) Work out, in terms of $\mathbf{b}$ and $\mathbf{c}$,

  i) $\overrightarrow{BC}$ [1]

     ii) $\overrightarrow{OA}$ [2]

     iii) the position vector of D. [2]

  b) The sides of the hexagon are each of length 10 cm.

     Calculate:

     i)   the size of angle OAB [2]

     ii) the area of triangle OAB [2]

     iii) the length of the straight line OB [2]

     iv) the area of the hexagon. [2]

4. Answer the whole of this question on one sheet of graph paper.

  a) Draw and label x- and y-axes from -8 to $+8$, using a scale of 1 cm to 1 unit on each axis. [1]

  b) Draw and label triangle ABC with $A(2, 1)$, $B(4, 1)$ and $C(4, 3)$. [1]

  c) On your grid:

     i)   translate triangle ABC by the vector $\begin{pmatrix} 2 \\ -5 \end{pmatrix}$ and label this image $A_1B_1C_1$ [2]

     ii) reflect triangle ABC in the line $x = 3$ and label this image $A_2B_2C_2$ [2]

     iii) rotate triangle ABC 90° clockwise about $(0, 0)$ and label this image $A_3B_3C_3$. [2]

5. Answer the whole of this question on a sheet of graph paper.

  a) Draw and label x- and y-axes from -6 to 6, using a scale of 1 cm to 1 unit. [1]

  b) Draw triangle ABC with $A(1, 1)$, $B(2, 2)$ and $C(2, 5)$. [1]

  c) Draw the reflection of triangle ABC in the line $y = -x$. Label this $A_1B_1C_1$. [2]

  d) Rotate triangle $A_1B_1C_1$ about $(0, 0)$ through 90° clockwise. Label this $A_2B_2C_2$. [2]

  e) Describe fully the single transformation which maps triangle ABC onto triangle $A_2B_2C_2$. [2]

13 Statistics

Florence Nightingale (1820–1910) was a nurse during the Crimean War, which took place between 1853 and 1856. She is generally considered to have founded the modern nursing profession, by establishing her own nursing school at St Thomas' Hospital in London in 1860. She was also a gifted mathematician, and used statistical diagrams to illustrate the conditions that existed in the hospitals where she worked. Although she did not invent the pie chart, she popularised its use, along with other diagrams such as the rose diagram, which is like a circular histogram. In 1859, she was elected the first female member of the Royal Statistical Society.

- Use tables of statistical data.
- Read, interpret, draw inferences from and compare data using tables, graphs and statistical diagrams and measures including an appreciation of limits on any conclusions made.
- Find the mean, median, mode, quartiles, range and interquartile range and choose the most appropriate statistical measures. Calculate an estimate of the mean and find the modal class from grouped data.
- Draw and interpret the following statistical diagrams including: bar charts, pie charts, pictograms, stem-and-leaf diagrams, and simple frequency distributions.
- scatter diagrams (including understanding correlation and drawing a line of best fit)
- histograms (including understanding and using frequency density).
- cumulative frequency diagrams (including the mean, percentiles, quartiles and interquartile range).

13.1 Pictograms, bar charts and pie charts

Pictograms

A pictogram is a way to show numerical data using pictures or symbols. Each picture or symbol represents a certain number of items.

The number of items being represented in each row of the pictogram is called the **frequency**. You represent the frequency by repeating the picture or symbol the appropriate number of times.

Every pictogram will have a **key** that tells you how many items each picture or symbol represents.

For example, this pictogram shows how many pizzas were sold on four days.

The key says that one full circle represents 4 pizzas. Thus, half a circle represents 2 pizzas, and a quarter circle represents 1 pizza. So, you can see that:

12 pizzas were sold on Monday

10 pizzas were sold on Tuesday

 8 pizzas were sold on Wednesday

17 pizzas were sold on Thursday.

The main disadvantage of a pictogram is showing fractions of the symbol which can sometimes only be approximate.

Mon	○ ○ ○
Tues	○ ○ ◖
Wed	○ ○
Thur	○ ○ ○ ○ ◿

Key: ○ represents 4 pizzas

Exercise 13.1A

1. The pictogram shows the money spent at a school café by four students.

Reena	$ $
Sharon	$ $ $ $
Tim	$ $
June	$ $ $

   Key: $ represents $1

   a) Who spent the most money?

   b) How much was spent altogether?

   c) How could you show that someone spent 50 cents?

2. The pictogram shows the make of cars in a car park.

   a) How many cars does the 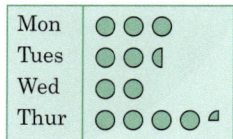 symbol represent?

   b) Copy and complete the pictogram.

Make	Number of cars	
Ford	4	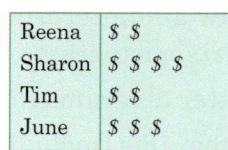
Renault		
Toyota	6	
Audi		

3. Charlotte started creating this pictogram but did not have time to finish it. The pictogram shows the number of library books borrowed at her school during one week.

Mon	◯ ◯ ◔
Tues	◯ ◔
Wed	◯ ◯ ◔
Thur	
Fri	
Sat	

   Key: ◯ = _____

   From Monday to Wednesday, a total of 78 library books were borrowed.

   15 books were borrowed on Thursday.

   24 books were borrowed on Friday.

   A total of 150 books were borrowed over the six days.

   Use the information to complete Charlotte's pictogram.

4. The frequency table shows the number of letters posted to six houses one morning. Draw a pictogram to represent the data.

House 1	House 2	House 3	House 4	House 5	House 6
5	3	2	7	1	4

Tally charts

Data needs to be collected before it can be displayed. One way of collecting data is by making a tally chart.

In a tally chart, items of data are represented by tally marks which are put into groups of five to make them easier to count.

Example 1

The marks obtained by 36 students in a test were as follows.

1	3	2	3	4	2	1	3	0
5	3	0	1	4	0	4	4	3
3	4	3	1	3	4	3	1	2
1	3	4	0	4	3	2	5	3

Show the data in a tally chart.

Create a table to organise the raw data. Each mark in the Tally column represents one person. The Frequency column shows the number of tally marks. As there were marks for 36 students in this data set, the total in the Frequency column should be 36.

Mark	Tally	Frequency
0	||||	4
1	卌 |	6
2	||||	4
3	卌 卌 ||	12
4	卌 |||	8
5	||	2
	Total:	36

Bar charts

The data from Example 1 can be presented in a bar chart where the height of each bar represents the frequency. The width of each bar has no significance. Each bar should be labelled and there should be gaps between the bars.

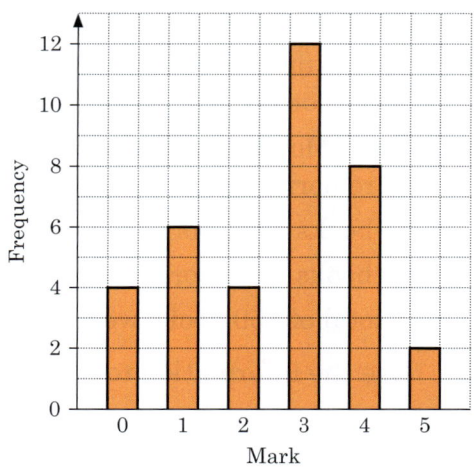

Pie charts

In a pie chart, data is displayed using sectors of a circle.

Example 2

The number of cars of various colours that were parked in a car park were counted and the data collected in this tally chart.

Display the data in a pie chart.

Colour	Tally	Frequency
Blue	ЦНТ II	7
Red	ЦНТ ЦНТ II	12
Yellow	ЦНТ II	7
Green	ЦНТ I	6
Other	I I I I	4

Total number of cars = $7 + 12 + 7 + 6 + 4 = 36$

First, calculate the angles.

Blue cars: $\dfrac{7}{36} \times 360 = 70°$

Red cars: $\dfrac{12}{36} \times 360 = 120°$

Yellow cars: $\dfrac{7}{36} \times 360 = 70°$

Green cars: $\dfrac{6}{36} \times 360 = 60°$

Other colours: $\dfrac{4}{36} \times 360 = 40°$

Colours of cars in a car park

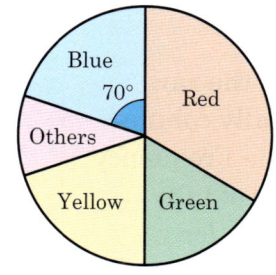

> **Tip**
>
> The order of the sectors is unimportant, as long as the angles are correct.

Next, draw a large circle.

Start with the first colour, blue, and use your protractor to measure an angle of 70°. Write 'Blue' in that sector. Now do the same for the other colours.

Exercise 13.1B

1. The bar chart shows the number of children playing various sports on a given day.

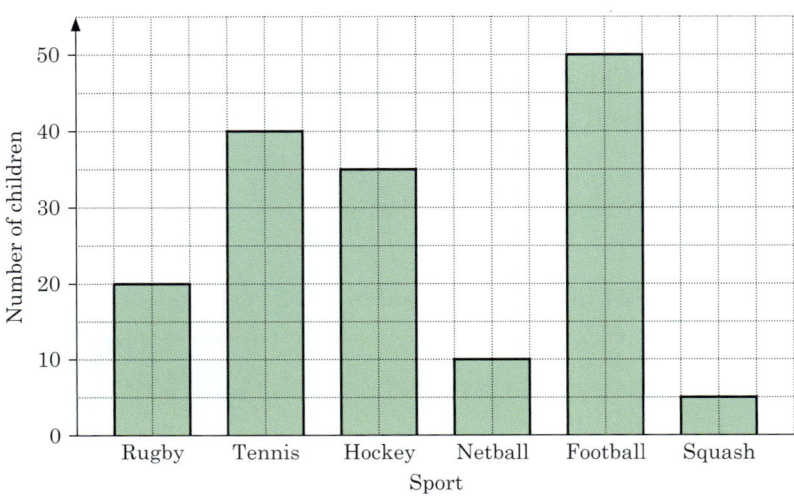

   a) Which sport had the fewest number of players?

   b) What was the total number of children playing?

   c) How many more footballers were there than tennis players?

2. In an experiment, two dice were rolled 60 times and the total score was recorded for each roll, as listed in the table here.

2	3	5	4	8	6	4	7	5	10
7	8	7	6	12	11	8	11	7	6
6	5	7	7	8	6	7	3	6	7
12	3	10	4	3	7	2	11	8	5
7	10	7	5	7	5	10	11	7	10
4	8	6	4	6	11	6	12	11	5

> **Tip**
>
> Don't forget to add a frequency column to your tally chart.

   Draw a tally chart to show the results of the experiment.

3. The table shows the number of different tropical fish in a large aquarium tank. Illustrate this data on a bar chart. What, if any, information is made obvious from the bar chart?

Fish	Pajama cardinal	Sailfin tang	Majestic angelfish	Three spot damsel	Cleaner wrasse	Tomato clownfish
Number	14	23	37	5	42	18

4. In a survey of a section of rainforest, a scientist logged the following:

37 Morpho butterflies	21 Orchid bees
18 Swallowtails	13 Rhinoceros beetles
26 Giraffe-necked weevils	44 Bee sphinx moths

Use the data to create a bar chart. Consider the frequencies involved to help you decide on a scale to use for the vertical axis. Don't forget to label the axes and give your chart a title.

5. The pie chart shows the values of various items sold at a garden centre.

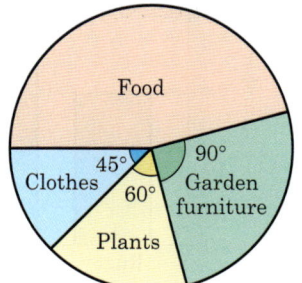

If the total value of the sales was $24 000, find the sales value of:

a) clothes

b) plants

c) garden furniture

d) food.

6. The table shows the number of students who signed up for after-school clubs.

Calculate the angles on a pie chart corresponding to each club.

Club	Drama	Clay workshop	Creative writing	Debate	Orchestra
Number	5	7	11	4	9

7. A recipe for cheese omelette has the following ingredients:

Ingredient	Eggs	Milk	Butter	Cheese	Salt
Mass	450 g	20 g	39 g	90 g	1 g

Calculate the angles on a pie chart corresponding to each ingredient.

8. Calculate the angles on a pie chart corresponding to the quantities given in the tables.

a)

Quantity	A	B	C	D	E
Number	3	5	3	7	6

b)

Quantity	A	B	C	D	E
Mass (g)	10	15	34	8	5

c)

Quantity	A	B	C	D	E
Length (cm)	7	11	9	14	11

9. A firm making artificial sand sold its products in four countries:

   5% were sold in Spain

   15% in France

   15% in Germany

   65% in the UK

   Find the angles that you would use on a pie chart to represent this information.

10. The amounts in kilograms of cumin, paprika and turmeric on a shelf are in the ratio $2:3:4$. Calculate the angles representing the three spices on a pie chart.

11. The cooking times for tortellini, egg-fried rice and tacos are in the ratio $3:7:x$. On a pie chart, the angle corresponding to tortellini is 60°. Find x.

12. The results of an opinion poll of 2000 people are represented on a pie chart. The angle corresponding to 'undecided' was 18°. How many people in the sample answered 'undecided'?

13. The pie chart illustrates the number of passengers on flights to Panama City on four different airlines.

    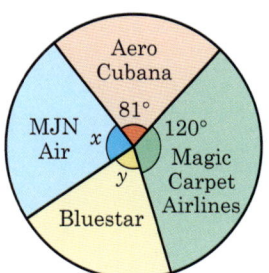

    a) What percentage of passengers flew with Aero Cubana?

    b) If Bluestar accounted for 12.5% of all passengers, calculate the angles x and y.

14. The graph shows the performance of a company in the year in which a new manager was appointed.

    In what way is the graph misleading?

    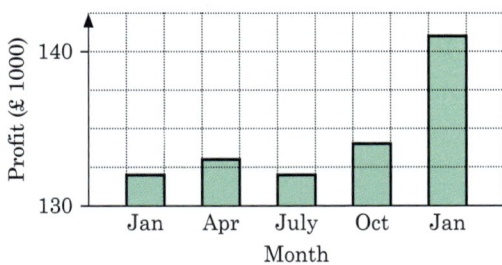

Two-way tables, dual and composite bar charts

Sometimes the data collected is subdivided into two (or more) groups, for example boys and girls, or adults and children.

In cases like this, it can be displayed in a **two-way table**.

Here is an example of a two-way table, showing the favourite sports of some men and some women.

	Cricket	Hockey	Basketball	Football
Men	12	14	7	3
Women	8	16	9	5

Data of this type can be displayed in two different ways, depending on exactly what you are trying to illustrate.

If you are comparing the number of men and women who like each sport, you can use a **dual** (or side-by-side) bar chart.

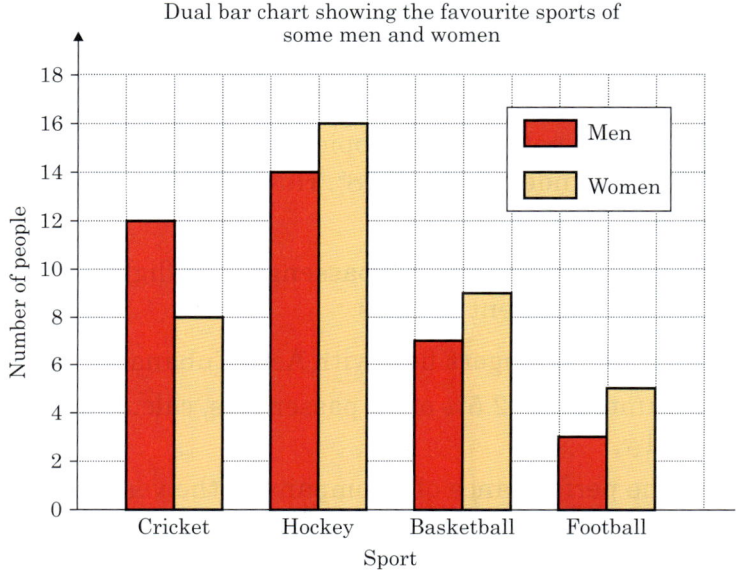

From this chart, you can clearly see that more men than women like cricket, and that more women than men like basketball.

It is difficult to see the total number of men and women from this type of chart since you would need to add up all the different bar heights. But if you display the data using a **composite** (or stacked) bar chart, then this information is clearly shown.

Now it is clear to see that there are more women than men. You can still compare the number who like each sport by looking at the relative height of each piece of the bar.
For example, the yellow piece is bigger for the women so there are more women who like football.

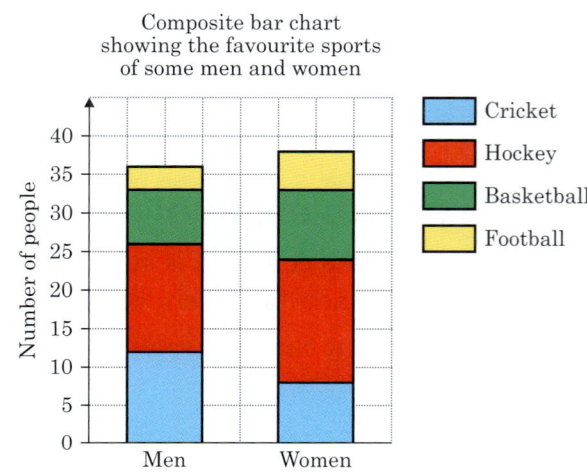

Exercise 13.1C

1. The two-way table shows the number of boys and girls who like different types of music.

	Rock	BritPop	Grunge	House
Boys	7	12	13	9
Girls	12	16	7	10

   a) Draw a composite bar chart to display this data.

   b) Draw a dual bar chart to show this data.

   c) Which diagram is best for comparing the total number of boys and girls?

2. A survey of some children and some adults is carried out.
   They are asked what their favourite food is.

   In the survey, 12 adults say their favourite food is curry, 15 say it is kebabs and 8 say it is dhal.

   Of the children surveyed, 9 say their favourite food is curry, 12 say it is kebabs and 16 say it is dhal.

   a) Show this information in a two-way table.

   b) Draw a dual bar chart to show this data.

   c) Draw a composite bar chart to show this data.

   d) Which diagram is best for comparing the number of adults and children who prefer kebabs?

3. Two shops record their daily sales of ice cream for a week. The results are shown in the two-way table.

	Monday	Tuesday	Wednesday	Thursday	Friday
Shakee's	80	70	55	60	80
Bargie's	60	55	20	65	70

   a) Draw a dual bar chart to show this data.

   b) Bargie's ran out of ice cream and had to close early on one of the days.
      Use your dual bar chart to identify the day.

   c) Draw a composite bar chart to show the data in the table.

   d) Which ice cream shop had the highest weekly sales?

4. A survey was carried out to find out the favourite type of chocolate of some children and some adults. A dual bar chart was drawn.

a) Draw a composite bar chart to show this data.

b) Were there more adults or children in the survey?

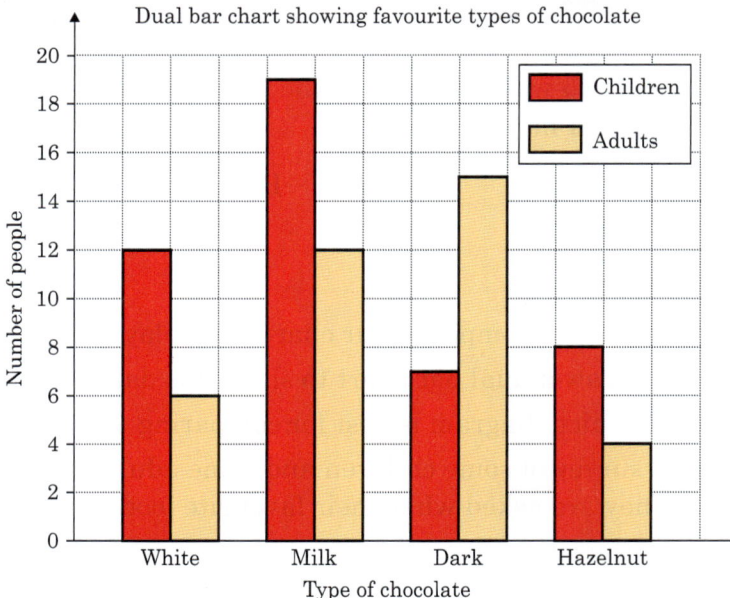

Dual bar chart showing favourite types of chocolate

13.2 Averages and spread

An **average** is a single number that is used to represent a set of numbers. The mean, median and mode are three different types of average.

- The **mean** of a data set is obtained by adding together all the numbers and dividing the result by however many numbers there are in the data set.

- The **median** of a data set is obtained by arranging the numbers in ascending order and then choosing the number in the middle. If there are two middle numbers then the median is the mean of these two numbers.

- The **mode** of a data set is the number or item which occurs most often.

Example 1

Find the mean, median and mode of this data set:

5, 4, 10, 3, 3, 4, 7, 4, 8, 5

Mean:

$$\frac{5 + 4 + 10 + 3 + 3 + 4 + 7 + 4 + 8 + 5}{10} = 5.3$$

The mean is 5.3.

Median:

Arrange the numbers in ascending order:

3, 3, 4, 4, 4, 5, 5, 7, 8, 10

There are 10 numbers, so the median is the mean of the 5th and 6th numbers, when arranged in order.

Median = $\dfrac{4 + 5}{2}$ = 4.5

Mode:

The mode is 4 because there are more 4s than any other number.

The reason why we use three types of average is because each one has its strengths and weaknesses.

- The mean is the most commonly used average and works best when there are not many extreme values in the data set.
- The median works well when there are extreme values, because it is not affected by them.
- The mode is a good average when there are a lot of values that are the same, and when that repeated value is a good representation of the group as a whole.

> **Tip**
>
> Ideally, it is good to know all three. This will give you the best picture of the data set.

Another important aspect of any data set is the **spread**. This tells you how consistent the data is.

The simplest way to measure this is to find the **range** of the data. You find this by subtracting the lowest value in the data set from the highest value.

$$\text{Range} = \text{highest value} - \text{lowest value}$$

Another way of thinking about how the data is distributed is to look at what value lies a quarter of the way into the data set and what value lies three quarters of the way into the data set. We call these values **the lower quartile** and the **upper quartile**.

The difference between these two values is called the **interquartile range** (or **IQR** for short).

$$\text{Interquartile range} = \text{upper quartile} - \text{lower quartile}$$

One advantage that the interquartile range has over the range is that it is not affected by extreme values in the data set.

There are several different ways of working out the upper and lower quartiles of a data set, but you should use the following method.

If there are n items in the data set, the lower quartile is the item at position $\dfrac{n+1}{4}$ and the upper quartile is the item at position $\dfrac{3(n+1)}{4}$.

Example 2

Find the range, lower quartile, upper quartile and interquartile range of this data set:

$$2, 2, 4, 5, 6, 9, 12, 15, 19, 22, 28$$

If the data is not already ordered, make sure you put it into ascending order before attempting to work out the lower and upper quartiles. The data in this data set is already in ascending order.

Range = highest value – lowest value = 28 – 2 = 26

There are 11 items of data, so the lower quartile is the data item in position $\dfrac{n+1}{4}$ which is position $\dfrac{12}{4} = 3$. The 3rd item of data is 4.   2, 2, **4**, 5, 6, 9, 12, 15, 19, 22, 28

The upper quartile is the data item in position $\dfrac{3(n+1)}{4}$ which is position $\dfrac{36}{4} = 9$.

The 9th item of data is 19.   2, 2, 4, 5, 6, 9, 12, 15, **19**, 22, 28

The interquartile range = upper quartile – lower quartile

$$= 19 - 4 = 15$$

Sometimes you may be asked to use these ideas within a more complicated question.

Example 3

The mean amount of money that five people have is $49. Klaus has $47, Diego has $56 and Luther has $16. Vanya has twice as much money as Allison.
How much money does Allison have?

Let x be the amount of money that Allison has. Vanya therefore has $2x$.

$$\frac{47 + 56 + 16 + x + 2x}{5} = 49$$

$$\frac{119 + 3x}{5} = 49$$

$$119 + 3x = 49 \times 5 = 245$$

$$3x = 245 - 119 = 126$$

$$x = 42$$

Allison has $42

Exercise 13.2A

1. Find the mean, median and mode of each of the following data sets:
   a) 3, 12, 4, 6, 8, 5, 4
   b) 7, 21, 2, 17, 3, 13, 7, 4, 9, 7, 9
   c) 12, 1, 10, 1, 9, 3, 4, 9, 7, 9
   d) 8, 0, 3, 3, 1, 7, 4, 1, 4, 4

2. Find the mean, median and mode of each of the following data sets:
   a) 3, 3, 5, 7, 8, 8, 8, 9, 11, 12, 12
   b) 7, 3, 4, 10, 1, 2, 1, 3, 4, 11, 10, 4
   c) −3, 4, 0, 4, −2, −5, 1, 7, 10, 5
   d) $1, \dfrac{1}{2}, \dfrac{1}{2}, \dfrac{3}{4}, \dfrac{1}{4}, 2, \dfrac{1}{2}, \dfrac{1}{4}, \dfrac{3}{4}$

3. Find the range, lower quartile, upper quartile and interquartile range of each of the following data sets:
   a) 4, 7, 9, 15, 21, 32, 38
   b) 1, 10, 14, 29, 37, 78, 100
   c) 10, 35, 4, 84, 46, 47, 21
   d) 20, 99, 129, 46, 81, 117, 150, 101, 34, 130, 62

4. The mean mass of five men is 76 kg. The masses of four of the men are 72 kg, 74 kg, 75 kg and 81 kg. What is the mass of the fifth man?

5. The mean length of six rods is 44.2 cm. The mean length of five of them is 46 cm. How long is the sixth rod?

6. a) A set contains the numbers 3, 7, 8, 10 and x. The mean of the set is 6. Find x.
   b) A set contains the numbers 3, 3, 7, 8, 10, x and x. The mean of the set is 7. Find x.

7. The mean height of 12 men is 1.70 m, and the mean height of 8 women is 1.60 m. Find:
   a) the total height of the 12 men
   b) the total height of the 8 women
   c) the combined mean height of the 20 men and women.

8. The total mass of 6 gymnasts is 540 kg and the mean mass of 14 ballet dancers is 40 kg. Find the mean mass of the group of 20 gymnasts and ballet dancers.

9. The mean mass of 8 leopards is 55 kg and the mean mass of a group of red kangaroos is 52 kg. The mean mass of all the animals is 53.2 kg. How many red kangaroos are there?

10. Find the mean and the median for this set of numbers:

       1, 3, 3, 3, 4, 6, 99

    Which average best describes the set of numbers?

11. In a history test, Andrew got 62%. For the whole class, the mean mark was 64% and the median mark was 59%. Which 'average' should Andrew use to claim that he is in the 'top' half of the class?

12. The mean age of three people is 22 and their median age is 20.

    The range of their ages is 16. How old is each person?

Frequency tables

If lots of data items are repeated, sometimes it is useful to group them in a table, where the frequency, f, of each item, x, is also recorded.

- When working out the mean of a grouped frequency table, first add an extra row to your table that contains the data item multiplied by the frequency. Divide the sum of this row by the sum of the frequency row to find the mean.

- The median is the middle value. You will need to work this out by keeping a running total of the frequencies and working out in which category the middle data item lies.

- The mode is the data item with the highest frequency.

Example

The marks obtained by 100 students in a test were as follows:

Mark, x	0	1	2	3	4
Frequency, f	4	19	25	29	23

Find:

a) the mean mark   **b)** the median mark   **c)** the modal mark.

a) Since the frequency row is just a shorthand way of writing out lots of individual numbers, to work out the total of all the marks, you need to multiply each mark by its frequency, and then add those answers together. It is helpful to add a new row in the table to contain this data.

Mark, x	0	1	2	3	4	Total
Frequency, f	4	19	25	29	23	100
Mark × frequency, xf	0	19	50	87	92	248

The mean is now the total of the *xf* row, divided by the total of the *f* row.

This is sometimes written: mean $= \dfrac{\sum xf}{\sum f}$

Mean $= \dfrac{(0 \times 4) + (1 \times 19) + (2 \times 25) + (3 \times 29) + (4 \times 23)}{100}$

$\qquad = \dfrac{248}{100} = 2.48$

Mean = 2.48 marks

b) The median mark is the number that is halfway through the data set. Because there are 100 data items in total, which is an even number, the list divides equally into two groups of 50 items; items 1 to 50, and items 51 to 100. The midpoint of the list is therefore halfway between the 50th and 51st items.

If you add the frequencies and keep a running total, you will see that the first three categories (0, 1 and 2) contain $4 + 19 + 25 = 48$ items of data. Since the next 29 items of data are all 3, this means that the 50th and 51st items are both 3. Since the median is the mean of these two numbers, it is also 3.

Median = 3 marks

c) The modal mark is the mark that has the highest frequency. This is also 3.

Mode = 3 marks

Exercise 13.2B

1. A group of 50 people were asked how many books they had read in the previous year; the results are shown in the frequency table below. Calculate the mean number of books read per person.

Number of books	0	1	2	3	4	5	6	7	8
Frequency	5	5	6	9	11	7	4	2	1

2. A number of people were asked how many coins they had in their pockets; the results are shown below. Calculate the mean number of coins per person.

Number of coins	0	1	2	3	4	5	6	7
Frequency	3	6	4	7	5	8	5	2

3. The following tables give the distribution of marks obtained by different classes in various tests. For each table, find the mean, median and mode.

a)

Mark	0	1	2	3	4	5	6
Frequency	3	5	8	9	5	7	3

b)

Mark	15	16	17	18	19	20
Frequency	1	3	7	1	5	3

c)

Mark	0	1	2	3	4	5	6
Frequency	10	11	8	15	25	20	11

4. One hundred golfers play a certain hole and their scores are summarised below.

Score	2	3	4	5	6	7	8
Number of players	2	7	24	31	18	11	7

Find:

a) the mean score

b) the median score.

5. The number of goals scored in a series of ice hockey games was as follows:

Number of goals	1	2	3
Number of games	8	8	x

a) If the mean number of goals is 2.04, find x.

b) If the modal number of goals is 3, find the smallest possible value of x.

c) If the median number of goals is 2, find the largest possible value of x.

6. In a survey of the number of occupants in a random selection of cars, the following data resulted.

Number of occupants	1	2	3	4
Number of cars	7	11	7	x

a) If the mean number of occupants is $2\frac{1}{3}$, find x.

b) If the mode is 2, find the largest possible value of x.

c) If the median is 2, find the largest possible value of x.

7. The numbers 3, 5, 7, 8 and N are arranged in ascending order.
   If the mean of the numbers is equal to the median, find N.

8. The mean of five numbers is 11. The numbers are in the ratio $1:2:3:4:5$.
   Find the smallest number.

9. The mean of a set of 7 numbers is 3.6 and the mean of a different set of 18 numbers is 5.1. Calculate the mean of the 25 numbers.

10. The marks obtained by the members of a class are summarised in the table.

Mark	x	y	z
Frequency	a	b	c

Calculate the mean mark in terms of a, b, c, x, y and z.

Grouped data

Sometimes it is more convenient to group data into categories called **class intervals**. There are many reasons why this could be the case. Perhaps there is a lot of data and you want to make it more manageable, or perhaps most of the data items are different and so most individual items would have a frequency of 1, again making it difficult to manage. Perhaps you don't know any exact values but you do know what categories the data items are in.

Because you are not using the actual items of data, any averages you calculate from a grouped data set will only be **estimates** of the actual values.

Example

The results of 51 students in a test are given in the frequency table.

Mark	30–39	40–49	50–59	60–69
Frequency	7	14	21	9

Find the   **a)** mean   **b)** median   **c)** modal class.

To find the mean, you approximate by saying that each class interval is represented by its midpoint. For the 30−39 interval you say that there are 7 marks of 34.5 (that is $(30 + 39) \div 2 = 34.5$).

Mark	30–39	40–49	50–59	60–69
Frequency	7	14	21	9
Midpoint	34.5	44.5	54.5	64.5

a) Mean $= \dfrac{(34.5 \times 7) + (44.5 \times 14) + (54.5 \times 21) + (64.5 \times 9)}{(7 + 14 + 21 + 9)}$

$= 50.7745098$

$= 51$ (2 s.f.)

b) The median is the 26th mark, which is in the class interval 50−59.

You cannot find the exact median.

> **Tip**
>
> The mean is only an estimate because you do not have the raw data and you have made an assumption with the midpoint of each class interval.

c) The modal class is 50–59 because it is the class interval with the highest frequency. You cannot find an exact mode with grouped data.

> **Tip**
>
> Later you will find out how to get an estimate of the median by drawing a cumulative frequency curve.

Exercise 13.2C

1. The table gives the number of words in each sentence on one page in a book.

   a) Copy and complete the table.

   b) Work out an estimate for the mean number of words in a sentence.

Number of words	Frequency, f	Midpoint, x	fx
1–5	6	3	18
6–10	5	8	40
11–15	4		
16–20	2		
21–25	3		
Totals	20	–	

2. The exam results of 24 students are given in the table.

Mark	Frequency
85–99	4
70–84	7
55–69	8
40–54	5

   a) Find the midpoint of each class interval and calculate an estimate of the mean mark.

   b) Explain why your answer is an estimate.

   c) The result from part **(a)** is then used to predict the mean exam results of 2000 students across a group of 10 schools. Why might this not be a good idea?

3. The table shows the number of letters delivered to the 26 houses in a street.
   Calculate an estimate of the mean number of letters delivered per house.

Number of letters delivered	Number of houses (frequency)
0–2	10
3–4	8
5–7	5
8–12	3

4. The mean age of a class of 25 six-year-olds and their 50-year-old teacher is 7.7. Why is this not a good average to use to represent the ages of the people in that group? Which average would be better?

5. The number of words in 100 reading books is counted. Why is the mode not suitable to represent the average number of words in the books?

6. A property company consists of 50 builders and their boss. Why might the median be a good choice for representing the average wage of someone in that company?

7. A group of people are asked what their favourite kind of music is from a list consisting of 10 different kinds of music. Why is the mode the best kind of average here?

Frequency charts

Grouped data can also be displayed on a frequency chart. This looks like a bar chart, but the horizontal axis is labelled instead of the bars and there are no gaps between the bars.

Example

The hand spans of 21 children were measured as follows:

14.8   20.0   16.9   20.7   18.1   17.5   18.7

19.0   19.8   17.8   14.3   19.2   21.7   17.4

16.0   15.9   18.5   19.3   16.6   21.2   18.4

Group the data and draw up a tally chart and frequency diagram.

The smallest value is 14.3 cm and the largest is 21.7 cm.
The data can be grouped as follows and the frequency diagram drawn.

Hand span, s	Tally	Frequency
$14 \leqslant s < 16$	$\lvert\,\lvert\,\lvert$	3
$16 \leqslant s < 18$	$\cancel{\lvert\lvert\lvert\lvert}\,\lvert$	6
$18 \leqslant s < 20$	$\cancel{\lvert\lvert\lvert\lvert}\,\lvert\lvert\lvert$	8
$20 \leqslant s < 22$	$\lvert\,\lvert\,\lvert\,\lvert$	4

> **Tip**
>
> Note that 20.0 goes into the last group $20 \leqslant s < 22$.

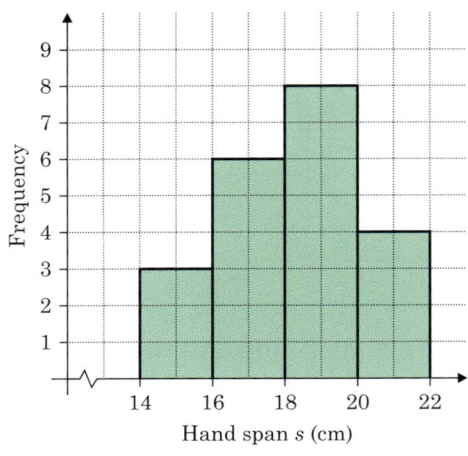

Exercise 13.2D

1. The graphs show the heights of two groups of people.
One graph represents high school students, the other one represents adults.

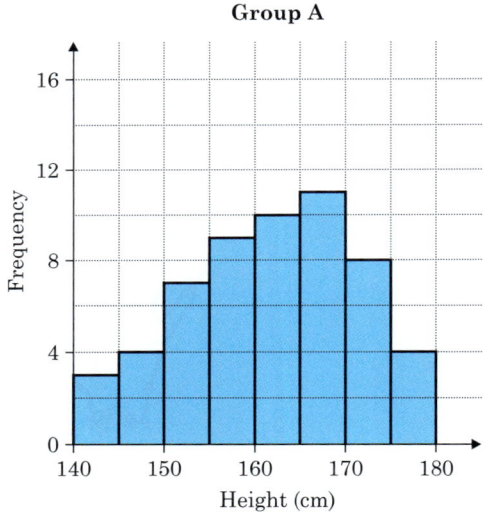

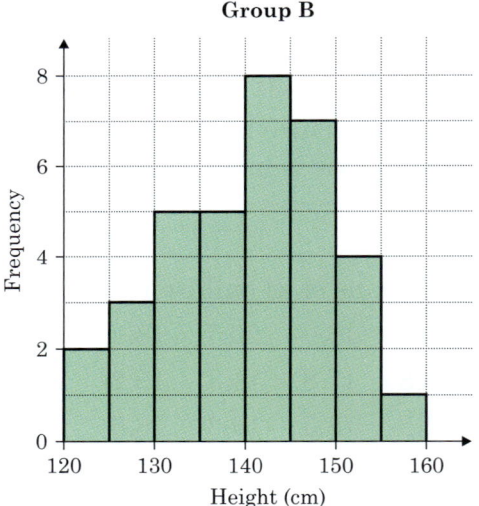

a) Which graph represents the high school students?

b) How many students were over 150 cm tall?

c) How many students were there?

d) How many adults were there?

e) What fraction of the adults were under 150 cm tall?

2. In a survey, the heights of children aged 15 were measured in four countries around the world. A random sample of children was chosen, not necessarily the same number from each country.

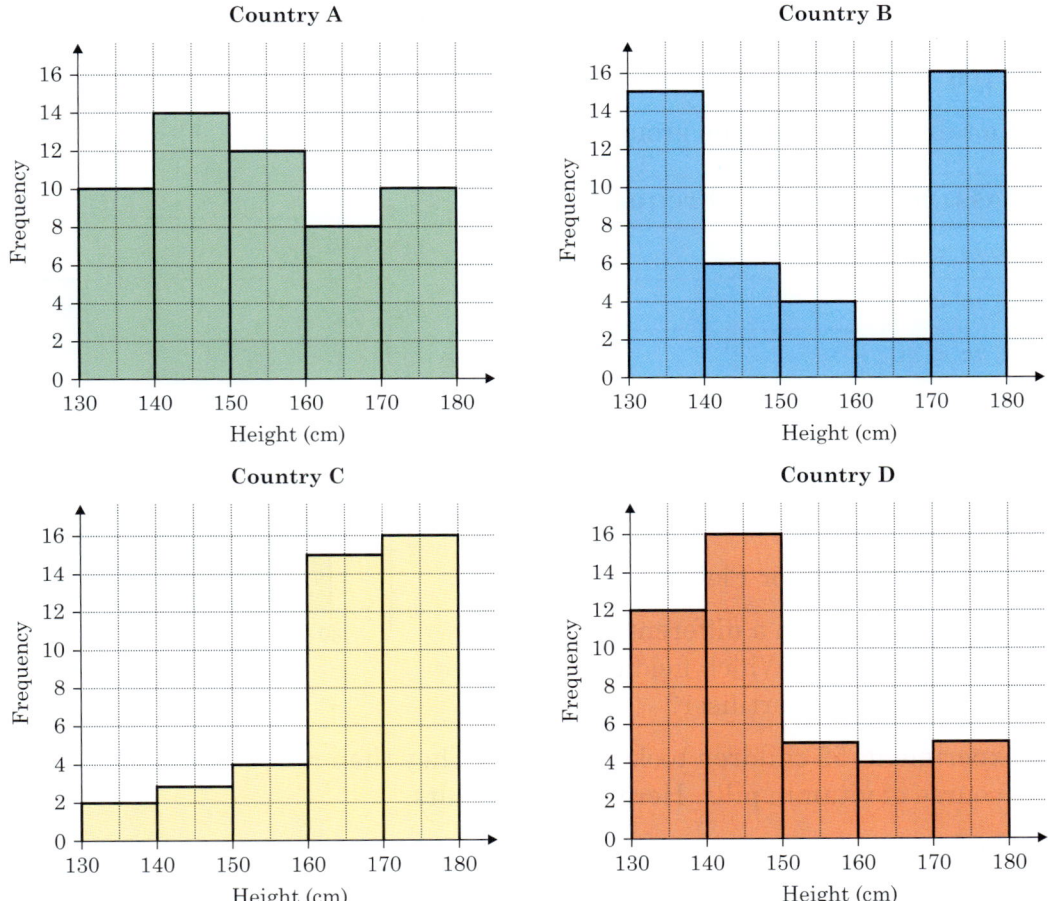

Use the graphs to identify the country in each of the statements below.

a) Two-thirds of the children from Country ____ were less than 150 cm tall.

b) There were 54 children in the sample from Country ____.

c) In Country ____, the heights were spread fairly evenly across the range 130 to 180 cm.

d) The smallest sample of children came from Country ____.

e) In Country ____, approximately three-quarters of the children were either relatively tall or relatively short.

3. A farmer grew carrots in two adjacent fields, A and B, and treated one of the fields with fertiliser. A random sample of 50 carrots was taken from each field and the mass found. Here are the results for Field A (all in grams).

118	91	82	105	72	92	103	95	73	109
63	111	102	116	101	104	107	119	111	108
112	97	100	75	85	94	76	67	93	112
70	116	118	103	65	107	87	98	105	117
114	106	82	90	77	88	66	99	95	103

Make a tally chart using the groups given.

Mass, m	Tally	Frequency
$60 \leqslant m < 70$		
$70 \leqslant m < 80$		
$80 \leqslant m < 90$		
$90 \leqslant m < 100$		
$100 \leqslant m < 110$		
$110 \leqslant m < 120$		

Field B

The frequency graph for Field B is shown.

Copy the graph and, in a different colour, draw the graph for Field A. Which field do you think was treated with the fertiliser?

4. In an experiment, 52 children took an IQ test. They then re-took the test after a course of vitamin pills. Here are the results.

Score before:

81	107	93	104	103	96	101	102	93	105	82	106	97
108	94	111	92	86	109	95	116	92	94	101	117	102
95	108	112	107	106	124	125	103	127	118	113	91	113
113	114	109	128	115	86	106	91	85	119	129	99	98

Score after:

93	110	92	125	99	127	114	98	107	128	103	91	104
103	83	125	91	104	99	102	116	98	115	92	117	97
126	100	112	113	85	108	97	101	125	93	102	107	116
94	117	95	108	117	96	102	87	107	94	103	95	96

a) Put the scores into convenient groups between 80 and 130.

b) Draw two frequency graphs to display the results.

c) Write a conclusion. Did the vitamin pills make a significant difference?

13.3 Stem-and-leaf, frequency polygons and histograms

Stem-and-leaf diagrams

Data can be displayed in groups using a stem-and-leaf diagram.

Here are the ages of 20 people who attended a concert.

| 25 | 65 | 43 | 16 | 28 | 32 | 57 | 21 | 17 | 61 |
| 21 | 43 | 36 | 21 | 14 | 35 | 22 | 44 | 52 | 47 |

You need to organise the data, and so you start by choosing a sensible way to group it. Here you can use the tens digit of the ages, giving the groups 10–19, 20–29, 30–39, 40–49, 50–59, 60–69.

You then use the tens digit as the 'stem' and the units digit as the 'leaf'.

Make the diagram, putting the data in numerical order.

You also need to include a key, containing a sample piece of data, so that people know how to interpret the diagram.

Stem	Leaf	Key
1	4 6 7	1 | 4 = 14 years old
2	1 1 1 2 5 8	
3	2 5 6	
4	3 3 4 7	
5	2 7	
6	1 5	

> **Tip**
>
> If there is a lot of data, you may want to make an unordered stem-and-leaf diagram first, to get the data into the correct categories before putting it in order.

Once your diagram is complete, the data can easily be read off in ascending order, making it quite straightforward to find the median, range, mode, lower quartile, upper quartile, and interquartile range.

Back-to-back stem-and-leaf diagrams

Two sets of data can be compared using a back-to-back stem-and-leaf diagram.

10 students who received coaching and 10 students who did not receive coaching all took part in a mathematics competition. Their scores are shown in this back-to-back stem-and-leaf diagram.

Key (Coached)	Coached		Not coached	Key (Not coached)
9 | 1 = a score of 19		0	4 8	1 | 5 = a score of 15
	9 5 4	1	0 2 5 9	
	7 6 0	2	4 8	
	6 5 4 1	3	2 4	

Because the two sets of data share the same stem, you can see that it looks like the students who were coached performed better in the competition than those who weren't. For example, the median score for the Coached group is 26.5, and the median score for the Not coached group is 17.

Exercise 13.3A

1. The marks scored by 25 students in a history test are as follows.

62	45	53	76	60	45	33	64	53	36
71	42	26	48	62	66	29	37	21	74
48	56	52	68	62					

   a) Draw a stem-and-leaf diagram to display this data.

   b) Find the median score for the students.

   c) Write down the range of the scores.

2. Here is a stem-and-leaf diagram showing the times taken by a group of amateur athletes to run 100 metres, measured to the nearest tenth of a second.

Stem	Leaf	Key
12	9	13 | 5 = 13.5 seconds
13	0 1 5 8	
14	1 6 8	
15	2 2 7	

   a) How many athletes' scores were recorded?

   b) What was the median time taken?

   c) What was the range of the times recorded?

   d) What was the modal time?

   e) What was the interquartile range of the times?

3. Ten girls and ten boys measured their hand spans in centimetres. Here are the results.

Girls	17.4	19.4	18.8	16.7	16.1	21.0	19.3	16.5	20.8	18.5
Boys	17.7	21.0	21.9	18.2	23.1	22.2	18.8	22.7	17.5	19.3

a) Copy and complete the following back-to-back stem-and-leaf diagram to display the data.

Key (Girls)
4 | 17 = 17.4 cm

	Girls		Boys	

Girls		Boys
	16	
	17	
	18	
	19	
	20	
	21	
	22	
	23	

Key (Boys)
19 | 3 = 19.3 cm

b) What are the median hand spans for the girls and for the boys?

c) What are the ranges of the hand spans for the girls and for the boys?

4. The lengths, to the nearest minute, of 10 horror films and 10 action films are collected.

Horror	99	90	94	85	105	92	88	95	89	100
Action	110	88	99	90	119	100	121	106	93	110

a) Display this data in a back-to-back stem-and-leaf diagram.

b) What is the median length of each type of film?

c) Based on this sample, which type of film is, on average, longer?

Frequency polygons

A frequency polygon can be drawn by joining the midpoints of the tops of the bars on a frequency chart.

Frequency polygons are used mainly to compare data.

- Here is a frequency chart showing the heights of babies treated at a hospital one day.

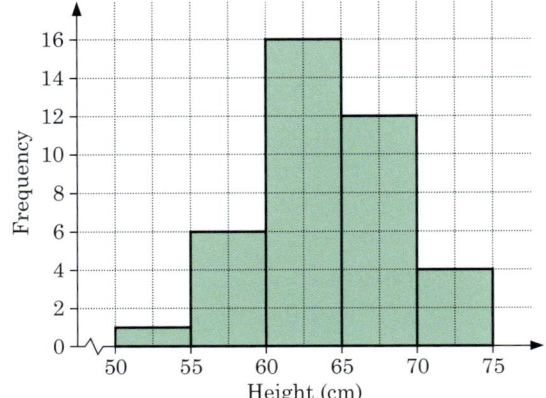

- Here is the corresponding frequency polygon, drawn by joining the midpoints of the tops of the bars.

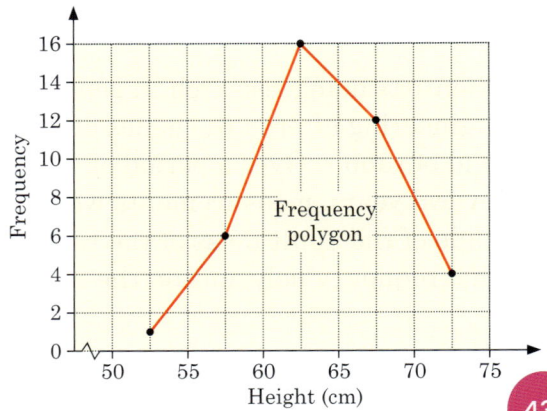

It is not necessary to draw the bars if you require only the frequency polygon.

This diagram shows the frequency polygons for the exam results of 34 students in two subjects, Maths and French.

Two main differences are apparent:

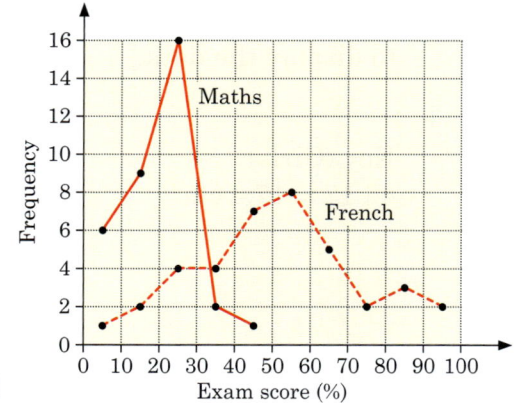

- The scores obtained in the Maths exam were significantly lower than French for most students.

- The scores in the French exam were more spread out than the Maths scores. The French scores were distributed fairly evenly over the range from 0 to 100%, whereas the Maths scores were mostly between 0 and 40%.

Exercise 13.3B

1. Draw a frequency polygon for the distribution of masses of children shown in the diagram.

2. In a supermarket survey, shoppers were asked two questions as they left:

   a) How much have you just spent?

   b) How far away do you live?

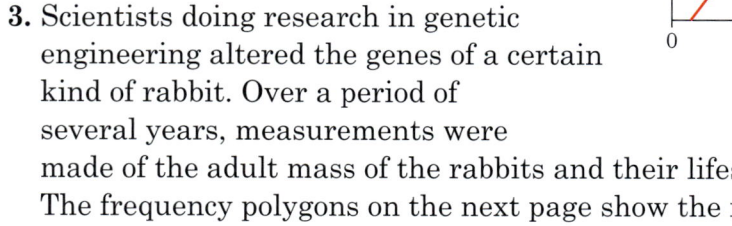

The results were separated into two groups: shoppers who lived less than 2 miles from the supermarket and shoppers who lived further away. The frequency polygons show how much shoppers in each group had spent.

Decide which polygon, P or Q, is most likely to represent shoppers who lived less than 2 miles from the supermarket. Give your reasons.

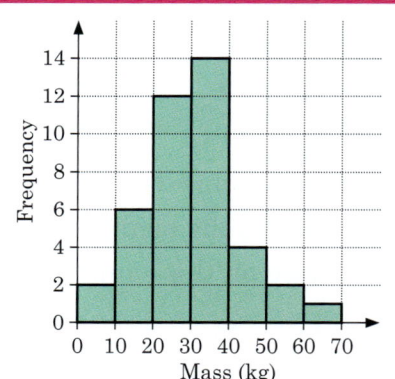

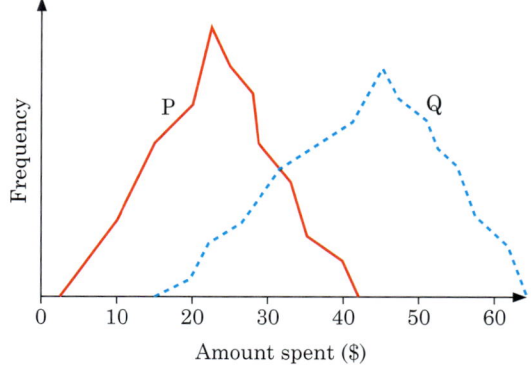

3. Scientists doing research in genetic engineering altered the genes of a certain kind of rabbit. Over a period of several years, measurements were made of the adult mass of the rabbits and their lifespans. The frequency polygons on the next page show the results.

What can you deduce from the two frequency polygons?
Write one sentence about mass and one sentence about lifespan.

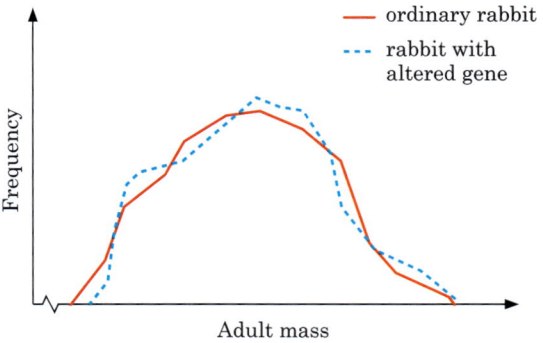

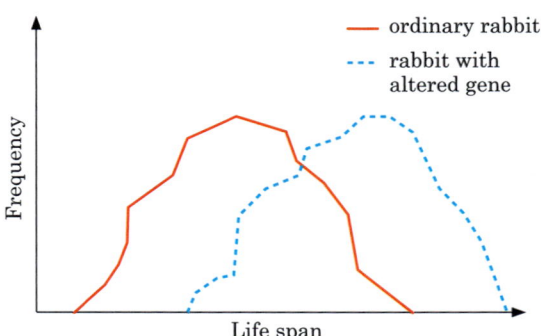

Histograms

Histograms resemble bar charts but are not to be confused with them.

In a bar chart, the frequency is shown by the height of each bar. In a histogram, the frequency of the data is shown by the *area* of each bar.

Histograms often have bars of varying widths, matching the widths of the class intervals whose data they are representing. Because the area of the bar represents the frequency, the height of the bar depends on its width. Unlike a bar chart, the vertical axis is not labelled frequency but frequency density. You can calculate the frequency density for a particular bar using the formula:

$$\text{frequency density} = \frac{\text{frequency}}{\text{class width}}$$

The main purpose of histograms is to represent continuous data, but they can also be used to represent grouped discrete data.

Example

Draw a histogram from the table shown for the distribution of ages of passengers travelling on a flight to Catania, Sicily.

Note that the data has been collected into class intervals of different widths.

Age x, years	Frequency
$0 \leqslant x < 20$	28
$20 \leqslant x < 40$	36
$40 \leqslant x < 50$	20
$50 \leqslant x < 70$	30
$70 \leqslant x < 100$	18

$\rightarrow$

To draw the histogram, the heights of the bars must be adjusted by calculating frequency density.

Age x, years	Frequency	Class width	Frequency density (f.d.)
$0 \leqslant x < 20$	28	20	$28 \div 20 = 1.4$
$20 \leqslant x < 40$	36	20	$36 \div 20 = 1.8$
$40 \leqslant x < 50$	20	10	$20 \div 10 = 2$
$50 \leqslant x < 70$	30	20	$30 \div 20 = 1.5$
$70 \leqslant x < 100$	18	30	$18 \div 30 = 0.6$

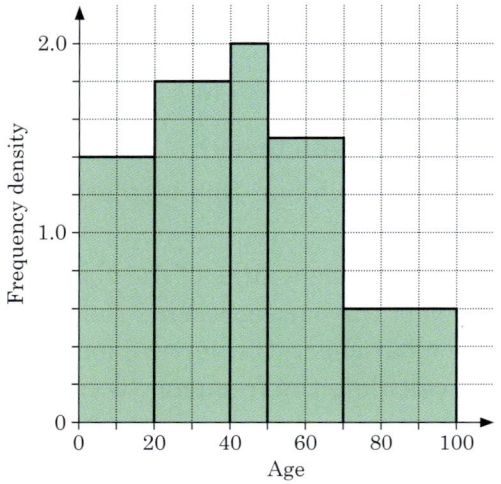

Tip

Remember that discrete data can only take certain values, but continuous data can take any value within a given range. More often than not, discrete data relates to things that you count, and continuous data relates to things that you measure.

Exercise 13.3C

1. The lengths of 20 copper nails were measured. The results are shown in the frequency table.

Length L, mm	Frequency	Frequency density (f.d.)
$0 \leqslant L < 20$	5	$5 \div 20 = 0.25$
$20 \leqslant L < 25$	5	
$25 \leqslant L < 30$	7	
$30 \leqslant L < 40$	3	

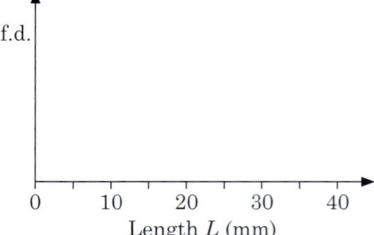

Calculate the rest of the frequency densities, then copy the axes and draw the histogram for the data.

2. The volumes of 55 containers were measured and the results were used to create this frequency table.

Volume V, mm³	Frequency
$0 \leqslant V < 5$	5
$5 \leqslant V < 10$	3
$10 \leqslant V < 20$	12
$20 \leqslant V < 30$	17
$30 \leqslant V < 40$	13
$40 \leqslant V < 60$	5

Calculate the frequency densities and draw the histogram.

3. The lengths of snakes and their frequencies are shown in the following histogram.

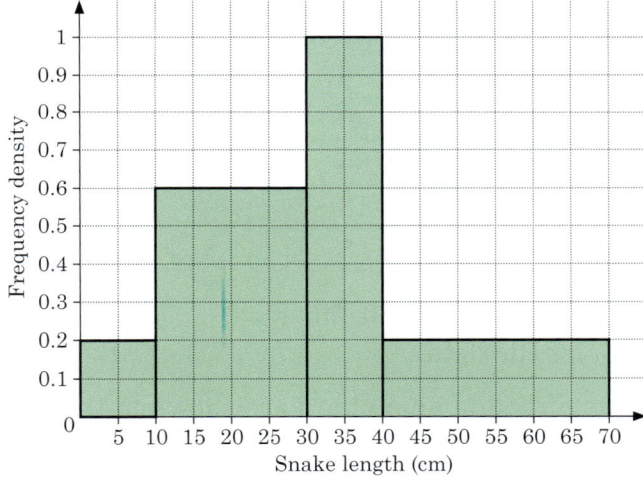

There are two snakes that are between 0 and 10 cm long.

a) How many snakes are between 30 and 40 cm long?

b) What is the modal class?

c) Work out an estimate of the mean length of the snakes in this group.

4. The table shows some results of a running race. Copy and complete the histogram using the data in the table.

Time t, seconds	Frequency
$0 \leqslant t < 20$	32
$20 \leqslant t < 30$	20
$30 \leqslant t < 50$	16
$50 \leqslant t < 60$	12

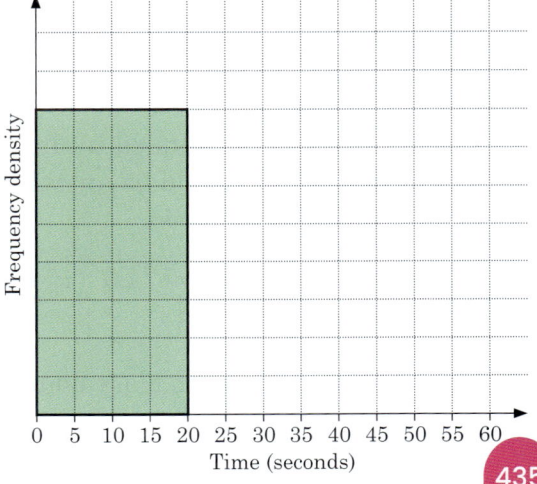

5. The masses of 30 Humboldt squid were measured, and are shown in the table. Draw a histogram to represent this data.

Mass (kg)	Frequency
30–40	5
40–45	7
45–50	10
50–55	5
55–70	3

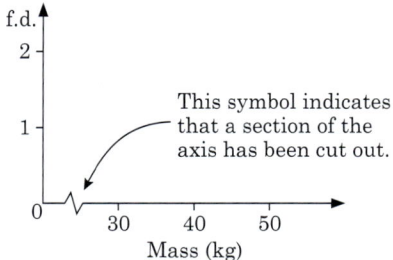

Note that the masses do not start at zero. This is shown on the graph above.

6. The ages of 120 people passing through an airport security gate were recorded and are shown in the frequency table.

Age A, years	Frequency
$0 \leqslant A < 10$	18
$10 \leqslant A < 15$	46
$15 \leqslant A < 20$	35
$20 \leqslant A < 30$	13
$30 \leqslant A < 40$	8

The class boundaries are 0, 10, 15, 20, 30, 40.
Draw the histogram for the data.

> **Tip**
>
> Be careful when the data set represents people's ages. Remember that although age is continuous, we treat it as though it were discrete. You do not round ages up or down.

7. The masses of plums picked in an orchard are shown in the table below.

Mass (g)	$0 < A \leqslant 20$	$20 < A \leqslant 30$	$30 < A \leqslant 40$	$40 < A \leqslant 60$	$60 < A \leqslant 80$
Frequency	11	18	7	5	0

Draw a histogram with class boundaries at 0, 20, 30, 40, 60, 80.

8. The heights of 50 Olympic athletes were measured as shown in the table.

Height (cm)	170–174	175–179	180–184	185–194
Frequency	8	17	14	11

These values were rounded to the nearest cm. For example, an athlete whose height h is 181 cm could be anywhere in the range 180.5 cm $\leqslant h <$ 181.5 cm. So, the table is as follows:

Height	169.5–174.5	174.5–179.5	179.5–184.5	184.5–194.5
Frequency	8	17	14	11

Draw a histogram with class boundaries at 169.5, 174.5, 179.5, . . .

9. Data representing the heights of tomato plants is to be displayed in a histogram.

   a) If the first class interval is $0 \leqslant x < 10$ and it has a frequency of 80, what would the frequency density be for that class interval?

   b) Sometimes, to make the histogram easier to construct or easier to read, the frequency densities will all be multiplied by a scale factor. If the scaled frequency density for the class interval $0 \leqslant x < 10$ is given as 80, what is the scale factor that has been used?

   c) Copy and complete the following table, filling in the missing scaled frequency densities.

Length	Frequency	Scaled frequency density
$0 \leqslant x < 10$	80	80
$10 \leqslant x \leqslant 20$	57	
$30 \leqslant x < 60$	42	
$60 \leqslant x \leqslant 80$	35	

13.4 Scatter diagrams

Sometimes you want to know if there is a connection or relationship between two sets of data.

Examples:

- Are more ice creams sold when the weather is hot?
- Do tall people have higher resting heart rates?
- Are people who are good at maths also good at science?
- Does eating bananas improve examination results?

If there is a relationship, it will be easy to spot if the data is plotted on a scatter diagram, which is a graph where one set of data is plotted on the horizontal axis and the other on the vertical axis.

Here is a scatter diagram showing the price of pears and the quantity sold.

You can see a *connection* – when the price of pears was low, sales were at their highest. As the price increased, the number of pears sold went down.

This scatter diagram shows the sales of a newspaper and the temperature. You can see that there is *no connection* between the two variables.

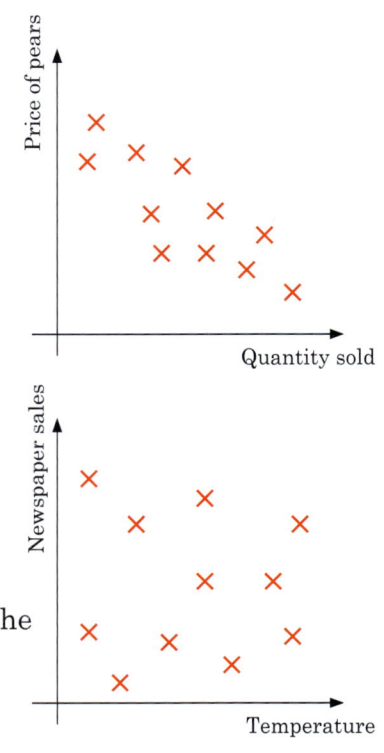

Correlation

The word **correlation** describes how things co-relate. There is correlation between two sets of data if there is a connection or relationship.

The correlation between two sets of data can be positive or negative and it can be strong or weak as indicated by the scatter diagrams below.

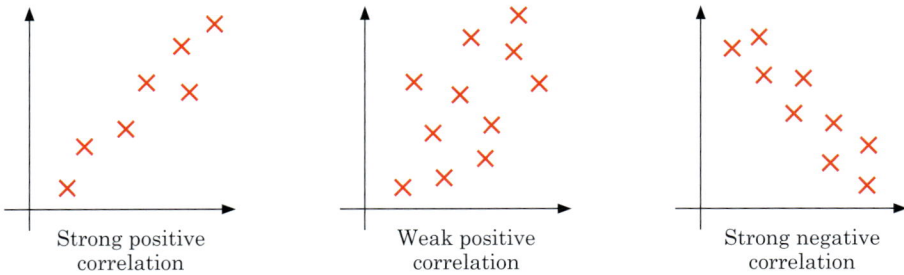

Strong positive correlation   Weak positive correlation   Strong negative correlation

When the correlation is positive, the points are around a line which slopes upwards to the right. When the correlation is negative, the 'line' slopes downwards to the right.

When the correlation is strong, the points are bunched close to a line through their midst. When the correlation is weak, the points are more scattered.

It is important to realise that often there is no correlation between two sets of data.

For example, if you take a group of students and plot their maths test results against their time to run 800 m, the graph might look like the one on the right.

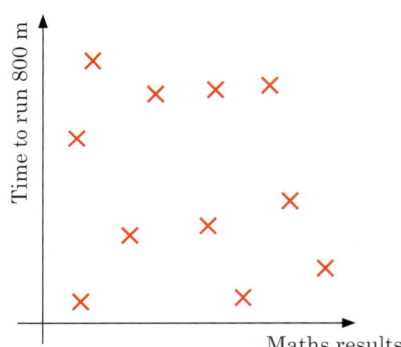

A common mistake in this topic is to 'see' a correlation on a scatter diagram where none exists. There is also *no* correlation in these two scatter diagrams.

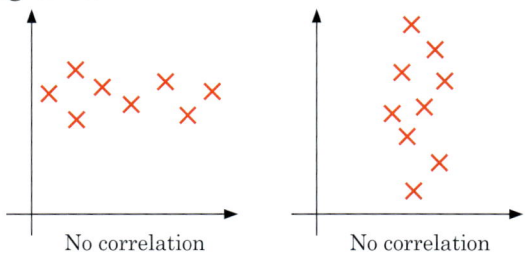

No correlation   No correlation

Line of best fit

When a scatter diagram shows either positive or negative correlation, a **line of best fit** can be drawn. The sums of the distances to points on either side of the line are equal and there should be roughly an equal number of points on each side of the line. The line is easier to draw when a transparent ruler is used.

Here are the marks obtained in two tests by nine students.

Student	Ben	Amy	Eli	Max	Hanna	Andy	Lisl	Oscar	Sakura
Maths mark	28	22	9	40	37	35	30	23	?
Physics mark	48	45	34	57	50	55	53	45	52

A line of best fit can be drawn as there is strong positive correlation between the two sets of marks.

The line of best fit can be used to estimate the maths result of Sakura, who missed the maths test but scored 52 in the physics test.

We can *estimate* that Sakura would have scored about 33 in the maths test. It is not possible to be *very* accurate using scatter diagrams. It is reasonable to state that 'she might have scored between 30 and 36 in the maths test'.

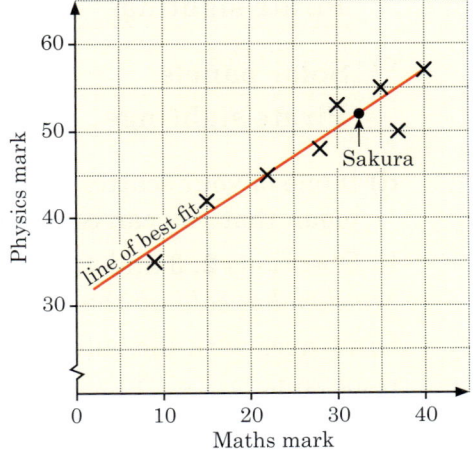

Here is a scatter diagram in which the heights of boys of different ages are recorded.
A line of best fit is drawn.

We can estimate that the height of an 8-year-old boy might be about 123 cm (say between 120 and 126 cm).

We can only predict a height within the range of values plotted. We could not extend the line of best fit and use it to predict the height of a 30-year-old. Why not?

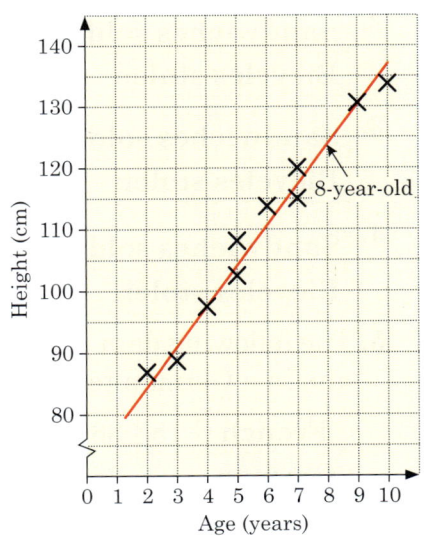

Tip

You cannot make an accurate prediction by extending the line of best fit beyond the range of the data collected because you cannot be sure that the same trend will continue.

Exercise 13.4A

1. Plot the points given on a scatter diagram, with Solar panels on the horizontal axis and Pirate sightings on the vertical. Use axis values from 0 to 20.

   Describe the correlation, if any, between the data sets.
   For example, 'strong negative', 'weak positive', etc.

a)

Solar panels	7	16	4	12	18	6	20	4	10	13
Pirate sightings	8	15	6	12	17	9	18	7	10	14

b)

Solar panels	3	8	12	15	16	5	6	17	9
Pirate sightings	4	2	10	17	5	10	17	11	15

c)

Solar panels	11	1	16	7	2	19	8	4	13	18
Pirate sightings	5	12	7	14	17	1	11	8	11	5

   d) If one of your scatter diagrams shows a strong positive correlation, does this mean that you can conclude that the pirates are attracted by the solar panels?

   In Questions **2**, **3** and **4**, plot the points given on a scatter diagram, with *Sandwiches sold* on the horizontal axis and *Bicycles stolen* on the vertical.

   Draw axes with the values from 0 to 20.

   If possible, draw a line of best fit on the graph.

   Where possible, estimate the number of *Bicycles stolen* on the line of best fit where the number of *Sandwiches sold* = 10.

2.

Sandwiches sold	2	14	14	4	12	18	12	6
Bicycles stolen	5	15	16	6	12	18	13	7

3.

Sandwiches sold	2	15	17	3	20	3	6
Bicycles stolen	13	7	5	12	4	13	11

4.

Sandwiches sold	4	10	15	18	19	4	19	5
Bicycles stolen	19	16	11	19	15	3	1	9

5. The following data gives the marks of 11 students in a French test and in a German test.

French	15	36	36	22	23	27	43	22	43	40	26
German	6	28	35	18	28	28	37	9	41	45	17

   a) Plot this data on a scatter diagram, with French marks on the horizontal axis.
   b) Draw the line of best fit.
   c) Estimate the German mark of a student who got 30 in French.

d) Estimate the French mark of a student who got 45 in German.

e) Two of the students joined the German class later than the other students. Which two students do you think it might have been?

6. The data below gives the petrol consumption figures of cars with the same size engine, when driven at different speeds.

Speed (miles per hour)	30	62	40	80	70	55	75
Petrol consumption (miles per gallon)	38	25	35	20	26	34	22

a) Plot a scatter diagram and draw a line of best fit.

b) Estimate the petrol consumption of a car travelling at 45 m.p.h.

c) Estimate the speed of a car whose petrol consumption is 27 m.p.g.

13.5 Cumulative frequency

Cumulative frequency is the total frequency up to a given point.

Cumulative frequency graphs are used for grouped data. The curve you draw connects the points that represent the cumulative frequency at the upper bound of every class interval.

You can use a cumulative frequency graph to make estimates of the median and of the lower and upper quartiles.

To find an estimate of the median:

- Divide the total frequency by 2.
- Draw a horizontal line from this point on the vertical axis until it meets the curve.
- Draw a vertical line down from that point until it meets the horizontal axis.
- The value at this point is your estimate of the median.

To find an estimate of the lower quartile, repeat the steps above, but begin by dividing the total frequency by 4 rather than 2. The lower quartile is sometimes called the 25th percentile, since it is a quarter (25%) of the way through the data.

You can find an estimate of the upper quartile (the 75th percentile) in a similar way.

Sometimes you may be asked to find other **percentiles**, such as the 10th percentile or the 60th percentile. To find these, work out what 10% or 60% of the total frequency is, then use that number as the place from which you draw the horizontal line from the vertical axis to meet the curve. Then draw in your vertical line and read off the value from the horizontal axis.

Tip

Because the median is the point halfway through the data, it is sometimes called the 50th percentile.

Example

The marks obtained by 80 students in an examination are shown below.

Mark	Frequency	Cumulative frequency	Marks represented by cumulative frequency
1–10	3	3	$\leqslant 10$
11–20	5	8	$\leqslant 20$
21–30	5	13	$\leqslant 30$
31–40	9	22	$\leqslant 40$
41–50	11	33	$\leqslant 50$
51–60	15	48	$\leqslant 60$
61–70	14	62	$\leqslant 70$
71–80	8	70	$\leqslant 80$
81–90	6	76	$\leqslant 90$
91–100	4	80	$\leqslant 100$

The table also shows the cumulative frequency.

Plot a cumulative frequency curve and hence estimate:

a) the median

b) the interquartile range

c) the 10th percentile.

> **Tip**
>
> To calculate the cumulative frequency for any interval, start with the frequency for the interval and add to it all frequencies from previous intervals.

The points on the graph are plotted at the upper bound of each class interval.

a) median = 55 marks

b) lower quartile = 37.5 marks

upper quartile = 68 marks

interquartile range = 68 – 37.5 = 30.5 marks

c) 10th percentile = 20

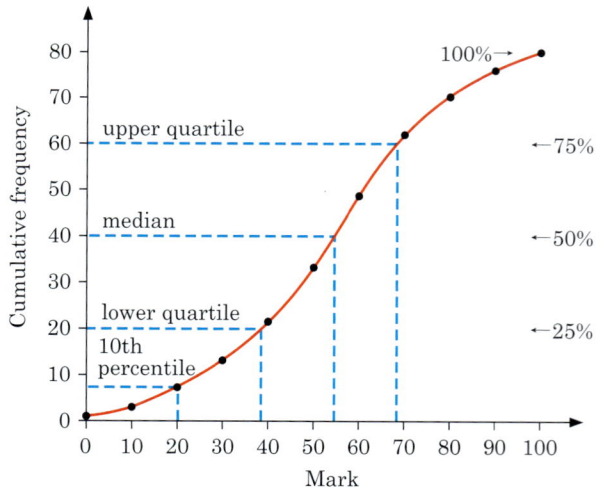

Exercise 13.5A

1. Figure 1 shows the cumulative frequency curve for the marks of 60 students in an examination.

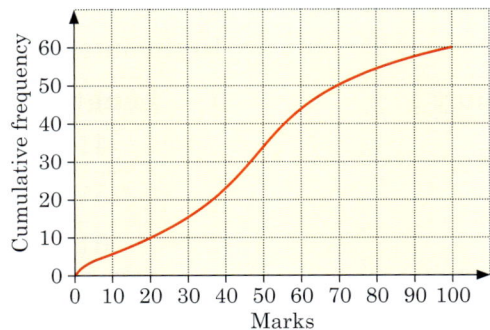

From the graph, estimate:

a) the median mark

b) the mark at the lower quartile and at the upper quartile

c) the interquartile range

d) the pass mark if two-thirds of the students passed

e) the number of students achieving fewer than 40 marks

f) the 10th percentile

g) the 90th percentile.

2. Figure 2 shows the cumulative frequency curve for the marks of 140 students in an examination.

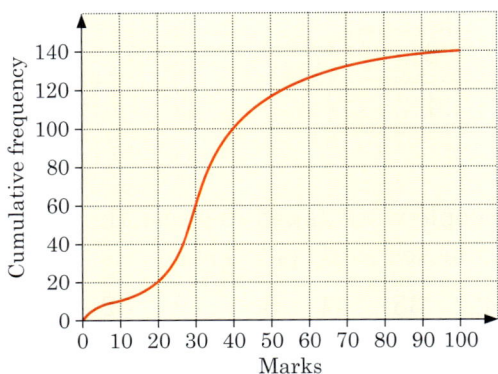

From the graph, estimate:

a) the median mark

b) the mark at the lower quartile and at the upper quartile

c) the interquartile range

d) the pass mark if three-fifths of the students passed

e) the number of students achieving more than 30 marks

f) the 15th percentile.

For Questions **3–6**, draw a cumulative frequency curve, and estimate:

a) the median **b)** the interquartile range.

3.

Mass (kg)	Frequency
1–5	4
6–10	7
11–15	11
16–20	18
21–25	22
26–30	10
31–35	5
36–40	3

4.

Length (cm)	Frequency
41–50	6
51–60	8
61–70	14
71–80	21
81–90	26
91–100	14
101–110	7
111–120	4

5.

Time (seconds)	Frequency
36–45	3
46–55	7
56–65	10
66–75	18
76–85	12
86–95	6
96–105	4

6.

Number of marks	Frequency
1–10	0
11–20	2
21–30	4
31–40	10
41–50	17
51–60	11
61–70	3
71–80	3

7. In an experiment, 50 people were asked to guess the mass of a bunch of flowers in grams. The guesses were as follows:

47	39	21	30	42	35	44	36	19	52
23	32	66	29	5	40	33	11	44	22
27	58	38	37	48	63	23	40	53	24
47	22	44	33	13	59	33	49	57	30
17	45	38	33	25	40	51	56	28	64

Construct a frequency table using intervals 0–9, 10–19, 20–29, etc.

Hence draw a cumulative frequency curve for this data set.

8. In a competition, 30 children had to pick up as many paper clips as possible in one minute using a pair of tweezers. The results were as follows:

3	17	8	11	26	23	18	28	33	38
12	38	22	50	5	35	39	30	31	43
27	34	9	25	39	14	27	16	33	49

Construct a frequency table using intervals 1–10, 11–20, and so on and hence draw a cumulative frequency curve.

a) From the curve, estimate the median number of clips picked up.

b) From the frequency table, estimate the mean of the distribution using the mid-interval values 5.5, 15.5, etc.

c) Calculate the exact value of the mean using the original data.

d) Why is it possible only to estimate the mean in part **b**?

13.6 Comparing data sets

Graphs and charts can often be used to compare two different sets of data.

Exercise 13.6A

1. After finishing dinner, Zac and Lucy had 4 hours before going to bed.

These pie charts show how they spent their time.

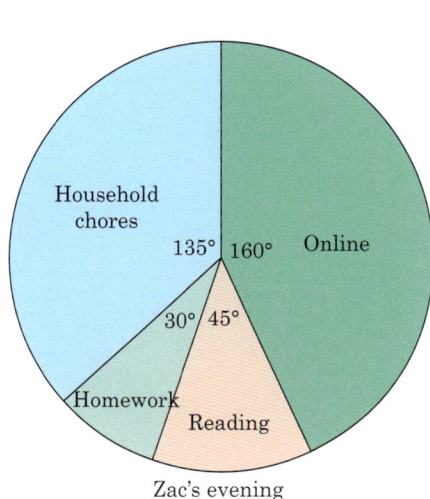

Zac's evening

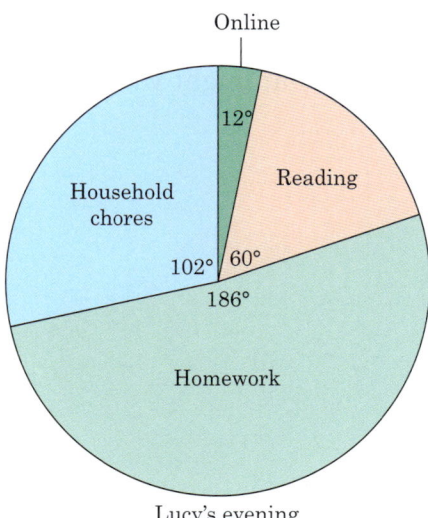

Lucy's evening

a) Who spent more time reading, Zac or Lucy?

b) How many minutes did Zac spend doing his homework?

c) How many more minutes did Zac spend doing household chores than Lucy?

2. A group of 60 children and a group of 60 adults were asked to guess how many olives there were in a large jar. Their responses have been illustrated in the following cumulative frequency graph.

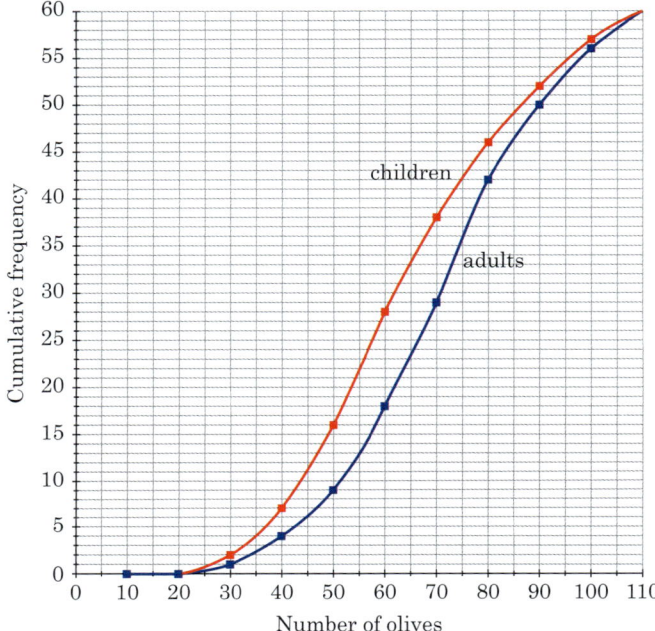

a) Work out estimates of the median and interquartile range for both groups.

b) Given that there were actually 70 olives in the jar, which group was better at guessing?

c) It was later discovered that the group of adults who were asked all enjoyed Italian cookery. What might you infer from the results?

Revision exercise 13

1. A pie chart is drawn with sectors to represent the following percentages:

   20%, 45%, 30%, 5%.

   What is the angle of the sector which represents 45%?

2. The pie chart shows the numbers of votes for candidates A, B and C in an election.

   What percentage of the votes were cast in favour of candidate C?

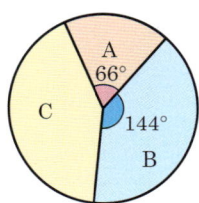

3. A pie chart is drawn showing the expenditure of a robotics club as follows:

Materials	$410
Travel	$90
Contest fees	$60
Miscellaneous	$40

   What is the angle of the sector showing the expenditure on travel?

4. The mean of four numbers is 21.

   a) Calculate the sum of the four numbers.

   Six other numbers have a mean of 18.

   b) Calculate the mean of all ten numbers.

5. A data set consists of these numbers:
   3, 1, 5, 4, 3, 8, 2, 3, 4, 1

   Find:

   a) the mean   b) the median

   c) the mode

6.

Marks	3	4	5	6	7	8
Number of students	2	3	6	4	3	2

   The table shows the number of students in a class who scored marks 3 to 8 in a test. Find:

   a) the mean mark   b) the modal mark

   c) the median mark.

7. The mean height of 10 boys is 1.60 m and the mean height of 15 girls is 1.52 m. Find the mean height of the 25 boys and girls.

8.

Marks	3	4	5
Number of students	3	x	4

   The table shows the number of students who scored marks 3, 4 or 5 in a test. Given that the mean mark is 4.1, find x.

9. Two classes of 19 students take a maths test. The scores for the students in Class 1 are as follows:

11	14	16	17	18	22	26
28	34	39	41	42	44	44
46	46	48	49	50		

   a) Draw a stem-and-leaf diagram to illustrate these results.

   b) Use the stem-and-leaf diagram to find the median and interquartile range of these results.

   Here is a summary of the results for students in Class 2.

   Lowest score: 23   Lower quartile: 30
   Median: 36   Upper quartile: 44

   Highest score: 48

   c) Compare the results from the two classes.

Examination-style exercise 13

1. The mass of each of 200 cupcakes was checked by an inspector in a factory.
   The results are shown by the cumulative frequency curve.

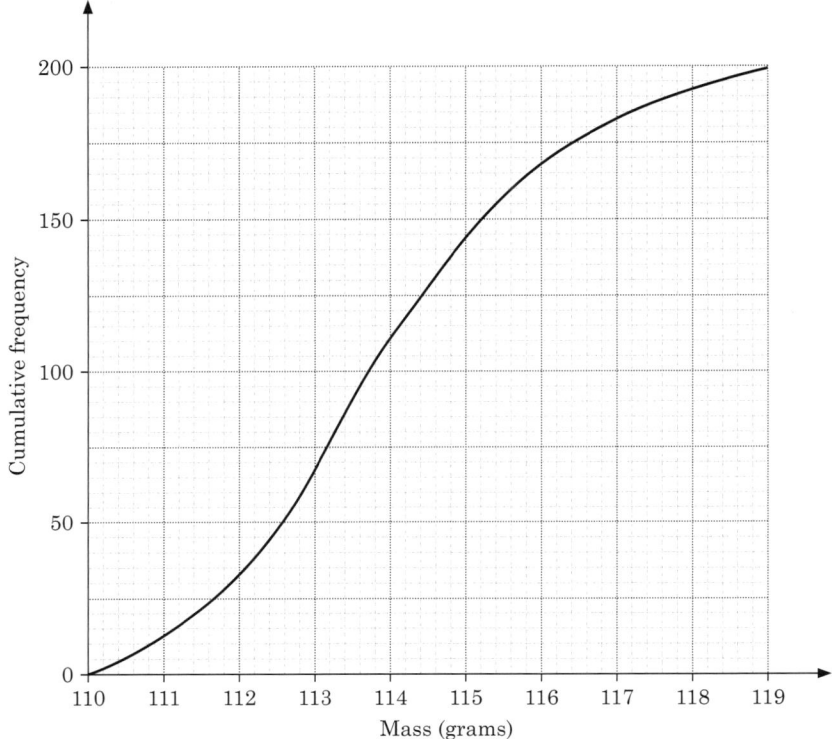

Use the cumulative frequency curve to work out:

a) the median mass, [1]

b) the interquartile range, [2]

c) the number of cupcakes with a mass greater than 116 grams. [1]

2. a) Each student in a class is given a bag of stones for a craft project.

   The students note the number of stones in their bag. The results
   are shown in the table, where $0 \leqslant x < 10$.

Number of stones	19	20	21
Frequency (number of bags)	12	10	x

   i)   State the mode. [1]

   ii)   Find the possible values of the median. [3]

   iii) The mean number of sweets is 19.64.

   Find the value of x. [3]

b) The mass, m grams, of each of 200 buttons is noted and the results are shown in the table.

Mass (m grams)	Frequency
$5 < m \leqslant 15$	21
$15 < m \leqslant 17$	19
$17 < m \leqslant 19$	22
$19 < m \leqslant 25$	18

i) Calculate an estimate of the mean mass of a button. [4]

ii) On a histogram, the height of the column for the $15 < m \leqslant 17$ interval is 19 cm. Calculate the heights of the other three columns.
Do not draw the histogram. [5]

3. The speeds (v kilometres/hour) of 150 cars passing a 60 km/h speed limit sign are recorded. A cumulative frequency curve to show the results is drawn below.

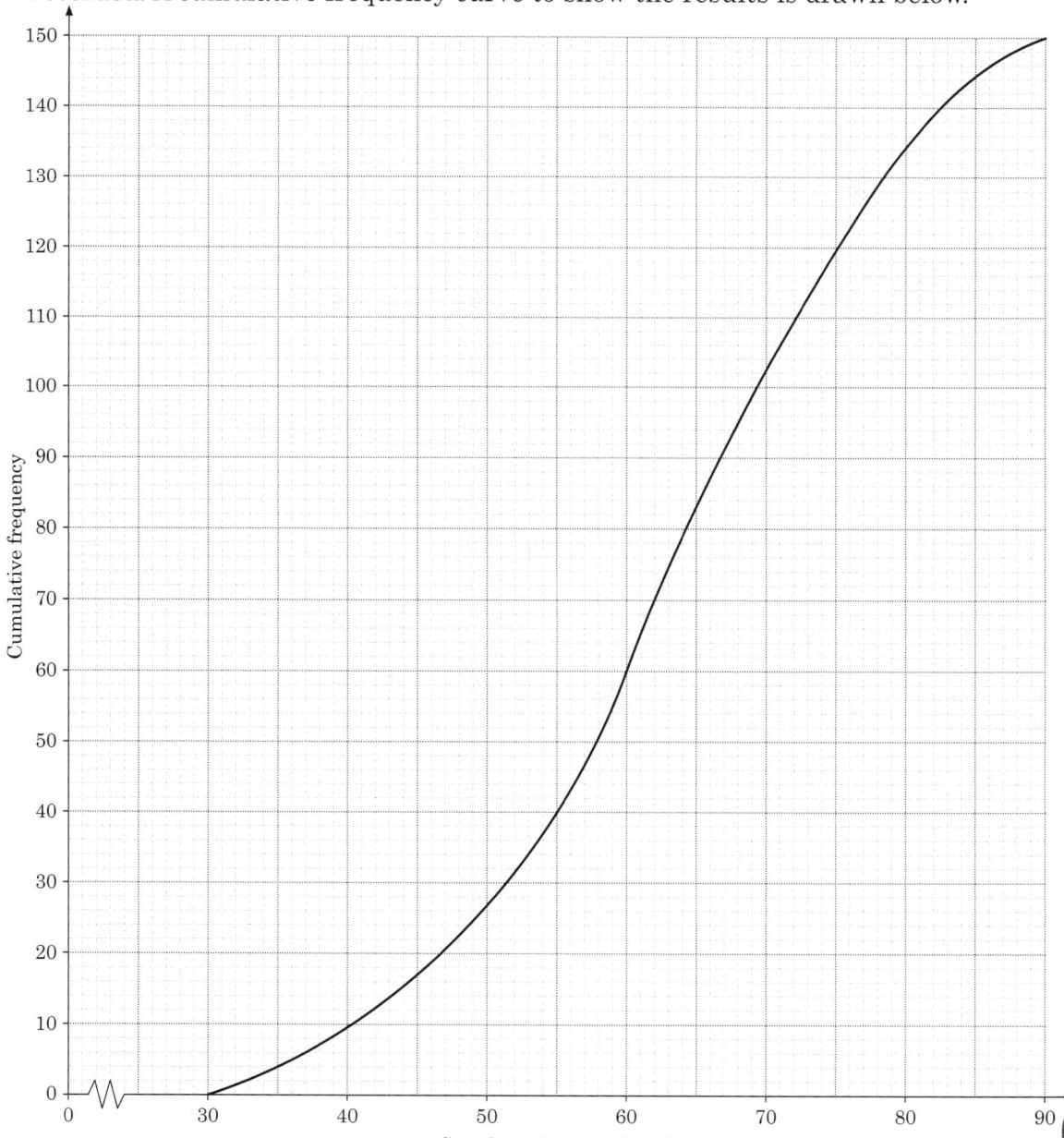

Speed (v kilometres/hour)

a) Use the graph to find:

   i)   the median speed,   [1]

   ii) the interquartile range of the speeds,   [2]

   iii) the number of cars travelling with speeds of more than 60 km/h.   [2]

b) A frequency table showing the speeds of the cars is

Speed (v km/h)	Frequency
$30 < v \leqslant 40$	10
$40 < v \leqslant 50$	17
$50 < v \leqslant 60$	n
$60 < v \leqslant 70$	42
$70 < v \leqslant 80$	32
$80 < v \leqslant 90$	16

   i) Find the value of n.   [1]

   ii) Calculate an estimate of the mean speed.   [4]

c) Answer this part of this question on a sheet of graph paper.

Another frequency table for the same speeds is:

Speed (v km/h)	$30 < v \leqslant 50$	$50 < v \leqslant 60$	$60 < v \leqslant 90$
Frequency	27	33	90

Draw an accurate histogram to show this information. Use 1 cm to represent 5 units on the speed axis and 3 cm to represent 1 unit on the frequency density axis (Your bars should be accurate to the nearest mm.)

14 Probability

Blaise Pascal (1623–1662) was a mathematical child prodigy who was educated by his father. Pascal's work on probability showed for the first time that absolute certainty is not a necessity in mathematics and science. His development of probability theory continues to be very important in economics, especially actuarial science. Pascal even designed and constructed a calculating device to help his father with his tax computations. It is considered to be the first digital calculator since it operated by counting integers.

- Understand and use probability including the language, notation and the scale from 0 to 1 including calculating the probability of an event and understanding the probability of an event not happing is 1 – the probability of the event happening.
- Understand and use relative frequency to estimate probability and find expected frequencies.
- Find the probability of combined events including conditional probabilities using these diagrams:
  - sample space diagrams
  - tables
  - Venn diagrams
  - tree diagrams.

14.1 Simple probability

Probability is about working out how likely it is that a particular event will happen. Because of this, it has many practical uses. All major airlines, for example, regularly overbook flights because they can usually predict with a great deal of accuracy how likely it is that a certain number of passengers will fail to arrive.

Here are some basic facts about probability that you need to learn:

- If an event **cannot** happen, the probability of it occurring is 0.
- If an event is **certain** to happen, the probability of it occurring is 1.
- All other probabilities lie between 0 and 1. You write probabilities using either fractions, decimals or percentages.
- You write the probability of an event A happening as P(A) and the probability of it not happening as P(A′), where A′ means 'not A'.
- Because either A or 'not A' must always happen, and there is no third option, we can always say that P(A′) = 1 − P(A).

Sometimes probabilities can be calculated exactly. Sometimes, however, they depend very much on the circumstances surrounding the event; for example, when and where it takes place.

Exercise 14.1A

1. Draw a probability scale from 0 to 1 and place the letter for each of the following events on the line to show what their probability is. Some of the probabilities you will be able to calculate exactly. Some will need to be estimated.

   A Tossing a coin and it landing on heads.

   B Rolling a six on a fair six-sided dice.

   C It will rain tomorrow.

   D A randomly chosen triangle will have three sides.

   E The sun will rise tomorrow morning.

   F At some point in the future, you will travel into space.

> **Tip**
>
> When a dice or coin is described as being fair, it means that all the possible outcomes are equally likely. If some outcomes are more likely than others, we say it is biased.

G You will use a smartphone tomorrow.

H You will go to school tomorrow.

I A randomly chosen day of the week will be a Saturday.

J Rolling a seven on a fair six-sided dice.

2. If the probability that it will rain tomorrow is 0.3, what is the probability that it will not rain tomorrow?

3. In a game that you either win or lose, if the probability that you win the game is 25%, what is the probability that you lose?

4. If the probability that I will be late to an appointment today is $\frac{1}{6}$, what is the probability that I will not be late?

Calculating probabilities

Suppose an event can have n equally likely outcomes and suppose that a 'success' can occur in s out of the n different ways. Then the probability of a 'success' $= \frac{s}{n}$. For example, if you roll a dice, there are 6 possible outcomes. If you want to roll a prime number, this can occur in 3 different ways: by rolling a two, three or five. The probability of success by rolling a prime number is therefore $\frac{3}{6} = \frac{1}{2}$.

Example 1

The numbers 1 to 20 are each written on cards.

The 20 cards are mixed together.

One card is chosen at random from the pack.

Find the probability that the number on the card is:

a) even   **b)** a factor of 24   **c)** prime   **d)** not prime.

Count the number of ways in which a 'success' can occur and divide by the number of possible results of a 'trial'.

a) There are 20 cards, and we are considering 'even' to be a 'success'. There are 10 even numbered cards.

$$P(\text{even}) = \frac{10}{20} = \frac{1}{2}$$

---

b) P(factor of 24) = P(1, 2, 3, 4, 6, 8, 12)

$$= \frac{7}{20}$$

c) P(prime) = P(2, 3, 5, 7, 11, 13, 17, 19)

$$= \frac{8}{20} = \frac{2}{5}$$

d) P(not prime) = 1 − P(prime) = $1 - \frac{2}{5} = \frac{3}{5}$

Sometimes, a useful way of listing all the possible outcomes so that you can see how many of them are a success is to make a sample space diagram. This usually takes the form of a table.

Example 2

A green dice and an orange dice are rolled at the same time and their scores are added together.

a) Display all the possible outcomes in a sample space diagram.

b) Find the probability of obtaining:

   i) a total of 5

   ii) a total of 11

   iii) a two on the green dice and a six on the orange dice.

a) There are 36 possible outcomes, shown in this sample space diagram.

+	1	2	3	4	5	6
1	2	3	4	5	6	7
2	3	4	5	6	7	8
3	4	5	6	7	8	9
4	5	6	7	8	9	10
5	6	7	8	9	10	11
6	7	8	9	10	11	12

b) **i)** There are four ways of obtaining a total of 5 on the two dice, highlighted pink in the diagram.

Probability of obtaining a total of 5 = $\frac{4}{36} = \frac{1}{9}$

   ii) There are two ways of obtaining a total of 11, highlighted yellow in the diagram.

P(total of 11) = $\frac{2}{36} = \frac{1}{18}$

   iii) There is only one way of obtaining a two on the green dice and a six on the orange dice, highlighted blue in the diagram.

P(two on green and six on orange) = $\frac{1}{36}$

Exercise 14.1B

In this exercise, all dice are fair, six-sided dice with faces numbered 1 to 6.

1. A fair dice is rolled once. Find the probability of obtaining:

   a) a six
   b) an even number
   c) a number greater than three
   d) a three or a five.

2. The two sides of a coin are known as a 'head' and a 'tail'. A 10c and a 5c coin are tossed at the same time.

   a) List all the possible outcomes in a sample space diagram.

   b) Find the probability of obtaining:

   i) two heads
   ii) a head and a tail.

3. A bag contains 6 red balls and 4 green balls.

   a) Find the probability of selecting at random:

   i) a red ball
   ii) a green ball.

   b) One red ball is removed from the bag. Find the new probability of selecting at random

   i) a red ball
   ii) a green ball.

4. One letter is selected at random from the word 'UNNECESSARY'.

   Find the probability of selecting:

   a) an R
   b) an E
   c) an O
   d) a C.

5. Three coins are tossed at the same time. List all the possible outcomes. Find the probability of obtaining:

   a) three heads
   b) two heads and one tail
   c) no heads
   d) at least one head.

6. A bag contains 10 red balls, 5 blue balls and 7 green balls. Find the probability of selecting at random:

   a) a red ball
   b) a green ball
   c) a blue *or* a red ball
   d) a red *or* a green ball.

7. Cards with the numbers 2 to 101 are placed in a hat. Find the probability of selecting:

   a) an even number
   b) a number less than 14
   c) a square number
   d) a prime number less than 20.

8. A red dice and a blue dice are rolled at the same time.
List all the possible outcomes in a sample space diagram.
Find the probability of obtaining:

a) a total of 10   **b)** a total of 12

c) a total less than 6   **d)** the same number on both dice

e) a total more than 9.

What is the most likely total?

9. A dice is rolled; when the result has been recorded, the dice
is rolled a second time. Find the probability of obtaining:

a) a total of 4 from the two rolls

b) a total of 8 from the two rolls

c) a total between 5 and 9 inclusive from the two rolls

d) a number on the second roll which is double the number
on the first roll

e) a number on the second roll which is four times the
number on the first roll.

10. Find the probability of:

a) rolling a number less than eight on a single dice

b) obtaining the same number of heads and tails when
five coins are tossed

c) selecting a square number from the set
A = {4, 9, 16, 25, 36, 49}

d) selecting a prime number from the set A.

11. Four coins are tossed at the same time.
List all the possible outcomes in a systematic way.
Find the probability of obtaining:

a) two heads and two tails   **b)** four tails

c) at least one tail   **d)** three heads and one tail.

12. Cards numbered 1 to 1000 are put in a box. Alison selects a
card at random. What is the probability that she selects a
card containing at least one '3'?

13. One ball is selected at random from a bag containing
12 balls, of which x are white.

a) What is the probability of selecting a white ball?

b) When a further 6 white balls are added the probability
of selecting a white ball is doubled. Find x.

14. Two dice and two coins are thrown at the same time.
Find the probability of obtaining:

a) two heads and a total of 12 on the dice

b) a head, a tail and a total of 9 on the dice

c) two tails and a total of 3 on the dice.

d) What is the most likely outcome?

15. A red, a blue and a green dice are all thrown at the same
time. Display all the possible outcomes in a suitable way.
Find the probability of obtaining:

a) a total of 18 on the three dice

b) a total of 4 on the three dice

c) a total of 10 on the three dice

d) a total of 15 on the three dice

e) a total of 7 on the three dice

f) the same number on each dice.

14.2 Relative frequency

To work out the probability of a drawing pin landing point up,
you can do an experiment in which a drawing pin is dropped
many times. If the pin lands 'point up' on x occasions out of a total
number of N trials, the **relative frequency** of it landing 'point up'
is $\dfrac{x}{N}$.

When an experiment is repeated many times, you can use the
relative frequency as an estimate of the probability of the event
occurring.

Suppose a dice, suspected of being biased, was rolled 300 times.
After each set of 25 rolls, the number of sixes obtained was noted
and the results were as follows:

5 4 6 6 6 5 3 7 6 5 6 5

After 25 rolls, the relative frequency of sixes $= \dfrac{5}{25} = 0.2$

After 50 rolls, the relative frequency of sixes $= \dfrac{5 + 4}{50} = 0.18$

After 75 rolls, the relative frequency of sixes $= \dfrac{5 + 4 + 6}{75} = 0.2$

The calculation is continued for each set of 25 rolls, and the results are plotted on this graph.

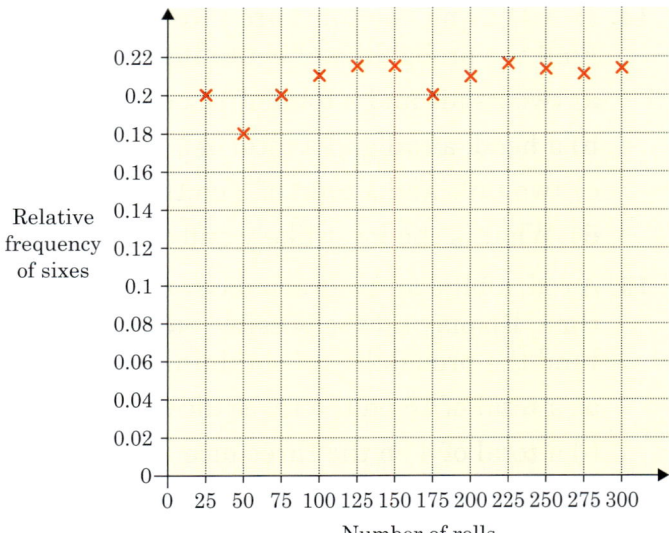

As you include more and more results, the average number of sixes per roll settles down at slightly over 0.21.

For this dice, the **relative frequency** of sixes was just over 0.21

If the dice was fair, you would expect to get a six on $\frac{1}{6}$ of the throws.

So the relative frequency would be 0.1̇6̇

The **expected frequency** would be equal to one sixth of the total, so in 300 rolls you would expect to get (approximately) 50 sixes. The dice in the experiment does appear to be biased so that sixes occur more frequently than you would expect for a fair dice.

Exercise 14.2A

1. **a)** Repeatedly roll two dice and multiply their scores together, writing down each time whether the product of the two numbers is odd or even.

   b) From your data, calculate an estimate of the probability of the product being odd using the relative frequency.

   c) Using a sample space diagram, work out what you think the probability of the product being odd is in theory.

   d) How similar or different are the two probabilities? If they are quite different, why do you think this might be?

2. A spinner has a red section and a blue section. Debbie spins the spinner 400 times.

   The table shows the relative frequency of the spinner landing on red after different numbers of spins.

Number of spins	Relative frequency of red
100	0.11
200	0.15
300	0.18
400	0.24

a) How many of the first 100 spins landed on red?

b) How many times did it land on red in total?

c) What is the best estimate of the probability of the spinner landing on red?

3. Veronica has a biased coin. The probability of it landing on heads is 0.7. Veronica is going to toss the coin 240 times. Work out an estimate for the number of times the coin will land on heads.

4. Javier rolls a dice 348 times. Work out an estimate for the number of times Javier rolls an even number.

5. The test results of 80 students are recorded in the two-way table shown.

	Grade			Total
	A	B	C	
Band 1	18	15	6	39
Band 2	10	14	17	41
Total	28	29	23	80

These results are used to predict the results of the following year's students.

The following year there are 100 students.

a) Find the probability that a randomly selected student will be:

i) in band 1 and get a grade A

ii) in band 2 and get a grade C.

b) Calculate an estimate of the number of students who, the following year, will:

i) get a grade B

ii) be in band 2 and get a grade A

iii) be in band 1 and get a grade C.

6. The spinner has an equal chance of landing on any digit from 0 to 9. Four friends do an experiment where they spin the pointer a different number of times and record the number of zeros they get.

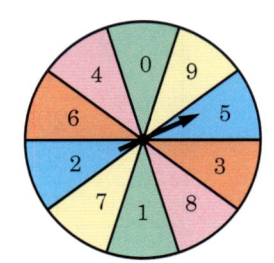

Here are their results.

	Number of spins	Number of zeros	Relative frequency
Steve	10	2	0.2
Nick	150	14	0.093
Mike	200	41	0.205
Jason	1000	104	0.104

One of the four recorded his results incorrectly. Say who you think this was and explain why.

14.3 Mutually exclusive and independent events

Two events are **mutually exclusive** if they cannot occur at the same time: for example, choosing a random number and it being both even and odd at the same time. Thus, 'even' and 'odd' are mutually exclusive.

The 'OR rule' says that for mutually exclusive events A and B:

$$P(A \text{ or } B) = P(A) + P(B)$$

Two events are **independent** if the probability of one event occurring is not affected by the other event occurring.

For example, if you roll a dice and toss a coin, the number that the dice lands on is not affected by the outcome of the coin toss.

The 'AND rule' says that for independent events A and B:

$$P(A \text{ and } B) = P(A) \times P(B)$$

> **Tip**
>
> For mutually exclusive events A and B,
>
> $P(A \text{ and } B) = 0$

Example 1

One ball is selected at random from a bag containing 5 red balls, 2 yellow balls and 4 white balls. Find the probability of selecting a red ball or a white ball.

The two events are mutually exclusive.

P (red ball *or* white ball) = P(red) + P(white)

$$= \frac{5}{11} + \frac{4}{11}$$

$$= \frac{9}{11}$$

Example 2

A fair coin is tossed and a fair dice is rolled. Find the probability of obtaining a 'head' and a 'six'.

The two events are independent.

P (head *and* six) = P(head) × P(six)

$$= \frac{1}{2} \times \frac{1}{6}$$

$$= \frac{1}{12}$$

Exercise 14.3A

1. A coin is tossed and a dice is rolled. Write down the probability of obtaining:

   a) heads on the coin

   b) an odd number on the dice

   c) heads on the coin and an odd number on the dice.

2. A sock is selected at random from a drawer containing 3 red socks, 4 black socks and 5 green socks. The first sock is replaced and a second is selected. Find the probability of obtaining:

   a) two red socks   **b)** two green socks.

3. The letters of the word 'INDEPENDENT' are written on individual cards and the cards are put into a box. A card is selected and then replaced and then a second card is selected. Find the probability of obtaining:

   a) the letter 'P' twice   **b)** the letter 'E' twice.

4. Three coins are tossed and two dice are thrown at the same time. Find the probability of obtaining:

   a) three heads and a total of 12 on the dice

   b) three tails and a total of 9 on the dice.

5. When a golfer plays any hole, he will take 3, 4, 5, 6, or 7 strokes with probabilities of $\frac{1}{10}, \frac{1}{5}, \frac{2}{5}, \frac{1}{5}$ and $\frac{1}{10}$ respectively. He never takes more than 7 strokes.

Find the probability of:

a) scoring 4 on each of the first three holes

b) scoring 3, 4 and 5 (in that order) on the first three holes

c) scoring a total of 28 for the first four holes

d) scoring a total of 10 for the first three holes

e) scoring a total of 20 for the first three holes.

6. A coin is biased so that it shows heads with a probability of $\frac{2}{3}$. The same coin is tossed three times.

Find the probability of obtaining:

a) two tails on the first two tosses

b) a head, a tail and a head (in that order)

c) two heads and one tail (in any order).

14.4 Tree diagrams

A tree diagram is a probability tool used to calculate the number of possible outcomes of an event, by presenting the possible outcomes in an organised way.

Example 1

A bag contains 5 red balls and 3 green balls. A ball is drawn at random and then put back in the bag. Another ball is drawn.

What is the probability that both balls are green?

The probability of this event is obtained by simply multiplying the fractions on the two branches.

The thicker branches represent the selection of a green ball twice.

$$P \text{ (two green balls)} = \frac{3}{8} \times \frac{3}{8} = \frac{9}{64}$$

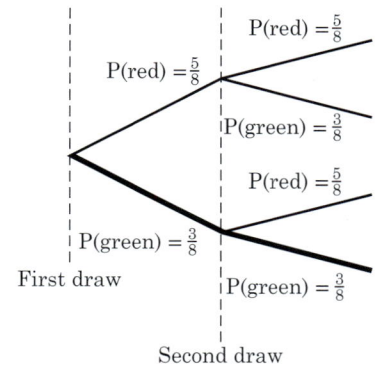

Example 2

A bag contains 5 red balls and 3 green balls. A ball is selected at random and not replaced. A second ball is then selected. Find the probability of selecting:

a) two green balls

b) one red ball and one green ball.

a) P(two green balls) $= \dfrac{3}{8} \times \dfrac{2}{7}$

$$= \dfrac{3}{28}$$

b) P(one red, one green)

$$= \left(\dfrac{5}{8} \times \dfrac{3}{7} \right) + \left(\dfrac{3}{8} \times \dfrac{5}{7} \right)$$

$$= \dfrac{15}{28}$$

P(red) $= \frac{5}{8}$

P(green) $= \frac{3}{8}$

First draw

P(red) $= \frac{4}{7}$ P(red, red) $= \frac{5}{8} \times \frac{4}{7}$

P(green) $= \frac{3}{7}$ P(red, green) $= \frac{5}{8} \times \frac{3}{7}$

P(red) $= \frac{5}{7}$ P(green, red) $= \frac{3}{8} \times \frac{5}{7}$

P(green) $= \frac{2}{7}$ P(green, green) $= \frac{3}{8} \times \frac{2}{7}$

Second draw

Exercise 14.4A

1. A bag contains 10 discs: 7 are black and 3 white. A disc is selected, and then replaced. A second disc is selected. Copy and complete the tree diagram showing all the probabilities and outcomes. Find the probability that:

   a) both discs are black   **b)** both discs are white.

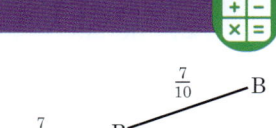

2. A bag contains 5 red balls and 3 green balls. A ball is drawn and then replaced before a ball is drawn again.

   Draw a tree diagram to show all the possible outcomes. Find the probability that:

   a) two green balls are drawn

   b) the first ball is red and the second is green.

3. A bag contains 7 green discs and 3 blue discs. A disc is drawn and *not* replaced. A second disc is drawn.

   Copy and complete the tree diagram. Find the probability that:

   a) both discs are green   **b)** both discs are blue.

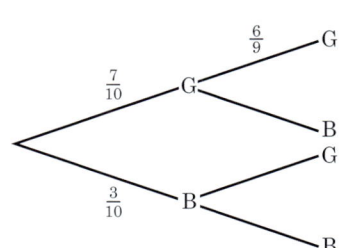

4. A bag contains 5 red balls, 3 blue balls and 2 yellow balls. A ball is drawn and not replaced. A second ball is drawn. Find the probability of drawing:

a) two red balls

b) one blue ball and one yellow ball

c) two yellow balls

d) two balls of the same colour.

5. A bag contains 4 red balls, 2 green balls and 3 blue balls. A ball is drawn and not replaced. A second ball is drawn. Find the probability of drawing:

a) two blue balls

b) two red balls

c) one red ball and one blue ball

d) one green ball and one red ball.

6. A six-sided dice is rolled three times. Draw a tree diagram, showing at each branch the two events: 'six' and 'not six'. What is the probability of throwing a total of:

a) three sixes

b) no sixes

c) one six

d) at least one six (use part **b**).

7. A bag contains 6 red marbles and 4 blue marbles. A marble is drawn at random and not replaced. Two further draws are made, again without replacement. Find the probability of drawing:

a) three red marbles   **b)** three blue marbles

c) no red marbles   **d)** at least one red marble.

8. When a cutting is taken from a geranium the probability that it grows is $\frac{3}{4}$. Three cuttings are taken. What is the probability that:

a) all three grow

b) none of them grow?

9. A dice has its six faces marked 0, 1, 1, 1, 6, 6. Two of these dice are rolled together and the total score is recorded. Draw a sample space diagram.

a) How many different totals are possible?

b) What is the probability of obtaining a total of 7?

10. A coin is biased so that the probability of a 'head' is $\frac{3}{4}$.
Find the probability that, when tossed three times,
it shows:

a) three tails
b) two heads and one tail
c) one head and two tails
d) no tails.

Write down the sum of the probabilities in (**a**), (**b**), (**c**) and (**d**).

11. A party box contains 3 white balloons, 5 yellow balloons
and 12 red balloons. Students line up to take a balloon at
random. Find the probability that:

a) the first three students all get a white balloon

b) the first three students all get a yellow balloon

c) the first three students all get different colour balloons

d) the first four students all get a yellow balloon.

(Do not cancel down the fractions.)

12. The probability that an amateur golfer actually hits the
ball is $\frac{1}{10}$. If four separate attempts are made, find the
probability that the ball will be hit:

a) four times
b) at least twice
c) not at all.

13. A box contains x milk chocolates and y plain chocolates.
Two chocolates are chosen at random. Find, in terms of x
and y, the probability of choosing:

a) a milk chocolate on the first choice

b) two milk chocolates

c) one of each sort

d) two plain chocolates.

14. Bag A contains 3 red balls and 3 blue balls.
Bag B contains 1 red ball and 3 blue balls.
A ball is taken at random from bag A and placed
in bag B. A ball is then chosen from bag B.
What is the probability that the ball taken from B is red?

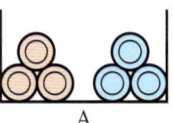
A

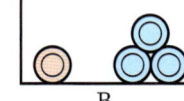
B

15. On a Monday or a Thursday, Cerys paints a 'masterpiece'
with a probability of $\frac{1}{5}$. On any other day, the probability of
producing a 'masterpiece' is $\frac{1}{100}$. Find the probability that
on one day chosen at random, she will paint a masterpiece.

16. Two four-sided dice, each with faces marked 1, 2, 3 and 4, are rolled together.

   a) What is the most likely total score on the faces pointing downwards?

   b) What is the probability of obtaining this score on three successive throws of the two dice?

17. A bag contains 3 red, 4 white and 5 green balls. Three balls are selected without replacement. Find the probability that the three balls chosen are:

   a) all red

   b) all green

   c) one of each colour.

   If the selection of the three balls was carried out 1100 times, how often would you expect to choose:

   d) three red balls

   e) one of each colour?

18. There are 1000 components in a box of which 10 are known to be defective. Two components are selected at random. What is the probability that:

   a) both are defective

   b) neither are defective

   c) just one is defective?

   (Do *not* simplify your answers.)

19. There are 10 boys and 15 girls in a class. Two children are chosen at random. What is the probability that:

   a) both are boys

   b) both are girls

   c) one is a boy and one is a girl?

20. There are 500 ball bearings in a box of which 100 are known to be undersized. Three ball bearings are selected at random. What is the probability that:

   a) all three are undersized

   b) none are undersized?

   Give your answers as decimals correct to three significant figures.

21. There are 9 boys and 15 girls in a class. Three children are chosen at random. Find the probability that:

    a) all three are boys

    b) all three are girls

    c) one is a boy and two are girls.

    Give your answers as fractions.

> **Tip**
>
> You don't have to simplify fractions when you answer probability questions.

14.5 Probability from Venn diagrams

Venn diagrams can be used to solve certain types of probability questions.

You are already used to the idea that 'the probability of A' can be written as P(A) and 'the probability of B' can be written as P(B). In a Venn diagram, events A and B are represented by sets.

Sometimes the different regions in the diagram contain the number of elements that belong to that region. Sometimes the different regions contain the probabilities of a randomly selected item belonging to that region.

The **intersection** of the two sets represents event A **and** event B both happening. The probability of this can be written as $P(A \cap B)$.

The **union** of the two sets represents event A **or** event B (or both) happening.

The probability of this is can be written as $P(A \cup B)$.

Example 1

A group of 30 cats were given two different types of food.

    7 cats liked only food A.

    5 cats liked only food B.

    16 liked both, and 2 liked neither food.

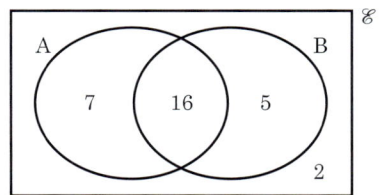

This information is displayed in the Venn diagram.

Find the probability that a randomly selected cat:

a) will like both foods A and B

b) will like only food A

c) does not like food B.

---

a) P(the cat likes both foods) $= \dfrac{16}{30} = \dfrac{8}{15}$

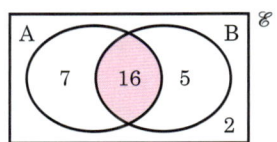

b) P(the cat likes only food A) $= \dfrac{7}{30}$

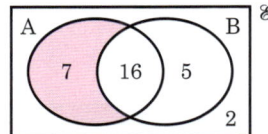

c) P(the cat does not like food B) $= \dfrac{9}{30}$

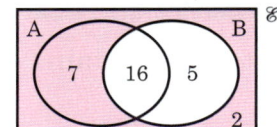

Example 2

A group of 25 students were offered an apple and a banana as part of a packed lunch. Set A represents the students who had an apple. Set B represents the students who had a banana.

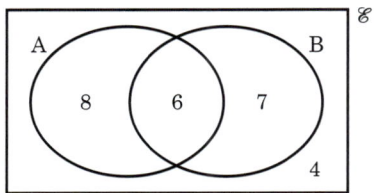

a) Find P(A ∩ B)
b) Find P(A ∪ B)
c) Find P(A′)
d) Find P(B′)

a) $P(A \cap B) = \dfrac{6}{25}$

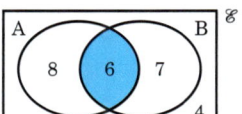

b) $P(A \cup B) = \dfrac{8 + 6 + 7}{25} = \dfrac{21}{25}$

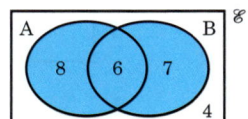

c) $P(A') = \dfrac{7 + 4}{25} = \dfrac{11}{25}$

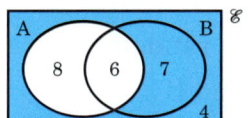

d) $P(B') = \dfrac{8 + 4}{25} = \dfrac{12}{25}$

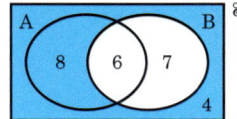

Exercise 14.5A

1. In a class of 25 students, some study French, some study German, some study both, and some study neither. This information is illustrated in the following Venn diagram.

   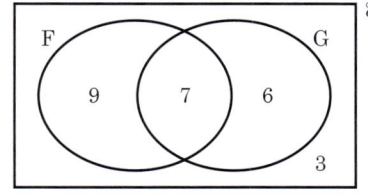

   $\mathscr{E}$ = {students in the class}

   F = {students who study French}

   G = {students who study German}

   a) If a student is chosen randomly from the class, find

   i) P(F) **ii)** P(F ∩ G)

   iii) P(F′ ∩ G′) **iv)** P(F′ ∩ G)

   b) Give a real-world interpretation of **a) iii)** and **iv)**

2. A group of 30 children were asked whether they liked eating carrots. Some said they liked eating them, some said they didn't like them but ate them anyway, and some said they refused to eat them. This information is illustrated in the following Venn diagram.

   $\mathscr{E}$ = {the group of children}

   C = {those who eat carrots}

   L = {those who like carrots}

   a) Find the probability that a randomly selected student:

   i) likes carrots

   ii) does not like carrots but does eat them

   iii) does not like carrots and refuses to eat them.

   b) What type of person does the number 4 in the diagram represent?

3. A group of 50 students have the option of going on two different school trips. 20 of them are going to the museum and to the theme park. 18 of them are going to the museum but not to the theme park. 3 are not going on either outing.

   a) Illustrate this information in a Venn diagram, where the set M represents the students going to the museum and set T represents the students going to the theme park.

   b) If a student is randomly selected, find

   i) P(M′ ∩ T) **ii)** P(M)

   iii) P(T) **iv)** P(M′ ∪ T)

4. A group of 12 friends were discussing the various places they had visited. Two of them had been to Spain, but not Italy. Four had been to Italy, but not Spain. The number who had been to both countries was twice the number who had been to neither.

a) Illustrate this information in a Venn diagram.

b) Find the probability that a randomly selected member of the group

i) had been to Italy and Spain

ii) had been to Italy

iii) had not been to Italy.

5. A book club has 30 members. Some of them like detective stories (D), some like historical fiction (H), some like science fiction (S) and one member does not like any of these genres.
This information is illustrated in the Venn diagram.

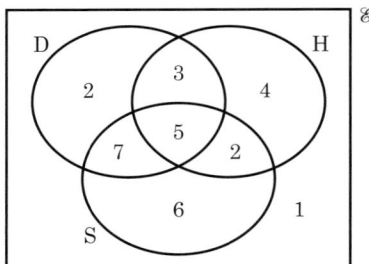

If a member of the group is randomly selected, find:

a) P(D)

b) P(H ∩ S)

c) P(S ∩ D′)

d) P(H′)

e) P(D ∩ H ∩ S)

6. In a school year group consisting of 120 students, each student studies one or more of the three sciences, Biology, Chemistry and Physics. Here is a Venn diagram illustrating this.

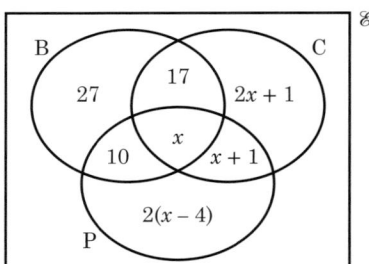

𝒮 = {students in the year group}

B = {students who study Biology}

C = {students who study Chemistry}

P = {students who study Physics}

a) Work out the value of x.

b) Find the probability that a randomly selected student

i) studies Biology

ii) studies Chemistry and Physics

iii) studies Chemistry but not Biology

iv) does not study Physics.

7. $\mathscr{E}$ = {positive whole numbers from 1 to 20}.

F, P and T are sets of positive whole numbers, such that

F = {1, 2, 3, 5, 8, 13}, P = {2, 3, 5, 7, 11, 13, 17, 19}, and

T = {3, 6, 9, 12, 15, 18}

a) Illustrate these three sets in a Venn diagram.

b) Calculate:

    i) $P(F \cap P)$ **ii)** $P(F \cup T)$

    iii) $P(P \cap T')$ **iv)** $P(F' \cup P')$ **v)** $P(F \cup T')$

14.6 Conditional probability

A **conditional probability** is the probability of an event, given that another event has occurred. The probability of event A, given that event B has already occurred, is called the probability of 'A given B' and is written $P(A|B)$. There are many ways to calculate conditional probabilities, including tree diagrams, Venn diagrams, and logic combined with a basic knowledge of probability.

You may find it useful to use the formula $P(A \mid B) = \dfrac{P(A \cap B)}{P(B)}$, but this is not required knowledge for this course.

> **Tip**
>
> An example of conditional probability is selecting a student with black hair given that they are a girl.

Example

A bookshop has a café on the top floor. Some people go into the shop just to use the café, some just to buy a book, some do both, and some do neither. The Venn diagram shows what a group of 50 people did in the bookshop one day.

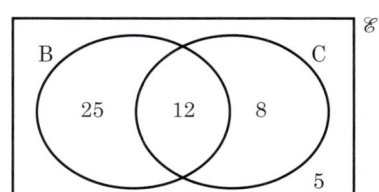

$\mathscr{E}$ = {the group of 50 people}

B = {those who bought a book}

C = {those who used the café)

Work out:

a) $P(B|C)$ **b)** $P(C|B)$

---

a) $P(B|C) = \dfrac{\text{the number of people who buy a book and use the café}}{\text{the number of people who use the café}} = \dfrac{12}{20}$

b) $P(C|B) = \dfrac{\text{the number of people who buy a book and use the café}}{\text{the number of people who buy a book}} = \dfrac{12}{37}$

> **Tip**
>
> Note that $P(B|C)$ and $P(C|B)$ are not the same so the denominators are different.

Exercise 14.6A

1. A regular pack of playing cards contains 26 red cards and 26 black cards.

   If you are asked to pick a card at random, what is the probability that you will choose a red card, given that one black card has already been removed from the pack and not replaced?

2. Tiye collected the following seashells one day: 3 Scotch bonnets, 4 lightning whelks and 2 calico clams. She chose one at random and gave it to Erica. She then chose another one at random for herself.

   a) What is the probability that Tiye's shell was a lightning whelk, given that:

   i) Erica's shell was a calico clam

   ii) Erica's shell was a Scotch bonnet?

   b) What is the probability that they both had lightning whelks?

3. A group of 50 people went to a restaurant for a meal. They each chose a main course and a dessert. Their choices are shown in the following table.

	Cheesecake	Gelato	Total
Rainbow trout	17	9	**26**
Chicken curry	10	14	**24**
Total	**27**	**23**	**50**

   Find the probability that a randomly selected member of the group will have chosen:

   a) chicken curry

   b) gelato

   c) cheesecake, given that they chose rainbow trout

   d) chicken curry, given that they chose gelato

   e) gelato, given that they chose chicken curry.

4. If Kebe is late for school, the probability that Lilian is late for school is 0.7.

   If Kebe is not late for school, there is still a probability of 0.2 that Lilian will be late.

The probability that Kebe will be late for school is 0.2.

Here is a tree diagram illustrating this information.

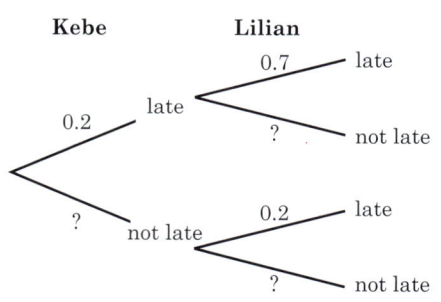

Kebe   **Lilian**

a) Copy and complete the tree diagram.

b) What is the probability that Lilian will not be late, given that Kebe is late?

c) What is the probability that Lilian will be late for school?

5. When Karl goes on holiday, he asks his friend Ellen to water his plant for him while he is away.

If Ellen does not water the plant correctly, the probability that the plant will die is 0.8.

If Ellen does water the plant correctly, there is still a probability of 0.2 that it will die.

The probability that Ellen will water the plant correctly is 0.7.

a) Use a tree diagram to work out the probability that the plant will be alive when Karl returns.

b) What is the probability that Ellen did not water the plant properly, given that Karl returns to find that his plant is dead?

6. A coffee shop manager asked 60 customers if they drank coffee or tea. Some drank only coffee, some drank only tea, some drank both and some drank neither. This information is illustrated in the following Venn diagram.

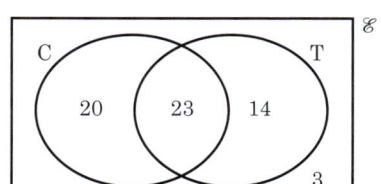

$\mathscr{E}$ = {the 60 customers}

C = {those who drink coffee}

T = {those who drink tea}

Find the probability that a customer, chosen at random:

a) drinks coffee, given that they also drink tea

b) does not drink tea, given that they drink coffee

c) does not drink coffee, given that they do not drink tea.

7. Let A and B be two events, such that
P(A) = 0.8, P(B) = 0.7, and P(A ∩ B) = 0.5.

The Venn diagram illustrates these
probabilities.

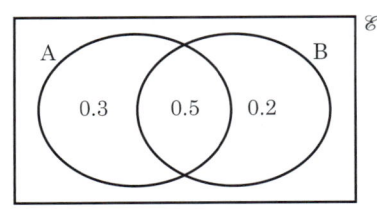

Find:

a) P(A | B)   **b)** P(B | A)   **c)** P(A | B′)   **d)** P(B′ | A′)

Revision exercise 14

1. When two dice are rolled
simultaneously, what is the
probability of obtaining the same
number on both dice?

2. A bag contains 20 discs of equal size
of which 12 are red, x are blue and the
rest are white.

   a) If the probability of randomly
   selecting a blue disc is $\frac{1}{4}$, find x.

   b) A disc is selected and then replaced.
   A second disc is selected. Find the
   probability that neither disc is red.

3. Three dice are rolled. What is the
probability that none of them shows a
1 or a 6?

4. A fair coin is tossed four times. What
is the probability of obtaining at least
three heads?

5. A bag contains 8 balls of which 2 are
red and 6 are white. A ball is randomly
selected and not replaced. A second
ball is selected. Find the probability
of obtaining:

a) two red balls

b) two white balls

c) one ball of each colour.

6. A bag contains x green discs and 5 blue
discs. A disc is randomly selected. A
second disc is selected. Find, in terms
of x, the probability of selecting:

   a) a green disc on the first draw

   b) a green disc on the first and second
   draws, if the first disc is replaced

   c) a green disc on the first and second
   draws, if the first disc is *not* replaced.

7. In a group of 20 people, 5 cannot swim.
If two people are selected at random,
what is the probability that neither of
them can swim?

8. **a)** What is the probability of winning
   the toss in five consecutive hockey
   matches?

   b) What is the probability of winning
   the toss in all the matches in the FA
   cup from the first round to the final
   (that is, 8 matches)?

9. Mr and Mrs Penumbra have three
children. If you know nothing about
them, what is the probability that:

   a) all the children are boys

   b) there are more girls than boys?

   (Assume that a boy is as likely
   as a girl.)

10. The probability that it will be wet today is $\frac{1}{6}$. If it is dry today, the probability that it will be wet tomorrow is $\frac{1}{8}$. What is the probability that both today and tomorrow will be dry?

11. Two dice are rolled. What is the probability that the *product* of the numbers on top is:

a) 12 **b)** 4 **c)** 11?

12. The probability of snow on January 1st is $\frac{1}{20}$. What is the probability that snow will fall on January 1st for the next three years?

13. In the Venn diagram:

$\mathscr{E}$ = {students in a class of 15}

G = {girls}

S = {swimmers}

F = {students who were born on a Friday}.

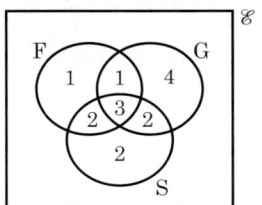

A student is chosen at random.
Find the probability that the student:

a) can swim

b) is a girl swimmer

c) is a boy swimmer who was born on a Friday.

Two students are chosen at random.
Find the probability that:

d) both are boys

e) neither can swim

f) both are girl swimmers who were born on a Friday.

Examination-style exercise 14

1. Rooms in a hotel are numbered from 1 to 29.
   Rooms are allocated at random as guests arrive.

   a) What is the probability that the first guest to arrive is given a room that is an even number? [2]

   b) The first guest to arrive is given a room which is an even number.
   What is the probability that the second guest to arrive is given a room which is an odd number? [1]

2. The table shows the grades gained by 32 students in a history test.

Grade	3	4	5	6	7	8	9
Number of students	1	2	3	9	8	5	4

   a) Write down the mode of the data. [1]

   b) Work out the median. [1]

   c) Calculate the mean. [3]

   d) Two students are chosen at random.
   Calculate the probability that they both gained grade 7. [2]

   e) From all the students who gained grades 6, 7, 8 or 9, two are chosen at random.
   Calculate the probability that they both gained grade 8. [2]

   f) Students are chosen at random, one by one, from the original 32, until
   the student chosen has a grade 4. Calculate the probability that this is the
   fourth student chosen. [2]

3. Scott goes to school by bus.

   The probability that the bus is late is 0.2. If the bus is late, the probability that Scott is late to school is 0.7.

   If the bus is not late, the probability that Scott is late to school is 0.1.

   a) Calculate the probability that the bus is late and Scott is late to school. [1]

   b) Calculate the probability that Scott is late to school. [3]

   c) The school term lasts 35 days.
   How many days would Scott expect to be late? [1]

4.

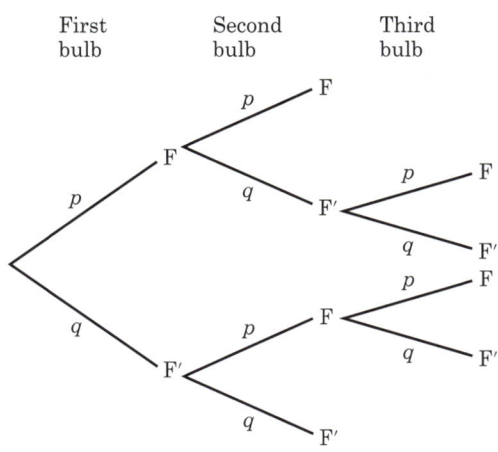

First bulb   Second bulb   Third bulb

F = faulty   F′ = not faulty

The tree diagram shows a testing procedure on light bulbs, taken from a large batch. **Each** time a bulb is chosen at random, the probability that it is faulty (F) is 0.02.

a) Write down the values of p and q. [1]

b) Two bulbs are chosen at random. Calculate the probability that

  i) neither are faulty, [2]

  ii) exactly one is faulty. [2]

c) If **exactly one** out of two bulbs tested is faulty, then a third bulb is chosen at random. Calculate the probability that exactly one of the first two bulbs is faulty **and** the third one is not faulty. [2]

d) The whole batch of bulbs is rejected **either** if the first two chosen are both faulty **or** if a third one needs to be chosen and it is faulty.

Calculate the probability that the whole batch is rejected. [2]

e) In one month, 2000 batches of bulbs are tested in this way.

How many batches are expected to be rejected? [1]

5. All 28 students in a class are asked if they like tennis and if they like badminton. Some of the results are shown in the Venn diagram.

$\mathscr{E}$ = {students in the class}

T = {students who like tennis}

B = {students who like badminton}

a) How many students like both sports? [1]

b) How many students do not like either sport? [1]

c) Write down the value of n(T ∪ B). [1]

d) Write down the value of n(T ∩ B′). [1]

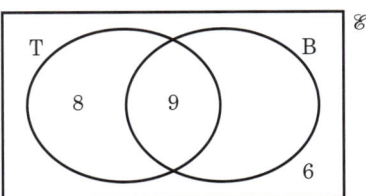

Tip

Remember that n before a set means the number of elements in the set.

e) A student from the class is selected at random.

What is the probability that this student likes tennis? [1]

f) A student who likes badminton is selected at random.

What is the probability that this student likes tennis? [1]

6. Two students are selected at random from a group of 14 boys and 13 girls.

Find the probability that:

a) they are both boys [2]

b) one is a boy and one is a girl. [3]

7. A play is being performed twice; first on a Friday and again on a Saturday. 100 people who wanted to see the play were asked which of the two performances they could attend. 58 people said they could attend the Friday performance, 74 said they could attend the Saturday performance, and 4 said they could attend neither.

a) Complete the Venn diagram to illustrate this information.

$\mathscr{E}$ = {the 100 people questioned}

F = {those who could attend on Friday}

S = {those who could attend on Saturday}

[3]

b) What is the probability that a randomly selected person from the 100 questioned:

i) could attend either performance [1]

ii) could only attend the Saturday performance [1]

iii) could not attend the Saturday performance? [1]

c) If one customer who wanted a ticket for the Saturday performance accidentally bought a ticket for the Friday performance, what is the probability that they would still be able to go? [2]

Answers

1 Number 1

Exercise 1.1A
1. 7.91
2. 22.22
3. 7.372
4. 0.066
5. 466.2
6. 1.22
7. 1.67
8. 1.61
9. 16.63
10. 24.1
11. 26.7
12. 3.86
13. 0.001
14. 1.56
15. 0.0288
16. 2.176
17. 0.02
18. 0.0001
19. 7.56
20. 0.7854
21. 360
22. 34 000
23. 18
24. 0.74
25. 2.34
26. 1620
27. 8.8
28. 1200
29. 0.00175
30. 13.2
31. 200
32. 0.804
33. 0.8
34. 0.077
35. 0.0009
36. 0.01
37. 184
38. 20
39. 0.099
40. 3

Exercise 1.1B
1. 98.7 degrees
2. 43.4 g
3. $2.55
4. 1.375 litres
5. $0.92
6. 13.2 N
7. 12 people
8. 46.85 s
9. £12.55
10. 20 calculators

Exercise 1.1C
1. $1\frac{11}{20}$
2. $\frac{11}{24}$
3. $1\frac{1}{2}$
4. $\frac{5}{12}$
5. $\frac{4}{15}$
6. $\frac{1}{10}$
7. $\frac{8}{15}$
8. $\frac{5}{42}$
9. $\frac{15}{26}$
10. $\frac{5}{12}$
11. $4\frac{1}{2}$
12. $1\frac{2}{3}$
13. $\frac{23}{40}$
14. $\frac{3}{40}$
15. $1\frac{7}{8}$
16. $1\frac{1}{12}$
17. $1\frac{1}{6}$
18. $2\frac{5}{8}$
19. $6\frac{1}{10}$
20. $9\frac{1}{10}$
21. $1\frac{9}{26}$
22. $\frac{1}{9}$
23. $\frac{2}{3}$
24. $5\frac{1}{4}$
25. $2\frac{2}{5}$
26. a) $\frac{1}{2},\frac{7}{12},\frac{2}{3}$
    b) $\frac{2}{3},\frac{3}{4},\frac{5}{6}$
    c) $\frac{1}{3},\frac{5}{8},\frac{17}{24},\frac{3}{4}$
    d) $\frac{5}{6},\frac{8}{9},\frac{11}{12}$
27. a) $\frac{1}{2}$
    b) $\frac{3}{4}$
    c) $\frac{17}{24}$
    d) $\frac{7}{18}$
    e) $\frac{3}{10}$
    f) $\frac{5}{12}$
28. 5
29. 9
30. same

Exercise 1.1D
1. 0.25
2. 0.4
3. 0.8
4. 0.75
5. 0.5
6. 0.375
7. 0.9
8. 0.625
9. $0.41\dot{6}$
10. $0.1\dot{6}$
11. $0.\dot{6}$
12. $0.8\dot{3}$
13. $0.\dot{2}8571\dot{4}$
14. $0.\dot{4}2857\dot{1}$
15. $0.\dot{4}$
16. $0.4\dot{5}$
17. 1.2
18. 2.625
19. $2.\dot{3}$
20. 75
21. 2.1875
22. $2.\dot{2}8571\dot{4}$
23. $2.\dot{8}5714\dot{2}$
24. 3.19
25. $\frac{1}{5}$
26. $\frac{7}{10}$
27. $\frac{1}{4}$
28. $\frac{9}{20}$
29. $\frac{9}{25}$
30. $\frac{13}{25}$
31. $\frac{1}{8}$
32. $\frac{5}{8}$
33. $\frac{21}{25}$
34. $2\frac{7}{20}$
35. $3\frac{19}{20}$
36. $1\frac{1}{20}$
37. $3\frac{1}{5}$
38. $\frac{27}{100}$
39. $\frac{7}{1000}$
40. $\frac{11}{100\,000}$
41. 0.58
42. 1.42
43. 0.65
44. 1.61
45. 0.07
46. 0.16
47. 3.64
48. 0.60
49. $\frac{4}{15},0.33,\frac{1}{3}$
50. $\frac{2}{7},0.3,\frac{4}{9}$
51. $\frac{7}{11},0.705,0.71$
52. $\frac{5}{18},0.3,\frac{4}{13}$
53. $\frac{2}{3}$
54. $\frac{4}{9}$
55. $\frac{4}{33}$
56. $\frac{43}{99}$
57. $\frac{134}{999}$
58. $\frac{731}{999}$
59. $\frac{23}{90}$
60. $\frac{611}{990}$
61. a) T
    b) F
    c) F

Exercise 1.2A
1. $5°$
2. $-4°$
3. $-1°$
4. $4°$
5. $-4°$
6. $12°$
7. $-7°$
8. $-5°$
9. $-4°$
10. $0°$
11. a) C
    b) B
12. -17 m

Exercise 1.2B

1. −12	**2.** −31	**3.** 6.1	**4.** −35	**5.** −9	**6.** −3
7. 3	**8.** −2	**9.** −14	**10.** −7	**11.** 181	**12.** −2.2
13. 8.2	**14.** 17	**15.** 2	**16.** −6	**17.** −15	**18.** −12
19. −80	**20.** −13.1	**21.** −4.2	**22.** 12.4	**23.** −7	**24.** 8
25. 4	**26.** −10	**27.** 11	**28.** −20	**29.** −5	**30.** −10
31. −26	**32.** −21	**33.** 8	**34.** −20.2	**35.** −50	**36.** −508
37. −29	**38.** 0	**39.** −21	**40.** −4	**41.** 6.7	**42.** 1
43. −850	**44.** 4	**45.** 6	**46.** −4	**47.** −12	**48.** −31

Exercise 1.2C

1. −8	**2.** 28	**3.** 12	**4.** 24	**5.** 18	**6.** −35
7. 49	**8.** −12	**9.** −2	**10.** 9	**11.** −4	**12.** 4
13. −4	**14.** 8	**15.** 70	**16.** −7	**17.** $\frac{1}{4}$	**18.** $-\frac{3}{5}$
19. −0.01	**20.** 0.0002	**21.** 121	**22.** 6	**23.** −600	**24.** −1
25. −20	**26.** −2.6	**27.** −700	**28.** 18	**29.** −1000	**30.** 640
31. −6	**32.** −42	**33.** −0.4	**34.** −0.4	**35.** −200	**36.** −35
37. −2	**38.** $\frac{1}{2}$	**39.** $-\frac{1}{4}$	**40.** −90		

Exercise 1.3A

1. 3, 11, 19, 23, 29, 31, 37, 47, 59, 61, 67, 73

2. a) 4, 8, 12, 16, 20 **b)** 6, 12, 18, 24, 30 **c)** 10, 20, 30, 40, 50
d) 11, 22, 33, 44, 55 **e)** 20, 40, 60, 80, 100

3. multiples of 4: 4, 8, 12, 16, 20, 24
multiples of 6: 6, 12, 18, 24, 30, 36
common multiples: 12, 24

4. multiples of 3: 3, 6, 9, 12, 15, 18
multiples of 5: 5, 10, 15, 20, 25, 30
LCM: 15

5. a) 1, 2, 3, 6 **b)** 1, 3, 9 **c)** 1, 2, 5, 10
d) 1, 3, 5, 15 **e)** 1, 2, 3, 4, 6, 8, 12, 24 **f)** 1, 2, 4, 8, 16, 32

6. a) Yes. Divide by 3, 5, 7, 11, 13, (i.e. odd prime numbers $< \sqrt{263}$) **b)** No

7. 2, 3, 5, 41, 67, 89

8. a) $2^3 \times 3$ **b)** $2^2 \times 3 \times 5$ **c)** $2 \times 3^2 \times 5$ **d)** $2^4 \times 3^2$ **e)** $2^3 \times 5^3$ **f)** $2^4 \times 5 \times 11$
9. a) 12 **b)** 18 **c)** 20 **d)** 8 **e)** 10 **f)** 12
10. a) 120 **b)** 90 **c)** 60 **d)** 24 **e)** 63 **f)** 210
11. a) 16 **b)** 36 **c)** 100 **d)** 27 **e)** 1000
12. a) 81 **b)** 441 **c)** 1.44 **d)** 0.04 **e)** 9.61
f) 10 000 **g)** 625 **h)** 75.69 **i)** 0.81 **j)** 6625.96
13. a) 4.41 cm² **b)** 0.36 cm² **c)** 196 m² **14.** $x = 8$
15. a) $\frac{1}{7}$ **b)** $\frac{1}{12}$ **c)** $-\frac{1}{4}$ **d)** $\frac{2}{7}$ **e)** 2 **f)** $\frac{5}{3}$

16. $\frac{1}{2}$ or 0.5 **17.** $\frac{1}{10}$ or 0.1 **18.** $\frac{1}{5}$ or 0.2 **19.** $\frac{1}{4}$ or 0.25 **20.** $\frac{1}{8}$ or 0.125

Exercise 1.3B

1. a, b, d, e, h, j, k, m, n and p
3. a) both irrational **b)** both rational
4. a) 6π cm, irrational **b)** 6 cm, rational **c)** 36 cm², rational
d) 9π cm², irrational **e)** 36 − 9π cm², irrational
6. A rational number can always be written exactly in the form $\frac{a}{b}$ where a and b are whole numbers. An irrational number cannot be written in the form $\frac{a}{b}$.
7. a) No **b)** Yes e.g. $\sqrt{8} \times \sqrt{2} = 4$

Exercise 1.4A

1. 18, 22; Add 4 **2.** 30, 37; Add 7 **3.** 63, 55; Subtract 8
4. −7, −12; Subtract 5 **5.** 21, 27 **6.** 2, −5
7. 16, 22 **8.** 16, 32 **9.** 25, 15 **10.** −4, −10
11. −4, −3 **12.** $7\frac{1}{2}$, $3\frac{3}{4}$ **13.** $\frac{1}{3}$, $\frac{1}{9}$ **14.** 2, $\frac{2}{3}$
15. 32, 47 **16.** 840, 6720 **17.** 5, −1 **18.** 2, 1

Exercise 1.4B

1. $4n + 1$ 2. $3n + 4$ 3. $5n - 1$ 4. $4n + 2$ 5. $3n + 2$ 6. $28 - 3n$

7. $5n$ 8. $n + 20$ 9. $\dfrac{n}{n + 1}$ 10. $7n$ 11. $10n + 2$ 12. $\dfrac{n + 2}{n}$

13. $4n - 1$ 14. $2n + 3$ 15. $9 - 2n$ 16. $4n - 9$

17. a) $2n + 6$ b) $4n - 1$ c) $5n + 3$

18. a) $8n + 3$ b) $2n + \frac{1}{2}$ c) $3n - 10$

19. a) $3n + 1$ b) 3001

Exercise 1.4C

1. $n^2 + 3$ 2. $2n^2$ 3. $n^2 - 1$ 4. $\frac{1}{2}n^2$ 5. $n^2 - 7$ 6. $-n^2$

7. $-n^2 + 1$ 8. $n^2 + 4n$ 9. $2n^2 - n$ 10. $n^2 + 3n - 1$ 11. $n^3 + 1$ 12. $2n^3$

13. $n^3 - 2$ 14. $2^n - 1$ 15. 3^n

Exercise 1.4D

1. n^3 2. 2^n 3. 3^{n-1} 4. $n^3 + 12$ 5. 2×3^n

6. $n^3 - 5$ 7. $2^n + 7$ 8. $n^3 + n$ 9. $n^3 - n^2$ 10. $n^3 + 2^n$

Exercise 1.5A

1. a) 8 b) 8.17 c) 8.17 2. a) 20 b) 19.6 c) 19.62

3. a) 20 b) 20.0 c) 20.04 4. a) 1 b) 0.815 c) 0.81

5. a) 311 b) 311 c) 311.14 6. a) 0 b) 0.275 c) 0.28

7. a) 0 b) 0.00747 c) 0.01 8. a) 16 b) 15.6 c) 15.62

9. a) 900 b) 900 c) 900.12 10. a) 4 b) 3.56 c) 3.56

11. a) 5 b) 5.45 c) 5.45 12. a) 21 b) 21.0 c) 20.96

13. a) 0 b) 0.0851 c) 0.09 14. a) 1 b) 0.515 c) 0.52

15. a) 3 b) 3.07 c) 3.07 16. 5.7 17. 0.8 18. 11.2

19. 0.1 20. 0.0 21. 11.1

Exercise 1.5B

1. 195.5 cm 2. 36.5 kg 3. 3.25 kg 4. 95.55 m 5. 28.65 s

6. a) 1.5, 2.5 b) 2.25, 2.35 c) 63.5, 64.5 d) 13.55, 13.65 e) 42.5, 47.5

7. B 8. C 9. a) Not necessarily b) 1 cm

10. a) $16.5 \leqslant m < 17.5$ b) $255.5 \leqslant d < 256.5$ c) $2.35 \leqslant l < 2.45$

d) $0.335 \leqslant m < 0.345$ e) $2.035 \leqslant v < 2.045$ f) $11.95 \leqslant x < 12.05$

g) $81.35 \leqslant T < 81.45$ h) $0.25 \leqslant M < 0.35$ i) $0.65 \leqslant m < 0.75$

j) $51\,500 \leqslant n < 52\,500$ k) $210 \leqslant t < 230$ l) $2725 \leqslant f < 2775$

11. No, max. card length 11.55 cm, min. envelope length 11.5 cm

Exercise 1.5C

1. a) 7.5, 8.5, 10.5 cm b) 26.5 cm 2. 46.75 cm^2

3. a) 7 b) 5 c) 10 d) 4 e) 2 f) 5

g) 2 h) 24

4. a) 13 b) 11 c) 3 d) 12.5

5. i) 10.5 ii) 4.3 6. i) 13, 11 ii) 3, 1 iii) 0.8 (1 d.p.), 0.6

7. 56 cm^2 8. 55.7

Exercise 1.5D

1. 70.56 2. 118.958 3. 451.62 4. 33 678.8 5. 0.6174

6. 1068 7. 19.53 8. 18 914.4 9. 38.72 10. 0.009 79

11. 2.4 12. 11 13. 41 14. 8.9 15. 4.7

16. 56 17. 0.0201 18. 30.1 19. 1.3 20. 0.31

21. 210.21 22. 294 23. 282.131 24. 35 25. 242

Exercise 1.6A

1. 6^2 2. 4^5 3. $3^2 \times 5^2$ 4. $2^3 \times 11$ 5. 8^{-3} 6. $3^{-3} \times 7^{-2}$

7. $13^{\frac{1}{2}}$ 8. $2^{\frac{1}{3}}$ 9. $10^{\frac{1}{5}}$ 10. $5^{\frac{3}{2}}$ 11. 3^{11} 12. 3^8

13. 3^{17} 14. 3^{-3} 15. 3^{20} 16. 3^{-4}

Exercise 1.6B
1. 27   **2.** 1   **3.** $\frac{1}{9}$ **4.** 25   **5.** 2
6. 4   **7.** 9   **8.** 2   **9.** 27   **10.** 3
11. $\frac{1}{3}$ **12.** $\frac{1}{2}$ **13.** 1   **14.** $\frac{1}{5}$ **15.** 10
16. 8   **17.** 32   **18.** 4   **19.** $\frac{1}{9}$ **20.** $\frac{1}{8}$
21. 18   **22.** 10   **23.** 1000   **24.** $\frac{1}{1000}$ **25.** $\frac{1}{9}$
26. 1   **27.** $1\frac{1}{2}$ **28.** $\frac{1}{25}$ **29.** $\frac{1}{10}$ **30.** $\frac{1}{4}$
31. $\frac{1}{4}$ **32.** 100 000   **33.** 1   **34.** $\frac{1}{32}$ **35.** 0.1
36. 0.2   **37.** 1.5   **38.** 1   **39.** 9   **40.** $1\frac{1}{2}$
41. $\frac{3}{10}$ **42.** 64   **43.** $\frac{1}{100}$ **44.** $1\frac{2}{3}$ **45.** $\frac{1}{100}$
46. 1   **47.** 100   **48.** 6   **49.** 750   **50.** -7

Exercise 1.7A
1. 4×10^3 **2.** 5×10^2 **3.** 7×10^4 **4.** 6×10 **5.** 2.4×10^3
6. 3.8×10^2 **7.** 4.6×10^4 **8.** 4.6×10 **9.** 9×10^5 **10.** 2.56×10^3
11. 7×10^{-3} **12.** 4×10^{-4} **13.** 3.5×10^{-3} **14.** 4.21×10^{-1} **15.** 5.5×10^{-5}
16. 1×10^{-2} **17.** 5.64×10^5 **18.** 1.9×10^7 **19.** 1.1×10^9 **20.** 1.67×10^{-24}
21. 5.1×10^8 **22.** 2.5×10^{-10} **23.** 37 100 000 000 000   **24.** 3×10^{10}

Exercise 1.7B
1. 8.2×10^4 **2.** 1.206×10^2 **3.** 5.86×10^{12} **4.** 5.18×10^{-2}
5. 3×10^8 **6.** 2.8×10^{-2} **7.** 7×10 **8.** 2×10^6
9. 4×10^{-6} **10.** 9×10^{-2} **11.** 6.6×10^{-8} **12.** 3.5×10^{-7}
13. 1×10^{-16} **14.** 8×10^9 **15.** 7.4×10^{-7} **16.** c, a, b
17. 13   **18.** 16   **19. i)** $8.75 \times 10^2, 3.75 \times 10^2$ **ii)** $1 \times 10^8, 4.29 \times 10^7$
20. 50 min   **21.** 6×10^2 **22. a)** 20.5 s   **b)** 6.3×10^{91} years

Exercise 1.8A
1. $\sqrt{14}$ **2.** $\sqrt{55}$ **3.** $\sqrt{10}$ **4.** $\sqrt{5}$ **5.** 3
6. 7   **7.** $\sqrt{15}$ **8.** $\sqrt{30}$ **9.** 635   **10.** $15\sqrt{14}$
11. $5\sqrt{5}$ **12.** 60   **13.** 4   **14.** 9   **15.** $5\sqrt{7}$
16. a) 90 cm^2 **b)** 120 cm^2 **17.** 2

Exercise 1.8B
1. a) 4   **b)** 2   **c)** 2
2. a) $3\sqrt{5}$ **b)** $2\sqrt{7}$ **c)** $6\sqrt{2}$ **d)** $3\sqrt{10}$ **e)** $\sqrt{5}$ **f)** $\sqrt{6}$ **g)** $\frac{\sqrt{5}}{4}$
3. Student's explanation e.g. no square number (other than 1) is a factor of 30.
4. $5\sqrt{12} = 5 \times \sqrt{4} \times \sqrt{3} = 5 \times 2 \times \sqrt{3} = 10\sqrt{3}$
5. a) $4\sqrt{3}$ **b)** $6\sqrt{5}$ **c)** $15\sqrt{2}$ **d)** $6\sqrt{2}$
6. a) $42\sqrt{3}$ **b)** $20\sqrt{42}$ **c)** $\frac{1}{9}$ **d)** $\frac{5\sqrt{3}}{2}$
7. Kyle's method is easier when the multiplication is harder to do.
Amir's method is quicker when the multiplication is easier to do.
8. a) 360   **b)** 2

Exercise 1.8C
1. a) $12\sqrt{5}$ **b)** $4\sqrt{3}$ **c)** $15\sqrt{3}$ **d)** $8\sqrt{2}$ **e)** $5\sqrt{5}$
   f) $13\sqrt{2}$ **g)** $9\sqrt{3}$ **h)** $\sqrt{5}$ **2.** $5\sqrt{11}$
3. a) 13   **b)** 600   **c)** 20   **d)** 3   **4.** $26\sqrt{10}$
5. $\left(\sqrt{12} + \sqrt{3}\right)^2 = \left(2\sqrt{3} + \sqrt{3}\right)^2 = \left(3\sqrt{3}\right)^2 = 3\sqrt{3} \times 3\sqrt{3} = 3 \times 3 \times \sqrt{3} \times \sqrt{3} = 9 \times 3 = 27$
6. 18   **7. a)** 6   **b)** $\frac{1}{4}$ **c)** 4   **8.** $\sqrt{3}$

Exercise 1.8D

1. a) $\dfrac{1}{\sqrt{11}} \times \dfrac{\sqrt{11}}{\sqrt{11}} = \dfrac{\sqrt{11}}{11}$ **b)** $\sqrt{\dfrac{1}{7}} = \dfrac{1}{\sqrt{7}} = \dfrac{1}{\sqrt{7}} \times \dfrac{\sqrt{7}}{\sqrt{7}} = \dfrac{\sqrt{7}}{7}$

c) $\dfrac{5\left(2+\sqrt{3}\right)}{\left(2-\sqrt{3}\right)\left(2+\sqrt{3}\right)} = \dfrac{10+5\sqrt{3}}{4+2\sqrt{3}-2\sqrt{3}-3} = \dfrac{10+5\sqrt{3}}{1} = 10+5\sqrt{3}$

2. a) $\dfrac{\sqrt{6}}{6}$ **b)** $\dfrac{2\sqrt{5}}{5}$ **c)** $3\sqrt{6}$ **d)** $\dfrac{\sqrt{11}}{11}$ **e)** $\sqrt{5}$ **f)** $\dfrac{4\sqrt{3}}{5}$

3. a) 2 **b)** 31 **c)** 52 **d)** 72 **e)** 50 **4.** 38

5. $a = 21, b = 2$ **6. a)** $\dfrac{5-\sqrt{3}}{22}$ **b)** $\dfrac{4+\sqrt{5}}{11}$ **c)** $-14 + 7\sqrt{5}$ **d)** $\dfrac{3+2\sqrt{3}}{3}$ **e)** $\dfrac{\sqrt{6}+\sqrt{3}}{3}$

f) $4 + 4\sqrt{5}$ **g)** $\dfrac{9+2\sqrt{14}}{5}$ **7.** $5\sqrt{2}$ **8. a)** $5\sqrt{6}$ **b)** $2\sqrt{6}$ **c)** $5\sqrt{6}$ **9.** 8

10. $4\sqrt{5} - 28$ **11.** 5 **12.** $\dfrac{3}{7}$ **13.** $7\sqrt{3}$ **14. a)** $\dfrac{2}{3}\sqrt{3}$ **b)** $\dfrac{7}{3}\sqrt{3}$

Exercise 1.9A

1. 3.041	**2.** 1460	**3.** 0.030 83	**4.** 47.98	**5.** 130.6
6. 0.4771	**7.** 0.3658	**8.** 37.54	**9.** 8.000	**10.** 0.6537
11. 0.037 16	**12.** 34.31	**13.** 0.7195	**14.** 3.598	**15.** 0.2445
16. 2.043	**17.** 0.3798	**18.** 0.7683	**19.** −0.5407	**20.** 0.070 40
21. 2.526	**22.** 0.094 78	**23.** 0.2110	**24.** 3.123	**25.** 2.230
26. 128.8	**27.** 4.268	**28.** 3.893	**29.** 0.6290	**30.** 0.4069
31. 9.298	**32.** 0.1010	**33.** 0.3692	**34.** 1.125	**35.** 1.677
36. 0.9767	**37.** 0.8035	**38.** 0.3528	**39.** 2.423	**40.** 1.639
41. 0.000 465 9	**42.** 0.3934	**43.** −0.7526	**44.** 2.454	

Exercise 1.9B

1. 40 000	**2.** 0.070 49	**3.** 405 400	**4.** 471.3
5. 20 810	**6.** 2.218×10^{6}	**7.** 1.237×10^{-24}	**8.** 3.003
9. 0.035 81	**10.** 47.40	**11.** −1748	**12.** 0.011 38
13. 1757	**14.** 0.026 35	**15.** 0.1651	**16.** 5447
17. 0.006 562	**18.** 0.1330	**19.** 0.4451	**20.** 0.036 16
21. 19.43	**22.** 1.296×10^{-15}	**23.** 5.595×10^{14}	**24.** 1.022×10^{-8}
25. 0.019 22	**26.** 0.9613		

Exercise 1.9C

1. a) 1850, 1850, 92.5 **b)** 4592, 4592, 14 **c)** 50.4, 50.4, 63 **d)** 31.6, 31.6, 221.2
e) 42.3, 42.3, 384.93 **f)** 39.51, 39.51, 13·71 **g)** 21.2, 21.2, 95.4 **h)** 42.4, 42.4
i) 6.2449 ..., 6.2449 ... **j)** 29.63, 29.63
2. a) A–T, B–P, C–S, D–R, E–Q
3. a) 281 **b)** 36 **c)** 101.16 **4.** $1000 **5.** 6 times
6. a) 5 **b)** 100 **c)** £3000 **d)** 1 **e)** 2
f) 100 **g)** £2000 **h)** 400

Exercise 1.9D

1. a) 2.218 hours **b)** 5.711 hours **c)** 1.114 hours
2. a) 2 hours 38 minutes 24 seconds **b)** 3 hours 52 minutes 48 seconds
c) 8 hours 17 minutes 24 seconds
3. a) 4 hours 22 minutes 12 seconds **b)** 14 hours 32 minutes 24 seconds
4. 530 **5.** $73.20 **6.** $26 875 **7.** $8.60 **8.** 2 hours 15 minutes

Revision exercise 1

1. a) 185 **b)** 150 **c)** 40 **d)** $\dfrac{11}{12}$ **e)** $2\dfrac{4}{5}$ **f)** $\dfrac{2}{5}$
2. a) 17 **b)** −13 **c)** 5 **d)** −10
3. a) −36 **b)** 21 **c)** −10 **d)** 5 **4.** 128 cm **5.** $\dfrac{2}{5}$
6. a) 0.0547 **b)** 0.055 **c)** 5.473×10^{-2} **7.** 1.238
8. a) 11 **b)** $\dfrac{1}{7}$ **c)** $\dfrac{1}{3}$ **d)** 64 **e)** 48 **f)** 1

9. a) 3×10^7 **b)** 3.7×10^4 **c)** 2.7×10^{13} **10.** 3.05
11. a) i) 3 **ii)** 10 **iii)** $1, 9$ **iv)** $1, 8$
  b) $m = 3, n = 9$ **c)** $p = 1, q = 3, r = 9, s = 8, t = 10$
12. About 3 **13.** 2.3×10^9
14. a) 600 **b)** $10\,000$ **c)** 3 **d)** 20
15. a) 0.5601 **b)** 3.215 **c)** 0.6161 **d)** 0.4743
16. a) 0.340 **b)** 4.08×10^{-6} **c)** 64.9 **d)** 0.119
17. a) $\frac{1}{20}$ or 0.05 **b)** 3 **c)** 2.5 **d)** $\frac{2}{3}$

18. 2^8 **19. a)** $\dfrac{\sqrt{5}}{5}$ **b)** $\dfrac{\sqrt{5} - 1}{2}$ **c)** $3 + 2\sqrt{2}$

20. a) $4n - 5$ **b)** $n^2 + 2n - 1$ **c)** $n^3 + 2$ **d)** 4^n
21. Lower bound: 75 cm, upper bound: 125 cm
22. a) 0.43 **b)** 0.2 **c)** 0.03 **d)** 0.125 **e)** 1.15
23. a) 0.25 **b)** 0.4 **c)** 0.875 **d)** $0.\dot{4}2857\dot{1}$ **e)** 2.5

Examination-style exercise 1

1. a) $\frac{9}{64}$ **b)** 0.140625 **2.** $\frac{37}{25}$ or $1\frac{12}{25}$ or 1.48
3. a) an irrational number between 1 and 2; for example $\sqrt{2}$ or $\sqrt{3}$ **b)** $71, 73$ or 79
4. a) $09{:}55$ **b)** $\$46.50$ **5. a)** -2.6 **b)** 33
6. a) 1170 **b)** $(n + 2)^2 + 10$ **7.** $237.5 \leqslant d$ km < 242.5
8. $30\,800$ km $\leqslant$ total distance travelled $< 31\,600$ km
9. 36.3375 cm^2 **10.** $\frac{3}{2} + \sqrt{2}$
11. 7 million km **12.** 1.9×10^{27} **13.** 4.17

2 Algebra 1

Exercise 2.1A
1. 7 **2.** 13 **3.** 13 **4.** 22 **5.** 1 **6.** -1
7. 18 **8.** -4 **9.** -3 **10.** 37 **11.** 0 **12.** -4
13. -7 **14.** -2 **15.** -3 **16.** -8 **17.** -30 **18.** 16
19. -10 **20.** 0 **21.** 7 **22.** -6 **23.** -2 **24.** -7
25. -5 **26.** 3 **27.** 4 **28.** -8 **29.** -2 **30.** 2
31. 0 **32.** 4 **33.** -4 **34.** -3 **35.** -9 **36.** 4

Exercise 2.1B
1. 9 **2.** 27 **3.** 4 **4.** 16 **5.** 36 **6.** 18
7. 1 **8.** 6 **9.** 2 **10.** 8 **11.** -7 **12.** 15
13. -23 **14.** 3 **15.** 32 **16.** 36 **17.** 144 **18.** -8
19. -7 **20.** 13 **21.** 5 **22.** -16 **23.** 84 **24.** 17
25. 6 **26.** 0 **27.** -25 **28.** -5 **29.** 17 **30.** $-1\frac{1}{2}$
31. 19 **32.** 8 **33.** 19 **34.** 16 **35.** -16 **36.** 12
37. 36 **38.** -12 **39.** 2 **40.** 11 **41.** -23 **42.** -26
43. 5 **44.** 31 **45.** $4\frac{1}{2}$

Exercise 2.1C
1. -20 **2.** 16 **3.** -42 **4.** -4 **5.** -90 **6.** -160
7. -2 **8.** -81 **9.** 4 **10.** 22 **11.** 14 **12.** 5 or -5
13. 1 or -1 **14.** $\sqrt{5}$ **15.** 4 **16.** $-6\frac{1}{2}$ **17.** 54 **18.** 25
19. 4 or -4 **20.** 312 **21.** 45 **22.** 22 **23.** 14 **24.** -36
25. -7 **26.** 1 or -1 **27.** 901 **28.** -30 **29.** -5 **30.** $7\frac{1}{2}$
31. -7 **32.** $-\frac{3}{13}$ **33.** 7 **34.** -2 **35.** 0 **36.** $-4\frac{1}{2}$
37. 6 or -6 **38.** 2 or -2 **39.** 26 **40.** -9 **41.** $3\frac{1}{4}$ **42.** $-\frac{5}{6}$
43. 4 **44.** $2\frac{2}{3}$ **45.** $3\frac{1}{4}$ **46.** $-2\frac{1}{6}$ **47.** -13 **48.** 12
49. $1\frac{1}{3}$ **50.** $-\frac{5}{36}$

Exercise 2.1D
1. 21 m/s
2. 1.62 s
3. 396 cm^2
4. 650
5. 63.8 m/s^2
6. 9×10^{12} kg m/s
7. 800 m
8. $ac + ab - a^2$
9. $r - p + q$

Exercise 2.2A
1. $3x + 11y$
2. $2a + 8b$
3. $3x + 2y$
4. $5x + 5$
5. $9 + x$
6. $3 - 9y$
7. $5x - 2y - x^2$
8. $2x^2 + 3x + 5$
9. $-10y$
10. $3a^2 + 2a$
11. $7 + 7a - 7a^2$
12. $5x$
13. $\dfrac{10}{a} - b$
14. $\dfrac{5}{x} - \dfrac{5}{y}$
15. $\dfrac{3m}{x}$
16. $\dfrac{1}{2} - \dfrac{2}{x}$
17. $\dfrac{5}{a} + 3b$
18. $-\dfrac{n}{4}$
19. $7x^2 - x^3$
20. $2x^2$
21. $x^2 + 5y^2$
22. $-12x^2 - 4y^2$
23. $5x - 11x^2$
24. $\dfrac{8}{x^2}$
25. $5x + 2$
26. $12x - 7$
27. $3x + 4$
28. $11 - 6x$
29. $-5x - 20$
30. $7x - 2x^2$
31. $3x^2 - 5x$
32. $x - 4$
33. $5x^2 + 14x$
34. $-4x^2 - 3x$
35. $5a + 8$
36. $a + 9$
37. $ab + 4a$
38. $y^2 + y$
39. $2x - 2$
40. $6x + 3$
41. $x - 4$
42. $7x + 5y$
43. $4x^2 - 11x$
44. $2x^2 + 14x$
45. $3y^2 - 4y + 1$
46. $12x + 12$
47. $4ab - 3a + 14b$
48. $2x - 4$

Exercise 2.2B
1. $x^2 + 4x + 3$
2. $x^2 + 5x + 6$
3. $y^2 + 9y + 20$
4. $x^2 + x - 12$
5. $x^2 + 3x - 10$
6. $x^2 - 5x + 6$
7. $a^2 - 2a - 35$
8. $z^2 + 7z - 18$
9. $x^2 - 9$
10. $k^2 - 121$
11. $2x^2 - 5x - 3$
12. $3x^2 - 2x - 8$
13. $2y^2 - y - 3$
14. $49y^2 - 1$
15. $9x^2 - 4$
16. $6a^2 + 5ab + b^2$
17. $3x^2 + 7xy + 2y^2$
18. $6b^2 + bc - c^2$
19. $-5x^2 + 16xy - 3y^2$
20. $15b^2 + ab - 2a^2$
21. $2x^2 + 2x - 4$
22. $6x^2 + 3x - 9$
23. $24y^2 + 4y - 8$
24. $6x^2 - 10x - 4$
25. $4a^2 - 16b^2$
26. $x^3 - 3x^2 + 2x$
27. $8x^3 - 2x$
28. $3y^3 + 3y^2 - 18y$
29. $x^3 + x^2y + x^2z + xyz$
30. $3za^2 + 3zam - 6zm^2$

Exercise 2.2C
1. $x^2 + 8x + 16$
2. $x^2 + 4x + 4$
3. $x^2 - 4x + 4$
4. $4x^2 + 4x + 1$
5. $y^2 - 10y + 25$
6. $9y^2 + 6y + 1$
7. $x^2 + 2xy + y^2$
8. $4x^2 + 4xy + y^2$
9. $a^2 - 2ab + b^2$
10. $4a^2 - 12ab + 9b^2$
11. $3x^2 + 12x + 12$
12. $9 - 6x + x^2$
13. $9x^2 + 12x + 4$
14. $a^2 - 4ab + 4b^2$
15. $2x^2 + 6x + 5$
16. $2x^2 + 2x + 13$
17. $5x^2 + 8x + 5$
18. $2y^2 - 14y + 25$
19. $10x - 5$
20. $-8x + 8$
21. $-10y + 5$
22. $3x^2 - 2x - 8$
23. $2x^2 + 4x - 4$
24. $-x^2 - 18x + 15$

Exercise 2.2D
1. $x^3 - 5x^2 - 2x + 24$
2. $x^3 - 4x^2 - 7x + 10$
3. $x^3 + 8x^2 - 3x - 90$
4. $2x^3 - x^2 - 2x + 1$
5. $6x^3 - 7x^2 - 9x - 2$
6. $8x^3 + 22x^2 + 3x - 18$
7. $36x^3 - 361x + 280$
8. $x^3 - 2x^2 - 7x - 4$
9. $x^3 - 7x^2 + 16x - 12$
10. $4x^3 + 8x^2 - 3x - 9$
11. $x^3 - 3x^2 + 3x - 1$
12. $27x^3 + 54x^2 + 36x + 8$
13. $-9x^2 + 9x - 9$
14. $21x^2 - 21x + 91$
15. $11x^3 + 21x^2 + 15x + 4$

Exercise 2.3A
1. 8
2. 9
3. 7
4. 10
5. $\dfrac{1}{3}$
6. 10
7. $1\dfrac{1}{2}$
8. -1
9. $-1\dfrac{1}{2}$
10. $\dfrac{1}{3}$
11. 35
12. 130
13. 14
14. $\dfrac{2}{3}$
15. $3\dfrac{1}{3}$
16. $-2\dfrac{1}{2}$
17. 3
18. $1\dfrac{1}{8}$
19. $\dfrac{3}{10}$
20. $-1\dfrac{1}{4}$
21. 10
22. 27
23. 20
24. 18
25. 28
26. -15
27. $\dfrac{99}{100}$
28. 0
29. 1000
30. $-\dfrac{1}{1000}$
31. 1
32. -7
33. -5
34. $1\dfrac{1}{6}$
35. 1
36. 2
37. -5
38. -3
39. $-1\dfrac{1}{2}$
40. 2
41. 1
42. $3\dfrac{1}{2}$
43. 2
44. -1
45. $10\dfrac{2}{3}$
46. 1.1
47. -1
48. 2
49. $2\dfrac{1}{2}$
50. $1\dfrac{1}{3}$

Exercise 2.3B
1. $-1\dfrac{1}{2}$
2. 2
3. $-\dfrac{2}{5}$
4. $-\dfrac{1}{3}$
5. $1\dfrac{2}{3}$
6. 6
7. $-\dfrac{2}{5}$
8. $-3\dfrac{1}{5}$
9. $\dfrac{1}{2}$
10. -4
11. 18
12. 5
13. 4
14. 3
15. $2\dfrac{3}{4}$
16. $-\dfrac{7}{22}$
17. $\dfrac{1}{4}$
18. 1

485

19. 4　　**20.** −11　　**21.** $-7\frac{1}{3}$　　**22.** $1\frac{1}{4}$　　**23.** −5　　**24.** 6

25. 3　　**26.** 6　　**27.** 2　　**28.** 3　　**29.** 4　　**30.** 3

31. $10\frac{1}{2}$　　**32.** 5　　**33.** 2　　**34.** −1　　**35.** −17　　**36.** $-2\frac{9}{10}$

37. $2\frac{10}{21}$　　**38.** $\frac{1}{3}$　　**39.** 14　　**40.** 15

Exercise 2.3C

1. $\frac{1}{4}$　　　**2.** −3　　　**3.** 4　　　**4.** $-7\frac{2}{3}$　　　**5.** −43

6. 11　　　**7.** $-\frac{1}{2}$　　　**8.** 0　　　**9.** 1　　　**10.** $-1\frac{2}{3}$

11. $\frac{1}{4}$　　　**12.** 0　　　**13.** $-\frac{6}{7}$　　　**14.** $1\frac{9}{17}$　　　**15.** $1\frac{22}{23}$

16. $\frac{2}{11}$　　　**17.** 4 cm　　　**18.** 5 m　　　**19.** 4

Exercise 2.3D

1. $\frac{1}{3}$　　**2.** $\frac{1}{5}$　　**3.** $1\frac{2}{3}$　　**4.** −3　　**5.** $\frac{5}{11}$　　**6.** −2

7. 6　　**8.** $3\frac{3}{4}$　　**9.** −7　　**10.** $-7\frac{2}{3}$　　**11.** 2　　**12.** 3

13. 4　　**14.** −2　　**15.** −3　　**16.** 3　　**17.** $1\frac{5}{7}$　　**18.** $4\frac{4}{5}$

19. 10　　**20.** 24　　**21.** 2　　**22.** 3　　**23.** 5　　**24.** −4

25. $6\frac{3}{4}$　　**26.** −3　　**27.** 0　　**28.** 3　　**29.** 0　　**30.** 1

31. 2　　**32.** 3　　**33.** 4　　**34.** $\frac{3}{5}$　　**35.** $1\frac{1}{8}$　　**36.** −1

37. 1　　**38.** 1　　**39.** $\frac{1}{4}$　　**40.** $-\frac{1}{3}$　　**41.** $\frac{9}{10}$　　**42.** 1

43. 2　　**44.** $-\frac{1}{7}$　　**45.** 2　　**46.** 3

Exercise 2.4A

1. 91, 92, 93　　　**2.** 21, 22, 23, 24　　　**3.** 57, 59, 61　　　**4.** 506, 508, 510

5. $12\frac{1}{2}$　　　**6.** $12\frac{1}{2}$　　　**7.** $11\frac{2}{3}$　　　**8.** $8\frac{1}{3}, 41\frac{2}{3}$

9. $1\frac{1}{4}, 13\frac{3}{4}$　　　**10.** $3\frac{1}{3}$ cm　　　**11.** 12 cm　　　**12.** 20

13. 5 cm　　　**14.** 7 cm　　　**15.** $18\frac{1}{2}, 27\frac{1}{2}$　　　**16.** 20°, 60°, 100°

17. 45°, 60°, 75°　　　**18.** 5　　　**19.** 6, 8　　　**20.** 12, 24, 30

21. 5, 15, 8　　　**22.** $59\frac{2}{3}$ kg, $64\frac{2}{3}$ kg, $72\frac{2}{3}$ kg　　　**23.** 24, 22, 15　　　**24.** 48, 12

25. 40, 8　　　**26.** 6　　　**27.** 168.84 cm²　　　**28.** 14

29. $45, $31　　　**30.** $21.50

Exercise 2.4B

1. $3700　　**2.** 3　　**3.** $1\frac{3}{7}$ m　　**4.** 80°, 100°　　**5.** 30°, 60°, 90°, 120°, 150°, 270°

6. 26, 58　　**7.** 21　　**8.** 23　　**9.** 15　　**10.** 2, 3, 4, 5

11. 2 km　　**12.** 8 km

Exercise 2.5A

1. $x = 2, y = 1$　　　**2.** $x = 4, y = 2$　　　**3.** $x = 3, y = 1$　　　**4.** $x = -2, y = 1$

5. $x = 3, y = 2$　　　**6.** $x = 5, y = -2$　　　**7.** $x = 2, y = 1$　　　**8.** $x = 5, y = 3$

9. $x = 3, y = -1$　　　**10.** $a = 2, b = -3$　　　**11.** $a = 5, b = \frac{1}{4}$　　　**12.** $a = 1, b = 3$

13. $m = \frac{1}{2}, n = 4$　　　**14.** $w = 2, x = 3$　　　**15.** $x = 6, y = 3$　　　**16.** $x = \frac{1}{2}, z = -3$

17. $m = 1\frac{15}{17}, n = \frac{11}{17}$　　　**18.** $c = 1\frac{16}{23}, d = -2\frac{12}{23}$

Exercise 2.5B

1. 1　　**2.** −3　　**3.** 2　　**4.** 15　　**5.** −12　　**6.** −3

7. −2　　**8.** −11　　**9.** −21　　**10.** 1　　**11.** 0　　**12.** 15

13. −10　　**14.** 3　　**15.** 6　　**16.** −11　　**17.** 2　　**18.** 5

19. −19　　**20.** −4　　**21.** x　　**22.** $-3x$　　**23.** $4x$　　**24.** $4y$

25. $9y$　　**26.** $3x$　　**27.** $-8x$　　**28.** $4x$　　**29.** $2x$　　**30.** $3y$

Exercise 2.5C

1. $x = 2, y = 4$　　　**2.** $x = 1, y = 4$　　　**3.** $x = 2, y = 5$　　　**4.** $x = 3, y = 7$

5. $x = 5, y = 2$　　　**6.** $a = 3, b = 1$　　　**7.** $x = 1, y = 3$　　　**8.** $x = 1, y = 3$

9. $x = -2, y = 3$ **10.** $x = 4, y = 1$ **11.** $x = 1, y = 5$ **12.** $x = 0, y = 2$

13. $x = \frac{5}{7}, y = 4\frac{3}{7}$ **14.** $x = 1, y = 2$ **15.** $x = 2, y = -3$ **16.** $x = 4, y = -1$

17. $x = 3, y = 1$ **18.** $x = 1, y = 2$ **19.** $x = 2, y = 1$ **20.** $x = -2, y = 1$

21. $x = 1, y = 2$ **22.** $a = 4, b = 3$ **23.** $x = -23, y = -78$ **24.** $x = 3, y = \frac{1}{2}$

25. $x = 4, y = 3$ **26.** $x = 5, y = -2$ **27.** $x = \frac{1}{3}, y = -2$ **28.** $x = 5\frac{5}{6}, y = -\frac{2}{3}$

29. $x = 3, y = -1$ **30.** $x = 5, y = 0.2$

Exercise 2.6A

1. $5\frac{1}{2}$, $9\frac{1}{2}$ **2.** 6, 3   **3.** 4, 10   **4.** $a = 2, c = 7$

5. $m = 4, c = -3$ **6.** $a = 1, b = -2$ **7.** carrot $0.01; lettuce $0.03

8. 1 torch is $2, 1 box of batteries is $4.50   **9.** 7, 3   **10.** white 2 g, brown $3\frac{1}{2}$ g

11. first part 120 cm, second part 240 cm   **12.** 150 m at 10 m/s, 350 m at 50 m/s

13. fourteen 10c coins; seven 50c coins   **14.** 20 people

15. current 4 m/s, speed in still water 10 m/s   **16.** $\frac{5}{7}$ **17.** owner 10, mouse 3

18. 4, 7   **19.** $y = 3x - 2$ **20.** 1×15, 5×5 **21.** man = 36, son = 9

22. current $4\frac{1}{2}$ knots, submarine $20\frac{1}{2}$ knots   **23.** $a = 1, b = 2, c = 5$ **24.** $y = 2x^2 - 3x + 5$

25. $y = x^2 + 3x + 4$ **26.** $y = x^2 + 2x - 3$

Revision exercise 2

1. a) $-2\frac{1}{2}$ **b)** $2\frac{2}{3}$

2. a) 14   **b)** 18   **c)** 28

3. a) $x = 3, y = -2$ **b)** $m = 1\frac{1}{2}, n = -3$ **c)** $x = 7, y = \frac{1}{2}$ **d)** $x = -1, y = -2$

4. a) 8   **b)** 140   **c)** 29   **d)** 42   **e)** 6   **f)** −6

5. a) $x^3 - 9x^2 + 26x - 24$ **b)** $8x^3 - 36x^2 + 54x - 27$

6. a) $x = 1$ **b)** $x = \frac{21}{2}$ **7.** $\frac{7}{8}$

8. a) $c = 5, d = -2$ **b)** $x = 2, y = -1$ **c)** $x = 9, y = -14$ **d)** $s = 5, t = -3$

9. a) $\frac{7}{11}$ **b)** 3

10. a) 2   **b)** −3   **c)** 36   **d)** 0   **e)** 36   **f)** 4

11. 8   **12.** 21   **13.** 20

Examination-style exercise 2

1. a) $x = 3$ **b)** $y = 5$ **2.** $x = 4, y = 1$

3. a) $x = 18$ **b)** $x = 7$ **4.** $x = 10, y = 7$

5. a) $3x^3 - 17x^2 + 21x + 9$ **b)** $3x^3 - 18x^2 + 17x + 5$

3 Number 2

Exercise 3.1A

1. a) $1:4$ **b)** $3:8$ **c)** $7:4$ **d)** $5:6$

   e) $3:7$ **f)** $10:3$ **g)** $1:2:5$ **h)** $7:3:2$

2. a) $1:3$ **b)** $1:6$ **c)** $1:50$ **d)** $1:1.6$

   e) $1:0.75$ **f)** $1:0.375$ **g)** $1:25$ **h)** $1:8$

3. a) $2.4:1$ **b)** $2.5:1$ **c)** $0.8:1$ **d)** $0.02:1$

4. a) $15, $25   **b)** $36, $84   **c)** 140 m, 110 m   **d)** $18, $27, $72

   e) 15 kg, 75 kg, 90 kg   **f)** 46 min, 69 min, 69 min

5. $39   **6.** 18 kg, 36 kg, 54 kg, 72 kg   **7.** $400, $1000, $1000, $1600

8. $5:3$ **9.** $200   **10.** $3:7$ **11.** $\frac{1}{7}x$ **12.** 6

13. 12   **14.** $120   **15.** 300 g   **16.** 625

17. a) $8:3$ **b)** A gets $320, B gets $80, C gets $120

Exercise 3.1B

1. $11.90   **2.** $84   **3.** 6 days   **4.** $2\frac{1}{2}$ litres   **5.** 60 km

6. 119 g   **7.** $68.40   **8.** $2\frac{1}{4}$ weeks   **9.** 80 c   **10. a)** 12 **b)** 2100

11. 4   **12.** 5.6 days   **13.** $175   **14.** 540°   **15.** $1.20
16. 190 m   **17.** 1250   **18.** 11.2 h   **19.** 57.1 min   **20.** 12 days

Exercise 3.1C
1. a) €20.60   **b)** £64.40   **c)** 29376 pesos
   d) 122.00 rupees   **e)** 331.20 yen   **f)** 0.28 dinars
2. a) $485.44   **b)** $2717.39   **c)** $0.09   **d)** $2903.23   **e)** $0.85   **f)** $490.20
3. £0.58   **4.** Cheaper in the UK by $6.16   **5.** €416.15
6. Kuwait £445.16, France £491.26, Japan £587.78   **7.** €471.24

Exercise 3.2A
1. a) 70 m   **b)** 16 m   **c)** 3.55 m   **d)** 108.5 m
2. a) 5 cm   **b)** 3.5 cm   **c)** 0.72 cm   **d)** 2.86 cm
3. a) 450 000 cm   **b)** 4500 m   **c)** 4.5 km
4. 12.3 km   **5.** 4.71 km   **6.** 50 cm   **7.** 64 cm   **8.** 5.25 cm

Exercise 3.2B
1. 40 m by 30 m; 12 cm²; 1200 m²   **2.** 1 m², 6 m²   **3.** 0.32 km²   **4.** 50 cm²
5. 150 km²   **6.** 18.75 hectares   **7.** 240 cm²   **8.** 1:50 000

Exercise 3.3A
1. a) $\frac{3}{5}$ **b)** $\frac{6}{25}$ **c)** $\frac{1}{50}$ **d)** $\frac{28}{25}$
2. a) 25%   **b)** 10%   **c)** $87\frac{1}{2}\%$ **d)** $33\frac{1}{3}\%$ **e)** 72%   **f)** 183%
3. a) 0.36   **b)** 0.07   **c)** 0.134   **d)** 1.29   **e)** 0.6   **f)** 0.875
4. a) 45%; $\frac{1}{2}$; 0.6   **b)** 4%; $\frac{6}{16}$; 0.38   **c)** 11%; 0.111; $\frac{1}{9}$ **d)** 0.3; 32%; $\frac{1}{3}$
5. a) 85%   **b)** 77.5%   **c)** 23.75%   **d)** 56%   **e)** 10%   **f)** 37.5%

Exercise 3.3B
1. a) $15   **b)** 900 kg   **c)** $2.80   **d)** 125
2. $32   **3.** 13.2c   **4.** 52.8 kg
5. a) $1.02   **b)** $21.58   **c)** $2.22   **d)** $0.53
6. $289.28   **7.** $26 182   **8.** 53.9%   **9.** 77.5%
10. 200   **11.** 29 000   **12.** 500 cm   **13. a)** $6.30   **b)** 42%
14. 400 kg   **15.** 325   **16.** $35.25   **17.** $8425.60

Exercise 3.3C
1. a) 25%, profit   **b)** 25%, profit   **c)** 10%, loss   **d)** 20%, profit
   e) 30%, profit   **f)** 7.5%, profit   **g)** 12%, loss   **h)** 54%, loss
2. 28%   **3.** $44\frac{4}{9}\%$ **4.** 46.9%   **5.** 12%   **6.** $5\frac{1}{3}\%$
7. a) $50   **b)** $450   **c)** $800   **d)** $12.40
8. $50   **9.** $12   **10.** $5   **11.** 60c   **12.** $2200
13. 14.3%   **14.** 20%   **15.** 1:1.375 or 8:11   **16.** 21%   **17.** 20%
18. $25.20   **19.** 175%   **20.** 275

Exercise 3.4A
1. a) $216   **b)** $115.50   **c)** 2 years   **d)** 5 years
2. $2295, $9045   **3.** $1600   **4.** 2.5%   **5.** 7.5%

Exercise 3.4B
1. 25.9 cm   **2.** $10 931   **3.** £262.50   **4.** 336   **5.** £409.50
6. $239.36   **7.** 56   **8.** 60   **9.** 69%   **10.** Either order gives the same final price.

Exercise 3.4C
1. a) $2180   **b)** $2376.20   **c)** $2590.06
2. a) $5550   **b)** $6838.16   **c)** $8425.29
3. $13 107.96   **4. a)** $36 465.19   **b)** $38 288.45
5. a) 9540   **b)** 11 362   **c)** 16 118
6. a) $14 033.01   **b)** $734.03   **c)** $107 946.25
7. $9211.88   **8.** 8 years   **9.** 11 years   **10.** 13 years   **11.** $20 000 at 12% compound interest

Exercise 3.4D
  1. $7250   **2.** $8800   **3.** $18 800   **4.** $3640

Exercise 3.5A
  1. 08:00   **2.** 21:30   **3.** 18:00   **4.** 05:30   **5.** 19:40
  6. 22:00   **7.** 19:15   **8.** 22:45   **9.** 08:30   **10.** 04:15
  11. 02:25   **12.** 13:30   **13.** 19:20   **14.** 06:50   **15.** 07:10
  16. 23:58   **17.** 21:30   **18.** 11:55   **19.** 15:30   **20.** 01:00
  21. 10:30   **22.** 00:20   **23.** 19:00   **24.** 12:06   **25.** 00:50
  26. 7.00 a.m.   **27.** 7.30 p.m.   **28.** 11.20 a.m.   **29.** 4.45 a.m.   **30.** 8.30 p.m.
  31. 9.15 p.m.   **32.** 9.10 a.m.   **33.** 11.45 a.m.   **34.** 11.10 p.m.   **35.** 8.00 p.m.
  36. noon   **37.** 1.40 a.m.   **38.** 4.00 a.m.   **39.** 7.07 a.m.   **40.** 1.13 p.m.
  41. 12.15 p.m.   **42.** 12.30 p.m.   **43.** 3.45 p.m.   **44.** 4.20 p.m.   **45.** 5.16 a.m.

Exercise 3.5B
  1. 1 h 10 mins   **2.** 2 h 10 mins   **3.** 55 mins
  4. 35 mins   **5.** 3 h 20 mins   **6.** 1 h 45 mins
  7. 2 h 20 mins   **8.** 1 h 53 mins   **9.** 53 mins
  10. 5 h 25 mins   **11.** 1 h 50 mins   **12.** 3 h 14 mins
  13. 1 h 15 mins   **14.** 4 h 35 mins   **15.** 2 h 20 mins
  16. 12 h   **17.** 14 h   **18.** 7 h 20 mins
  19. 3 h 15 mins   **20.** 7 h 05 mins   **21.** 5 h
  22. 4 h 40 mins   **23.** 8 h 30 mins   **24.** 2 h 25 mins
  25. 8 h 10 mins   **26.** 19 h   **27.** 19 h
  28. 17 h 30 mins   **29.** 9 h 25 mins   **30.** 34 h

Exercise 3.5C
  1. a) 25 mins   **b)** 45 mins   **c)** 1 h 6 mins   **2.** 7
  3. 09:54   **4.** 11:35   **5.** 15 mins   **6.** 12:52
  7. a) 1 h 42 mins   **b)** 2 h 32 mins   **c)** 3 h 43 mins   **8.** 2
  9. 14:07   **10.** 09:21   **11.** 27 mins   **12.** 12:01
  13. 18:00   **14.** 13:02   **15.** 21:40

Exercise 3.6A
  1. a) $2\frac{1}{2}$ h   **b)** $3\frac{1}{8}$ h   **c)** 75 s   **d)** 4 h
  2. a) 20 m/s   **b)** 30 m/s   **c)** $83\frac{1}{3}$ m/s   **d)** 108 km/h   **e)** 79.2 km/h
     f) 1.2 cm/s   **g)** 90 m/s   **h)** 25 mph   **i)** 0.03 miles per second
  3. a) 75 km/h   **b)** 4.52 km/h   **c)** 7.6 m/s   **d)** 4×10^6 m/s   **e)** 2.5×10^8 m/s
     f) 200 km/h   **g)** 3 km/h
  4. a) 110 000 m   **b)** 10 000 m   **c)** 56 400 m   **d)** 4500 m   **e)** 50 400 m
     f) 80 m   **g)** 960 000 m
  5. a) 3.125 h   **b)** 76.8 km/h   **6. a)** 4.45 h   **b)** 23.6 km/h
  7. 46 km/h   **8. a)** 8 m/s   **b)** 7.6 m/s   **c)** 102.6 s   **d)** 7.79 m/s
  9. 1230 km/h   **10.** 3 h   **11.** 100 s   **12.** $1\frac{1}{2}$ minutes   **13.** 600 m
  14. $53\frac{1}{3}$ s   **15.** 5 cm/s   **16.** 60 s   **17.** 120 km/h

Exercise 3.6B
  1. a) 0.8   **b)** 16   **c)** 390   **d)** 4800   **e)** 1460
  2. a) 1.5   **b)** 2.5   **c)** 90   **d)** 36
  3. $13\frac{1}{3}$ litres per minute   **4.** 12.6 kwh/day   **5.** $8\frac{1}{3}$ minutes
  6. a) 2500   **b)** $66\frac{2}{3}$ **7.** 250 N/m^2 **8.** 1.5 m^2
  9. 243 kg   **10.** 14 000 000   **11.** 41.2 people/km^2

Revision exercise 3
  1. a) $26   **b)** 6:5   **c)** 6   **2.** $75
  3. a) i) 57.2%   **ii)** $87\frac{1}{2}$%   **b)** 40%   **c)** 80 c
  4. 5% increase   **5. a)** $500 **b)** $37\frac{1}{2}$%   **6.** $357.88
  7. a) 2.4 km   **b)** 1 km^2 **8. a)** 300 m   **b)** 60 cm   **c)** 150 cm^2

9. a) 1:50 000   **b)** 1:4 000 000   **10. a)** 22%   **b)** 20.8%   **c)** $240
11. a) i) 7 m/s   **ii)** 200 m/s   **iii)** 5 m/s   **b) i)** 144 km/h   **ii)** 2.16 km/h
12. a) 0.005 m/s   **b)** 1.6 s   **c)** 172.8 km   **13.** $33\frac{1}{3}$ km/h   **14.** 33.1%

Examination-style exercise 3
1. a) Coraline $180, Davina $300, Edward $420
    b) $168   **c)** $210   **d)** 28:35:34   **e)** $257.55
2. a) $29 357.80   **b)** 4%   **3.** 15   **4. a)** $5000   **b)** $56.69
5. a) 1.68   **b)** $1225   **c)** 43.8 cents per kg   **d)** $0.36 per kilogram
6. a) i) 2100 km   **ii)** 2.00 cm   **b) i)** 1:12 000 000   **ii)** 799 km/h
7. a) i) $2875   **ii)** $2000   **b) i)** 232   **ii)** $8816   **iii)** 253%
8. a) 22 500 ml   **b)** 2250 seconds or 37.5 minutes

4 Trigonometry 1

Exercise 4.1A
1. 5 cm   **2.** 13 cm   **3.** 12 cm   **4.** 8 cm
5. 24 cm   **6.** 11 cm   **7.** 65 mm   **8.** 77 m

Exercise 4.1B
1. 10 cm   **2.** $\sqrt{17}$ cm   **3.** $\sqrt{162}$ cm   **4.** $\sqrt{18}$ cm   **5.** $\sqrt{76}$ cm
6. $\sqrt{32}$ cm   **7.** $\sqrt{44}$ cm   **8.** 5 cm   **9.** 17 cm   **10.** $x = 18$ cm

Exercise 4.1C
1. 9.85 cm   **2.** 7.07 cm   **3.** 3.46 m   **4.** 13.6 cm   **5.** 6.34 m
6. 4.58 cm   **7.** 84.9 km   **8.** 24 cm   **9.** 18.5 km
10. 5, 4, 3; 13, 12, 5; 25, 24, 7; 41, 40, 9; 61, 60, 11   **11.** $x = 4$ m, 20.6 m   **12.** 9.49 cm

Exercise 4.2B
1. 4.54   **2.** 3.50   **3.** 3.71   **4.** 6.62   **5.** 8.01
6. 31.9   **7.** 45.4   **8.** 4.34   **9.** 17.1   **10.** 13.2
11. 38.1   **12.** 3.15   **13.** 516   **14.** 79.1   **15.** 5.84
16. 2.56   **17.** 18.3   **18.** 8.65   **19.** 11.9   **20.** 10.6
21. 119   **23.** 3.36 cm   **24.** 4.05 cm   **25.** 11.7 cm   **26.** 9.48 cm
27. 5.74 cm   **28.** 9.53 cm   **29.** 100 m   **30.** 56.7 m   **31.** 16.3 cm
32. 0.952 cm   **33.** 8.27 m

Exercise 4.2C
1. 5.00, 5.55   **2.** 13.1, 27.8   **3.** 34.6, 41.3   **4.** 20.4, 11.7   **5.** 94.1, 94.1
6. 15.2, 10.0, 6.43   **7.** 4.26   **8.** 3.50   **9.** 26.2   **10.** 8.82
11. a) 17.4 cm   **b)** 11.5 cm   **c)** 26.5 cm
12. a) 6.82 cm   **b)** 6.01 cm   **c)** 7.31 cm

Exercise 4.2D
1. 36.9°   **2.** 44.4°   **3.** 48.2°   **4.** 60°   **5.** 36.9°   **6.** 50.2°
7. 29.0°   **8.** 56.4°   **9.** 38.9°   **10.** 43.9°   **11.** 41.8°   **12.** 39.3°
13. 60.3°   **14.** 50.5°   **15.** 13.6°   **16.** 34.8°   **17.** 60.0°   **18.** 42.0°
19. 36.9°   **20.** 51.3°   **21.** 19.6°   **22.** 17.9°   **23.** 32.5°   **24.** 59.6°
25. 54.8°   **26.** 46.3°

Exercise 4.2E
1. a) 1   **b)** 4   **c)** 2   **d)** $3\sqrt{3}$ **e)** $4\sqrt{3}$ **f)** 1
    g) $\frac{1}{2}$ **h)** 0   **i)** $\frac{5}{6}$ **j)** $2\sqrt{3}$
2. a) $6\sqrt{3}$ **b)** 14   **c)** $10\sqrt{3}$ **d)** $7\sqrt{2}$ **e)** $\dfrac{5}{\sqrt{3}}$ **f)** $\dfrac{16}{\sqrt{3}}$

3. $\sin x = \dfrac{\sqrt{12}}{\sqrt{48}} = \dfrac{2\sqrt{3}}{4\sqrt{3}} = \dfrac{1}{2}$ so $x = 30°$ **4.** $4 + 5\sqrt{2}$ **5. a)** $\sqrt{2}$ **b)** $\dfrac{2\sqrt{3}}{3}$

6. $k = 3, c = 2$ **7.** $\cos x = \dfrac{\sqrt{32}}{\sqrt{50} + \sqrt{18}} = \dfrac{4\sqrt{2}}{5\sqrt{2} + 3\sqrt{2}} = \dfrac{4\sqrt{2}}{8\sqrt{2}} = \dfrac{1}{2}$ so $x = 60°$

Exercise 4.3A
1. $314°$ 2. $239°$ 3. a) 26.0 km b) 23.4 km
4. a) 88.6 km b) 179.3 km 5. 40.3 km
6. a) 484 km b) 858 km c) 985 km, $060.6°$
7. 954 km, $133°$ 8. 98.6 km, $023.5°$

Exercise 4.4A
1. 93.3 m 2. $36.9°$ 3. 133 m 4. 67.1 m 5. 139 m
6. 4.41 m 7. 180 m 8. Yes; distance from A to B is 2.13 m
9. a) 11.1 m b) 11.1 s 10. 22.6 m 11. 55.0 m 12. 7.26 m

Exercise 4.4B
1. $19.5°$ 2. 4.12 m 3. 4.13 m 4. 8.60 m 5. 83.2 km
6. $56.3°$ 7. $35.5°$ 8. $71.6°$ 9. $91.8°$ 10. $36.4°$
11. 10.3 cm 12. $71.1°$ 13. $60°$ 14. 13.9 cm

Exercise 4.5A
1. 100 m 2. 89 miles 3. 103 km 4. 99 km; $024°$
5. 9190 km/h; $255°$ 6. 11 km

Exercise 4.6A
1. a) 13 cm b) 13.6 cm c) $17.1°$
2. a) 4.04 m b) $38.9°$ c) 11.2 m d) $19.9°$
3. a) 8.49 cm b) 8.49 cm c) 10.4 cm d) $35.3°$ e) $35.3°$
4. a) 14.1 cm b) 18.7 cm c) $69.3°$ d) $29.0°$ e) $41.4°$
5. a) 4.47 m b) 7.48 m c) $63.4°$ d) $74.5°$ e) $53.3°$
6. 10.8 cm; $21.8°$ 7. a) $h \tan 65°$ or $\dfrac{h}{\tan 25°}$ b) $h \tan 57°$ or $\dfrac{h}{\tan 33°}$ c) 22.7 m
8. $43.3°$

Revision exercise 4
1. $x = 9.43$ cm, $y = 13.4$ cm 2. 4.12 cm
3. a) $45.6°$ b) $58.0°$ c) 3.89 cm d) 33.8 m
4. a) 1.75 b) $60.3°$ 5. 3 6. $30°$
7. $2\sqrt{6}$ 8. 5.39 cm 9. a) $220°$ b) $295°$
10. 0.335 m 11. a) 6.61 cm b) 12.8 cm c) 5.67 cm
12. 52.4 m 13. a) 14.1 cm b) $35.3°$ c) $35.3°$
14. a) 6.63 cm b) $41.8°$

Examination-style exercise 4
1. a) 3 cm b) 5.66 cm 2. a) 12.7 cm b) 5.92 cm c) $36.1°$
3. $\dfrac{6 + \sqrt{2}}{8}$ 4. a) 86.9 cm b) 53.6 cm c) 133 cm
5. 33.1 m 6. 31.1 cm 7. a) 11.3 cm b) 8.25 cm c) $55.6°$
8. a) $5.6°$ b) $281.3°$
9. a) 360 m^3 b) 11.7 m c) $59.0°$ d) 12.5 m e) $53.1°$
10. a) $24\sqrt{3}$ b) $30°$

5 Mensuration

Exercise 5.1A
1. 10.2 m^2 2. 22 cm^2 3. 103 m^2 4. 9 cm^2 5. 31 m^2
6. 6000 cm^2 or 0.6 m^2 7. 26 m^2 8. 18 cm^2 9. 20 cm^2

Exercise 5.1B
1. 13 m 2. 15 cm 3. 56 m 4. 8 m, 10 m 5. 12 cm
6. 2500 7. 6 square units 8. 14 square units 9. 1100 m 10. 1849

Exercise 5.1C

1. 48.3 cm²   **2.** 28.4 cm²   **3.** 66.4 m²   **4.** 3.07 cm²   **5.** 18.2 cm²
6. 12.3 cm²   **7.** 2.78 cm²   **8.** 36.4 m²   **9.** 62.4 m²   **10.** 30.4 m²
11. 44.9 cm²   **12.** 0.227 m²   **13.** 63 m²   **14.** 70.7 m²   **15.** 14 m²
16. 65.8 cm²   **17.** 18.1 cm²   **18.** 8.03 m²   **19.** 52.0 cm²   **20.** 14 m²
21. 124 cm²   **22.** 69.8 m²   **23.** 57.1 cm²   **24.** 10.7 cm   **25.** 50.9°
26. 4.10 m   **27.** 4.85 m   **28.** 7.23 cm   **29.** 60°; 3.90 cm², 23.4 cm²
30. 292   **31.** 110 cm²   **32.** 18.7 cm
33. a) $\dfrac{360°}{n}$ **b)** $\dfrac{n}{2}\sin\dfrac{360°}{n}$ **c)** 2.60, 2.94, 3.1414, 3.1416, 3.14159 as n increases, $A \to \pi$

Exercise 5.2A

1. 12.566 cm, 12.566 cm²   **2.** 50.265 cm, 201.062 cm²   **3.** 31.416 cm, 78.540 cm²
4. 43.982 cm, 153.938 cm²   **5.** 21.991 cm, 38.485 cm²   **6.** 34.558 cm, 95.033 cm²

Exercise 5.2B

1. a) 10π **b)** 25π **2. a)** 6π **b)** 9π **3. a)** $20 + 10\pi$ **b)** 50π
4. a) $14 + 4\pi$ **b)** $24 + 8\pi$ **5. a)** $20 + 2\pi$ **b)** $27 + 2\pi$ **6. a)** $14 + 3.5\pi$ **b)** 12.25π
7. a) $20 + 5\pi$ **b)** $100 - 25\pi$ **8. a)** 16π **b)** $48 + 40\pi$ **9. a)** 7π **b)** $49 - 12.25\pi$
10. a) 3π **b)** $\sqrt{3} + 1.5\pi$ **11. a)** 8π **b)** 8π **12. a)** 6π **b)** 4π

Exercise 5.2C

1. 2.19 cm   **2.** 30.2 m   **3.** 2.65 km   **4.** 9.33 cm   **5.** 14.2 mm
6. 497000 km²   **7.** 21.5 cm²   **8. a)** 40.8 m²   **b)** 6   **9.** 5305
10. 29   **11.** 970   **12. a)** 80   **b)** 7   **13.** 5.39 cm $\left(\sqrt{29}\right)$
14. a) 33.0 cm   **b)** 70.9 cm²   **15. a)** 98 cm²   **b)** 14.0 cm²
16. 1 : 4 : 9   **17.** 796 m²   **18.** 57.5°   **19.** 2π m

Exercise 5.3A

1. a) 2.09 cm; 4.19 cm²   **b)** 7.85 cm; 39.3 cm²   **c)** 8.20 cm; 8.20 cm²
2. 31.9 cm²   **3.** 31.2 cm²
4. a) 7.07 cm²   **b)** 19.5 cm²   **5. a)** 85.9°   **b)** 57.3°   **c)** 6.25 cm
6. a) 12 cm   **b)** 30°   **7. a)** 3.98 cm   **b)** 74.9°
8. a) 30°   **b)** 10.5 cm   **9. a)** 18 cm   **b)** 38.2°
10. a) 10 cm   **b)** 43.0°   **11. a)** 6.14 cm   **b)** 27.6 m   **c)** 28.6 cm²

Exercise 5.4A

1. a) 14.5 cm   **b)** 72.6 cm²   **c)** 24.5 cm²   **d)** 48.1 cm²
2. a) 5.08 cm²   **b)** 82.8 m²   **c)** 5.14 cm²
3. a) 60°, 9.06 cm²   **b)** 106.3°, 11.2 cm²   **4.** 3 cm   **5.** 3.97 cm
6. 13.5 cm², 405 cm³   **7.** 130 cm²; 184 cm²   **8.** 459 cm², 651 cm²
9. 19.6 cm²   **10.** $0.313r^2$ **11. a)** 8.37 cm   **b)** 54.5 cm   **c)** 10.4 cm

Exercise 5.5A

1. a) 30 cm³   **b)** 168 cm³   **c)** 110 cm³   **d)** 94.5 cm³   **e)** 240π cm³   **f)** 90π cm³
2. a) 160π cm³   **b)** 242π cm³   **c)** 3.969π cm³

Exercise 5.5B

1. 3.98 cm   **2.** 6.37 cm   **3.** 1.89 cm   **4.** 5.37 cm   **5.** 9.77 cm
6. 7.38 cm   **7.** 12.7 m   **8.** 4.24 litres   **9.** 106 cm/s
10. a) 1570 cm³   **b)** 12.6 kg   **11.** 3 : 4   **12.** cubes by 77 cm³
13. Yes; to 1 s.f., the number of bricks is 40000   **14.** 1.19 cm   **15.** 53 times
16. 191 cm

Exercise 5.5C

1. $\dfrac{20}{3}\pi$ cm³   **2.** $\dfrac{500}{3}\pi$ cm³   **3.** $\dfrac{4000}{3}\pi$ cm³   **4.** 32π cm³   **5.** $\dfrac{256}{3}\pi$ cm³
6. $\dfrac{4}{3}x^2\pi$ cm³   **7.** $\dfrac{1}{750}\pi$ cm³   **8.** 3 cm³   **9.** $\dfrac{280}{3}$ cm³   **10.** 48 m³
11. $\dfrac{160\sqrt{3}}{3}$ cm³   **12.** $\dfrac{250}{3}\pi$ cm³

Exercise 5.5D
1. 235 cm³ **2.** 400.6 cm³ **3.** 5 m **4.** 2.43 cm **5.** 23.9 cm
6. 6 cm **7.** 3.72 cm **8.** 1.93 kg **9.** 106 s
10. a) 125 **b)** 2744 **c)** 2.7×10^7 **11. a)** 0.36 cm **b)** 0.427 cm
12. a) 6.69 cm **b)** 39.1 cm **13.** $10\frac{2}{3}$ cm³ **14.** 1.05 cm³ **15.** 488 cm³
16. 4 cm **17.** 53.6 cm³ **18.** 74.5 cm³ **19.** 4.24 cm **20.** 123 cm³
21. 54.5 litres **22. a)** 16π **b)** 8 cm **c)** 6 cm **23.** 471 cm³
24. 2720 cm³ **25.** 943 cm³ **26.** 5050 cm³

Exercise 5.6A
1. a) 36π cm² **b)** 72π cm² **c)** 60π cm² **d)** 2.38π m² **e)** 400π m²
f) 65π cm² **g)** 192π mm² **h)** 10.2π cm² **i)** 0.0004π m² **j)** 98π cm², 147π cm²
2. 1.64 cm **3.** 2.12 cm **4.** 3.46 cm
5. a) 3 cm **b)** 4 cm **c)** 3 cm **d)** 0.2 m **e)** 6 cm **f)** 2.5 cm **g)** 7 m
6. 303 cm² **7.** \$1179 **8.** \$3870 **9.** 94.0 cm³
10. 44.6 cm² **11.** 675 cm² **13.** 377 cm² **14.** 116 cm²
15. 336 cm² **16.** 198 cm² **17.** 592 cm² **18.** 184 cm²

Exercise 5.6B
1. 200 mm² **2.** 4500 mm² **3.** 16 cm² **4.** 0.48 cm² **5.** 30 000 cm²
6. 260 000 cm² **7.** 0.86 m² **8.** 0.076 m² **9.** 5 000 000 m² **10.** 4.5 km²
11. 8000 mm³ **12.** 21 000 cm³ **13.** 48 cm³ **14.** 6 000 000 cm³ **15.** 28 m³
16. a) 24 000 mm³ **b)** 5200 mm² **17.** 0.32 m²
18. a) 4 830 000 cm² (3 s.f.) **b)** 998 m³ **c)** 998 000 000 cm³ (3 s.f.)
19. 400 000 mm³ **20.** 95.4 mm (3 s.f.)

Exercise 5.7A
1. $a = 2\frac{1}{2}$ cm, $e = 3$ cm **2.** $x = 6$ cm, $y = 10$ cm **3.** $x = 12$ cm, $y = 8$ cm
4. $m = 10$ cm, $a = 16\frac{2}{3}$ cm **5.** $y = 6$ cm **6.** $x = 4$ cm, $w = 1\frac{1}{2}$ cm
7. $e = 9$ cm, $f = 4\frac{1}{2}$ cm **8.** $x = 13\frac{1}{3}$ cm, $y = 9$ cm **9.** $m = 6$ cm, $n = 6$ cm
10. $m = 5\frac{1}{3}$ cm, $z = 4\frac{4}{5}$ cm **11.** $v = 5\frac{1}{3}$ cm, $w = 6\frac{2}{3}$ cm **12.** No
13. BO = 2 cm, DO = 6 cm **14. a)** Yes **b)** No **c)** No **d)** Yes **e)** Yes **f)** No **g)** No **h)** Yes
17. 16 m **18.** 0.618; 1.618 : 1

Exercise 5.7B
1. 16 cm² **2.** 27 cm² **3.** $11\frac{1}{4}$ cm² **4.** $14\frac{1}{2}$ cm² **5.** 128 cm² **6.** 12 cm²
7. 8 cm **8.** 18 cm **9.** $4\frac{1}{2}$ cm **10.** $7\frac{1}{2}$ cm **11.** $2\frac{1}{2}$ cm **12.** 6 cm

Exercise 5.7C
1. A = 32 cm² **2.** B = 27.9 cm² **3.** C = 40 cm² **4.** D = 225 cm²
5. a) $16\frac{2}{3}$ cm² **b)** $10\frac{2}{3}$ cm² **6. a)** 25 cm² **b)** 21 cm²
7. 8 cm² **8.** 6 cm **9.** 24 cm²
10. a) $1\frac{4}{5}$ cm **b)** 3 cm **c)** 3 : 5 **d)** 9 : 25
11. 150 **12.** 360 **13.** The amount of peel removed is not directly proportional to the volume, but is directly proportional to the surface area.

Exercise 5.7D
1. 480 cm³ **2.** 540 cm³ **3.** 160 cm³ **4.** 4500 cm³ **5.** 81 cm³
6. 11 cm³ **7.** 16 cm³ **8.** $85\frac{1}{3}$ cm³ **9.** 4 cm **10.** 21 cm
11. 4.6 cm **12.** 9 cm **13.** 6.6 cm **14.** $4\frac{1}{2}$ cm **15.** $168\frac{3}{4}$ cm³
16. 106.3 cm³ **17.** 12 cm **18. a)** 2 : 3 **b)** 8 : 27 **19.** 8 : 125
20. $x_1^{\ 3} : x_2^{\ 3}$ **21.** 54 kg **22.** 240 cm² **23.** $9\frac{3}{8}$ litres **24.** $2812\frac{1}{2}$ cm²

Revision exercise 5
1. **a)** 14 cm^2 **b)** 54 cm^2 **c)** 50 cm^2 **d)** 18 m^2
2. **a)** 56.5 m, 254 m^2 **b)** 10.8 cm   **c)** 3.99 cm
3. **a)** 9π cm^2 **b)** 8:1   **4.** 3.43 cm^2, 4.57 cm^2
5. **a)** 12.2 cm   **b)** 61.1 cm^2
6. **a)** 11.2 cm   **b)** 10.3 cm   **c)** 44.7 cm^2 **d)** 31.5 cm^2 **e)** 13.2 cm^2
7. 103.1°   **8.** 9.95 cm   **9. a)** 905 cm^3 **b)** 5.76 cm
10. 8.06 cm   **11.** 99.5 cm^3 **12.** 333 cm^3, 201 cm^3 **13.** 4 cm
14. **a)** 15.6 cm^2 **b)** 93.5 cm^2 **c)** 3741 cm^3 **15.** 104 cm^2 **16.** 5.14 cm^2
17. 68c   **18.** 25   **19.** 20 cm^2 **20. b)** 6 cm   **21.** $3\frac{2}{3}$ cm, $1\frac{1}{11}$ cm
22. 6 cm   **23.** 250 cm^3 **24. a)** 1 m^2 **b)** 1000 cm^3

Examination-style exercise 5
1. **c)** 2.8 cm   **2.** 15$\sqrt{2}$ cm^2 **3. a)** 1350 cm^3 **b)** 1008 cm^2
4. **a)** $3\frac{1}{3}$ cm   **b)** 1620 cm^3
5. **a)** 325 cm^2 **b)** 16 250 cm^3 **c)** 5650 cm^2 **6.** $\frac{75}{2}\pi$ cm^3
7. **a)** 42 590 km   **b)** 6780 km   **8.** 0.370 cm   **9.** 34.2 cm^2
10. $r = 96$ cm, $h = 180$ cm   **11. b)** 6069 kg

6 Algebra 2

Exercise 6.1A
1. $5(a + b)$ **2.** $7(x + y)$ **3.** $x(7 + x)$ **4.** $y(y + 8)$
5. $y(2y + 3)$ **6.** $2y(3y - 2)$ **7.** $3x(x - 7)$ **8.** $2a(8 - a)$
9. $3c(2c - 7)$ **10.** $3x(5 - 3x)$ **11.** $7y(8 - 3y)$ **12.** $x(a + b + 2c)$
13. $x(x + y + 3z)$ **14.** $y(x^2 + y^2 + z^2)$ **15.** $ab(3a + 2b)$ **16.** $xy(x + y)$
17. $2a(3a + 2b + c)$ **18.** $m(a + 2b + m)$ **19.** $2k(x + 3y + 2z)$ **20.** $a(x^2 + y + 2b)$
21. $xk(x + k)$ **22.** $ab(a^2 + 2b)$ **23.** $bc(a - 3b)$ **24.** $ae(2a - 5e)$
25. $ab(a^2 + b^2)$ **26.** $x^2y(x + y)$ **27.** $2xy(3y - 2x)$ **28.** $3ab(b^2 - a^2)$
29. $a^2b(2a + 5b)$ **30.** $ax^2(y - 2z)$ **31.** $2ab(x + b + a)$ **32.** $yx(a + x^2 - 2yx)$

Exercise 6.1B
1. $(a + b)(x + y)$ **2.** $(x + 1)(m + n)$ **3.** $(a + b)(h - k)$ **4.** $(m + n)(a - b)$
5. $(h + k)(s + t)$ **6.** $(a - b)(x - y)$ **7.** $(x - y)(s - t)$ **8.** $(h - b)(x - y)$
9. $(m - n)(a - b)$ **10.** $(x - z)(k - m)$ **11.** $(2a + b)(x + 3y)$ **12.** $(2a + b)(x + y)$
13. $(2m - 1)(h - k)$ **14.** $(m - n)(2h + 3k)$ **15.** $(2x + y)(3a + b)$ **16.** $(2a - b)(x - y)$
17. $(x^2 + y)(a + b)$ **18.** $(m - n)(s + 2t^2)$

Exercise 6.1C
1. $(x + 2)(x + 5)$ **2.** $(x + 3)(x + 4)$ **3.** $(x + 3)(x + 5)$ **4.** $(x + 3)(x + 7)$
5. $(x + 2)(x + 6)$ **6.** $(y + 5)(y + 7)$ **7.** $(y + 3)(y + 8)$ **8.** $(y + 5)(y + 5)$
9. $(y + 3)(y + 12)$ **10.** $(a + 2)(a - 5)$ **11.** $(a + 3)(a - 4)$ **12.** $(z + 3)(z - 2)$
13. $(x + 5)(x - 7)$ **14.** $(x + 3)(x - 8)$ **15.** $(x - 2)(x - 4)$ **16.** $(y - 2)(y - 3)$
17. $(x - 3)(x - 5)$ **18.** $(a + 2)(a - 3)$ **19.** $(a + 5)(a + 9)$ **20.** $(b + 3)(b - 7)$
21. $(x - 4)(x - 4)$ **22.** $(y + 1)(y + 1)$ **23.** $(y - 7)(y + 4)$ **24.** $(x - 5)(x + 4)$
25. $(x - 20)(x + 12)$ **26.** $(x - 15)(x - 11)$ **27.** $(y + 12)(y - 9)$ **28.** $(x - 7)(x + 7)$
29. $(x - 3)(x + 3)$ **30.** $(x - 4)(x + 4)$

Exercise 6.1D
1. $(2x + 3)(x + 1)$ **2.** $(2x + 1)(x + 3)$ **3.** $(3x + 1)(x + 2)$ **4.** $(2x + 3)(x + 4)$
5. $(3x + 2)(x + 2)$ **6.** $(2x + 5)(x + 1)$ **7.** $(3x + 1)(x - 2)$ **8.** $(2x + 5)(x - 3)$
9. $(2x + 7)(x - 3)$ **10.** $(3x + 4)(x - 7)$ **11.** $(2x + 1)(3x + 2)$ **12.** $(3x + 2)(4x + 5)$
13. $(3x - 2)(x - 3)$ **14.** $(y - 2)(3y - 5)$ **15.** $(4y - 3)(y - 5)$ **16.** $(2y + 3)(3y - 1)$
17. $(2x - 5)(3x - 6)$ **18.** $(5x + 2)(2x + 1)$ **19.** $(6x - 1)(x - 3)$ **20.** $(4x + 1)(2x - 3)$
21. $(6x + 5)(2x - 1)$ **22.** $(16x + 3)(x + 1)$ **23.** $(2a - 1)(2a - 1)$ **24.** $(x + 2)(12x - 7)$

25. $(x + 3)(15x - 1)$ **26.** $(8x + 1)(6x + 5)$ **27.** $(16y - 3)(4y + 1)$ **28.** $(15x - 1)(8x + 5)$
29. $(3x - 1)(3x + 1)$ **30.** $(2a - 3)(2a + 3)$

Exercise 6.1E

1. $(y - a)(y + a)$ **2.** $(m - n)(m + n)$ **3.** $(x - t)(x + t)$
4. $(y - 1)(y + 1)$ **5.** $(x - 3)(x + 3)$ **6.** $(a - 5)(a + 5)$
7. $\left(x - \frac{1}{2}\right)\left(x + \frac{1}{2}\right)$ **8.** $\left(x - \frac{1}{3}\right)\left(x + \frac{1}{3}\right)$ **9.** $(2x - y)(2x + y)$
10. $(a - 2b)(a + 2b)$ **11.** $(5x - 2y)(5x + 2y)$ **12.** $(3x - 4y)(3x + 4y)$
13. $\left(x - \frac{y}{2}\right)\left(x + \frac{y}{2}\right)$ **14.** $\left(3m - \frac{2}{3}n\right)\left(3m + \frac{2}{3}n\right)$ **15.** $\left(4t - \frac{2}{5}s\right)\left(4t + \frac{2}{5}s\right)$
16. $\left(2x - \frac{z}{10}\right)\left(2x + \frac{z}{10}\right)$ **17.** $x(x - 1)(x + 1)$ **18.** $a(a - b)(a + b)$
19. $x(2x - 1)(2x + 1)$ **20.** $2x(2x - y)(2x + y)$ **21.** $3x(2x - y)(2x + y)$
22. $2m(3m - 2n)(3m + 2n)$ **23.** $5\left(x - \frac{1}{2}\right)\left(x + \frac{1}{2}\right)$ **24.** $2a(5a - 3b)(5a + 3b)$
25. $3y(2x - z)(2x + z)$ **26.** $4ab(3a - b)(3a + b)$ **27.** $2a^3(5a - 2b)(5a + 2b)$
28. $9xy(2x - 5y)(2x + 5y)$ **29.** 161 **30.** 404
31. 4400 **32.** 2421 **33.** 4329
34. 0.75 **35.** 4.8 **36.** -2469
37. 0.0761 **38.** $-10\,900$ **39.** 53.6
40. $0.000\,005$

Exercise 6.1F

1. $x(x + 1)(x + 2)$ **2.** $x(x + 2)(x - 3)$ **3.** $x(x - 1)(x + 4)$
4. $x(x + 3)(x + 5)$ **5.** $x(x - 6)(x + 10)$ **6.** $x(x + 7)(x - 4)$
7. $x(x - 5)(x - 3)$ **8.** $x(x - 4)(x - 11)$ **9.** $x(2x + 1)(x - 2)$
10. $x(3x - 1)(x + 2)$ **11.** $x(2x + 3)(x - 1)$ **12.** $x(4x - 3)(x + 1)$
13. $x(5x - 3)(x + 4)$ **14.** $x(2x + 1)(3x - 1)$ **15.** $x(5x - 3)(x + 4)$
16. $x(3x + 2)(5x + 1)$ **17.** $x(6x - 1)(2x + 7)$ **18.** $x(3x + 8)(2x - 5)$
19. $2x(x + 1)(x - 1)$ **20.** $3x(x - 2)(x + 1)$ **21.** $5x(3x - 2)(x + 4)$
22. $4x(3x + 4)(x - 3)$ **23.** $-2x(x + 7)(x + 9)$ **24.** $-5x(2x + 3)(3x - 5)$

Exercise 6.2A

1. $-3, -4$ **2.** $-2, -5$ **3.** $3, -5$ **4.** $2, -3$ **5.** $2, 6$
6. $-3, -7$ **7.** $2, 3$ **8.** $5, -1$ **9.** $-7, 2$ **10.** $-\frac{1}{2}, 2$
11. $\frac{2}{3}, -4$ **12.** $1\frac{1}{2}, -5$ **13.** $\frac{2}{3}, 1\frac{1}{2}$ **14.** $\frac{1}{4}, 7$ **15.** $\frac{3}{5}, -\frac{1}{2}$
16. $7, 8$ **17.** $\frac{5}{6}, \frac{1}{2}$ **18.** $7, -9$ **19.** $-1, -1$ **20.** $3, 3$
21. $-5, -5$ **22.** $7, 7$ **23.** $-\frac{1}{3}, \frac{1}{2}$ **24.** $-1\frac{1}{4}, 2$ **25.** $13, -5$
26. $-3, \frac{1}{6}$ **27.** $\frac{1}{10}, -2$ **28.** $1, 1$ **29.** $\frac{2}{9}, -\frac{1}{4}$ **30.** $-\frac{1}{4}, \frac{3}{5}$

Exercise 6.2B

1. $0, 3$ **2.** $0, -7$ **3.** $0, 1$ **4.** $0, \frac{1}{3}$ **5.** $4, -4$
6. $7, -7$ **7.** $\frac{1}{2}, -\frac{1}{2}$ **8.** $\frac{2}{3}, -\frac{2}{3}$ **9.** $0, -1\frac{1}{2}$ **10.** $0, 1\frac{1}{2}$
11. $0, 5\frac{1}{2}$ **12.** $\frac{1}{4}, -\frac{1}{4}$ **13.** $\frac{1}{2}, -\frac{1}{2}$ **14.** $0, \frac{5}{8}$ **15.** $0, \frac{1}{12}$
16. $0, 6$ **17.** $0, 11$ **18.** $0, 1\frac{1}{2}$ **19.** $0, 1$ **20.** $0, 4$
21. $0, 3$ **22.** $\frac{1}{2}, -\frac{1}{2}$ **23.** $1\frac{1}{3}, -1\frac{1}{3}$ **24.** $3, -4$ **25.** $0, 2\frac{2}{5}$
26. $\frac{1}{3}, -\frac{1}{3}$ **27.** $0, \frac{1}{4}$ **28.** $0, \frac{1}{6}$ **29.** $\frac{1}{4}, -\frac{1}{4}$ **30.** $0, \frac{1}{5}$

Exercise 6.2C

1. $-0.5, -5$ **2.** $-\frac{2}{3}, -3$ **3.** $-0.5, -\frac{2}{3}$ **4.** $\frac{1}{3}, 3$

5. $0.4, 1$ **6.** $\frac{1}{3}, 1.5$ **7.** $\dfrac{-3 \pm \sqrt{3}}{2}$ **8.** $-2 \pm \sqrt{3}$

9. $\dfrac{5 \pm \sqrt{5}}{10}$ **10.** $\dfrac{7 \pm \sqrt{41}}{2}$ **11.** $\dfrac{-5 \pm \sqrt{33}}{4}$ **12.** $\dfrac{-1 \pm \sqrt{37}}{6}$

13. $\dfrac{-4 \pm \sqrt{34}}{3}$ **14.** $-\frac{5}{3}, 4$ **15.** $-1.5, 5$ **16.** $\dfrac{3 \pm \sqrt{17}}{2}$

17. $-0.5, 2\frac{1}{3}$ **18.** $-\frac{1}{3}, -8$ **19.** $\frac{5}{3}, -1$ **20.** $-\frac{2}{3}, 0.5$

21. $-2.25, 1.4$ **22.** $1.5, -4$ **23.** $-3, \frac{5}{3}$ **24.** $-2, \frac{5}{3}$

25. $-3.5, 0.2$ **26.** $-3, 0.8$ **27.** $-8.5, 11$ **28.** $0.16, -3.16$
29. $2.28, 0.22$ **30.** $-0.35, -5.65$ **31.** $-0.58, 2.58$ **32.** $-2.69, 0.19$
33. $0.22, -1.55$ **34.** $-0.37, 5.37$ **35.** $-0.83, 1.75$ **36.** $-0.78, 1.25$

Exercise 6.2D

1. $-3, 2$ **2.** $-3, -7$ **3.** $-\frac{1}{2}, 2$ **4.** $1, 4$

5. $-1\frac{2}{3}, \frac{1}{2}$ **6.** $-0.39, -4.28$ **7.** $-0.16, 6.16$ **8.** 3

9. $2, -1\frac{1}{3}$ **10.** $-3, -1$ **11.** $0, 3\frac{1}{2}$ **12.** $-\frac{1}{4}, \frac{1}{4}$

Exercise 6.2E

1. $(x + 4)^2 - 16$ **2.** $(x - 6)^2 - 36$ **3.** $\left(x + \frac{1}{2}\right)^2 - \frac{1}{4}$ **4.** $(x + 2)^2 - 3$

5. $(x - 3)^2$ **6.** $(x + 1)^2 - 16$ **7.** $2(x + 4)^2 - 27$ **8.** $2(x - 2.5)^2 - 12.5$
9. $10 - (x - 2)^2$ **10.** $4 - (x + 1)^2$

11. a) $x = \pm\sqrt{7} - 2$ **b)** $x = \dfrac{3 \pm \sqrt{17}}{2}$ **c)** $x = \pm\sqrt{37} - 6$

12. $(x + 3)^2 + 1$ requires finding $\sqrt{-1}$, which has no real solutions

13. $y = (x + 3)^2 + 3$ since $(x + 3)^2 \geq 0$ for all
   values of x, so $y \geq 3$ **14.** $y = (x - 3.5)^2 - 12$ since $(x - 3.5)^2 \geq 0$
   for all values of x, so $y \geq -12$

15. a) 3 **b)** $x = -2$ **c)** $\frac{1}{3}$

Exercise 6.3A

1. $8, 11$ **2.** $11, 13$ **3.** 12 cm   **4.** 6 cm
5. $x = 11$ **6.** 10 cm $\times 24$ cm   **7.** 8 km north, 15 km east   **8.** 12 eggs
9. 13 eggs   **10.** $x = 2$ **11.** $x = 3$ or 9.5 **12.** 9 cm or 13 cm

Exercise 6.4A

1. $x = 6, y = 8$ and $x = 8, y = 4$ **2.** $x = 1, y = -2$ and $x = 3, y = 10$
3. $x = 1, y = 0$ **4.** $x = 1, y = 7$ and $x = 3, y = 3$
5. $x = -5, y = 19$ **6.** $x = 0.59, y = 33.31$ and $x = 3.41, y = 10.69$
7. $x = -0.73, y = 6.07$ and $x = 2.73, y = 19.93$ **8.** $x = -6.24, y = 5.58$ and $x = -1.76, y = 32.42$
9. $x = -5.73, y = 8.46$ and $x = -2.27, y = 1.54$ **10.** $x = -3.59, y = -4.88$ and $x = 2.09, y = 3.63$
11. $x = 0, y = 5$ and $x = 0.83, y = 3.89$ **12.** $x = -2.20, y = -3.13$ and $x = 1.31, y = -0.79$
13. $x = -2.16$ and $y = -1.16$, or $x = 1.16$ and $y = 2.16$ **14.** $x = -0.56$ and $y = -3.56$, or $x = 3.56$ and $y = 0.56$
15. $x = -1.13$ and $y = 2.17$, or $x = 1.77$ and $y = -1.69$

Revision exercise 6

1. a) $(2x - y)(2x + y)$ **b)** $2(x + 3)(x + 1)$ **c)** $(2 - 3k)(3m + 2n)$
   d) $(2x + 1)(x - 3)$ **e)** $2x(2x + 1)(x + 2)$

2. a) $0, 3\frac{1}{2}$ **b)** $-3, -2$ **c)** 12

3. a) $z(z - 4)(z + 4)$ **b)** $(x^2 + 1)(y^2 + 1)$ **c)** $(2x + 3)(x + 4)$

4. a) $x = 0, y = 4$ and $x = -3, y = 1$
   b) $x = 0.58, y = 1.36$ and $x = 2.18, y = 3.76$

5. a) $\frac{1}{2}, -\frac{1}{2}$ **b)** $0, 5$

6. a) 1.78, −0.28   **b)** 1.62, −0.62   **c)** 0.87, −1.54   **d)** 1.54, −4.54
7. a) $x = 9$ **b)** $x = 10$
8. $15 = x(x + 2)$; speed $= 5$ km/h   **9.** 8 cm × 6.5 cm   **10. a)** −2, 4   **b)** 6.19, 0.81
11. $x = 13$ **12.** 6 cm   **13.** $x = -3.28$, $y = -2.28$ and $x = 2.28$, $y = 3.28$

Examination-style exercise 6

1. $p = 3$, $q = -21$ **2. a)** $k = 9$ **b)** $b(a + 3b)(a - 3b)(a^2 + 9b^2)$
3. $-2 \pm \sqrt{15}$ **4. b)** $x = 9$ or -10 **c)** 16 cm
5. $x = -4$ and $y = 3$, $x = 3$ and $y = -4$ **6. a) i)** $x^2 + 6x + 8$ **b)** 5.1
7. $x = 0.618$ and $y = 1.618$ or $x = -1.618$ and $y = -0.618$ **8. a)** −4   **b)** 4

7 Geometry

Exercise 7.1A
1. 95°   **2.** 49°   **3.** 100°   **4.** 77°
5. 129°   **6.** 95°   **7.** $a = 30°$ **8.** $e = 30°$, $f = 60°$
9. 110°   **10.** $x = 54°$ **11.** $a = 40°$ **12.** $a = 36°$, $b = 72°$, $c = 144°$, $d = 108°$
13. 105°   **14.** $a = 30°$, $b = 120°$, $c = 150°$ **15.** $x = 20°$, $y = 140°$
16. $a = 120°$, $b = 34°$, $c = 26°$ **17.** $a = 68°$, $b = 58.5°$
18. $e = 25°$ **19.** $x = 44°$ **20.** $a = 30°$, $b = 60°$, $c = 150°$, $d = 120°$
21. $a = 10°$, $b = 76°$ **22.** $e = 71°$, $f = 21°$ **23.** 144°
24. 70°   **25.** $\hat{WZX} = 41°$, $\hat{XZY} = 66°$ **26.** D = 46°, B = 122°   **27.** 36°

Exercise 7.1B
1. $a = 72°$, $b = 108°$ **2.** $x = 60°$, $y = 120°$ **3.** $m = 60°$ **4.** $a = 128.6°$ (1 d.p.)   **5.** $x = 120°$
6. 15   **7.** 12   **8.** 9   **9.** 18   **10.** 12   **11.** 36°

Exercise 7.1C
1. $a = 116°$, $b = 64°$, $c = 64°$ **2.** $a = 64°$, $b = 40°$ **3.** $x = 68°$
4. $a = 40°$, $b = 134$, $c = 134°$ **5.** $m = 69°$, $y = 65°$ **6.** $t = 48°$, $u = 48°$, $v = 42°$
7. $a = 118°$, $b = 100°$, $c = 62°$ **8.** $a = 34°$, $b = 76°$, $c = 70°$, $d = 70°$ **9.** $2x = 72°$, $3x = 108°$

Exercise 7.2A
1. a) i) 1 **ii)** 1   **b) i)** 1 **ii)** 1   **c) i)** 2 **ii)** 2   **d) i)** 2 **ii)** 2
     e) i) 4 **ii)** 4   **f) i)** 0 **ii)** 2   **g) i)** 0 **ii)** 1   **h) i)** 0 **ii)** 2
     i) i) 0 **ii)** 2   **j) i)** 0 **ii)** 2   **k) i)** ∞ **ii)** ∞   **l) i)** 0 **ii)** 4
4. square 4, 4; rectangle 2, 2; parallelogram 0, 2; rhombus 2, 2; trapezium 0, 1; kite 1,1; equilateral triangle 3, 3; regular hexagon 6, 6; scalene triangle 0, 1

Exercise 7.2B
1. 34°, 56°   **2.** 35°, 35°   **3.** 72°, 108°, 28°   **4.** 40°, 30°, 110°
5. 116°, 32°, 58°   **6.** 55°, 55°   **7.** 26°, 26°, 77°   **8.** 52°, 26°, 64°

Exercise 7.2C
1. 4   **2. a)** 4   **b)** 3   **c)** 4   **d)** 2
3.

4. No
5. Yes, it has an infinite number of axes halfway down the length of the cylinder that pass through the centre of the cross-section. The cylinder has rotational symmetry of order 2 around each of these axes.

6. For example, a sphere (any line through centre) or a cylinder (see Question **5**).

7. 4

Exercise 7.2D

1. 3   **2. a)** 1   **b)** 1   **c)** 2   **3. a)** Multiple answers   **b)**   9

4. 7   **5.**   9   **6.** $n + 1$ **7.** $n + 1$

8.

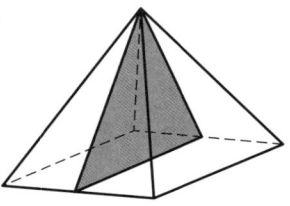 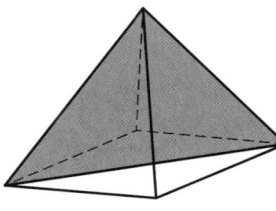 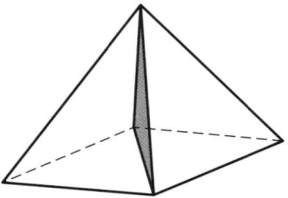

A square based pyramid has 4 planes of symmetry.

9. 4

10. a) an infinite number

     b) an infinite number running through the tip of the cone to the centre of the base

Exercise 7.3A

1. $a = 27, b = 30°$ **2.** $c = 58°, d = 41°, e = 30°$ **3.** $f = 40°, g = 55°, h = 55°$

4. $a = 32°, b = 80°, c = 43°$ **5.** $x = 34°, y = 34°, z = 56°$ **6.** $b = 42°$

7. $e = 49°, f = 41°$ **8.** $x = 48°$ **9.** $y = 32°$ **10.** $a = 36°, x = 36°$

Exercise 7.3B

1. $a = 94°, b = 75°$ **2.** $c = 101°, d = 84°$ **3.** $x = 92°, y = 116°$ **4.** $h = 37°$

5. $e = 36°, f = 72°$ **6.** $m = 90°$ **7.** $a = 30°$ **8.** $n = 58°, t = 64°, w = 45°$

9. $a = 32°, b = 40°, c = 40°$ **10.** $a = 18°, c = 72°$ **11.** $x = 55°$

12. $x = 30°, y = 115°$

Exercise 7.3C

1. $a = 18°$ **2.** $x = 40°, y = 65°, z = 25°$ **3.** $c = 30°, e = 15°$

4. $f = 50°, g = 40°$ **5.** $h = 40°, i = 40°$ **6.** $n = 36$

7. $k = 50°, m = 50°, p = 80°$ **8.** $n = 16°, p = 46°$

Exercise 7.3D

1. $70°$ **2.** $23°$ **3.** $49°$ **4.** $85°$ **5.** $36°$ **6.** $57°$ **7.** $136°$ **8.** $44°$

Exercise 7.3E

1. $x = 6, y = 8$ **2.** $x = 10$ **3.** $x = 8$

4. $x = 3, y = 4$ **5.** $x = 50, y = 80, z = 140$ **6.** Area $= 48$

Exercise 7.4A

1. $63°$ **2.** $35°$ **3.** $62°$ **4.** $30°$ **5.** $37°$ **6.** $94°$ **7.** $93°$ **8.** $36°$

Exercise 7.5A

1. a), b), d)   **2. a)** $a = 4$ cm, $x = 4$ cm, $y = 6$ cm   **b)**   240 cm³

3. a) $a = 10$ cm, $b = 6$ cm, $c = 10$ cm, $d = 10$ cm   **b)**   64 cm³

4. a) 168 mm²   **b)**   16 800 mm³

Revision exercise 7

2. $80°$ **3. a)** $30°$ **b)** $22\frac{1}{2}°$ **4.**   18   **5. a)** $40°$ **b)** $100°$

6. a) $50°$ **b)** $128°$ **c)** $c = 50°$ $d = 40°$ **d)** $x = 62°$ $y = 56°$ $z = 68°$

7. a) $55°$ **b)** $45°$ **9. a)**   6   **b)**   6   **10.** 1

11. 6   **12. a)** yes   **b)**   no

Examination-style exercise 7

1. a) $40°$ **b)** $20°$ **2.** $x = 36°, y = 54°, z = 72°$

3. a) $50°$ **b)** $125°$ **c)** $40°$ **4.** $x = 70°, y = 55°, z = 20°$

8 Algebra 3

Exercise 8.1A

1. $\dfrac{5x}{7}$
2. $\dfrac{7y}{8}$
3. $5y$
4. $\dfrac{1}{2}$
5. 4
6. $\dfrac{x}{2y}$
7. 2
8. $\dfrac{a}{2}$
9. $\dfrac{2b}{3}$
10. $\dfrac{a}{5b}$
11. a
12. $\dfrac{7}{8}$
13. $\dfrac{5 + 2x}{3}$
14. $\dfrac{3x + 1}{x}$
15. $\dfrac{25 + 7x}{25}$
16. $\dfrac{4 + 5a}{5}$
17. $\dfrac{3}{4 - x}$
18. $\dfrac{b}{3 + 2a}$
19. $\dfrac{5x + 4}{8x}$
20. $\dfrac{2x + 1}{y}$
21. $\dfrac{x + 2y}{3xy}$
22. $\dfrac{6 - b}{2a}$
23. $\dfrac{2b + 4a}{b}$
24. $x - 2$

Exercise 8.1B

1. $\dfrac{x + 2}{x - 3}$
2. $\dfrac{x}{x + 1}$
3. $\dfrac{x + 4}{2(x - 5)}$
4. $\dfrac{x + 5}{x - 2}$
5. $\dfrac{x + 3}{x + 2}$
6. $\dfrac{x + 5}{x - 2}$
7. $\dfrac{x + 2}{x}$
8. $\dfrac{3x}{x + 5}$
9. $\dfrac{1}{2}$
10. $\dfrac{3x}{x - 5}$
11. $\dfrac{3x - 5}{x}$
12. $\dfrac{x - 2}{x - 1}$

Exercise 8.1C

1. $\dfrac{2x^2}{15}$
2. $\dfrac{10}{3}$
3. $\dfrac{10}{x^2}$
4. 1
5. x^2
6. $\dfrac{3}{49x^2}$
7. $\dfrac{2x}{5}$
8. $\dfrac{x}{8}$
9. $\dfrac{x + 3}{5x}$
10. $\dfrac{3}{2}$
11. $\dfrac{8x^2}{15}$
12. $\dfrac{3}{7}$
13. x^2
14. $-\dfrac{25}{81}$
15. 6
16. $2x$
17. $\dfrac{(x - 2)^2}{3}$
18. $5(x + 1)$

Exercise 8.1D

1. $\dfrac{3x}{5}$
2. $\dfrac{3}{x}$
3. $\dfrac{4x}{7}$
4. $\dfrac{4}{7x}$
5. $\dfrac{7x}{8}$
6. $\dfrac{7}{8x}$
7. $\dfrac{5x}{6}$
8. $\dfrac{5}{6x}$
9. $\dfrac{23x}{20}$
10. $\dfrac{23}{20x}$
11. $\dfrac{x}{12}$
12. $\dfrac{1}{12x}$
13. $\dfrac{5x + 2}{6}$
14. $\dfrac{7x + 2}{12}$
15. $\dfrac{9x + 13}{10}$
16. $\dfrac{1 - 2x}{12}$
17. $\dfrac{2x - 9}{15}$
18. $\dfrac{-3x - 12}{14}$
19. $\dfrac{13x - 45}{6}$
20. $\dfrac{2(7x - 3)}{15}$
21. $\dfrac{5(3x + 1)}{14}$
22. $\dfrac{3x + 1}{x(x + 1)}$
23. $\dfrac{7x - 8}{x(x - 2)}$
24. $\dfrac{8x + 9}{(x - 2)(x + 3)}$
25. $\dfrac{4x + 11}{(x + 1)(x + 2)}$
26. $\dfrac{-3x - 17}{(x + 3)(x - 1)}$
27. $\dfrac{11 - x}{(x + 1)(x - 2)}$

Exercise 8.1E

1. 4 or -1
2. $2, 5$
3. $\dfrac{40}{x}$ h, $\dfrac{40}{x - 2}$ h, 10 km/h
4. 4 km/h
5. 60 km/h
6. 5 km/h
7. 157 km
8. $\dfrac{3}{4}$

Exercise 8.2A

1. $2\frac{1}{2}$
2. $\dfrac{B}{A}$
3. $\dfrac{K}{M}$
4. $\dfrac{4}{y}$
5. $\dfrac{D}{4}$
6. $\dfrac{T + N}{9}$
7. $\dfrac{B - R}{A}$
8. $\dfrac{N - R^2}{L}$
9. $\dfrac{R - S^2}{N}$
10. $T - A$
11. $M - B$
12. $L - D^2$
13. $T - N^2$
14. $N + M - L$
15. $R - S - Z$
16. 7
17. $A + R$
18. $F + B$
19. $F^2 + B^2$
20. $A + B + D$

21. $A^2 + E$

22. $L + B$

23. $\dfrac{N - C}{A}$

24. $\dfrac{H + F}{N}$

25. $\dfrac{Q - m}{V}$

26. $\dfrac{n + a + m}{t}$

27. $\dfrac{s - t - n}{q}$

28. $\dfrac{t + s^2}{n}$

29. $\dfrac{c - b}{V^2}$

30. $\dfrac{r + 6}{n}$

31. $\dfrac{s - d}{m}$

32. $\dfrac{t + b}{m}$

33. 2

34. $2\frac{2}{3}$

35. $\dfrac{C - AB}{A}$

36. $\dfrac{a - hn}{h}$

37. $\dfrac{q + bd}{b}$

38. $\dfrac{n - rt}{r}$

39. $\dfrac{b + 4t}{t}$

Exercise 8.2B

1. 12

2. BD

3. bm

4. 26

5. $BT + A$

6. $B^2N - Q$

7. $ge + r$

8. $4\frac{1}{2}$

9. $\dfrac{DC - B}{A}$

10. $\dfrac{vS + t}{r}$

11. $\dfrac{qt + m}{z}$

12. $\dfrac{bc - m}{A}$

13. $\dfrac{AE - D}{B}$

14. $\dfrac{nh + f}{e}$

15. $\dfrac{qr - b}{g}$

16. 4

17. -2

18. 2

19. $A - B$

20. $D - H$

21. $n - m$

22. $q - t$

23. $\dfrac{v^2 - r}{r}$

24. $\dfrac{w - t^2}{n}$

25. $\dfrac{n - 2}{q}$

26. $\frac{1}{4}$

27. $\dfrac{D - NB}{E}$

28. $\dfrac{h - bx}{f}$

29. $\dfrac{v^2 - Cd}{h}$

30. $\dfrac{NT - MB}{M}$

31. $\dfrac{mB + ef}{fN}$

32. $\dfrac{TM - EF}{T}$

33. $\dfrac{yx - zt}{y}$

Exercise 8.2C

1. $\frac{1}{2}$

2. $\dfrac{B}{C}$

3. $\dfrac{n}{m}$

4. $\dfrac{B}{x}$

5. $6\frac{2}{3}$

6. $\dfrac{ND}{B}$

7. $1\frac{1}{2}$

8. $3\frac{1}{3}$

9. $\dfrac{B - DC}{C}$

10. $\dfrac{Q + TC}{T}$

11. $\dfrac{L}{MB}$

12. $\dfrac{m}{cd}$

13. $\dfrac{xy - z}{x}$

14. 1

15. $\frac{5}{6}$

16. $\dfrac{A}{C - B}$

17. $\dfrac{r}{n + t}$

18. $\dfrac{b}{d - h}$

19. $\dfrac{d}{C - e}$

20. $\dfrac{m}{r - e^2}$

21. $\dfrac{n}{b - t^2}$

22. $\dfrac{d}{mn - b}$

23. $\dfrac{M - Nq}{N}$

24. $\dfrac{Y + Tc}{T}$

25. $\dfrac{N - 2MP}{2M}$

26. $\dfrac{B - 6Ac}{6A}$

27. $\dfrac{K}{(C - B)M}$

28. $\dfrac{z}{y(y + z)}$

29. $\dfrac{m^2}{n - p}$

30. $\dfrac{q}{w - t}$

Exercise 8.2D

1. 4

2. 11

3. $B^2 - a$

4. $H^2 + E$

5. $\dfrac{c^2 - b}{a}$

6. $a^2 + m$

7. $\dfrac{b^2 + t}{g}$

8. $b - r^2$

9. $b^2 + d$

10. $\dfrac{M - P^2}{N}$

11. $\dfrac{D - B}{A}$

12. $A^4 + D$

13. $\pm\sqrt{g}$

14. ± 4

15. $\pm\sqrt{(M + A)}$

16. $\pm\sqrt{(b - a)}$

17. $\pm\sqrt{(C - m)}$

18. $\pm\sqrt{(d - N)}$

19. $\dfrac{at}{z}$

20. $\pm\sqrt{\left(\dfrac{m + t}{a}\right)}$

21. $\pm\sqrt{(a - n)}$

22. $\pm\sqrt{(B^2 + A)}$

23. $\pm\sqrt{(t^2 - m)}$

24. 8

25. $\dfrac{M^2 - A^2B}{A^2}$

26. $\dfrac{M}{N^2}$

27. $a - b^2$

28. $\pm\sqrt{(a^2 - t^2)}$

29. $\pm\sqrt{(m - x^2)}$

30. $\dfrac{4}{\pi^2} - t$

31. $\dfrac{B^2}{A^2} - 1$

32. $\pm\sqrt{\left(\dfrac{C^2 + b}{a}\right)}$

33. $\pm\sqrt{\left(\dfrac{b^2 + a^2x}{a^2}\right)}$

34. $\pm\sqrt{(x^2 - b)}$

35. $\pm\sqrt{(c - b)a}$

36. $\dfrac{c^2 - b^2}{a}$

Exercise 8.2E

1. $3\frac{2}{3}$

2. $\dfrac{D - B}{2N}$

3. $\dfrac{nb - ma}{m - n}$

4. $\dfrac{a - ab}{b + 1}$

5. $\dfrac{d - c}{d + c}$

6. $\dfrac{m^2 + 5}{2 - m}$

7. $\dfrac{2 + n^2}{n - 1}$

8. $\dfrac{3x}{a + x}$

9. $\dfrac{e - c}{a - d}$ or $\dfrac{c - e}{d - a}$

10. $\dfrac{d}{a - b - c}$

11. $2x$

12. $\dfrac{a(b + c)}{b - 2a}$

13. $\dfrac{5x}{3}$

14. $\dfrac{mn}{p^2 - m}$

15. $\dfrac{mn + n}{4 + m}$

Exercise 8.2F

1. $-\left(\dfrac{by + c}{a}\right)$

2. $\pm\sqrt{\dfrac{e^2 + ab}{a}}$

3. $\dfrac{n^2}{m^2} + m$

4. $3y$

5. $\dfrac{t^2 g}{4\pi^2}$

6. $\pm\sqrt{\dfrac{a}{3}}$

7. $\pm\sqrt{\dfrac{t^2 e - ba}{b}}$

8. $\dfrac{1}{a^2 - 1}$

9. $\pm\sqrt{(x^4 - b^2)}$

10. $\dfrac{c - a}{b}$

11. $\dfrac{a^2 - b}{a + 1}$

12. $\pm\sqrt{\left(\dfrac{G^2}{16\pi^2} - T^2\right)}$

13. $\pm\sqrt{\left(\dfrac{a^2 m}{b^2} + n\right)}$

14. $\dfrac{P - M}{E}$

15. $\dfrac{RP - Q}{R}$

16. $\dfrac{z - t^2}{x}$

17. $(g - e)^2 - f$

18. $\dfrac{4np + me^2}{mn}$

Exercise 8.3A

1. a) $S = ke$ b) $y = k\sqrt{x}$ c) $T = k\sqrt{L}$ d) $C = kr$ e) $A = kr^2$ f) $V = kr^3$

2. a) 9   b) $2\frac{2}{3}$ 3. a) 35   b) 11

5.
x	1	3	4	$5\frac{1}{2}$
z	4	12	16	22

6.
r	1	2	4	$1\frac{1}{2}$
V	4	32	256	$13\frac{1}{2}$

7.
h	4	9	25	$2\frac{1}{4}$
w	6	9	15	$4\frac{1}{2}$

8. $333\frac{1}{3}$ N/cm^3

9. 180 m; 2 s

10. 675 J; $\sqrt{\dfrac{4}{3}}$ cm.

11. 4 cm; 49 h

12. $15\frac{5}{8}$ h

13. 9000 N; 25m/s

14. $15^4 : 1$ (50 625 : 1)

Exercise 8.3B

1. a) $x = \dfrac{k}{y}$ b) $s = \dfrac{k}{t^2}$ c) $t = \dfrac{k}{\sqrt{q}}$ d) $m = \dfrac{k}{w}$ e) $z = \dfrac{k}{t^2}$

2. a) 1   b) 4   3. a) $2\frac{1}{2}$ b) $\frac{1}{2}$ 4. a) 36   b) ± 4

5. a) 1.2   b) ± 2 6. a) 16   b) ± 10 7. a) 6   b) 16

8. a) $\frac{1}{2}$ b) $\frac{1}{20}$

9.
y	2	4	1	$\frac{1}{4}$
z	8	4	16	64

10.
t	2	5	20	10
v	25	4	$\frac{1}{4}$	1

11.
x	1	4	256	36
r	12	6	$\frac{3}{4}$	2

12. a) 0.36   b) 6

13. $k = 100$, $n = 3$

x	1	2	4	10
z	100	$12\frac{1}{2}$	$1\frac{9}{16}$	$\frac{1}{10}$

14. $k = 12$, $n = 2$

v	1	4	36	10000
y	12	6	2	$\frac{3}{25}$

15. 2.5 m^3; 200 N/m^2

16. 3 h; 48 men

17. 6 cm

Exercise 8.4A

1. x^7
2. y^{13}
3. z^4
4. m
5. e^{-5}
6. y^2
7. w^6
8. $y^1 = y$
9. x^{10}
10. $x^0 = 1$
11. w^{-5}
12. w^{-5}
13. x^7
14. k^3
15. $e^0 = 1$
16. y^2
17. x^6
18. t^{-4}
19. $4x^6$
20. $6x^4$
21. $10y^5$
22. $15a^4$
23. $8a^3$
24. $3x^0 = 3$

25. $4y^2$ **26.** $108x^5$ **27.** $4z^{-3}$ **28.** $2x^{-4}$ **29.** $\dfrac{5y^5}{2}$ **30.** 1

31. $2n^4$ **32.** $2x$ **33.** $2x^{-3.5}$ **34.** $\frac{1}{7}x^{2.5}$ **35.** $\dfrac{27x^{15}}{64}$ **36.** $\frac{50}{3}x^{-6.5}$

37. $\frac{1}{10}x^{3.5}$ **38.** $\dfrac{81x^2}{16}$ **39.** $\dfrac{25}{4x}$

Exercise 8.4B

1. $25x^4$ **2.** $49y^6$ **3.** $100a^2b^2$ **4.** $4x^2y^4$ **5.** $2x$ **6.** $\dfrac{1}{9y}$

7. x^2 **8.** $\dfrac{x^2}{2}$ **9.** 1 **10.** $\dfrac{2}{x}$ **11.** $36x^4$ **12.** $25y$

13. $16x^2$ **14.** $27y$ **15.** 25 **16.** 1 **17.** 49 **18.** 1

19. $8x^6y^3$ **20.** $100x^2y^6$ **21.** $\dfrac{3x}{2}$ **22.** $\dfrac{2}{x}$ **23.** x^3y^5 **24.** $12x^3y^2$

25. $10y^4$ **26.** $3x^3$ **27.** $x^3y^2z^4$ **28.** x **29.** $3y$ **30.** $27x^{\frac{3}{2}}$

31. $10x^3y^5$ **32.** $32x^2$ **33.** $\frac{5}{2}x^2$ **34.** $\dfrac{9}{x^2}$ **35.** $2a^2$ **36.** $a^3b^3c^6$

37. 16 **38.** $\frac{1}{4}$ **39.** $\frac{1}{6}$ **40.** 1 **41.** $16\frac{1}{8}$ **42.** $\frac{3}{8}$

43. $\frac{1}{4}$ **44.** $\frac{5}{256}$ **45.** $1\frac{1}{16}$ **46.** 0 **47.** $\frac{1}{4}$ **48.** $\frac{1}{4}$

Exercise 8.4C

1. a) 2^5 **b)** 2^7 **c)** 2^6 **d)** 2^0 **2. a)** 3^{-3}
   b) 3^{-4} **c)** 3^{-1} **d)** 3^{-2} **3.** 3 **4.** 4
5. -1 **6.** -2 **7.** 3 **8.** 3 **9.** 1
10. $\frac{1}{5}$ **11.** 0 **12.** -4 **13.** 2 **14.** -5
15. 1 **16.** $\frac{1}{18}$ **17. a)** 3.60 **b)** 5.44 **18.** 1
19. 3 **20.** 0 **21.** -1 **22.** x can be any value

Exercise 8.5A

1. $x > 13$ **2.** $x < -1$ **3.** $x < 12$ **4.** $x \leqslant 2\frac{1}{2}$ **5.** $x > 3$ **6.** $x \geqslant 8$
7. $x < \frac{1}{4}$ **8.** $x \geqslant -3$ **9.** $x < -8$ **10.** $x < 4$ **11.** $x > -9$ **12.** $x < 8$
13. $x > 3$ **14.** $x \geqslant 1$ **15.** $x < 1$ **16.** $x > 2\frac{1}{3}$

Exercise 8.5B

1. $x > 5$ **2.** $x \leqslant 3$ **3.** $x > 6$ **4.** $x \leqslant 4$ **5.** $x < 1$
6. $x < -3$ **7.** $x > 0$ **8.** $x > 4$ **9.** $x > 2$ **10.** $x < -3$
11. $1 < x < 4$ **12.** $-2 \leqslant x \leqslant 5$ **13.** $1 \leqslant x < 6$ **14.** $0 \leqslant x < 5$ **15.** $-1 \leqslant x \leqslant 7$
16. $0.2 < x < 2$ **17.** $x > 80$ **18.** $x > 10$ **19.** $x < -2.5$ **20.** $0 < x < 4$
21. $5 \leqslant x \leqslant 9$ **22.** $-1 < x < 4$ **23.** $5.5 \leqslant x \leqslant 6$ **24.** $\frac{1}{2} < x < 8$ **25.** $-8 < x < 2$
26. $3 < x \leqslant 7$ **27.** $-1 \leqslant x \leqslant 4$ **28.** $0 < x < 5$ **29.** $-3 < x < -1$ **30.** $-5 \leqslant x < 5$

Exercise 8.5C

1. $\{1, 2, 3, 4, 5, 6\}$ **2.** $\{7, 11, 13, 17, 19\}$ **3.** $\{2, 4, 6, 8, 10\}$
4. $\{4, 9, 16, 25, 36, 49\}$ **5.** $\{5, 10\}$ **6.** $\{-4, -3, -2, -1\}$
7. $\{2, 3, 4, \dots 12\}$ **8.** $\{1, 4, 9\}$ **9.** $\{2, 3, 5, 7, 11\}$ **10.** $\{2, 4, 6, \dots 18\}$
11. $n = 5$ **12.** $x = 7$ **13.** $y = 5$ **14.** $4 < z < 5$
15. $4 < p < 5$ **16.** $\frac{1}{2}$ (or other values)   **17.** $1, 2, 3, \dots 14$ **18.** 19
19. 19 **20.** 17 **21. a)** $21x + 75 \geqslant 330$ **b)** \$12.15
22. a) $12y + 300 \leqslant 700$ **b)** \$33.33   **23. a)** $30d + 240 \leqslant 470$ **b)** 7 days

Revision exercise 8

1. a) $\dfrac{9x}{20}$ **b)** $\dfrac{7}{6x}$ **c)** $\dfrac{5x - 2}{6}$ **d)** $\dfrac{5x + 23}{(x - 1)(x + 3)}$

2. a) $(x - 2)(x + 2)$ **b)** $\dfrac{3}{x + 2}$

3. a) $s = t(r + 3)$ **b)** $r = \dfrac{s - 3t}{t}$ **c)** $t = \dfrac{s}{r + 3}$

4. a) $z = x - 5y$ **b)** $m = \dfrac{11}{k + 3}$ **c)** $z = \dfrac{T^2}{C^2}$

5. a) 50   **b)** 50   **6. a)** 16   **b)** ± 4

7. a) 4   **b)** 0   **8.** 12 and 18

9. a) 9, 10   **b)** 2, 3, 4, 5

10. $\dfrac{t^2}{k^2} - 5$ **11.** $\dfrac{z + 2}{z - 3}$ **12. a)** $\frac{3}{5}$ **b)** $\dfrac{k(1 - y)}{y}$

13. a) $1\frac{5}{6}$ **b)** 0.09   **14.** 21

15. a) $\dfrac{5 + a^2}{2 - a}$ **b)** $-\left(\dfrac{cz + b}{a}\right)$ **c)** $\dfrac{a^2 + 1}{a^2 - 1}$

16. a) $\frac{2}{3}$ **b)** x **c)** $\dfrac{7}{2x}$ **d)** $\dfrac{3a + 7}{a^2 - 4}$

   e) $\dfrac{x - 8}{x(x + 1)(x - 2)}$ **17.** $s = \dfrac{2}{t^2}$

18. a) 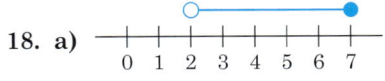   **b)**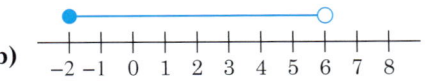

   c)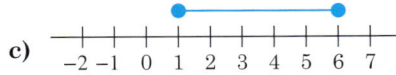

Examination-style exercise 8

1. $a = -4$, $b = 29$, $c = 5$ **2.** $16x^2$ **3. a)** 0   **b)** $\dfrac{1}{4}$ **c)** $\dfrac{3}{4}$

4. -1 **5.** $\dfrac{1}{b}$ **6.** $7\frac{2}{5}$ **7.** $b = 4(a + 2)^2$

8. a) $p^3(c + d)$ **b)** $p = \sqrt[3]{\dfrac{a^2 + b^3}{c + d}}$ **9.** 24   **10.** It is divided by 4.

11. $-\frac{1}{5}, 3$ **12. c)** $x = 2$ **d)** 3.48 km/h

9 Graphs

Exercise 9.1A
For Questions **1** to **10** end points of lines are given.

1. $(-3, -5)$ and $(3, 7)$ **2.** $(-3, -13)$ and $(3, 5)$ **3.** $(-3, -7)$ and $(3, 5)$

4. $(-2, 10)$ and $(4, 4)$ **5.** $(-2, 14)$ and $(4, 2)$ **6.** $(-3, 1)$ and $(3, 4)$

7. $(-3, -15)$ and $(3, 3)$ **8.** $\left(-3, \frac{1}{2}\right)$ and $\left(3, 3\frac{1}{2}\right)$ **9.** $(-2, -7)$ and $(4, 5)$

10. $(-2, 18)$ and $(4, 0)$ **11.** $(0, 0), (1, 4), (2, 2)$ **12.** $(0, 1), (2, 2), (3.5, 8)$

13. $(-2, -6), (1, 3), (4, 0)$ **14.** $(0, 6), (-2, -5), (4, -2)$ **15.** $(-2, 3), (2, 2), (5, 5), (1, 9)$

16. $(-1.5, 1.5), (0.67, 8), (3.5, 8), (3.5, -3.5)$

17. a) $560   **b)** 2400 km   **18. a)** 3.4 kg   **b)** 3 h 20 m

19. a) $440   **b)** 42 km/h   **c)** $210   **20. a)** $4315   **b)** 26 000 km

Exercise 9.2A

1. $1\frac{1}{2}$ **2.** 2   **3.** $1\frac{1}{2}$ **4.** $\frac{1}{2}$ **5.** $-\frac{1}{6}$

6. -7 **7.** -1 **8.** 4   **9.** -4 **10.** 5

11. $-1\frac{3}{7}$ **12.** 0   **13.** 0   **14.** undefined   **15.** undefined

16. $\dfrac{n + b}{m - a}$ **17.** $\dfrac{2f}{a}$ **18.** -4 **19.** 0   **20.** $-\dfrac{6d}{c}$

21. a) $-1\frac{1}{5}$ **b)** $\frac{1}{10}$ **c)** $\frac{4}{5}$ **22. a)** infinite **b)** $-\frac{3}{10}$ **c)** $\frac{3}{10}$ **23.** $3\frac{1}{2}$

24. a) $\dfrac{n+4}{2m-3}$ **b)** $n = -4$ **c)** $m = 1\frac{1}{2}$

Exercise 9.2B
1. Midpoint = (4, 2.5), length = $\sqrt{13}$ **2.** Midpoint = (2, 3), length = $2\sqrt{5}$

3. Midpoint = (3.5, 1.5), length = $\sqrt{10}$ **4.** Midpoint = (0, 4.5), length = $\sqrt{13}$

5. Midpoint = (–1, –0.5), length = $\sqrt{5}$ **6.** Midpoint = (4, 5.5), length = $\sqrt{37}$

7. Midpoint = (1.5, 0.5), length = $5\sqrt{2}$ **8.** Midpoint = (–1, –1), length = $2\sqrt{2}$

9. Midpoint = $\left(\dfrac{5}{8}, \dfrac{3}{2}\right)$, length = $\dfrac{1}{4}\sqrt{17}$ **10.** Midpoint = $\left(-\dfrac{1}{4}, 0\right)$, length = $\dfrac{\sqrt{17}}{2}$

11. Midpoint = (3.15, 2.25), length = $\sqrt{0.26}$ **12.** Midpoint = $\left(-\dfrac{7}{2}, 5\right)$, length = $\sqrt{149}$

13. (8, –1)   **14.** 12 or –12

Exercise 9.3A
1. 1, 3   **2.** 1, –2   **3.** 2, 1   **4.** 2, –5   **5.** 3, 4

6. $\frac{1}{2}$, 6   **7.** 3, –2   **8.** 2, 0   **9.** $\frac{1}{4}$, –4   **10.** –1, 3

11. –2, 6   **12.** –1, 2   **13.** –2, 3   **14.** $-\frac{1}{3}, -\frac{4}{3}$ **15.** $\frac{3}{2}$, 3

16. $-\frac{1}{3}$, 3   **17.** 4, –5   **18.** $1\frac{1}{2}$, –4   **19.** –1, 0   **20.** 0, 4

Pair of parallel lines: **11** and **13**; **14** and **16**; **12** and **19**; **15** and **18**

Exercise 9.3B
1. $y = 3x + 7$ **2.** $y = 2x - 9$ **3.** $y = -x + 5$ **4.** $y = 2x - 1$

5. $y = 3x + 5$ **6.** $y = -x + 7$ **7.** $x - 2y = 6$ **8.** $2x - y = 3$

9. $3x - y = 11$ **10.** $x + y = 5$ **11.** $x + 3y = 12$

12. $-\dfrac{a}{b}$ **13.** The gradient is undefined, therefore there is no value for m, and they do not cross the y-axis, therefore there is no value for c.

14. $x = 1$ **15. a)** $y = 3$ **b)** Yes, $m = 0$ and $c = 3$.

Exercise 9.3C
1. $y = 2x + 4$ **2.** $y = x + 2$ **3.** $x + 3y = 9$ **4.** $y = -2$

5. $x = -6$ **6. a)** A: $y = 3x - 4$, B: $y = x + 2$ **b)** $y = 3x + 1$ **c)** $y = x - 2$

7. a) $y = 2x + 5$ **b)** $5x + 4y = 12$

Exercise 9.3D
1. $y = -x + 7$ **2.** $y = 2x - 5$ **3.** $x + 4y = 23$ **4.** $y = 6x - 30$

5. $x + 5y = 17$ **6.** $x + 3y = -1$ **7.** $y = x - 1$ **8.** $x + 2y = 12$

9. $x = 4$ **10. a)** $y = -2x + 1$ **b)** 4.02   **11.** 0.32   **12.** 4.31

Exercise 9.4A
1. 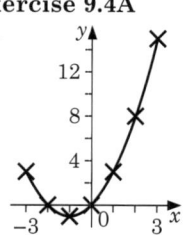   **2.** 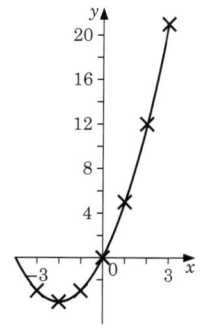   **3.** 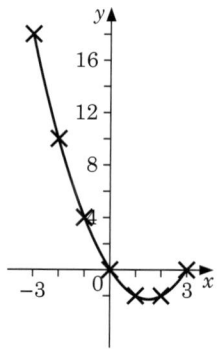   **4.**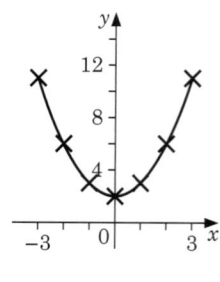

5.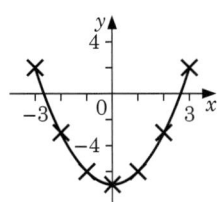

6.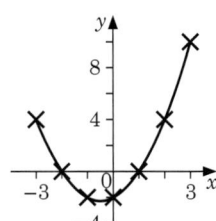

7.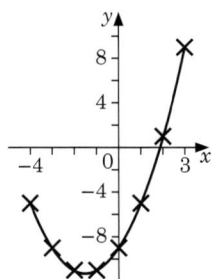

8.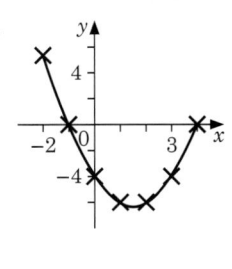

9.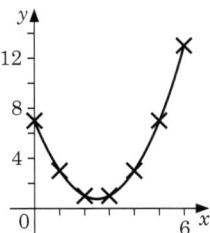

10.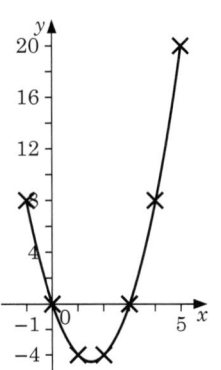

11.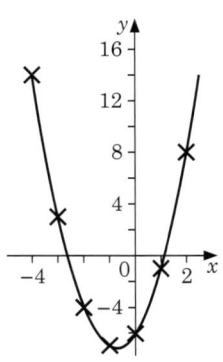

12.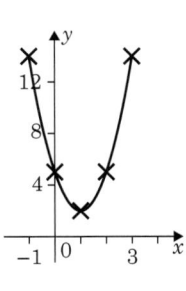

13.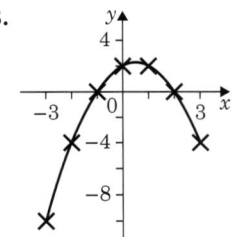

14.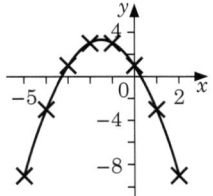

15.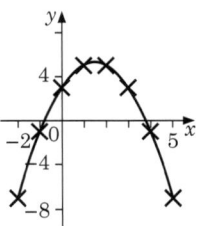

16.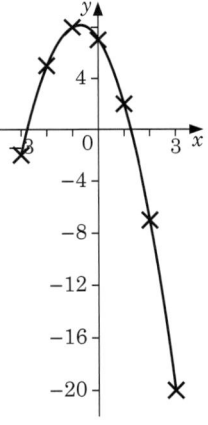

17.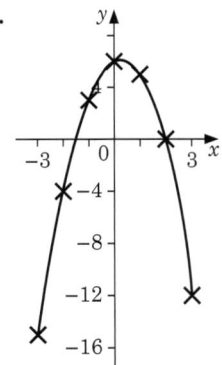

18.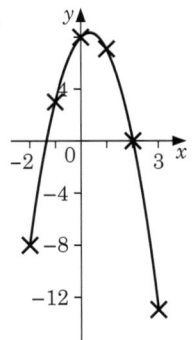

19.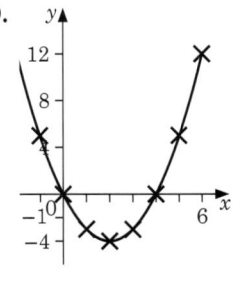

20.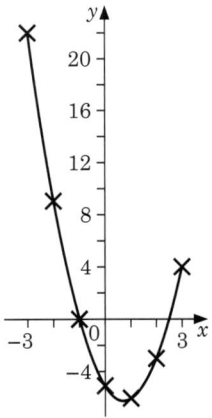

Exercise 9.4B

1. a) 3   **b)** –5   **c)** 1.5

2. a) 7.25   **b)** –2   **c)** –0.8, 3.8

3.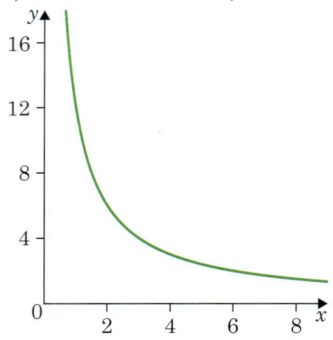

4.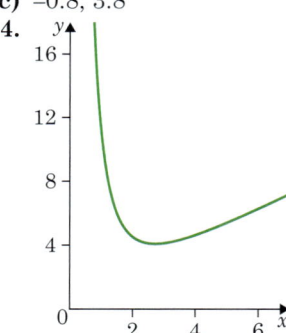

5.

6.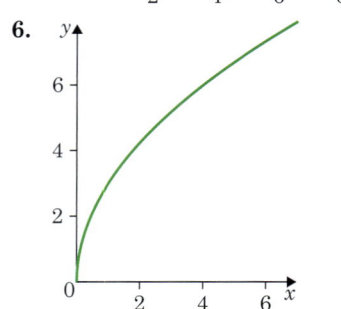

7.

8. 15 m × 30 m

9. a) 2.5 s   **b)** 31.3 m   **c)** $2 < t < 3$

10. a) 108 m/s   **b)** 1.4 s   **c)** $2.3 < t < 3.6$

11. Approximately 3.3

Exercise 9.4C

1. a) 4

b)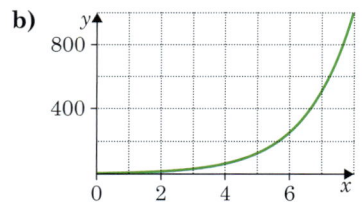

c) Around 7.2 mins

2. a) 600

b)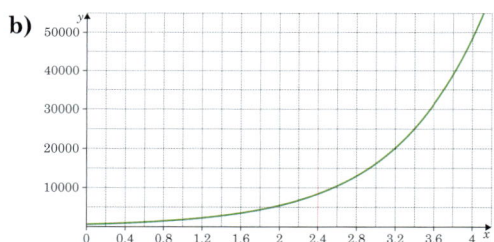

c) 3.6 hours

3.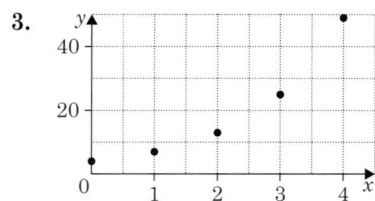

4.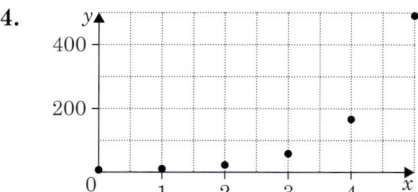

5. a) 996

b)

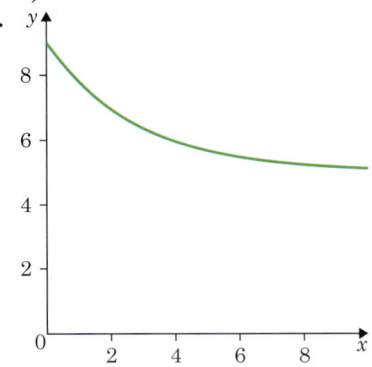

c) 5.6 hours

d) 950

e) The value of the function will be negative.

6.

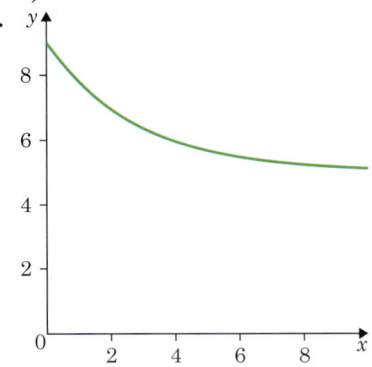

7. a) $80 000

b)

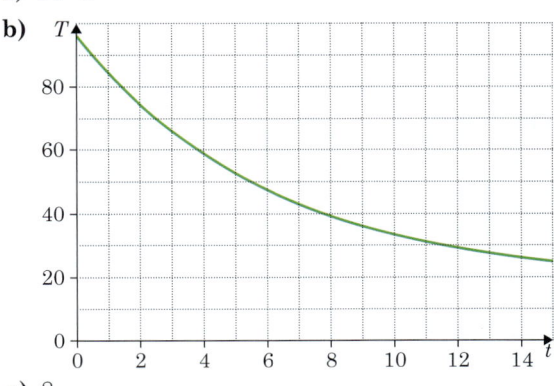

c) $50 000

d) 9

8. a) 96 °C

b)

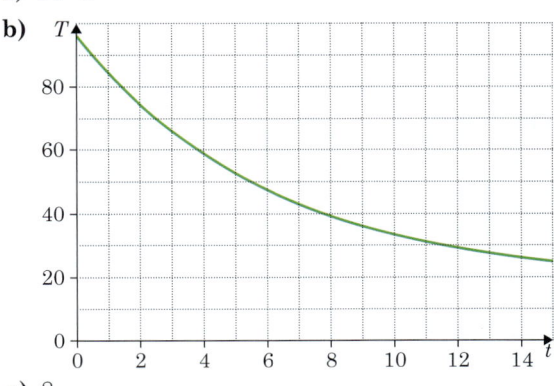

c) 8

d) That the temperature of the room stays constant.

Exercise 9.4D

1. linear	**2.** cubic	**3.** exponential	**4.** quadratic
5. exponential	**6.** reciprocal	**7.** linear	**8.** reciprocal
9. quadratic	**10.** cubic	**11.** linear	**12.** cubic
13. linear	**14.** cubic	**15.** quadratic	**16.** reciprocal
17. cubic	**18.** exponential	**19.** linear	**20.** quadratic
21. linear	**22.** square root	**23.** reciprocal of x^2	**24.** reciprocal of square root

Exercise 9.4E

All non-integer coordinates given to 2 decimal places.

1. Straight line, axis intercepts at (1.33, 0) and (0, –4)
2. Quadratic curving upward, touches both axes at (0, 0)
3. y-intercept at (0, 1), asymptote $y = 0$
4. Curve crosses both axes at (0, 0), positive for positive x and negative for negative x
5. No axis intercepts, asymptotes $y = 0$ and $x = 0$
6. y-intercept (0, –4), x-intercept (1.50, 0)
7. Straight line, y-intercept (0, 3), x-intercept (4, 0)
8. x-intercept (–2, 0), asymptotes $y = 1$ and $x = 0$
9. Quadratic curving upward, y-intercept (0, –3), x-intercepts (–1, 0) and (3, 0)
10. y-intercept (0, 3), asymptote $y = 2$

11. Horizontal line, y-intercept $(0, -1)$

12. y-intercept $(0, 0)$, x-intercepts $(-3, 0)$, $(-1, 0)$ and $(0, 0)$

13. x-intercepts at $(1, 0)$, $(0, 0)$ and $(-2, 0)$

14. Quadratic curving downward, x-intercepts at $(-2, 0)$ and $(2, 0)$

15. x-intercepts $(-3, 0)$, $(0, 0)$ and $(3, 0)$

Exercise 9.5A

1. a) i) 40 km   **ii)** 24 km   **iii)** 72 km   **iv)** 8 km

   b) i) 40 miles   **ii)** 35 miles   **iii)** 10 miles   **iv)** 20 miles

2. a) i) €28   **ii)** €112   **iii)** €70

   b) i) £40   **ii)** £60   **iii)** £100   **c)** £110

3. a) 180   **b)** $C = 0.2x + 35$

4. a) 30 litres   **b) i)** 8 km/litre   **ii)** 6 km/litre

   c) $6\frac{2}{3}$ km/litre   **d)** 30 litres

5. a) 2000   **b)** 200   **c)** $1.6 \leqslant x \leqslant 2.4$

6. a) Yes   **b)** No   **c)** About \$250 – \$300

Exercise 9.5B

1. $x \leqslant 3$ **2.** $y \geqslant 2\frac{1}{2}$ **3.** $1 \leqslant x \leqslant 6$

4. $x < 7, y < 5$ **5.** $y \geqslant x$ **6.** $x + y < 10$

7. $x < 8, y > -2, y < x$ **8.** $x \geqslant 0, y \geqslant x - 1, x + y \leqslant 7$ **9.** $y \geqslant 0, y \leqslant x + 2, x + y \leqslant 6$

10. 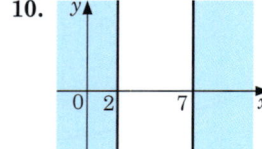   **11.** 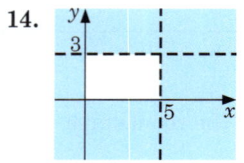   **12.** 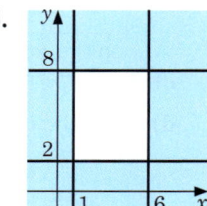   **13.**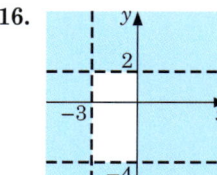

14. 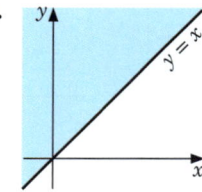   **15.** 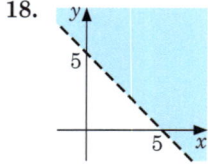   **16.** 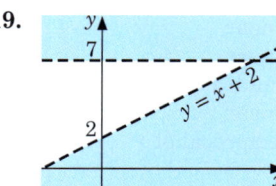   **17.**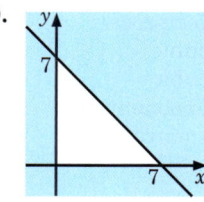

18. 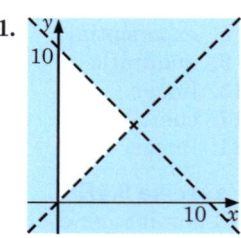   **19.** 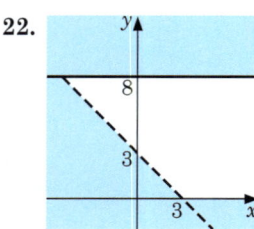   **20.** 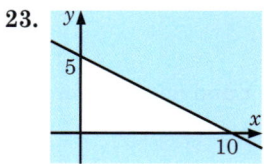   **21.**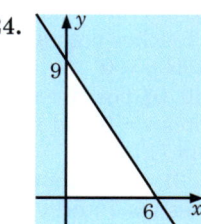

22. 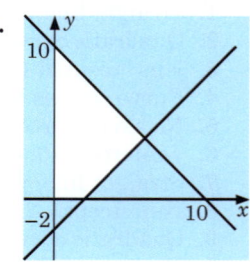   **23.**   **24.**   **25.**

26.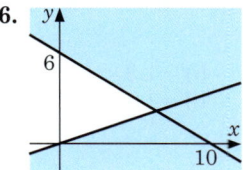

27.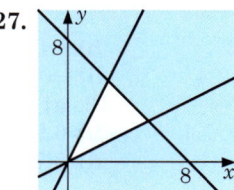

Exercise 9.5C

1. a) 45 min   **b)** 09:15   **c)** 60 km/h   **d)** 100 km/h   **e)** 57.1 km/h
2. a) 09:20   **b)** 64 km/h   **c)** 37.6 km/h   **d)** 44 km   **e)** 80 km/h
3. a) i) B   **ii)** A   **b)** 8 s to 18 s   **c)** About 8 s   **d)** About 17 s   **e)** C
   f) A   **g)** About 26 m/s
4. 11:05   **5.** 12:42   **6.** 12:35   **7.** $1\frac{1}{8}$ h   **8.** 1 h

9. Hanna started quickly, stood still for a while and then sped up quickly again before stopping and going backwards. Fateema started fairly slowly, sped up in the middle and then slowed down again. Carine started very slowly and then gradually sped up so that she overtook the other two and won the race.

Exercise 9.5D

1. a) $1\frac{1}{2}$ m/s²   **b)** 675 m   **c)** $11\frac{1}{4}$ m/s
2. a) 600 m   **b)** 20 m/s   **c)** 225 m   **d)** −2 m/s²
3. Approximately 8 m/s²
4. a) 600 m   **b)** $387\frac{1}{2}$ m   **c)** 0 m/s²
5. a) 20 m/s   **b)** 750 m
6. a) 8 s   **b)** 496 m   **c)** 12.4 m/s
7. a) 30 m/s   **b)** $-2\frac{1}{7}$ m/s²   **c)** 20 s
8. a) 15 m/s   **b)** $2\frac{1}{4}$ m/s²   **9. a)** 40 m/s   **b)** 10 s
10. a) 50 m/s   **b)** 20 s   **11. a)** 20 m/s   **b)** 20 s

Exercise 9.5E

1. 225 m   **2.** 120 m   **3.** 1 km
4. 10 s   **5.** 60 s   **6.** 50 m
7. 31.25 m   **8.** 1.39 km   **9.** 250 m
10. Yes. Stopping distance = 46.5 m
11. 94 375 m   **12. a)** 0.8 m/s²   **b)** 670 m
13. a) 0.35 m/s²   **b)** 260 m

Exercise 9.6A

1. $x = 0,\ x = 3$ **2.** $x = 0,\ x = 5$ **3.** $x = -3,\ x = 2$ **4.** $x = -2,\ x = 1$
5. $x = 0,\ x = 2$ **6.** $x = -1$ **7.** $x = -1,\ x = 0,\ x = 2$ **8.** $x = -1,\ x = 0,\ x = 1$
9. $x = 0,\ x = 3$ **10.** $x = -1,\ x = 2$

Exercise 9.6B

1. $x = 1, y = 3$ **2.** $x = 3, y = 1$ **3.** $x = 1, y = -2$
4. $x = 6, y = 2$ **5.** $x = -1, y = 1$ and $x = 2, y = 4$
6. $x = -1, y = 3$ and $x = 2, y = 0$ **7.** $x = 1.5, y = 3.5$ **8.** $x = 0.25, y = 3.5$
9. $x = -0.4, y = 2.7$ **10.** $x = 2.1, y = 4.4$ and $x = -1.4, y = 2.1$

Exercise 9.6C

1. a) −0.4, 2.4   **b)** −0.8, 3.8   **c)** −1, 3   **d)** −0.4, 2.4
2. −0.3, 3.3   **3.** 0.6, 3.4   **4.** 0.3, 3.7
5. a) $y = 3$ **b)** $y = -2$ **c)** $y = x + 4$ **d)** $y = x$ **e)** $y = 6$
6. a) $y = 6$ **b)** $y = 0$ **c)** $y = 4$ **d)** $y = 2x$ **e)** $y = 2x + 4$
7. a) $y = -4$ **b)** $y = 2x$ **c)** $y = x - 2$ **d)** $y = -3$ **e)** $y = 2$
8. a) $y = 5$ **b)** $y = 2x$ **c)** $y = 0.2$ **d)** $y = 3 - x$ **e)** $y = 3$
9. a) $y = 0$ **b)** $y = -2\frac{1}{2}$ **c)** $y = -8x$ **d)** $y = -3$ **e)** $y = -5\frac{1}{2}x$

10. a) −1.7, 3.7   **b)** −1.3, 2.3   **c)** −1.5, 3.5

11. a) 1.7, 5.3   **b)** 0.2, 4.8   **12. a)** −3.3, 0.3   **b)** −4.6, −0.4

13. a) −2.35, 0.85   **b)** −2.8, 1.8   **14. a) i)** −0.4, 2.4   **ii)** −0.5, 2   **b)** $-1.3 < x < 2.8$

15. a) 3.4, −5.4   **b)** 2.4, 7.6   **c)** ±4.2   **16. a)** ±3.7   **c)** ±2.8

17. a) 1.7   **b)** 0, ±1.4   **18. a)** $1.6 < x < 7.4$ **b)** 6.9

19. a) 2.6   **b)** 0.5, 3.3   **c)** 0.6   **d)** 5.7

20. a) −1.6, 0.6   **b)** $-\frac{1}{2}, 1$

Exercise 9.7A

1. (3, −7)   **2.** (−2, −7)   **3.** $\left(-\frac{5}{2}, -\frac{33}{4}\right)$ **4.** $\left(\frac{7}{2}, -\frac{29}{4}\right)$ **5.** (−2, 10)

6. $\left(-\frac{3}{2}, \frac{25}{4}\right)$ **7.** $\left(\frac{3}{2}, \frac{1}{2}\right)$ **8.** (−1, −7)   **9.** $\left(-\frac{3}{4}, \frac{41}{8}\right)$ **10.** $\left(-\frac{5}{8}, \frac{137}{16}\right)$

Exercise 9.7B

1. $6x$ **2.** $6x^2 - 4$ **3.** $24x^3$ **4.** $10x^4 - 8x$

5. $16x^3 - 9x^2 + 10x$ **6.** $-6x - 12x^3$ **7.** $7x^6 + 6x^5 + 5x^4$ **8.** $\frac{3}{2}x^2 + \frac{4}{3}x$

9. $\frac{4}{5}x^3 + \frac{9}{4}x^2 - \frac{4}{5}x$ **10.** $\frac{1}{4}x^3 - x^2$ **11.** $15x^2 - 12x$ **12.** $30x^4 - 16x^3$

13. $40x - 25x^4 + 2$ **14.** $56x^7 - 13$ **15.** $\frac{7}{8}x^6 - \frac{5}{6}x^4$ **16.** $\frac{40}{9}x^4 + \frac{1}{5}x^2$

17. a) $70x^4 - 64x^3 - 13$ **b)** $72x^8 - 10x$ **c)** $\frac{1}{2}x^6 - 5x^5 + \frac{3}{4}x^2$

Exercise 9.7C

1. a) −5   **b)** −128   **c)** −245   **2. a)** 43   **b)** 427   **c)** −2

3. a) 245   **b)** 329   **c)** $\frac{35}{3}$ **4.** $\frac{3}{2}$ **5.** −3   **6.** (−2, 5)

7. $1, -\frac{7}{3}$ **8.** $\left(1, -\frac{25}{6}\right), \left(-2, \frac{28}{3}\right)$ **9.** (0, 0), (2, −14), (−2, −2)

10. $(4, -48), \left(-\frac{2}{3}, \frac{76}{27}\right)$

Exercise 9.7D

1. a) (1.5, −7.25)   **b)** (0.875, −3.0625)   **c)** (−0.75, 3.125)

2. a) Min   **b)** Min   **c)** Max

3. a) (0.7, 3.55)   **4. a)** $(0, -3), \left(\frac{2}{3}, -\frac{89}{27}\right)$ **b)** Max, Min

5. a) (−1, −1), (1, −9)   **b)** Max, Min   **6. a)** (−2, −13), (2, 19)   **b)** Min, Max

7. You show that the quadratic formed when you differentiate has no solutions when = 0.

8. $k < -\frac{1}{3}$

Revision exercise 9

1. a) $y = x - 7$ **b)** $y = 2x + 5$ **c)** $y = -2x + 10$ **d)** $y = \dfrac{x + 1}{2}$

2. a) 2   **b)** 1   **c)** $-3\frac{1}{2}$ **d)** 0   **e)** 10

3. a) 2, −7   **b)** −4, 5   **c)** $\frac{1}{2}, 4$ **d)** $-\frac{1}{2}, 5$

    e) −2, 12   **f)** $-\frac{2}{3}, 8$

4. A : $y = 6$;   B : $y = \frac{1}{2}x - 3$;   C : $y = 10 - x$;   D : $y = 3x$

5. A : $4y = 3x - 16$;   B : $2y = x - 8$;   C : $2y + x = 8$;   D : $4y + 3x = 16$

6. a) $y = 2x - 3$ **b)** $y = 3x + 4$ **c)** $y = 10 - x$ **d)** $y = 7$

7. a) A(0, −8), B(4,0)   **b)** 2   **c)** $y = 2x - 8$

8. 25 sq. units   **9.** 3.13   **10.** −3   **11.** 219

13. a) $y = 3x$ **b)** $y = 0$ **c)** $y = 11 - x$ **d)** $y = 5x$

14. a) 1.6, −2.6   **b)** ±2.2   **c)** ±2.6

15. a) 0.8, 4.2   **b)** $0.7 < x < 3.9$ **c)** 3.3

16. a) 9.2   **b)** 0.6   **c)** 1.4   **d)** 1.7

17. $y \geqslant 2$, $x + y \leqslant 6$, $y \leqslant 3x$ **18.** $x \geqslant 0$, $y \geqslant x - 2$, $x + y \leqslant 7$, $y \geqslant 0$

19. a) 0.3 m/s^2 **b)** 1050 m   **c)** 40 s

20. a) 30 m/s   **b)** 600 m

21. $12x^3 - 12x$ **22. a)** $\frac{3}{2}x^5 - \frac{6}{5}x^2 + \frac{7}{4}x$ **b)** 46.7

23. −0.52 (Max), 4.52 (Min)

Examination-style exercise 9

1. a) $y = -2x - 5$ **b)** (−2.5, 0)

2. a) $y = -\frac{5}{2}x - 5$ **b)** $-\frac{5}{2}$ **c)** (0, −5)

3. $y = 4x + 3$ **4.** $x = 2$ is a minimum, $x = -1$ is a maximum

5. a) i) −3   **ii)** −6   **b)** $x = -1.2, 1.5, 5.7$ **c)** 5, 11   **d)** $0 < x < 4$

6. a) 0.3 m/s^2 **b)** 297 km   **c)** 297 km/h

7. a) $y = -2x + 17$ **b)** 0.894

8. a) $3x^2 - 4x - 4$ **b)** $\left(-\frac{2}{3}, \frac{40}{27}\right)$ and (2, −8)

9. a) $6x^2 - 8x + 5$ **b)** 2.5   **c)** No, there are no solutions to the equation $\frac{dy}{dx} = 0$.

10 Trigonometry 3

Exercise 10.1A

1. a) 1, 0.87, 0.5, 0, −0.5, −0.87, −1, −0.87, −0.5, 0, 0.5, 0.87, 1

b) 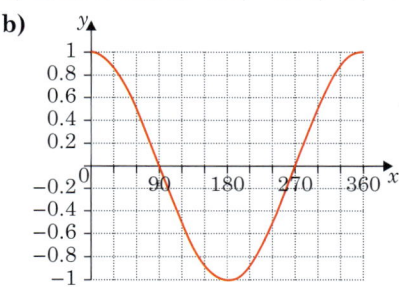   **2.**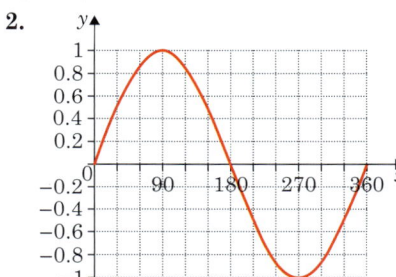

3.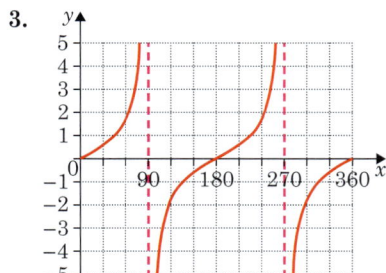

4. 162°   **5.** 153°   **6.** 310°   **7. a)** 140°   **b)** 50°   **c)** 240°

8. 290°   **9.** 255°   **10.** 160°, 200°   **11.** 216°   **12.** 292°

13. a) 60°, 120°   **b)** 25.8°, 334.2°   **c)** 26.6°, 206.6°   **d)** 135°, 225°   **e)** 228.6°, 311.4°
     f) 99.5°, 279.5°

14. a) 30°, 150°   **b)** 48.2°, 311.8°   **c)** 74.1°, 254.1°   **d)** 199.5°, 340.5°   **e)** 143.1°, 216.9°
     f) 126.9°, 306.9°   **g)** 15°, 105°   **h)** 90°, 270°

Exercise 10.1B

1. −0.5   **2.** 0.5   **3.** $\frac{\sqrt{3}}{2}$ **4.** −0.5   **5.** −0.5   **6.** $-\frac{\sqrt{2}}{2}$ **7.** $\frac{\sqrt{2}}{2}$

8. $-\frac{\sqrt{3}}{2}$ **9.** −0.5   **10.** −0.5   **11.** $\frac{\sqrt{3}}{3}$ **12.** $-\frac{\sqrt{3}}{2}$ **13.** $-\frac{\sqrt{2}}{2}$ **14.** $-\frac{\sqrt{2}}{2}$

15. $-\frac{\sqrt{3}}{2}$ **16.** $-\frac{\sqrt{2}}{2}$ **17.** $\frac{\sqrt{3}}{2}$ **18.** $-\frac{\sqrt{2}}{2}$ **19.** 1   **20.** $-\frac{\sqrt{3}}{2}$ **21.** $\sqrt{3}$

Exercise 10.2A
1. 6.38 m   **2.** 12.5 m   **3.** 5.17 cm   **4.** 40.4 cm   **5.** 7.81 m, 7.10 m
6. 8.61 cm   **7.** 99.7 cm   **8.** 8.52 cm   **9.** 15.2 cm   **10.** 35.8°
11. 32.3°   **12.** 37.8°   **13.** $\hat{R} = 35.5°$, $\hat{T} = 48.5°$ **14.** $\hat{X} = 68.8°$, $\hat{Y} = 80.0°$ **15.** 64.6°
16. 34.2°   **17.** 50.6°   **18.** 39.1°   **19.** 39.5°   **20.** 21.6°

Exercise 10.3A
1. 6.25 cm   **2.** 6.05 cm   **3.** 5.47 cm   **4.** 10.1 cm   **5.** 8.99 cm
6. 5.87 cm   **7.** 4.24 cm   **8.** 11.9 cm   **9.** 154 cm   **10.** 25.2°
11. 78.5°   **12.** 115.0°   **13.** 24.0°   **14.** 92.5°   **15.** 99.9°
16. 38.2°   **17.** 137.8°   **18.** 34.0°   **19.** 60.2°   **20.** 8.72 cm
21. 1.40 cm   **22.** 7.38 cm

Exercise 10.3B
1. 6.69 cm   **2.** 10.8 m   **3.** 35.6 km   **4.** 25.2 m
5. 38.6°, 48.5°, 92.9°   **6.** 40.4 m   **7. a)** 9.85 km   **b)** 085.7°
8. a) 29.6 km   **b)** 050.5°   **9. a)** 10.8 m   **b)** 72.6°   **c)** 32.6°
10. 378 km, 048.4°   **11. a)** 62.2°   **b)** 2.33 km
12. 9.64 m   **13.** 8.6°

Revision exercise 10
1. a) 11.5° and 168.5°   **b)** 41.0° and 221.0°
2. 6.68 m   **3.** 42.9°   **4.** 9.27 cm   **5.** 111.1°
6. from A: 45.2 km, from B: 33.6 km   **7.** 73.4°   **8.** YZ = 8.76 m, XZ = 9.99 m   **9.** 0.539
10. AB = 4.12 cm, AD = 9.93 cm   **11.** 26.4°   **12.** $\cos x$

Examination-style exercise 10
1. 210, 330   **2.** $x = 6.00$
3. a) 37.9 km   **b) i)** 275°   **ii)** 95°
4. a) 205°   **b)** 154.3°   **5. b)** 17.5 cm
6. a) i) 50°   **ii)** 0.958   **b) i)** 155°   **ii)** 56.8°   **iii)** 1.22 km   **c)** 0.893 km²
7. a) 10 m   **b)** 7.81 m   **c)** 9.43 m   **d)** 70.2°

11 Sets and functions

Exercise 11.1A
1. a) 8   **b)** 3   **c)** 4   **d)** 18   **e)** 7
2. a) 9   **b)** 5   **c)** 4   **d)** 20   **e)** 31
3. a) 8   **b)** 3   **c)** 3   **d)** 2   **e)** 18   **f)** 0
4. a) 59   **b)** 11   **c)** 5   **d)** 40   **e)** 11   **f)** 124
5. a) 120   **b)** 120   **c)** 490   **d)** 80   **e)** 40   **f)** 10   **g)** 500

Exercise 11.1B
1. a) {5, 7}   **b)** {1, 2, 3, 4, 5, 6, 7, 8, 9, 11, 13}   **c)** 5   **d)** 11
   e) true   **f)** true   **g)** false   **h)** true
2. a) {2, 3, 5, 7}   **b)** {1, 2, 3, ..., 9}   **c)** 4   **d)** ∅   **e)** false
   f) true   **g)** false   **h)** true
3. a) false   **b)** true   **c)** false   **d)** false
4. a) true   **b)** true   **c)** true   **d)** true
5. a) {2, 4, 6, 8, 10}   **b)** {16, 18, 20}   **c)** ∅   **d)** 15   **e)** 11
   f) 21   **g)** false   **h)** false   **i)** true   **j)** true
6. a) {1, 3, 4, 5}   **b)** {1, 5}   **c)** 1   **d)** {1, 5}   **e)** {1, 3, 5, 10}
   f) 4   **g)** true   **h)** false   **i)** true
7. a) 4   **b)** 3   **c)** {b, d}   **d)** {a, b, c, d, e}   **e)** 5   **f)** 2
8. a) 2   **b)** 4   **c)** {1, 2, 4, 6, 7, 8, 9}   **d)** {7, 9}
   e) {1, 2, 4}   **f)** {1, 2, 4, 7, 9}   **g)** {1, 2, 4, 6, 8}   **h)** {6, 7, 8, 9}
   i) {1, 2, 4, 7, 9}

Exercise 11.1C

1. a)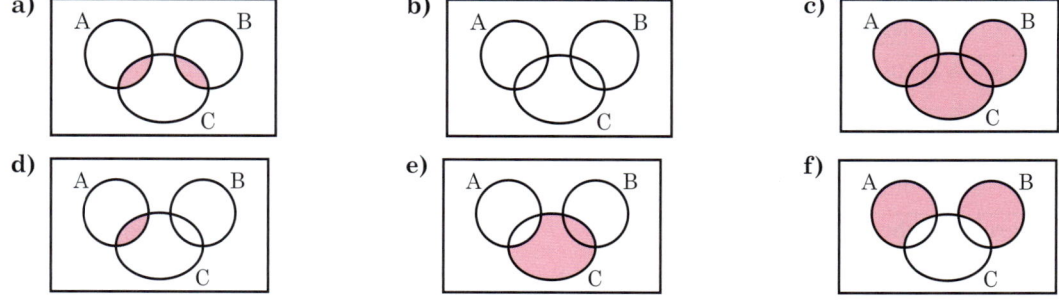
   b)
   c)

   d)
   e)
   f)

2. a)
   b)
   c)

   d)

3. a)
   b)
   c)
   d)

4. a)
   b)
   c)
   d)

   e)
   f)
   g)
   h)

   i)

5. a)
   b)
   c)

   d)
   e)
   f)

g)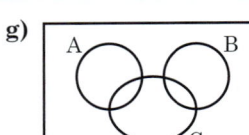

h)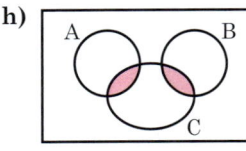

i)

6. a)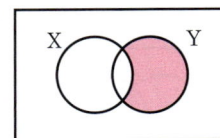

b)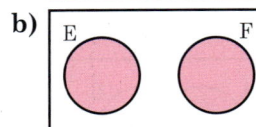

c)

d)
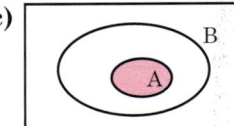

7. a) $A \cup B$ **b)** $A' \cap B$ **c)** $(A \cup B)'$ **d)** $X \cap Y'$

Exercise 11.2A

1. **a)** $10 - x$ **b)** $13 - x$ **d)** 5   2. **b)** 9   3. 14
4. 3   5. 36   6. 3   7. 11   8. 5
9. 28   10. $x = 6$; 26   11. 34   12. **a)** 12   **b)** $\frac{1}{2}$
13. $x = 10$; 30   14. 2
15. **a)** All good swimmers are skydivers.   **b)** No good swimmers are skydivers
     c) There are some good swimmers who are skydivers.
16. **a)** The surfers are all girls   **b)** The ice skaters are all boys
     c) Some students surf and ice skate   **d)** There are no girls who ice skate
     e) $G \cap S = \varnothing$ **f)** $(S \cup I)' = \varnothing$
17. **a)** $S \cap C = \varnothing$ b) $F \subseteq C$ c) $S \cap F \neq \varnothing$
     d) All living creatures are either spiders, animals that fly, or animals that are cute.
     e) All animals that are cute are spiders

Exercise 11.3A

1. **a)** 5, 10, 1   **b)** 21, 101, −29

2. $x \rightarrow \boxed{\times 5} \rightarrow \boxed{+4} \rightarrow 5x + 4$

3. $x \rightarrow \boxed{-4} \rightarrow \boxed{\times 3} \rightarrow 3(x - 4)$

4. $x \rightarrow \boxed{\times 2} \rightarrow \boxed{+7} \rightarrow \boxed{\text{square}} \rightarrow (2x + 7)^2$

5. $x \rightarrow \boxed{\times 5} \rightarrow \boxed{+9} \rightarrow \boxed{\div 4} \rightarrow \dfrac{5x + 9}{4}$

6. $x \rightarrow \boxed{\times - 3} \rightarrow \boxed{\text{subtract from 4}} \rightarrow \boxed{\div 5} \rightarrow \dfrac{4 - 3x}{5}$

7. $x \rightarrow \boxed{\text{square}} \rightarrow \boxed{\times 2} \rightarrow \boxed{+1} \rightarrow 2x^2 + 1$

8. $x \rightarrow \boxed{\text{square}} \rightarrow \boxed{\times 3} \rightarrow \boxed{\div 2} \rightarrow \boxed{+5} \rightarrow \dfrac{3x^2}{2} + 5$

9. $x \rightarrow \boxed{\times 4} \rightarrow \boxed{-5} \rightarrow \boxed{\text{square root}} \rightarrow \sqrt{(4x - 5)}$

10. $x \rightarrow \boxed{\text{square}} \rightarrow \boxed{+10} \rightarrow \boxed{\text{square root}} \rightarrow \boxed{\times 4} \rightarrow 4\sqrt{(x^2 + 10)}$

11. $x \rightarrow \boxed{\times 3} \rightarrow \boxed{\text{subtract from 7}} \rightarrow \boxed{\text{square}} \rightarrow (7 - 3x)^2$

12. $x \rightarrow \boxed{\times 3} \rightarrow \boxed{+1} \rightarrow \boxed{\text{square}} \rightarrow \boxed{\times 4} \rightarrow \boxed{+5} \rightarrow 4(3x + 1)^2 + 5$

13. $x \rightarrow \boxed{\text{square}} \rightarrow \boxed{\text{subtract from 5}} \rightarrow 5 - x^2$

14. $x \to \boxed{\text{square}} \to \boxed{+1} \to \boxed{\text{square root}} \to \boxed{\times 10} \to \boxed{+6} \to \boxed{\div 4} \to \dfrac{10\sqrt{(x^2 + 1)} + 6}{4}$

15. $x \to \boxed{\text{cube}} \to \boxed{\div 4} \to \boxed{+1} \to \boxed{\text{square}} \to \boxed{\text{subtract 6}} \to \left(\dfrac{x^3}{4} + 1\right)^2 - 6$

16. a) $-9, 11, \frac{1}{2}$ **b)** $0.8, -2.7, \frac{1}{80}$ **c)** $4, 1.2, 36$

17. a) 0 **b)** 6 **c)** 12

18. a) 10 **b)** $\frac{1}{2}$ **c)** 2

19. a) $6, 24, 6$ **b)** $0, \sqrt{2}, \sqrt{6}$ **c)** $-6, 6, 9\frac{3}{4}$

20. a) ± 3 **b)** ± 3 **c)** ± 2 **d)** ± 6

21. a) 5 **b)** 17 **c)** $1\frac{1}{2}$ **d)** 3

22. $a = 3, b = 5$ **23.** $a = 2, b = -5$ **24.** $a = 7, b = 1$

Exercise 11.3B

1. $x = 22, y = 7, z = 107$

2. a) 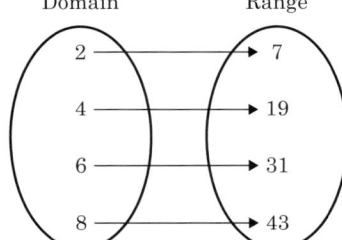   **b)**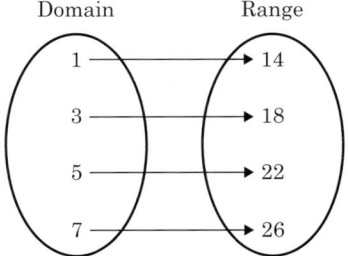

3. a) 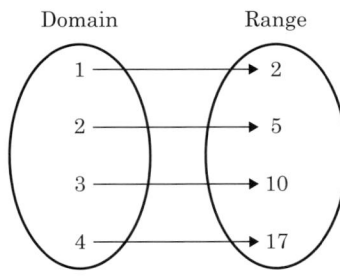   **b)**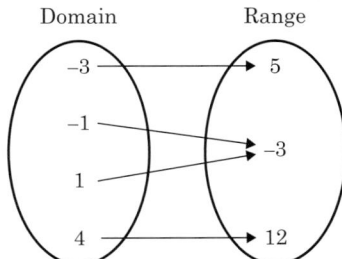

4. a) 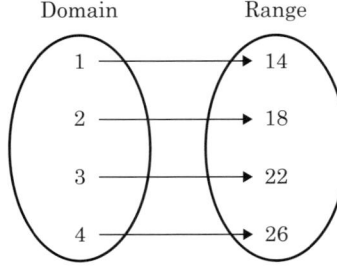   **b)**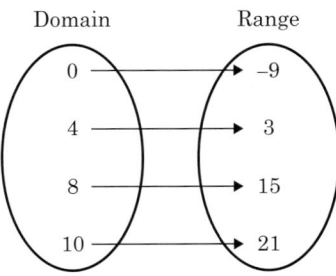

5. a) $f(x) = 3x - 4$ **b)** $f(x) = (x - 1)^2$

6. $\{9, 15, 57, 249\}$ **7.** $\{1, 2, 5, 9\}$

Exercise 11.4A

1. a) $4x + 20$ **b)** $4x + 5$ **c)** $16x^2$ **d)** $4x^2$ **e)** $x^2 + 5$

2. a) -2.5 **b)** $\pm\sqrt{\dfrac{5}{3}}$

3. $f^{-1}(x) = \dfrac{x + 2}{5}$ **4.** $f^{-1}(x) = \dfrac{x}{5} + 2$ **5.** $f^{-1}(x) = \dfrac{x}{6} - 2$

6. $g^{-1}(x) = \dfrac{3x - 1}{2}$

7. $f^{-1}(x) = \dfrac{4x}{3} + 1$

8. $g^{-1}(x) = \dfrac{x - 2}{6}$

9. a) $6x - 1$ **b)** $6x + 2$ **c)** $2x^2 + 1$ **d)** $9x^2 - 6x + 1$

10. a) 11 **b)** 9 **c)** -10 **d)** 14

11. a) 2 **b)** $0, 2$ **c)** $\pm\sqrt{2}$

12. a) 242 **b)** 11 **c)** 21

13. $h^{-1}(x) = \dfrac{2x - 24}{5}$

14. $k^{-1}(x) = \dfrac{3 - x}{7}$

15. $j^{-1}(x) = \dfrac{12 - 3x}{5}$

16. $n^{-1}(x) = 10 - 3x$

17. $m^{-1}(x) = \dfrac{4(5x + 3) + 1}{2} = \dfrac{20x + 13}{2}$

18. $f^{-1}(x) = \dfrac{30 - 7x}{6}$

19. $g^{-1}(x) = 20x - 164$

20. It is many-to-one, so the inverse would be one-to-many and this is not a function.

Revision exercise 11

1. a) {5}   **b)** {1, 3, 5, 6, 7}   **c)** {2, 4, 6, 7, 8}   **d)** {2, 4, 8}
   e) {1, 2, 3, 4, 5, 8}   **2.** 32

3. a) 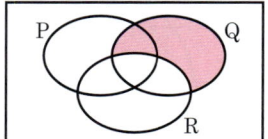   **b)** 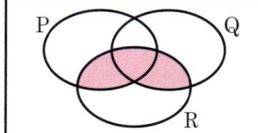   **c)**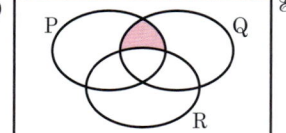

4. a) $(A \cup B)' \cap C$ **b)** $(A \cup B) \cap C'$

5. a) i) $S \subset T$ **ii)** $S \cap M' \neq \phi$
   b) There are no women on the train over 25 years old.

6. a) 4 **b)** 11 **c)** 17

7. a) -5 **b)** 0 **c)** -3 **d)** 8

8. $f^{-1}(x) = \dfrac{x - 4}{3}$ **a)** 3 **b)** $5\frac{1}{3}$ **9. a)** 3 **b)** $0, 5$

9. $f(x)$ and $f^{-1}(x)$ are the same.   **10. a)** $y = \dfrac{x + 1}{4}$ **b)** 10

Examination-style exercise 11

1. a) 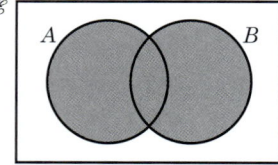   **b)** 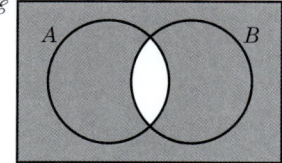   **c)**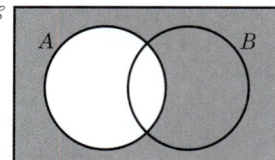

2. a) 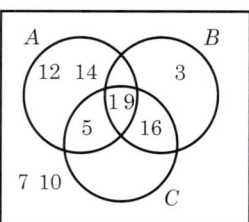   **b)** 1

3. a) $\mathscr{E}$ **b)** $\varnothing$ **c)** $\varnothing$

4. a) -27 **b)** $gf(x) = 3x^3 - 6x^2 + 15x - 2$ **c)** $g^{-1}(x) = \dfrac{x - 1}{3}$

5. a) 11   **b)** $f^{-1}(x) = \dfrac{7-x}{2}$ **c)** 4

6. a) 0.5   **b)** 0   **c)** $\dfrac{\sin(x)-6}{3}$

7. a) $\frac{17}{3}$ **b)** $\dfrac{4x+1}{4x-1}$ **c)** $g^{-1}(x) = \dfrac{2}{x-1}$ **d)** 19683   **e)** −2

12 Vectors and transformations

Exercise 12.1A

1. d	**2. 2c**	**3. 3c**	**4. 3d**	**5. 5d**
6. 3c	**7. −2d**	**8. −2c**	**9. −3c**	**10. −c**
11. c + d	**12. c + 2d**	**13. 2c + d**	**14. 3c + d**	**15. 2c + 2d**
16. 2c + 3d	**17. 2c − d**	**18. 3c − d**	**19. −c + 2d**	**20. −c + 3d**
21. −c + d	**22. −c − 2d**	**23. −2c − 2d**	**24. −3c − 6d**	**25. −2c + 3d**
26. c + 6d	**27.** $\overline{QI}$	**28.** $\overline{QU}$	**29.** $\overline{QH}$	**30.** $\overline{QB}$
31. $\overline{QF}$	**32.** $\overline{QJ}$	**33.** $\overline{QZ}$	**34.** $\overline{QL}$	**35.** $\overline{QE}$
36. $\overline{QX}$	**37.** $\overline{QW}$	**38.** $\overline{QK}$		

39. a) −a   **b)** b − a   **c)** −b   **d)** a + b
40. a) a + b   **b)** a − 2b   **c)** −a + b   **d)** −a − b
41. a) −a − b   **b)** 3a − b   **c)** 2a − b   **d)** −2a + b
42. a) a − 2b   **b)** a − b   **c)** 2a   **d)** −2a + 3b
43. a) 2a − c   **b)** 2a − c   **c)** 3a   **d)** a + b + c   **e)** −3a − b
44. a) b − c   **b)** 2b + 2c   **c)** a + 2b + 2c   **d)** −a − b   **e)** c − a − b
45. a) a + c   **b)** −a + c   **c)** a + b + c   **d)** b − c   **e)** −a + 2c

Exercise 12.1B

1. a) a   **b)** −a + b   **c)** 2b   **d)** −2a   **e)** −2a + 2b
   f) −a + b   **g)** a + b   **h)** b   **i)** −b + 2a   **j)** −2b + a
2. a) a   **b)** −a + b   **c)** 3b   **d)** −2a   **e)** −2a + 3b
   f) $-a + \frac{3}{2}b$ **g)** $a + \frac{3}{2}b$ **h)** $\frac{3}{2}b$ **i)** −b + 2a   **j)** −3b + a
3. a) 2a   **b)** −a + b   **c)** 2b   **d)** −3a   **e)** −3a + 2b
   f) $-\frac{3}{2}a + b$ **g)** $\frac{3}{2}a + b$ **h)** $\frac{1}{2}a + b$ **i)** −b + 3a   **j)** −2b + a
4. a) $\frac{1}{2}a$ **b)** −a + b   **c)** 4b   **d)** $-\frac{3}{2}a$ **e)** $-\frac{3}{2}a + 4b$
   f) $-a + \frac{8}{3}b$ **g)** $\frac{1}{2}a + \frac{8}{3}b$ **h)** $-\frac{1}{2}a + \frac{8}{3}b$ **i)** $\frac{3}{2}a - b$ **j)** a − 4b
5. a) 5a   **b)** b − a   **c)** $\frac{3}{2}b$ **d)** −6a   **e)** $\frac{3}{2}b - 6a$
   f) b − 4a   **g)** 2a + b   **h)** a + b   **i)** 6a − b   **j)** $a - \frac{3}{2}b$
6. a) 4a   **b)** b − a   **c)** 3b   **d)** −5a   **e)** 3b − 5a
   f) $\frac{3}{4}b - \frac{5}{4}a$ **g)** $\frac{15}{4}a + \frac{3}{4}b$ **h)** $\frac{11}{4}a + \frac{3}{4}b$ **i)** 5a − b   **j)** a − 3b
7. $\frac{1}{2}s - \frac{1}{2}t$ **8.** $\frac{1}{3}a + \frac{2}{3}b$ **9.** a + c − b   **10.** 2m + 2n
11. a) b − a   **b)** b − a   **c)** 2b − 2a   **d)** b − 2a   **e)** b − 2a   **f)** 2b − 3a
12. a) y − z   **b)** $\frac{1}{2}y - \frac{1}{2}z$ **c)** $\frac{1}{2}y + \frac{1}{2}z$ **d)** $-x + \frac{1}{2}y + \frac{1}{2}z$
   e) $-\frac{2}{3}x + \frac{1}{3}y + \frac{1}{3}z$ **f)** $\frac{1}{3}x + \frac{1}{3}y + \frac{1}{3}z$

Exercise 12.2A

1.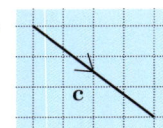

2.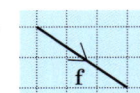

3.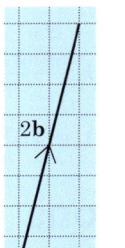

4.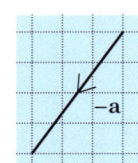

5.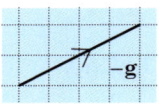

6.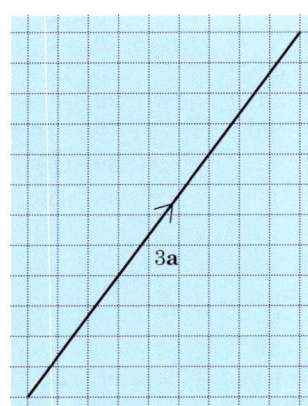

7.

8.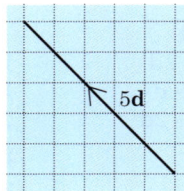

9.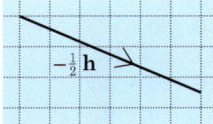

10.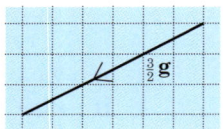

11.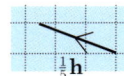

12.

13. $\begin{pmatrix} -11 \\ 9 \end{pmatrix}$

14. $\begin{pmatrix} -1 \\ -4 \end{pmatrix}$

15. $\begin{pmatrix} 4 \\ 8 \end{pmatrix}$

16. $\begin{pmatrix} 4 \\ 3 \end{pmatrix}$

17. $\begin{pmatrix} 8 \\ -7 \end{pmatrix}$

18. $\begin{pmatrix} 18 \\ -1 \end{pmatrix}$

19. $\begin{pmatrix} 7 \\ -4 \end{pmatrix}$

20. $\begin{pmatrix} -18 \\ -16 \end{pmatrix}$

21. $\begin{pmatrix} 13 \\ 19 \end{pmatrix}$

22. $\begin{pmatrix} 8 \\ 5 \end{pmatrix}$

23. $\begin{pmatrix} 10 \\ -13 \end{pmatrix}$

24. $\begin{pmatrix} 17 \\ 35 \end{pmatrix}$

25. $\begin{pmatrix} 4 \\ 8 \end{pmatrix}$

26. $\begin{pmatrix} 4 \\ 3 \end{pmatrix}$

27. $\begin{pmatrix} -1 \\ 1 \end{pmatrix}$

28. $\begin{pmatrix} -16 \\ 3 \end{pmatrix}$

29. $\begin{pmatrix} -2\frac{1}{2} \\ -3 \end{pmatrix}$

30. $\begin{pmatrix} -3\frac{1}{2} \\ \frac{1}{2} \end{pmatrix}$

31. $\begin{pmatrix} -3 \\ -7 \end{pmatrix}$

32. $\begin{pmatrix} -2 \\ 12 \end{pmatrix}$

33. $\begin{pmatrix} 4 \\ 8 \end{pmatrix}$

34. $\begin{pmatrix} -5\frac{1}{2} \\ 4\frac{1}{2} \end{pmatrix}$

35. $\begin{pmatrix} 0 \\ 0 \end{pmatrix}$

36. $\begin{pmatrix} -2\frac{1}{2} \\ -6 \end{pmatrix}$

37. b) l and s; n and r; p and t; m and q

38. a) true   **b)** true   **c)** true   **d)** true   **e)** false   **f)** false

39. a)    **b)**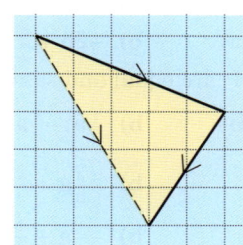

40. a) 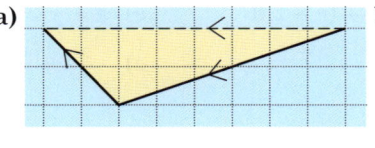   **b)** 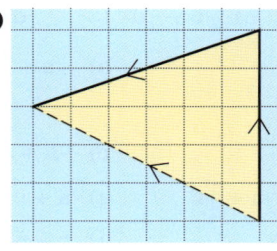   **c)** 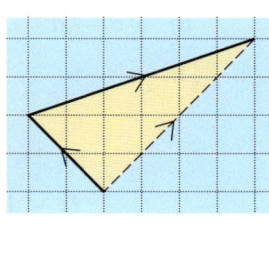   **d)**

Exercise 12.2B

1. $\begin{pmatrix} 2 \\ -2 \end{pmatrix}$ **2.** $\begin{pmatrix} 6 \\ -2 \end{pmatrix}$ **3. b)** $\begin{pmatrix} 0 \\ 3 \end{pmatrix}$; $\begin{pmatrix} -5 \\ -5 \end{pmatrix}$ **4. b)** $\begin{pmatrix} 4 \\ 2 \end{pmatrix}$; $\begin{pmatrix} -7 \\ 0 \end{pmatrix}$

5. a) $\begin{pmatrix} 3 \\ -3 \end{pmatrix}$ **b)** $\begin{pmatrix} 1\frac{1}{2} \\ -1\frac{1}{2} \end{pmatrix}$ **c)** $\begin{pmatrix} 3\frac{1}{2} \\ 3\frac{1}{2} \end{pmatrix}$; $M\left(3\frac{1}{2}, 3\frac{1}{2}\right)$

6. a) $\begin{pmatrix} -1 \\ 6 \end{pmatrix}$ **b)** $\begin{pmatrix} -\frac{1}{2} \\ 3 \end{pmatrix}$ **c)** $\begin{pmatrix} 5\frac{1}{2} \\ -4 \end{pmatrix}$; $M\left(5\frac{1}{2}, -4\right)$

7. a) i) $\begin{pmatrix} -6 \\ 3 \end{pmatrix}$ **ii)** $\begin{pmatrix} -2 \\ 1 \end{pmatrix}$ **iii)** $\begin{pmatrix} 2 \\ 3 \end{pmatrix}$ **b) i)** $\begin{pmatrix} 0 \\ -9 \end{pmatrix}$ **ii)** $\begin{pmatrix} 0 \\ -3 \end{pmatrix}$ **iii)** $\begin{pmatrix} -2 \\ 2 \end{pmatrix}$

8. $\begin{pmatrix} 1 \\ -2 \end{pmatrix}$ or $\begin{pmatrix} -1 \\ 2 \end{pmatrix}$ **9.** $\begin{pmatrix} 0 \\ 2 \end{pmatrix}$ or $\begin{pmatrix} 0 \\ -2 \end{pmatrix}$

10. a) q – p   **b)** q + 2p   **c)** p + q

11. a) $\begin{pmatrix} 1 \\ -3 \end{pmatrix}$ **b)** $\begin{pmatrix} -1 \\ 3 \end{pmatrix}$ **c)** $\begin{pmatrix} 3 \\ 1 \end{pmatrix}$ **d)** $\begin{pmatrix} -3 \\ -1 \end{pmatrix}$

Exercise 12.2C

1. 5   **2.** $\sqrt{17}$ **3.** 13   **4.** 3   **5.** 5

6. $\sqrt{45}$ **7.** $\sqrt{74}$ **8.** $\sqrt{208}$ **9.** 10   **10.** $\sqrt{89}$

11. a) $\sqrt{320}$ **b)** no   **12. a)** $\sqrt{148}$ **b)** no

13. $\sqrt{29}$ **14.** $\sqrt{26}$ **15.** $\sqrt{10}$

16. a) 5   **b)** $n = \pm 4$ **17. a)** 13   **b)** $m = \pm 13$

18. a) 5   **b)** $p = 0$ **19. a)** 9   **b)** 6   **c)** 5

20. a) 30   **b)** 5   **c)** $\sqrt{50}$ **d)** 4

Exercise 12.3A

1. a) 2a; 3b   **b)** –b + a   **c)** –3b + 2a   **d)** 4a – 3b

     e) 4a – 6b   **f)** $\overrightarrow{EC} = 2\overrightarrow{ED}$

2. a) $2\mathbf{b}$; $\frac{5}{2}\mathbf{a}$ **b)** $-\mathbf{a} + \mathbf{b}$ **c)** $-\frac{5}{2}\mathbf{a} + 2\mathbf{b}$ **d)** $-5\mathbf{a} + 6\mathbf{b}$

   e) $-\frac{15}{2}\mathbf{a} + 6\mathbf{b}$ **f)** $\overrightarrow{XC} = 3\overrightarrow{XY}$

3. a) $-\mathbf{b} + \mathbf{a}$; $-3\mathbf{b} + 3\mathbf{a}$ **b)** $-2\mathbf{b} + \frac{3}{2}\mathbf{a}$ **c)** $-\frac{1}{2}\mathbf{a}$; $-2\mathbf{b} + \frac{3}{2}\mathbf{a}$

   d) Since $\overrightarrow{RQ}$ and $\overrightarrow{QP}$ are equal and share a common point, R, Q and P lie on a straight line.

4. a) $-\mathbf{a} + \mathbf{b}$; $-\frac{2}{3}\mathbf{a} + \frac{2}{3}\mathbf{b}$ **b)** $\frac{1}{2}\mathbf{a}$; $-\frac{1}{6}\mathbf{a} + \frac{2}{3}\mathbf{b}$ **c)** $-\frac{1}{2}\mathbf{a} + 2\mathbf{b}$ **d)** $\overrightarrow{MX} = 3\overrightarrow{MP}$

5. a) $-\mathbf{b} + \mathbf{a}$; $-3\mathbf{a} + \mathbf{b}$ **b)** $-\frac{3}{2}\mathbf{a} + \frac{1}{2}\mathbf{b}$ **c)** $\left(k - \frac{3}{2}\right)\mathbf{a} + \left(\frac{1}{2} - k\right)\mathbf{b}$ **d)** $k = \frac{3}{2}$

6. a) $-\mathbf{a} + \mathbf{b}$ **b)** $-\frac{1}{4}\mathbf{a} + \frac{1}{4}\mathbf{b}$ **c)** $\mathbf{a} + (m - 1)\mathbf{b}$ **d)** $m = \frac{4}{3}$

7. a) $-\mathbf{c} + \mathbf{d}$ **b)** $-\frac{1}{5}\mathbf{c} + \frac{1}{5}\mathbf{d}$ **c)** $\frac{4}{5}\mathbf{c} + \frac{1}{5}\mathbf{d}$ **d)** $\mathbf{c} + (n - 1)\mathbf{d}$ **e)** $n = \frac{5}{4}$

8. a) $-\mathbf{a} + \mathbf{b}$; $-\frac{1}{2}\mathbf{a} + \frac{1}{2}\mathbf{b}$; $\frac{1}{2}\mathbf{a} + \frac{1}{2}\mathbf{b}$ **b)** $\frac{1}{3}\mathbf{a} + \frac{1}{3}\mathbf{b}$ **c)** $-\frac{2}{3}\mathbf{a} + \frac{1}{3}\mathbf{b}$

   d) $-\mathbf{a} + \frac{1}{2}\mathbf{b}$ **e)** $m = \frac{2}{3}$

9. a) $-\mathbf{a} + \mathbf{b}$ **b)** $\frac{1}{2}\mathbf{b}$ **c)** $-\mathbf{a} + \mathbf{c}$ **d)** $-\frac{1}{2}\mathbf{a} + \frac{1}{2}\mathbf{c}$

   e) $\frac{1}{2}\mathbf{a} + \frac{1}{2}\mathbf{c}$ **f)** $-\frac{1}{2}\mathbf{b} + \frac{1}{2}\mathbf{a} + \frac{1}{2}\mathbf{c}$ **g)** $\mathbf{a} + \mathbf{c} = \mathbf{b}$

10. a) $-\mathbf{b} + \mathbf{a}$ **c)** $4\mathbf{a} + 2\mathbf{b}$ **d)** $n = \frac{1}{6}$, $m = \frac{2}{3}$

11. a) $-\mathbf{c} + \mathbf{d}$; $-\frac{1}{4}\mathbf{c} + \frac{1}{4}\mathbf{d}$; $\frac{3}{4}\mathbf{c} + \frac{1}{4}\mathbf{d}$ **b)** $-\mathbf{c} + \frac{1}{2}\mathbf{d}$

   c) $(1 - h)\mathbf{c} + \frac{h}{2}\mathbf{d}$ **d)** $(1 - h)\mathbf{c} + \frac{h}{2}\mathbf{d} = \frac{3k}{4}\mathbf{c} + \frac{k}{4}\mathbf{d}$; $h = \frac{2}{5}$, $k = \frac{4}{5}$

Exercise 12.4A

1. 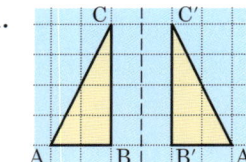   **2.** 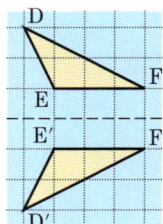   **3.** 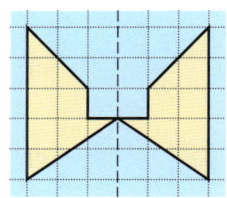   **4.**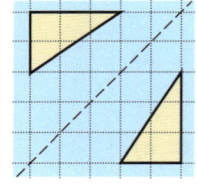

5. 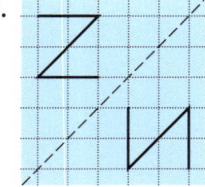   **6.**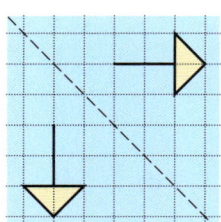

    7. $x = 0$ **8.** $y = x$

    9. $y = 1$ **10.** $y = -x$

    11. $y = x + 2$ **12.** $y = -x + 4$

Exercise 12.4B

  1. c) i) $(-6, 8)$ **ii)** $(6, -4)$ **iii)** $(8, 6)$

  2. c) i) $(8, 8)$ **ii)** $(8, -6)$ **iii)** $(-8, 6)$

  3. c) i) $(3, -1)$ **ii)** $(4, 2)$ **iii)** $(-1, 1)$

  4. b) i) $y = 1$ **ii)** $y = x$ **iii)** $y = -x$ **iv)** $y = 2$

  5. f) $(1, -1)$, $(-3, -1)$, $(-3, -3)$ **6. f)** $(8, -2)$, $(6, -6)$, $(8, -6)$

Exercise 12.4C

1.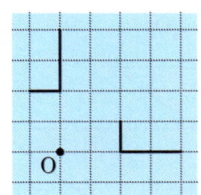

2.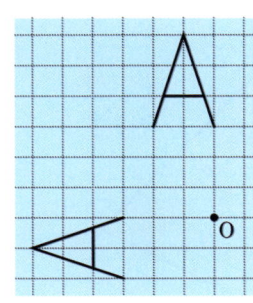

3.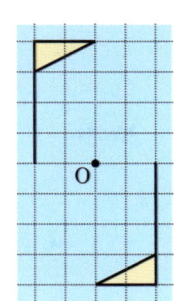

4.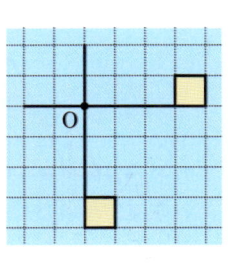

5.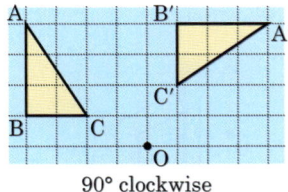

90° clockwise

6.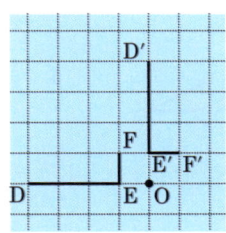

90° clockwise

7.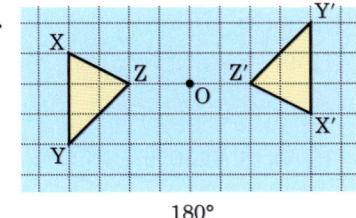

180°

8.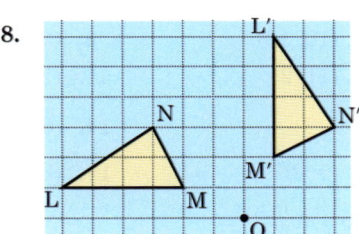

90° clockwise

Exercise 12.4D

1. a) A′(3, −1) B′(6, −1) C′(6, −3)
   b) D′(3, −3) E′(3, −6) F′(1, −6)
   c) P′ (−7, −4) Q′(−5, −4) R′(−5, −1)

2. b) i) (4, −1), (7, −1), (7, −3)
   ii) (−1, −4), (−1, −7), (−3, −7)
   iii) (−4, 1), (−7, 1), (−7, 3)

3. c) (−2, 1), (−2, −1), (1, −2)
   4. e) (−5, 2), (−5, 6), (−3, 5)

5. b) i) 90° anticlockwise, centre (0, 0)
   ii) 180°, centre (2, 1)

   iii) 90° clockwise, centre (2, 0)
   iv) 180°, centre $\left(3\frac{1}{2}, 2\frac{1}{2}\right)$

   v) 90° anticlockwise, centre (6, 1)
   vi) 90° clockwise, centre (1, 3)

6. e) i) 180°, centre $\left(\frac{1}{2}, \frac{1}{2}\right)$
   ii) 90° anticlockwise, centre (−2, 4)

Exercise 12.4E

1. a) $\begin{pmatrix} 7 \\ 3 \end{pmatrix}$ **b)** $\begin{pmatrix} 0 \\ -9 \end{pmatrix}$ **c)** $\begin{pmatrix} 9 \\ 10 \end{pmatrix}$ **d)** $\begin{pmatrix} -10 \\ 3 \end{pmatrix}$ **e)** $\begin{pmatrix} -1 \\ 13 \end{pmatrix}$ **f)** $\begin{pmatrix} 10 \\ 0 \end{pmatrix}$ **g)** $\begin{pmatrix} -9 \\ -4 \end{pmatrix}$ **h)** $\begin{pmatrix} -10 \\ 0 \end{pmatrix}$

2. (5, 2)   **3.** (5, 6)   **4.** (8, −5)   **5.** (0, 6)   **6.** (4, −7)

7. (−3, 4)   **8.** (−3, −5)   **9.** (−1, −8)   **10.** (5, 2)   **11.** (−2, 1)

Exercise 12.4F

1.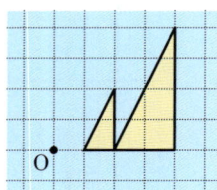

2.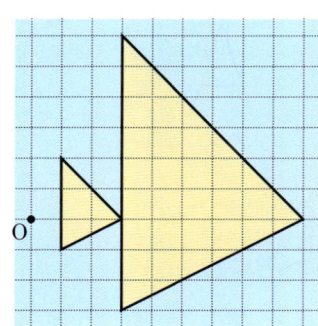

3.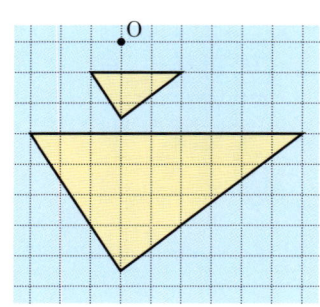

4.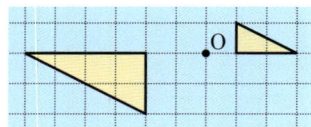

5.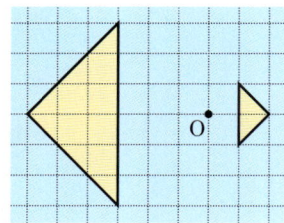

6.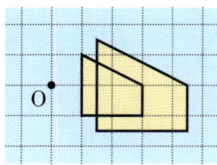

7. (4, 8), (8, 4), (10, 10)

8. (3, 6), (7, 2), (9, 8)

9. (1, 1), (10, 4), (4, 7)

10. (1, 4), (7, 8), (11, 2)

11. (2, 1), +3

12. (11, 9), $+\frac{1}{2}$

13. (5, 4), –2

14. (6, 6), –1

15. $\left(\frac{1}{2}, 1\right), \left(6\frac{1}{2}, 1\right), \left(\frac{1}{2}, 5\right)$

16. (3, 4), (3, 3), (5, 3)

17. (3, 7), (1, 7), (3, 3)

18. (10, 7), (6, 7), (6, 5)

19. (6, 5), $\left(3\frac{1}{2}, 5\right), \left(3\frac{1}{2}, 3\right)$

Exercise 12.4G

1. a) Rotation 90° clockwise, centre (0, –2)

b) Reflection in $y = x$

c) Translation $\begin{pmatrix} 3 \\ 7 \end{pmatrix}$

d) Enlargement, scale factor 2, centre (–5, 5)

e) Translation $\begin{pmatrix} -7 \\ -3 \end{pmatrix}$

f) Reflection in $y = x$

2. a) Rotation 90° clockwise, centre (4, –2)

b) Translation $\begin{pmatrix} 8 \\ 2 \end{pmatrix}$

c) Reflection in $y = x$

d) Enlargement, scale factor $\frac{1}{2}$, centre (7, –7)

e) Rotation 90° anticlockwise, centre (–8, 0)

f) Enlargement, scale factor 2, centre (–1, –9)

g) Rotation 90° anticlockwise, centre (7, 3)

3. a) Enlargement, scale factor $1\frac{1}{2}$, centre (1, –4)

b) Rotation 90° clockwise, centre (0, –4)

c) Reflection in $y = -x$

d) Translation $\begin{pmatrix} 11 \\ 10 \end{pmatrix}$

e) Enlargement, scale factor $\frac{1}{2}$, centre (–3, 8)

f) Rotation 90° anticlockwise, centre $\left(\frac{1}{2}, 6\frac{1}{2}\right)$

g) Enlargement, scale factor 3, centre (–2, 5)

Exercise 12.5A

1. a) (5, –1) **b)** (4, –6) **c)** (0, 0) **d)** (–6, 4) **e)** (3, –2)
f) (3, 2) **g)** (3, 6) **h)** (–3, 2) **i)** (–2, 3) **j)** (–4, 2)
k) (–3, –2) **l)** (7, –4) **m)** (1, 4) **n)** (–7, –3) **o)** (–4, –1)

Exercise 12.5B

1. a) $(-4, 4)$ **b)** $(2, -2)$ **c)** $(0, 0)$ **d)** $(0, 4)$ **e)** $(0, 0)$

2. a) $(-2, 5)$ **b)** $(-4, 0)$ **c)** $(2, -2)$ **d)** $(1, -1)$

3. a) reflection in y-axis   **b)** rotation 180°, centre $(-2, 2)$

   c) rotation 90° clockwise, centre $(2, 2)$

4. a) rotation 90° anticlockwise, centre $(0, 0)$ **b)** translation $\begin{pmatrix} -2 \\ 5 \end{pmatrix}$

   c) rotation 90° anticlockwise, centre $(2, -4)$ **d)** rotation 90° anticlockwise, centre $\left(-\frac{1}{2}, 3\frac{1}{2}\right)$

5. a) rotation 90° anticlockwise, centre $(2, 2)$ **b)** enlargement, scale factor $\frac{1}{2}$, centre $(8, 6)$

   c) rotation 90° clockwise, centre $\left(-1\frac{1}{2}, -4\frac{1}{2}\right)$

Revision exercise 12

1. a) $\mathbf{r} - \mathbf{p}$ **b)** $\frac{1}{2}\mathbf{r} - \frac{1}{2}\mathbf{p}$ **c)** $\frac{1}{2}\mathbf{r} + \frac{1}{2}\mathbf{p}$

2. a) 5   **b)** $\sqrt{68}$ **c)** $\sqrt{41}$ **3.** $n = 2$, $m = -15$

4. a) $\begin{pmatrix} -1 \\ 4 \end{pmatrix}$ **b)** $\begin{pmatrix} 4 \\ 4 \end{pmatrix}$ **c)** $\begin{pmatrix} 6 \\ -4 \end{pmatrix}$ **d)** $\begin{pmatrix} 2 \\ 2 \end{pmatrix}$

5. a) $\mathbf{a} - \mathbf{c}$ **b)** $\frac{1}{2}\mathbf{a} + \mathbf{c}$ **c)** $\frac{1}{2}\mathbf{a} - \frac{1}{2}\mathbf{c}$ CA is parallel to NM and CA = 2NM.

6. $m = 3$, $n = 2$ **7. a)** $\begin{pmatrix} -3 \\ 2 \end{pmatrix}$ **b)** $\begin{pmatrix} -1\frac{1}{2} \\ 1 \end{pmatrix}$ **c)** $\begin{pmatrix} 1\frac{1}{2} \\ 3 \end{pmatrix}$

8. a) $(4, -1)$ **b)** $(4, 1)$ **c)** $(-3, 2)$

9. a) A'$(-3, -1)$ B'$(1, -1)$ C'$(-3, -7)$ **b)** A'$(2, -2)$ B'$(6, -2)$ C'$(2, -8)$

   c) A'$(1, 1)$ B'$(2, 1)$ C'$\left(1, -\frac{1}{2}\right)$ **d)** A'$(4, 2)$ B'$(3, 2)$ C'$\left(4, 3\frac{1}{2}\right)$

   e) A'$(-2, 2)$ B'$(-6, 2)$ C'$(-2, 8)$

10. a) reflection in y-axis   **b)** reflection in $y = x$ **c)** rotation, $-90°$, centre $(0, 0)$

   d) reflection in $y = -x$ **e)** rotation, 180°, centre $(0, 0)$ **f)** rotation, $-90°$, centre $(0, 0)$

11. a) reflection in $x = \frac{1}{2}$ **b)** reflection in $y = -x$ **f)** rotation, 180°, centre $(1, 1)$

12. a) $(-1, -3)$ **b)** $(-1, 3)$ **c)** $(6, 2)$

   d) $(-3, 1)$ **e)** $(-2, 6)$ **f)** $(0, 2)$

Examination-style exercise 12

1. a) $2\mathbf{a} + \mathbf{g}$ **b)** $1\frac{1}{2}\mathbf{a} + \frac{1}{2}\mathbf{b}$

2. a)   **b)** $\frac{1}{2}\mathbf{a} + \mathbf{c}$ **c)** $\frac{1}{3}\mathbf{a} + \frac{1}{3}\mathbf{c}$

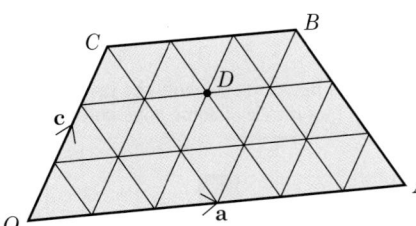

3. a) i) $\mathbf{c} - \mathbf{b}$ **ii)** $\mathbf{b} - \frac{1}{2}\mathbf{c}$ **iii)** $2\mathbf{c} - \mathbf{b}$

   b) i) 120°   **ii)** $25\sqrt{3}\,\text{cm}^2$ **iii)** $10\sqrt{3}\,\text{cm}$ **iv)** $150\sqrt{3}\,\text{cm}^2$

4.

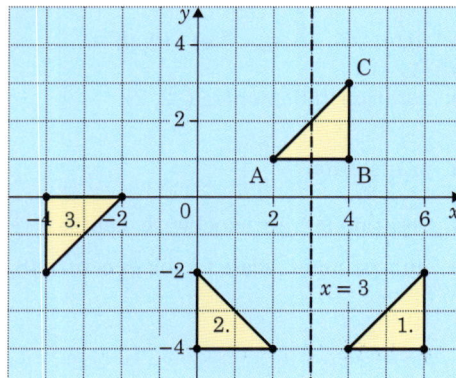

5.

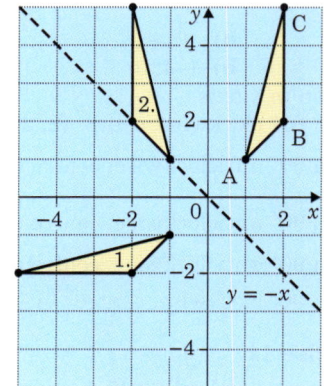

e) Reflection in the line $x = 0$

13 Statistics

Exercise 13.1A

1. a) Sharon   **b)** $11   **c)** Half of a $ symbol

2. a) 2

b)

Make	Number of cars	
Ford	4	
Renault	6	
Toyota	6	
Audi	3	

3. Key is ⬤ = 12 books; Saturday there were 33 books borrowed.

4. Student's own pictogram

Exercise 13.1B

1. a) Squash   **b)** 160   **c)** 10

2. Student's tally chart   **3.** Student's bar chart and observations   **4.** Student's bar chart

5. a) $3000   **b)** $4000   **c)** $6000   **d)** $11 000

6. Drama 50°; Clay workshop 70°; Creative writing 110°; Debate 40°; Orchestra 90°

7. Eggs 270°; milk 12°; butter 23.4°; cheese 54°; salt 0.6°

8. a) A 45°; B 75°; C 45°; D 105°; E 90°   **b)** A 50°; B 75°; C 170°; D 40°; E 25°

c) A 48.5°; B 76.2°; C 62.3°; D 96.9°; E 76.2°

9. 18°, 54°, 54°, 234°   **10.** 80°, 120°, 160°   **11.** $x = 8$ **12.** 100

13. a) 22.5%   **b)** $x = 45°, y = 114°$ **14.** You can only see the very tops of the bars.

Exercise 13.1C

1. a)

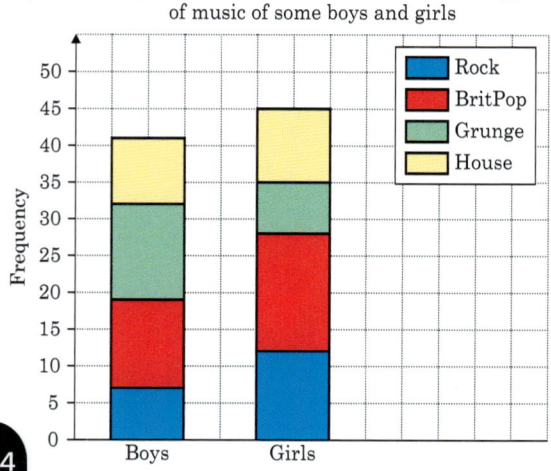

b)

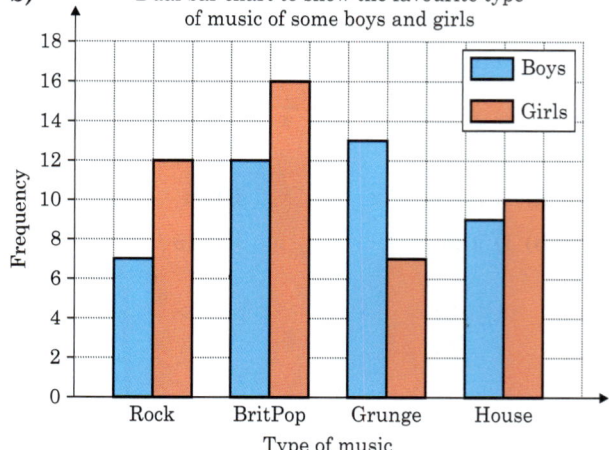

c) The composite bar chart (can compare the total height of the bar)

2. a)

	Curry	Kebab	Dhal
Adults	12	15	8
Children	9	12	16

b)

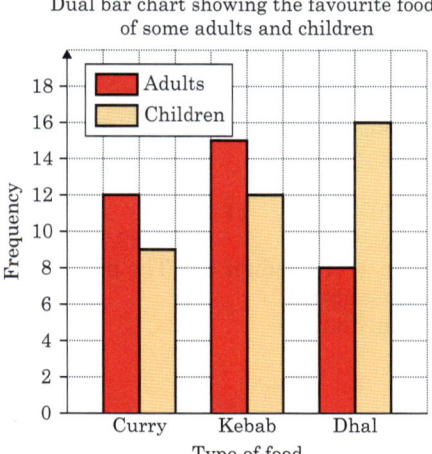

Dual bar chart showing the favourite foods of some adults and children

c)

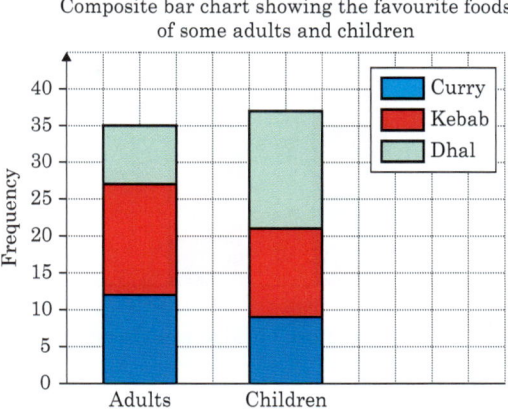

Composite bar chart showing the favourite foods of some adults and children

d) The dual bar chart (can directly compare the height of the kebab bars)

3. a)

Dual bar chart showing sales of ice cream

b) Wednesday – the bar is much lower than the Shakee's bar and also much lower than the other Bargie's' bars

c)

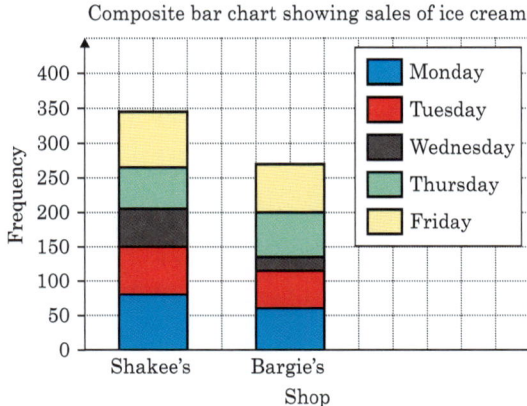

Composite bar chart showing sales of ice cream

d) Shakee's – the bar is much taller than for Bargie's

4. a)

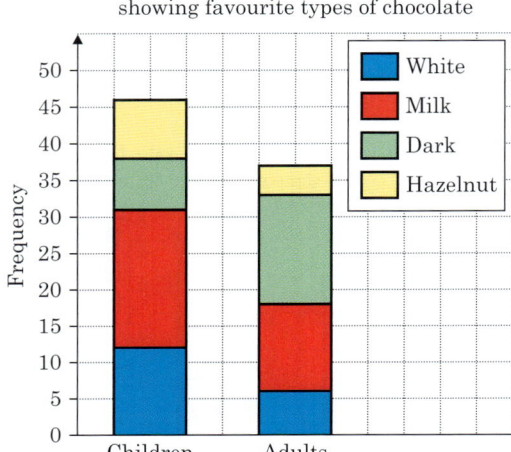

Composite bar chart
showing favourite types of chocolate

Frequency / White / Milk / Dark / Hazelnut

Children   Adults

b) There were more children in the survey.

Exercise 13.2A
1. **a)** mean = 6; median = 5; mode = 4.
   b) mean = 9; median = 7; mode = 7.
   c) mean = 6.5; median = 8; mode = 9.
   d) mean = 3.5; median = 3.5; mode = 4.
2. **a)** mean = 7.82; median = 8; mode = 8.
   b) mean = 5; median = 4; mode = 4.
   c) mean = 2.1; median = 2.5; mode = 4.
   d) mean = $\frac{13}{18}$; median = $\frac{1}{2}$; mode = $\frac{1}{2}$.
3. **a)** 34, 7, 32, 25   **b)** 99, 10, 78, 68
   c) 80, 10, 47, 37   **d)** 130, 46, 129, 83
4. 78 kg   5. 35.2 cm
6. **a)** 2   **b)** 9
7. **a)** 20.4 m   **b)** 12.8 m   **c)** 1.66 m
8. 55 kg   9. 12
10. mean = 17, median = 3. The median is more representative.
11. the median   **12.** 15, 20, 31

Exercise 13.2B
1. 3.38   **2.** 3.475
3. **a)** mean = 3.025; median = 3; mode = 3.   **b)** mean = 17.75; median = 17; mode = 17.
   c) mean = 3.38; median = 4; mode = 4.
4. **a)** 5.17   **b)** 5   **5. a)** 9   **b)** 9   **c)** 15
6. **a)** 5   **b)** 10   **c)** 10   **7.** 12   **8.** $3\frac{2}{3}$
9. 4.68   **10.** $\dfrac{ax + by + cz}{a + b + c}$

Exercise 13.2C
1. **a)**   **b)** 10.75

number of words	frequency f	midpoint x	fx
1–5	6	3	18
6–10	5	8	40
11–15	4	13	52
16–20	2	18	36
21–25	3	23	69
Totals	20	—	215

2. **a)** 68.25
   b) The raw data is unavailable and an assumption has been made using the midpoint of each interval.
   c) the sample is small, and different schools may be different.
3. 3.77
4. It is not a good description of anybody's ages in the group. The median or mode would be better.
5. All the books will have different word counts.
6. The boss may be an extreme value that might skew a mean.
7. Because the data is non-numerical.

Exercise 13.2D
1. **a)** Group B   **b)** 5   **c)** 35   **d)** 56   **e)** $\frac{1}{8}$
2. **a)** D   **b)** A   **c)** A   **d)** C   **e)** B
3. Field A   **4. c)** No significant change.

Exercise 13.3A

1. a)

Stem	Leaf
2	1 6 9
3	3 6 7
4	2 5 5 8 8
5	2 3 3 6
6	0 2 2 2 4 6 8
7	1 4 6

b) 53 **c)** 55

2. a) 11 **b)** 14.1 **c)** 2.8
d) 15.2 **e)** 2.1

4. a)

	Action			Horror	
		8	8	5 8	9
9	3	0	9	0 2	4
				5 9	
	6	0	10	0 5	
9	0	0	11		
		1	12		

b) Median: Action = 103, Horror = 93
c) Action films

3. a)

	Girls				Boys	
7	5	1	16			
		4	17	5	7	
	8	5	18	2	8	
	4	3	19	3		
		8	20			
		0	21	0	9	
			22	2	7	
			23	1		

b) Median: Boys = 20.15, Girls = 18.65
c) Range: Boys = 5.6, Girls = 4.9

Exercise 13.3B

1.

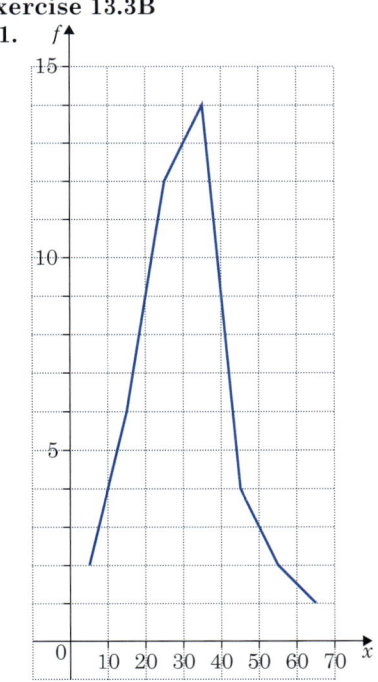

2. P – spend smaller amounts because probably visit more often since live closer.
3. Genetic engineering has little effect on mass. Genetic engineering makes a big difference to life span, extending it significantly.

Exercise 13.3C

Frequency densities for histograms are given here.

1. 1, 1.4, 0.3 **2.** 1, 0.6, 1.2, 1.7, 1.3, 0.25
3. a) 10 **b)** 10 to 30 **c)** 31 cm
4.

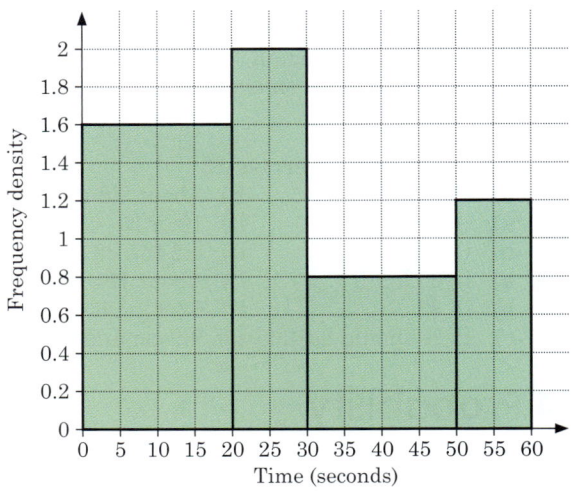

5. Frequency densities are: 0.5, 1.4, 2, 1, 0.2
6. Frequency densities are: 1.8, 9.2, 7, 1.3, 0.8
7. Frequency densities are: 0.55, 1.8, 0.7, 0.25, 0
8. Frequency densities are: 1.6, 3.4, 2.8, 1.1
9. a) 8 **b)** 10 **c)** 57, 14, 17.5

Exercise 13.4A

1. a) strong positive correlation   **b)** no correlation   **c)** weak negative correlation
    d) No. Correlation does not imply causation. Also, not every data set agrees with this conclusion.
2. 11   **3.** 9   **4.** no correlation
5. c) about 26   **d)** about 46   **e)** The ones with the marks 6 and 9.
6. b) 33 m.p.g.   **c)** 63 m.p.h.

Exercise 13.5A

1. a) 47   **b)** 30, 63   **c)** 33   **d)** 37   **e)** 23   **f)** 10   **g)** 80
2. a) 32   **b)** 26, 43   **c)** 17   **d)** 28   **e)** 80   **f)** 20
3. a) 20 kg   **b)** 10.5 kg   **4. a)** 85.5 cm   **b)** 25 cm   **5. a)** 71 s   **b)** 20 s
6. a) 45   **b)** 20   **8. a)** 26   **b)** 25.2   **c)** 26.1

Exercise 13.6A

1. a) Lucy   **b)** 20   **c)** 22
2. a) Median: Children = 62, Adults = 71
     IQR: Children = 78 − 49 = 29, Adults = 83 − 57 = 26
   b) The adults were better at guessing.
   c) Maybe the adults had used these olives before and so had some idea in advance of how many were in the jar.

Revision exercise 13

1. 162°   **2.** 41.7%   **3.** 54°   **4. a)** 84   **b)** 19.2
5. a) 3.4   **b)** 3   **c)** 3   **6. a)** 5.45   **b)** 5   **c)** 5
7. 1.552 m   **8.** 3
9. a)

Stem	Leaf	Key
1	1 4 6 7 8	1 | 4 means 14
2	2 6 8	
3	4 9	
4	1 2 4 4 6 6 8 9	
5	0	

   b) median = 39, interquartile range = 46 − 18 = 28
   c) For Class 2, median = 36 and IQR = 14
   This suggests that, on average, Class 1 performed better in the test, but their results were also more spread out.

Examination-style exercise 13

1. a) 113.7 g   **b)** About 2.6 g   **c)** 30
2. a) i) 19   **ii)** 19 or 20   **iii)** 3
   b) i) 16.325   **ii)** 4.2 cm, 22 cm, 6 cm
3. a) i) 63 km/h   **ii)** About 19   **iii)** 90
   b) i) 33   **ii)** 62.8 km/h
   c) Bars should be 4.05 cm, 9.9 cm and 9 cm tall.

14 Probability

Exercise 14.1A

1. Student's own scale with A at 0.5, B at $\frac{1}{6}$, D and E at 1, I at $\frac{1}{7}$, J at 0; C, F, G, H included.

2. 0.7   **3.** 75%   **4.** $\frac{5}{6}$

Exercise 14.1B

1. a) $\frac{1}{6}$ **b)** $\frac{1}{2}$ **c)** $\frac{1}{2}$ **d)** $\frac{1}{3}$

2. a)

	10c	
	H	T
5c H	HH	TH
T	HT	TT

  b) i) $\frac{1}{4}$ ii) $\frac{1}{2}$

3. a) i) $\frac{3}{5}$ ii) $\frac{2}{5}$ b) i) $\frac{5}{9}$ ii) $\frac{4}{9}$

4. a) $\frac{1}{11}$ b) $\frac{2}{11}$ c) 0   d) $\frac{1}{11}$

5. a) $\frac{1}{8}$ b) $\frac{3}{8}$ c) $\frac{1}{8}$ d) $\frac{7}{8}$

6. a) $\frac{5}{11}$ b) $\frac{7}{22}$ c) $\frac{15}{22}$ d) $\frac{17}{22}$

7. a) $\frac{1}{2}$ b) $\frac{3}{25}$ c) $\frac{9}{100}$ d) $\frac{2}{25}$

8. a) $\frac{1}{12}$ b) $\frac{1}{36}$ c) $\frac{5}{18}$ d) $\frac{1}{6}$ e) $\frac{1}{6}$; most likely total = 7

9. a) $\frac{1}{12}$ b) $\frac{5}{36}$ c) $\frac{2}{3}$ d) $\frac{1}{12}$ e) $\frac{1}{36}$

10. a) 1   b) 0   c) 1   d) 0

11. a) $\frac{3}{8}$ b) $\frac{1}{16}$ c) $\frac{15}{16}$ d) $\frac{1}{4}$

12. $\frac{271}{1000}$ 13. a) $\frac{x}{12}$ b) 3

14. a) $\frac{1}{144}$ b) $\frac{1}{18}$ c) $\frac{1}{72}$ d) head, tail and total of 7

15. a) $\frac{1}{216}$ b) $\frac{1}{72}$ c) $\frac{1}{8}$ d) $\frac{5}{108}$ e) $\frac{5}{72}$ f) $\frac{1}{36}$

Exercise 14.2A

1. a) b) and d) Student's own answers c) 0.25
2. a) 11   b) 96   c) 0.24   3. 168   4. 174
5. a) i) $\frac{18}{80}$ ii) $\frac{17}{80}$ b) i) 36   ii) 13   iii) 8
6. Mike. With a large number of spins, we would expect him to get zero on about $\frac{1}{10}$ of the spins.

Exercise 14.3A

1. a) $\frac{1}{2}$ b) $\frac{1}{2}$ c) $\frac{1}{4}$ 2. a) $\frac{1}{16}$ b) $\frac{25}{144}$

3. a) $\frac{1}{121}$ b) $\frac{9}{121}$ 4. a) $\frac{1}{288}$ b) $\frac{1}{72}$

5. a) $\frac{1}{125}$ b) $\frac{1}{125}$ c) $\frac{1}{10\,000}$ d) $\frac{3}{500}$ e) $\frac{3}{500}$

6. a) $\frac{1}{9}$ b) $\frac{4}{27}$ c) $\frac{4}{9}$

Exercise 14.4A

1. a) $\frac{49}{100}$ b) $\frac{9}{100}$ 2. a) $\frac{9}{64}$ b) $\frac{15}{64}$

3. a) $\frac{7}{15}$ b) $\frac{1}{15}$ 4. a) $\frac{2}{9}$ b) $\frac{2}{15}$ c) $\frac{1}{45}$ d) $\frac{14}{45}$

5. a) $\frac{1}{12}$ b) $\frac{1}{6}$ c) $\frac{1}{3}$ d) $\frac{2}{9}$

6. a) $\frac{1}{216}$ b) $\frac{125}{216}$ c) $\frac{25}{72}$ d) $\frac{91}{216}$

7. a) $\frac{1}{6}$ b) $\frac{1}{30}$ c) $\frac{1}{30}$ d) $\frac{29}{30}$ 8. a) $\frac{27}{64}$ b) $\frac{1}{64}$

9. a) 6   b) $\frac{1}{3}$ 10. a) $\frac{1}{64}$ b) $\frac{27}{64}$ c) $\frac{9}{64}$ d) $\frac{27}{64}$; Sum = 1

11. a) $\frac{6}{6840}$ b) $\frac{60}{6840}$ c) $\frac{1080}{6840}$ d) $\frac{120}{116\,280}$

12. a) $\frac{1}{10\,000}$ **b)** $\frac{523}{10\,000}$ **c)** $\frac{9^4}{10^4}$

13. a) $\frac{x}{x+y}$ **b)** $\frac{x(x-1)}{(x+y)(x+y-1)}$ **c)** $\frac{2xy}{(x+y)(x+y-1)}$ **d)** $\frac{y(y-1)}{(x+y)(x+y-1)}$

14. $\frac{3}{10}$ **15.** $\frac{9}{140}$ **16. a)** 5   **b)** $\frac{1}{64}$

17. a) $\frac{1}{220}$ **b)** $\frac{1}{22}$ **c)** $\frac{3}{11}$ **d)** 5   **e)** 300

18. a) $\frac{10\times9}{1000\times999}$ **b)** $\frac{990\times989}{1000\times999}$ **c)** $\frac{2\times10\times990}{1000\times999}$

19. a) $\frac{3}{20}$ **b)** $\frac{7}{20}$ **c)** $\frac{1}{2}$ **20. a)** 0.00781   **b)** 0.511

21. a) $\frac{21}{506}$ **b)** $\frac{455}{2024}$ **c)** $\frac{945}{2024}$

Exercise 14.5A

1. a) i) $\frac{16}{25}$ **ii)** $\frac{7}{25}$ **ii)** $\frac{3}{25}$ **iv)** $\frac{6}{25}$
  b) iii) They study neither French nor German   **iv)** They study German but not French

2. a) i) $\frac{14}{30}$ **ii)** $\frac{7}{30}$ **iii)** $\frac{9}{30}$
  b) Children who like carrots but do not eat them

3. a)

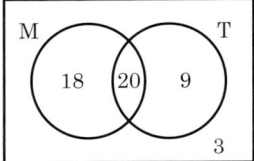

  b) i) $\frac{9}{50}$ **ii)** $\frac{38}{50}$ **iii)** $\frac{29}{50}$ **iv)** $\frac{32}{50}$

4. a)

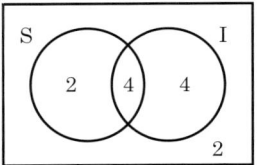

  b) i) $\frac{4}{12}$ **ii)** $\frac{8}{12}$ **iii)** $\frac{4}{12}$

5. a) $\frac{17}{30}$ **b)** $\frac{7}{30}$ **c)** $\frac{8}{30}$ **d)** $\frac{16}{30}$ **e)** $\frac{5}{30}$

6. a) $x=12$ **b) i)** $\frac{66}{120}$ **ii)** $\frac{25}{120}$ **iii)** $\frac{38}{120}$ **iv)** $\frac{69}{120}$

7. a)

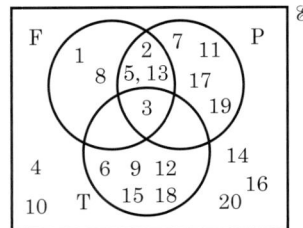

  b) i) $\frac{4}{20}$ **ii)** $\frac{11}{20}$ **iii)** $\frac{7}{20}$ **iv)** $\frac{16}{20}$ **v)** $\frac{15}{20}$

Exercise 14.6A

1. $\frac{26}{51}$ **2. a) i)** $\frac{4}{8}$ **ii)** $\frac{4}{8}$ **b)** $\frac{12}{72}$

3. a) $\frac{24}{50}$ **b)** $\frac{23}{50}$ **c)** $\frac{17}{26}$ **d)** $\frac{14}{23}$ **e)** $\frac{14}{24}$

4. a)

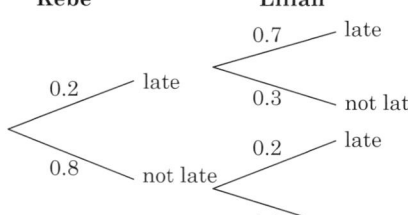

b) 0.3 **c)** 0.3

5. a) 0.62 **b)** 0.632 **6. a)** $\frac{23}{37}$ **b)** $\frac{20}{43}$ **c)** $\frac{3}{23}$

7. a) $\frac{5}{7}$ **b)** $\frac{5}{8}$ **c)** 1 **d)** 0

Revision exercise 14

1. $\frac{1}{6}$ **2. a)** 5 **b)** $\frac{4}{25}$ **3.** $\frac{8}{27}$ **4.** $\frac{5}{16}$

5. a) $\frac{1}{28}$ **b)** $\frac{15}{28}$ **c)** $\frac{3}{7}$

6. a) $\frac{x}{x+5}$ **b)** $\left(\frac{x}{x+5}\right)^2$ **c)** $\frac{x(x-1)}{(x+5)(x+4)}$

7. $\frac{1}{19}$ **8. a)** $\frac{1}{32}$ **b)** $\frac{1}{256}$ **9. a)** $\frac{1}{8}$ **b)** $\frac{1}{2}$

10. $\frac{35}{48}$ **11. a)** $\frac{1}{9}$ **b)** $\frac{1}{12}$ **c)** 0 **12.** $\frac{1}{20^3}$

13. a) $\frac{3}{5}$ **b)** $\frac{1}{3}$ **c)** $\frac{2}{15}$ **d)** $\frac{2}{21}$ **e)** $\frac{1}{7}$ **f)** $\frac{1}{35}$

Examination-style exercise 14

1. a) $\frac{14}{29}$ **b)** $\frac{15}{28}$

2. a) 6 **b)** 7 **c)** 6.625 **d)** $\frac{56}{992}$ **e)** $\frac{20}{650}$ **f)** $\frac{48720}{863040}$

3. a) 0.14 **b)** 0.22 **c)** 8 days (rounded from 7.7)

4. a) $p = 0.02$, $q = 0.98$ **b) i)** 0.9604 **ii)** 0.0392 **c)** 0.038416 **d)** 0.001184
e) 2 (rounded from 2.368)

5. a) 9 **b)** 6 **c)** 22 **d)** 8 **e)** $\frac{17}{28}$ **f)** $\frac{9}{14}$

6. a) $\frac{182}{702}$ **b)** $\frac{364}{702}$

7. a)

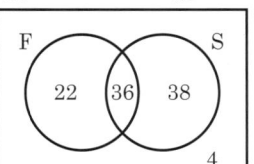

b) i) $\frac{36}{100}$ **ii)** $\frac{38}{100}$ **iii)** $\frac{26}{100}$ **c)** $\frac{36}{74}$

Index